Mastercam® X9

Training Guide

Lathe

By Matthew Manton and Duane Weidinger

camInstructor

Mastercam® X9 Training Guide Lathe
Published by
CamInstructor Inc.
330 Chandos Crt.
Kitchener, Ontario
N2A 3C2
www.caminstructor.com

Date: May 1, 2015
Author: Matthew Manton and Duane Weidinger
ISBN: 978-1-927359-74-7

National Library of Canada Cataloguing in Publication

To order additional copies of the book contact CamInstructor at:

Canadian Office	Phone 1-877-873-6867
330 Chandos Crt	Fax 1-866-741-8421
Kitchener, ON	email sales@caminstructor.com
N2A 3C2	

Printed in Canada

Requirements

Use of this book requires Mastercam X9 Lathe. Use of the Multi-media DVD requires a computer with speakers and a DVD ROM.
May 1, 2015

Contents at a Glance

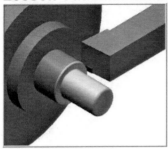

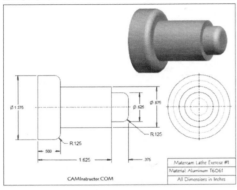

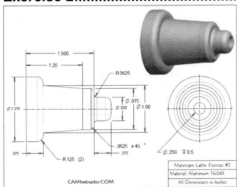

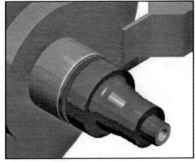

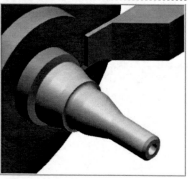

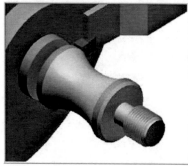

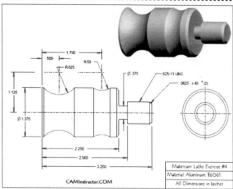

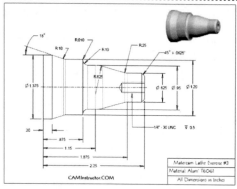

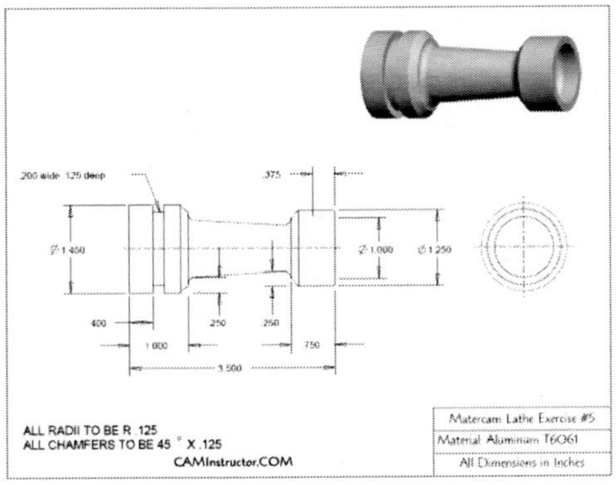
.200 wide .125 deep
.375
Ø 1.450
Ø 1.000
Ø 1.250
.400
.250
.250
1.000
.750
3.500
ALL RADII TO BE R .125
ALL CHAMFERS TO BE 45 ° X .125
CAMInstructor.COM
Matercam Lathe Exercise #5
Material: Aluminium T6061
All Dimensions in Inches

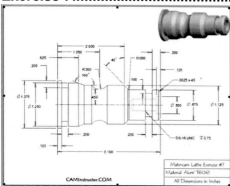

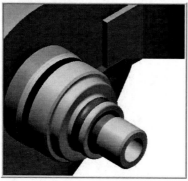

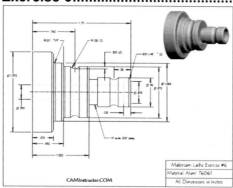

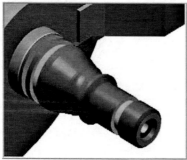

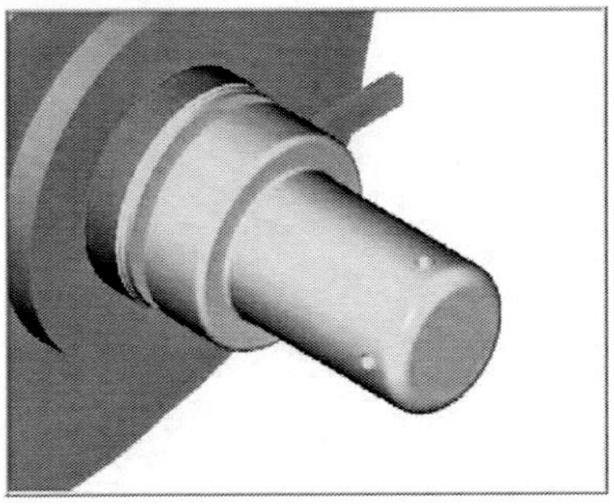

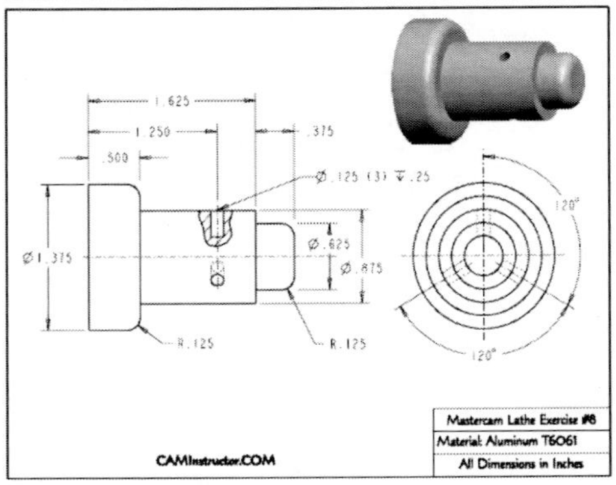
1.625
1.250
.375
.500
Ø.125 (3) ↧.25
Ø1.375
Ø.625
Ø.875
R.125
R.125
120°
120°
Mastercam Lathe Exercise #8
Material: Aluminum T6061
All Dimensions in Inches
CAMInstructor.COM

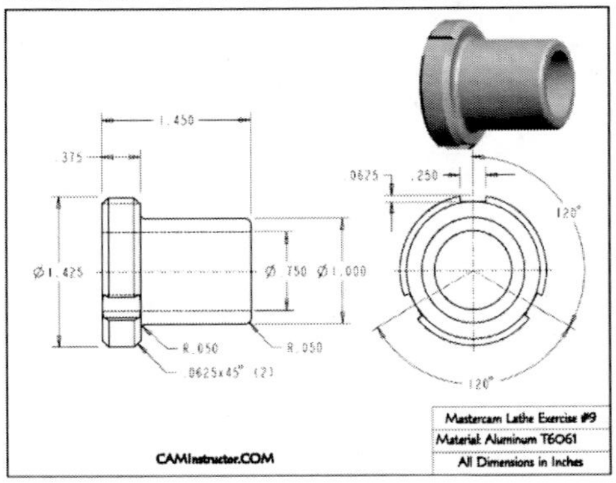
1.450
.375
.0625
.250
120°
Ø1.425
Ø.750
Ø1.000
R.050
R.050
.0625x45° (2)
120°
Mastercam Lathe Exercise #9
Material: Aluminum T6061
All Dimensions in Inches
CAMInstructor.COM

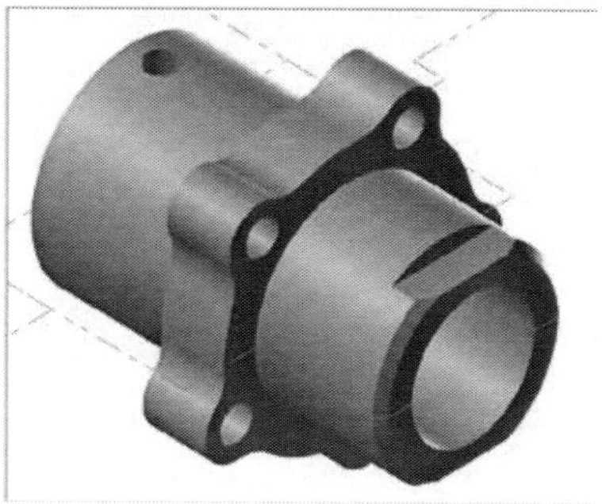

What's on the CD/DVD?

1. Training Videos

Getting Started-Video

- An overview of how the CD/DVD works

Setting the Mastercam Environment

Tips and Techniques-Videos

- Getting Help – 6 Minutes
- Lathe Diameter & Radius – 7 Minutes
- Creating Lines – 12 Minutes
- Creating Arcs and Circles – 12 Minutes
- Trim and Extend – 5 Minutes
- Xform – 9 Minutes
- Stock Setup – 8 Minutes
- Backplot and Verify – 5 Minutes

Lesson-1 through Lesson-9 Videos

- Video instructions on how to complete each Lesson from start to finish.

Sample-Files

- Mastercam files required by certain Lessons in the book
- CAD files required by Lesson 5B

Mastercam HLE Installation Software

Install it onto your computer so you can practice and work in Mastercam. **Please note**; Mastercam HLE Software is a full working copy of Mastercam, however it will NOT allow you to create NC code.

How To Use The Training Guides

This book set includes 1 book and 2 DVDs;

1. Mastercam Training Guide for Lathe
2. Mastercam Training Multi-media instruction for Lathe
3. Mastercam HLE Software – Installation disk

The software required to use this book is as follows:

- Mastercam X9 Lathe

Use of the Multi-media DVD requires a computer with speakers and a DVD ROM.

Both the book and DVD are meant to be used in conjunction with each other, for example Lesson 1 in the Mastercam Training Guide relates to Lesson 1 in on the DVD.

Each Lesson has all the information required to create the Geometry, Toolpaths and G-Code (NC code) for the part.

Lesson 1 is the easiest Lesson to complete. Each Lesson gets progressively more detailed, therefore it is important for new users to start with Lesson 1 and progress through each Lesson in order.

We recommend the following as a guideline;

Mastercam Experience	Lessons
No Mastercam Experience	Start with Lesson 1 and then complete 2, 3, 4, 5, 6, 7, 8 and 9 in that order.
Experience using V8 or V9 Lathe	Start with Lesson 1, then jump to Lesson 3 then complete 4, 5, 6, 7, 8 and 9
Experience using any previous VX Lathe	Start with Lesson 4, then complete 5, 6, 7, 8 and 9.

All the Lessons in this book are designed to be machined using 6061 Aluminum. In most cases the parts are machined from standard 1.5 inch diameter stock.

Material Size and required Cutters for each Lesson is listed in the Setup Sheet at the beginning of each Lesson.

If you have any suggestions on how this Training Guide can be improved please email duane.weidinger@caminstructor.com.

Mastercam® X9

TRAINING GUIDE

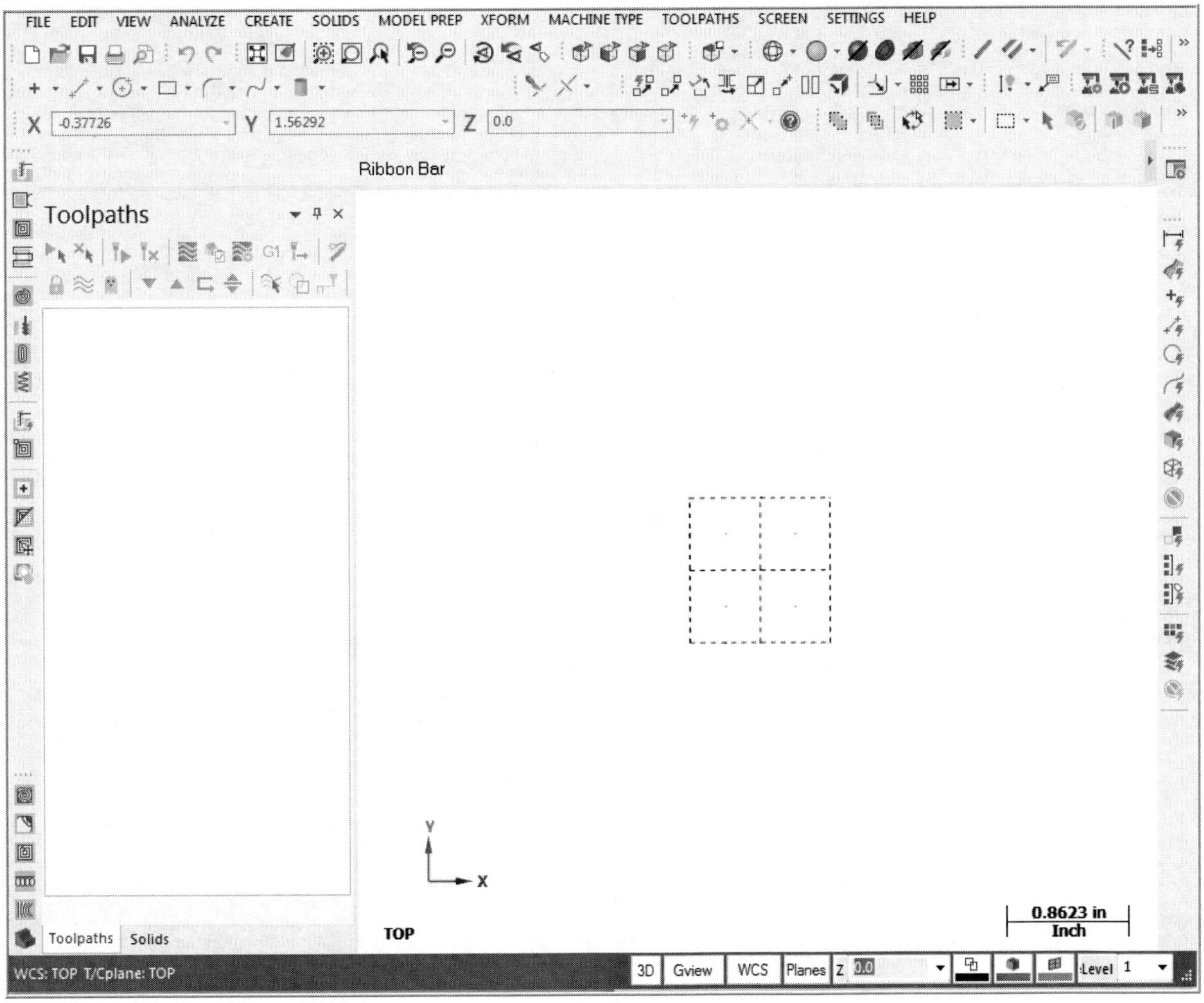

LATHE

SETTING THE ENVIRONMENT

camInstructor

SETTING THE ENVIRONMENT
COMPLETE THESE STEPS BEFORE STARTING EACH MODULE

Before starting the geometry creation and generating the toolpaths you should:

- Set the Grid. This will help identify the location of the origin.
- Customize the toolbars to machine a lathe part.
- Set the machine type to Lathe Default.

SETTING THE GRID:

1. Launch **Mastercam**.
2. Select from the pull down menu **SETTINGS>Configuration**.

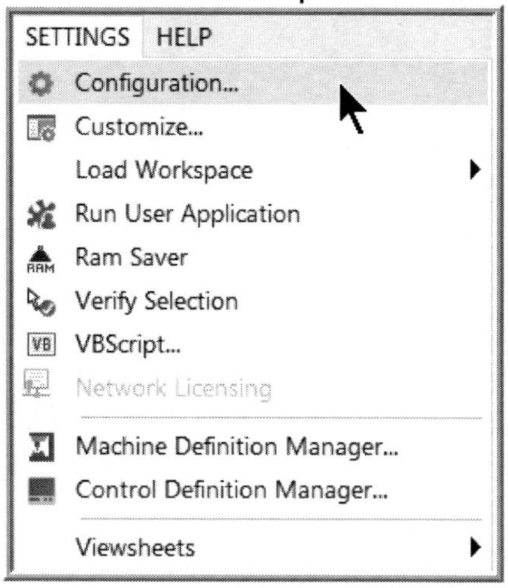

3. From the window on the left side of this window expand the **Screen** topic by selecting the **+ sign** and then select **Grid Settings**.
4. Enable the **Visible Grid** and change the **Size to 1**.

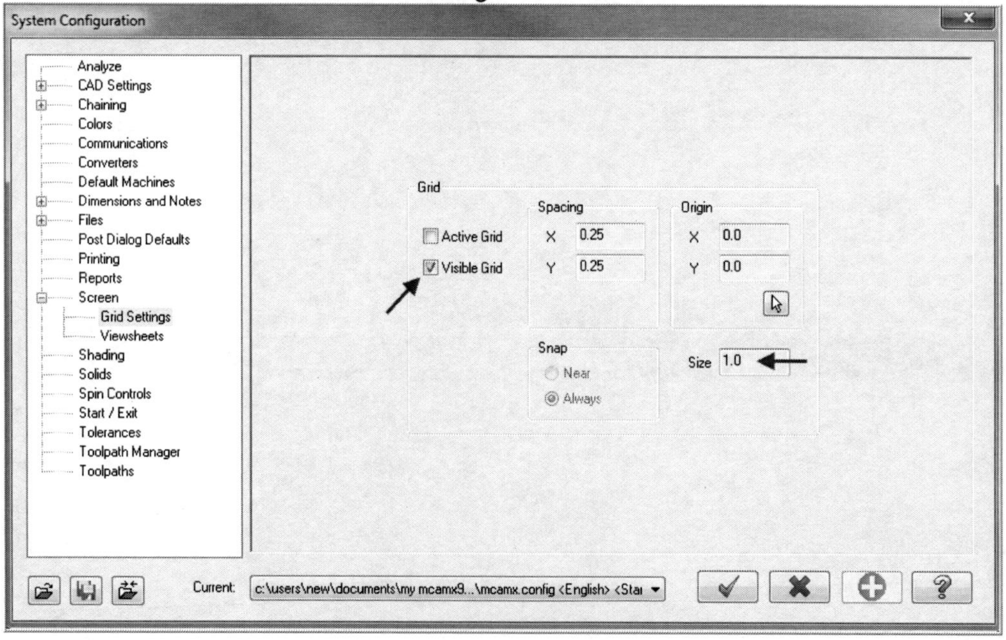

5. Select the **OK** button  to complete this function.
6. When prompted to **"Save settings to configuration file"** select **Yes.**

SELECTING THE TYPE OF MACHINE:

- For Lathe-Lessons 1 through 7 you will use the **Default Lathe** to machine the part.
- For Lathe-Lessons 8 and 9 you will use the **C-AXIS SLANT BED Lathe** to machine the part.
- To set the machine type to **Default** Lathe do the following:

1. Select from the pull down menu **Machine Type>Lathe**.
2. Click on **Default** as shown below:

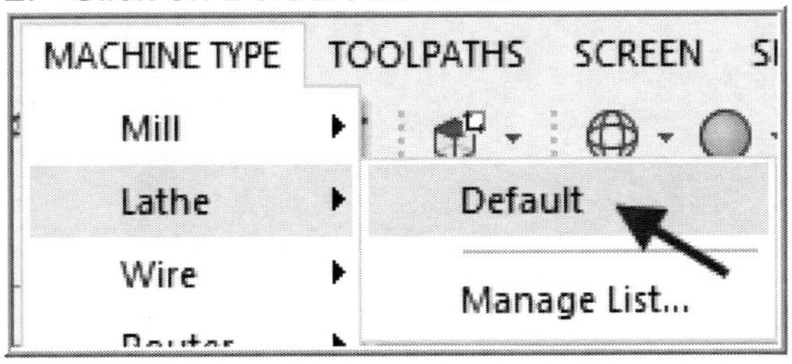

3. Your screen should look like the image shown below:

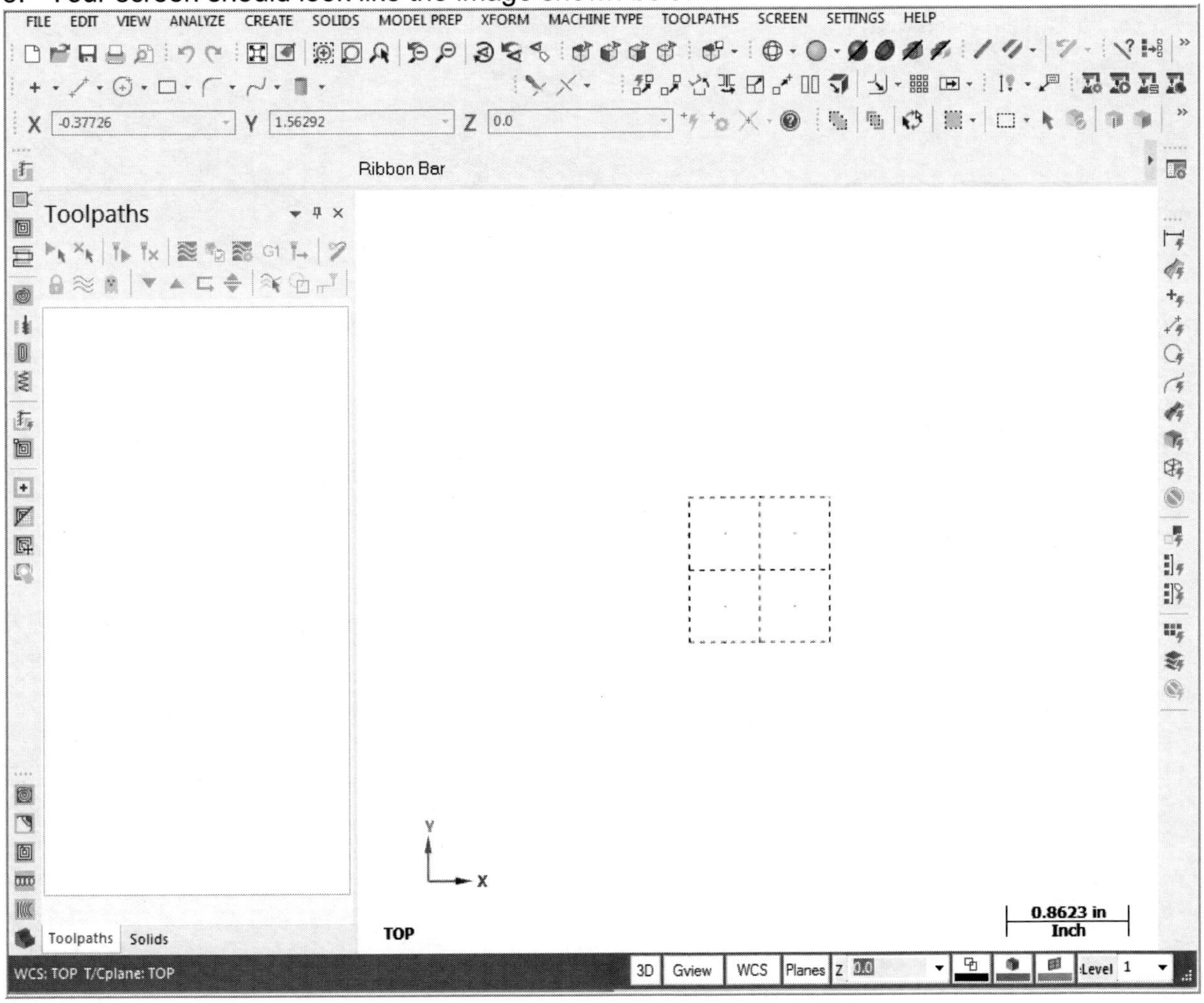

SETTING THE TOOLBARS FOR GEOMETRY CREATION AND MACHINING A LATHE PART:

1. Select from the pull down menu **Settings>Load Workspace>Lathe**.

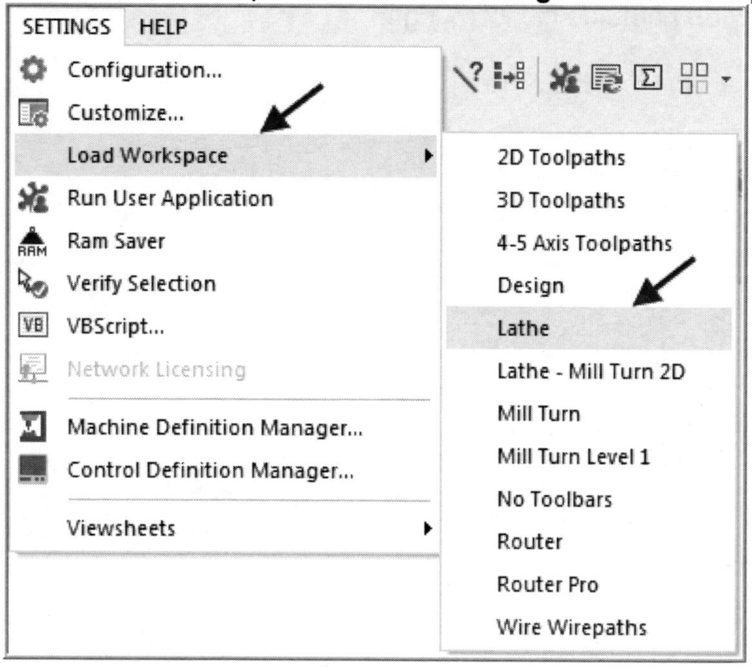

DISPLAYING THE TOOLPATHS MANAGER:

1. You can close the Toolpath/Solids Manager by clicking the **Close** button in the upper right corner. To open the Managers again, choose **View**, **Toggle Toolpaths Manager** or **View**, **Toggle Solids Manager**.

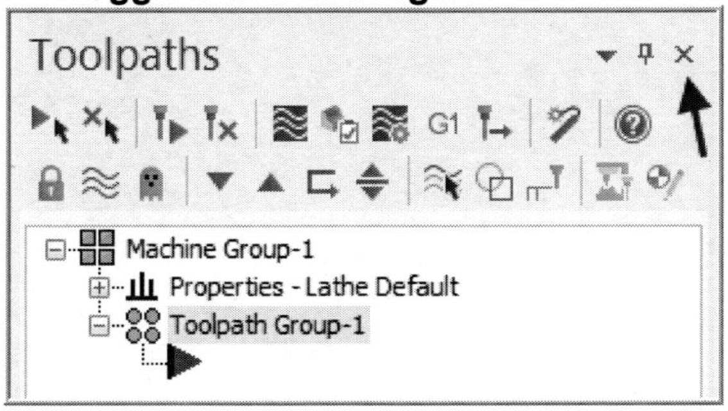

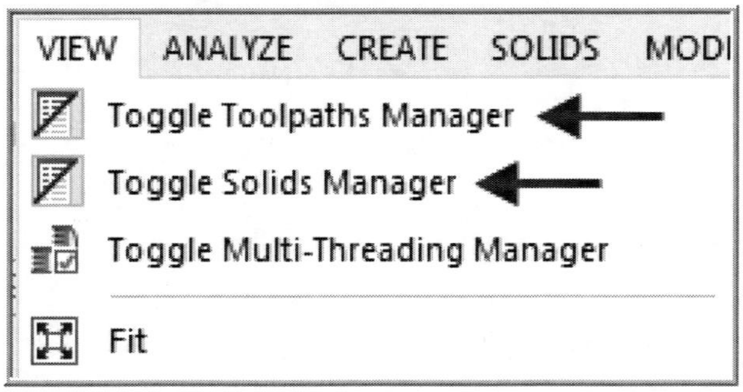

Note: Your settings for the Managers are modal between Mastercam sessions. This means that Mastercam "remembers" and maintains the position and size of the Managers, even if you close and re-open Mastercam.

Toolpaths Manager Hidden

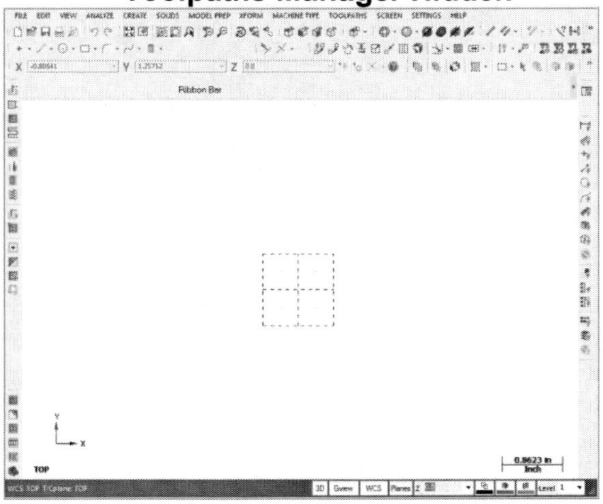

Toolpaths Manager Displayed

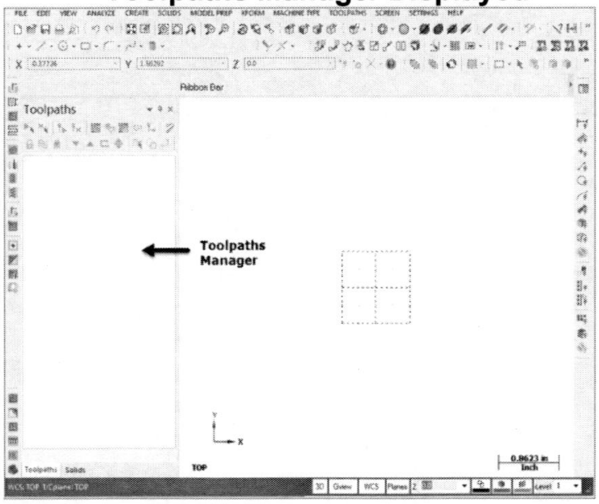

Mastercam allows you to move the Toolpath Manager and Solids Manager to a different location, re-size their window, and close or re-open them whenever you want.

By default, the Toolpath and Solids Manger are docked to the left side of the graphics window. You can undock the Managers and dock them where you like. To do so, drag the Manager pane to a screen position or to one of the docking icons that appear as you drag.

For more information on the **Toolpaths Manager** see the **Tips and Techniques** section on the **Multimedia DVD** supplied with this text.

Mastercam® X⁹

TRAINING

GUIDE

LATHE-LESSON-1

FACE, ROUGH, FINISH AND CUTOFF

camInstructor

Objectives

You will create the geometry for Lathe-Lesson-1, and then generate a toolpath to machine the part on a CNC lathe. This lesson covers the following topics:

➲ **Create a 2-dimensional drawing by:**
Creating lines.
Creating fillets.

➲ **Establish Stock and Chuck settings:**
Stock size.
Chuck Configuration.
Material for the part.
Feed calculation.

➲ **Generate a 2-dimensional lathe toolpath consisting of:**
Lathe Face.
Lathe Rough.
Lathe Finish.
Lathe Cutoff.

➲ **Inspect the toolpath using Mastercam's Verify and Backplot by:**
Launching the Verify function to machine the part on the screen.
Using Backplot to identify the correctness of the toolpaths.
Generating the NC- code.

LATHE-LESSON-1 DRAWING

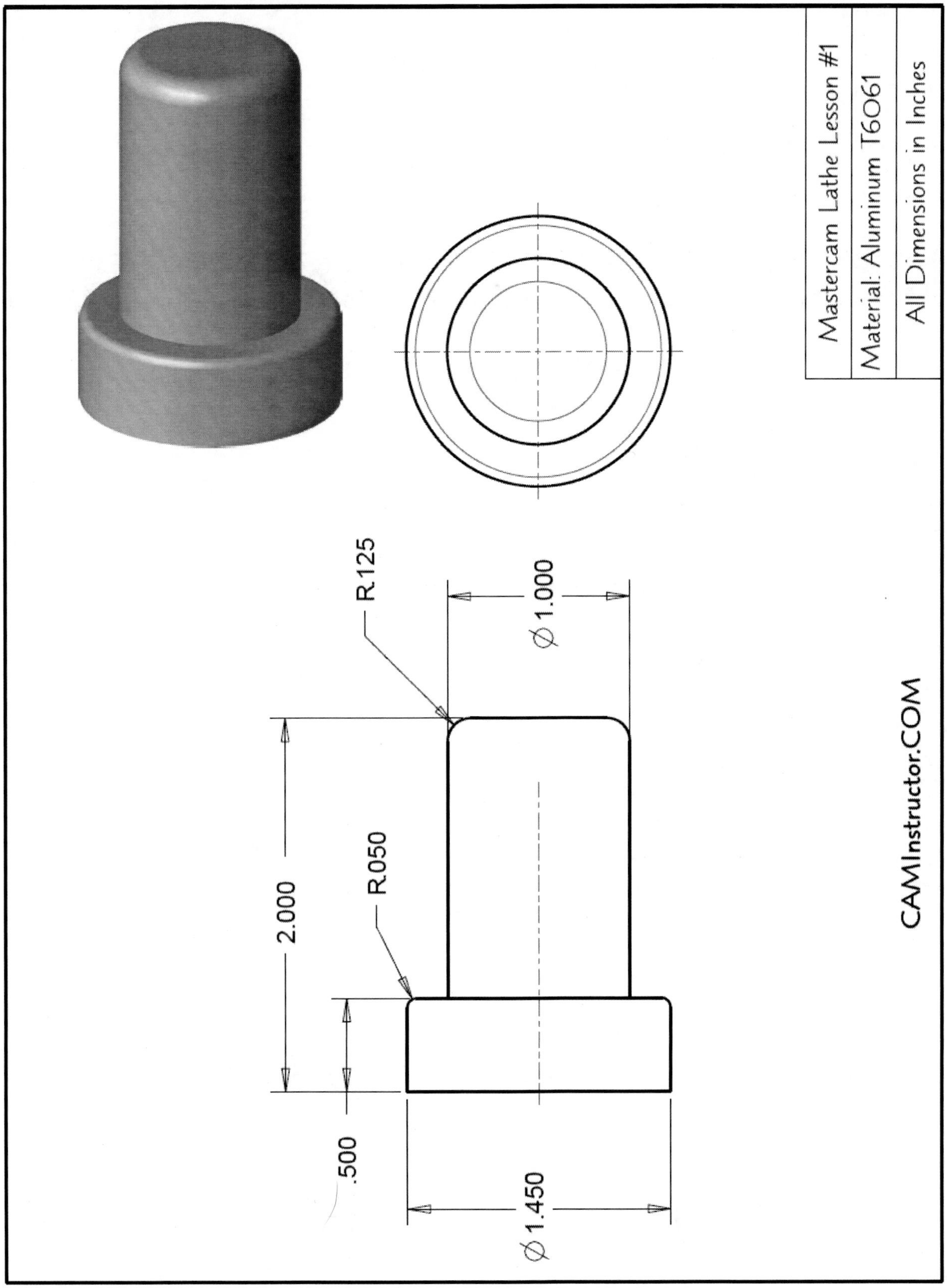

TOOL LIST

Two tools will be used to create this part.

➲ **Tool #1 Face, Rough and Finish the outside diameters**
Holder: Outside Diameter Rough Right Hand - DCGNR-164D.
Insert: 80 Degree Diamond Insert – CNMG-432.

➲ **Tool #2 Cutoff the part**
Holder: Outside Diameter Cut-off Right Hand.
Insert: 0.125" Wide.

LATHE - LESSON - 1 - THE PROCESS

Geometry Creation

TASK 1: Setting the Environment
TASK 2: Setting the Construction Planes
TASK 3: Create the Geometry
TASK 4: Create the Fillets (Radius)
TASK 5: Save the Drawing

Toolpath Creation

TASK 6: Define the Stock and Chuck Parameters
TASK 7: Face the Front of the Part
TASK 8: Rough the Outside Diameters
TASK 9: Finish the Outside Diameters
TASK 10: Cut off the Part
TASK 11: Backplot the Toolpath
TASK 12: Verify the Toolpath
TASK 13: Save the Updated Mastercam File
TASK 14: Post and Create the CNC Code File

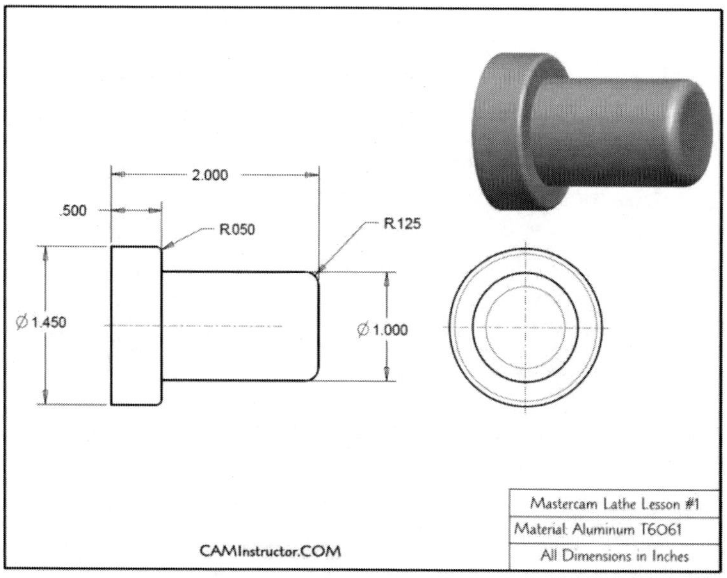

Geometry Creation

TASK 1:
SETTING THE ENVIRONMENT

Before starting the geometry creation you should set up the grid and toolbars as outlined in the **Setting the Environment** section at the beginning of this text:

1. Set up the **Grid**. This will help identify the location of the origin.
2. Load the Workspace – **SETTINGS>Load Workspace>Lathe** to machine a part on the Lathe.
3. Set the **MACHINE TYPE** to the **Lathe Default**.

TASK 2:
SETTING THE CONSTRUCTION PLANES:

➲ **Set the Construction Plane to Lathe diameter +D +Z (WCS)**

1. Click on **Planes** at the bottom of the screen as shown below:

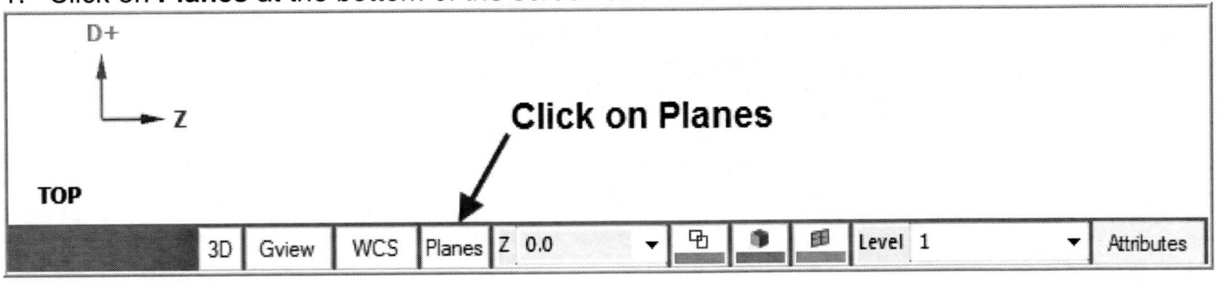

2. Click on **Lathe diameter>+D +Z (WCS)** as shown below:

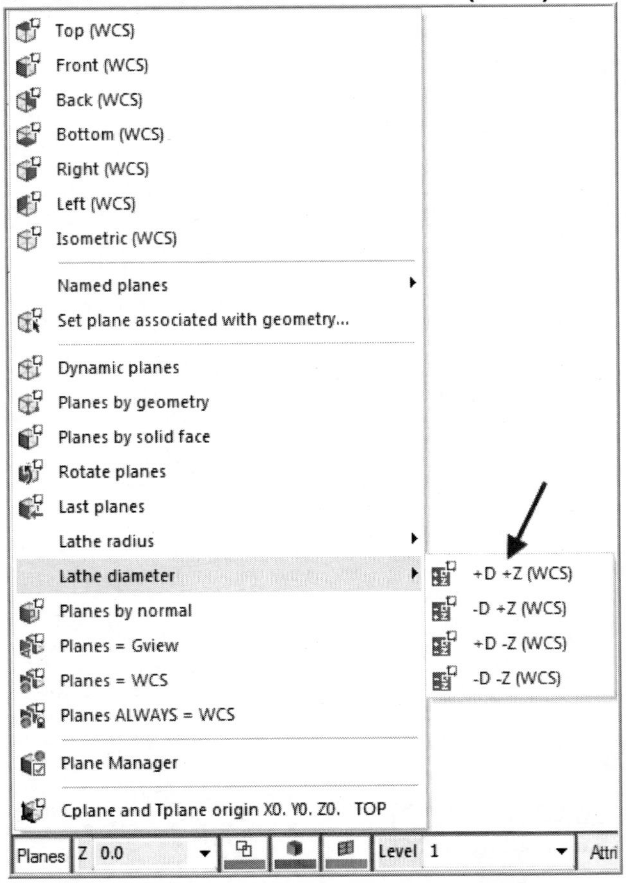

TASK 3:
CREATE THE GEOMETRY – THE RIGHT HAND FACE IS AT Z0

- ➲ This task explains how to create the geometry of this part. In this lathe part you only need to create **half of the geometry**, the geometry above the center line.
- ➲ Lines 1 through 5 will be created first and then the fillet and chamfer will be created.

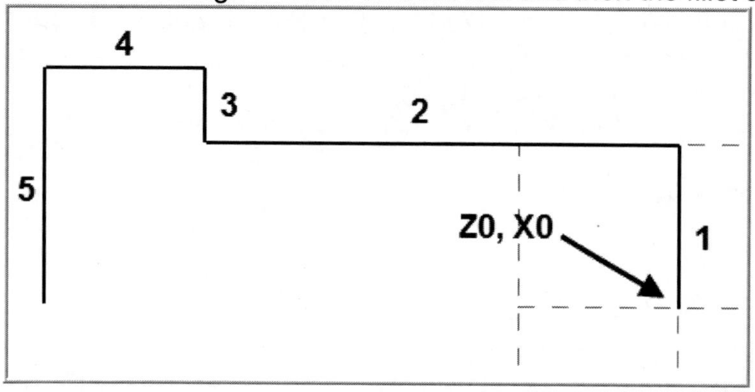

➲ **Create Line #1**

1. Watch the videos **Lesson-1 - Introduction** and **Lesson-1 - Task 1 to 3**.
2. Select from the pull down menu **CREATE>Line>Endpoint…**

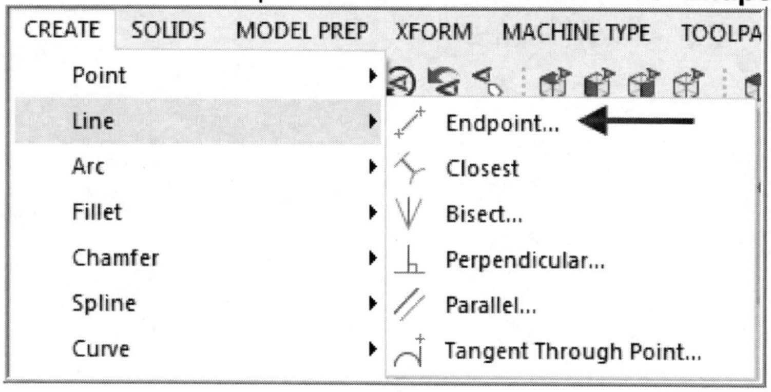

3. The **Line ribbon bar** appears.

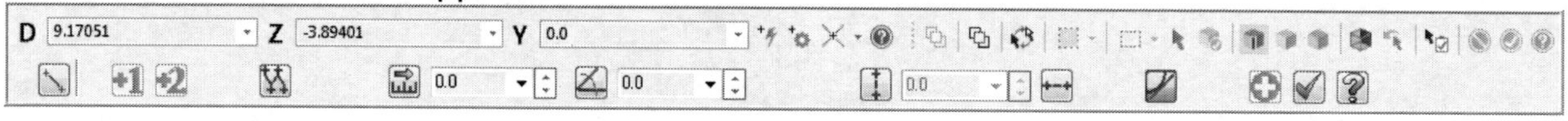

4. Move the cursor over the **center of the grid** and as you get close to the origin a visual cue appears.  With this visual cue highlighted click the **left mouse** button.

➲ The following are Mastercam Visual Cues:

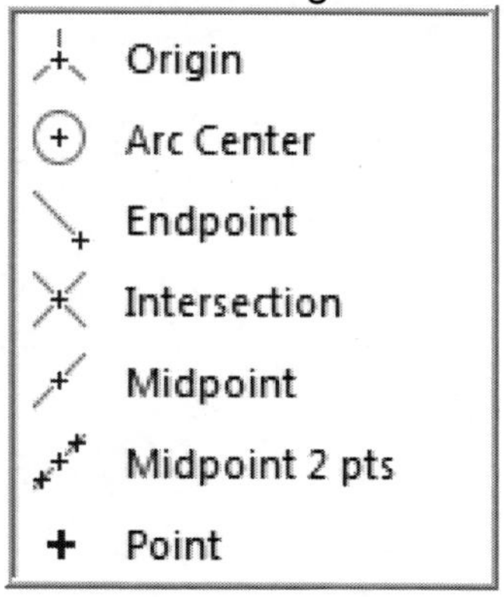

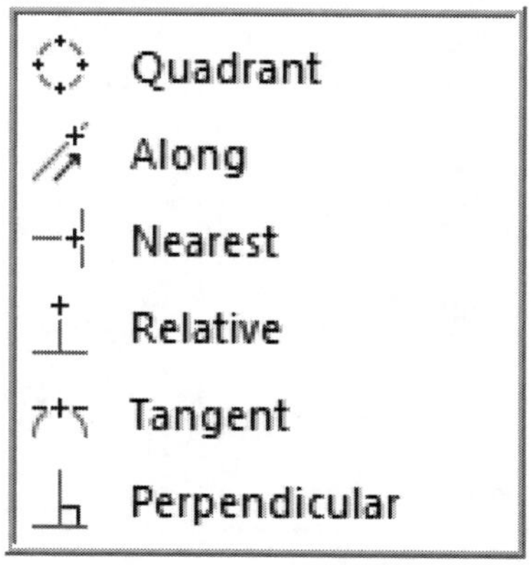

5. You are prompted to **"Specify the second endpoint".** Click in the **D** value space (Diameter) (as shown by the arrow below) and enter a value of **1.0**. Hit the Enter key and enter a value of **0 for the Z**, hit the Enter key again. **Note** the value of Y is set to **Zero**, this does not need to be input.

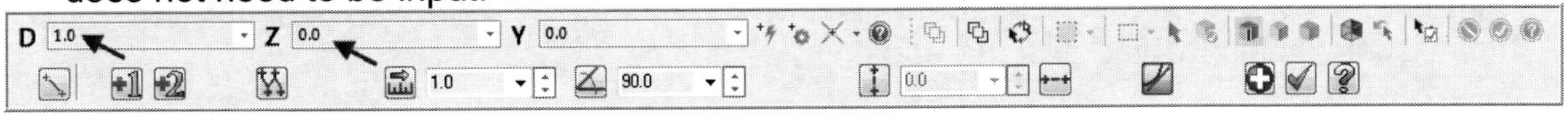

6. Click on Apply .
7. A **vertical line** should be visible as shown below:

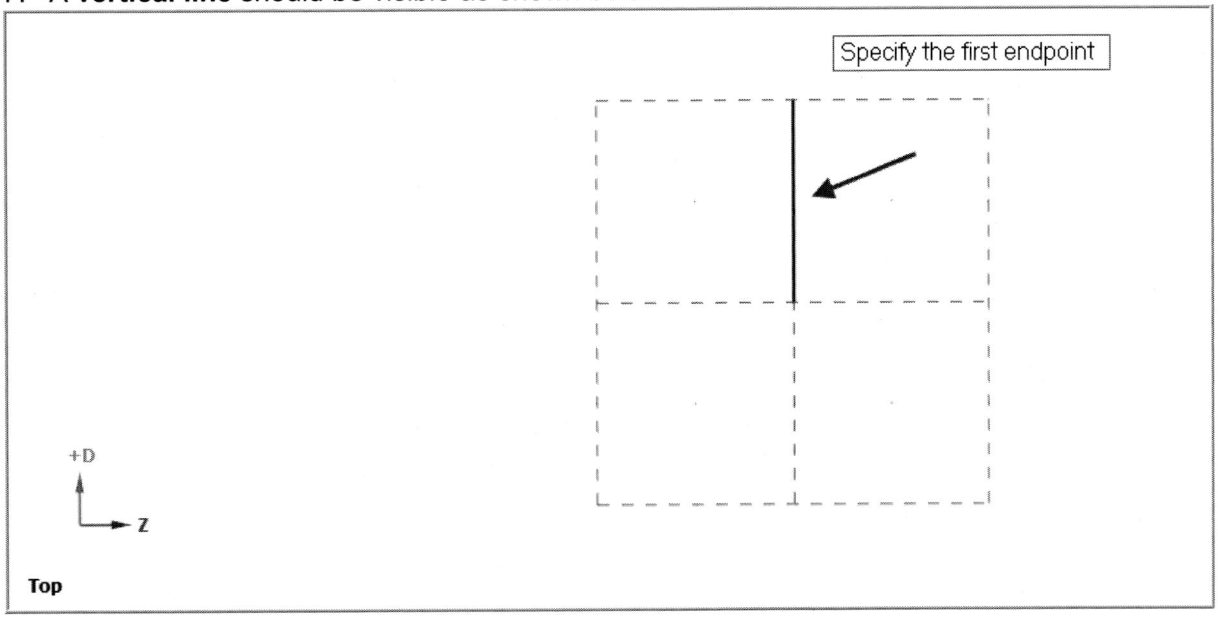

NOTE: If you make a mistake creating lines, click on the **Accept** icon and click on the **Undo** icon . Then redo the Line.

➲ **Create Line #2.**

8. You are next prompted to **"Specify the first endpoint".** Click on the **end of the line** that was just created as shown below and as you get close to the end point a visual cue appears.  This is the cue that will allow you to snap to the endpoint of this line. With this visual cue highlighted pick the end point of the line.

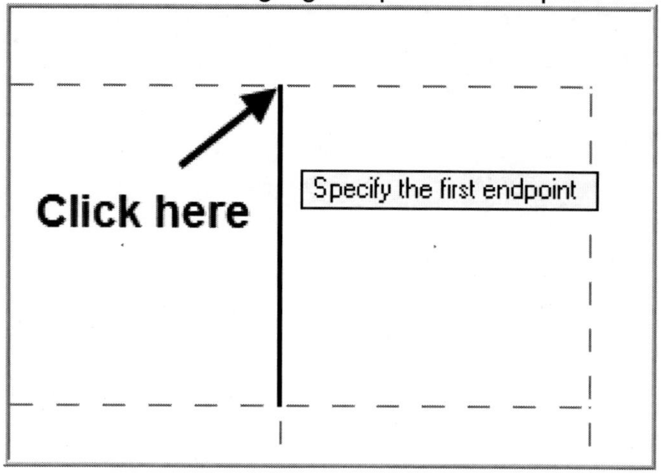

9. You are next prompted to **"Specify the second endpoint".** On the Line ribbon bar click in the **D** value space and enter **1.0**. Hit the Enter key and enter a value of **-1.5 for the Z**. **Note** the value of Y is set to **Zero**, this does not need to be input. Hit the Enter key once again to complete this line.

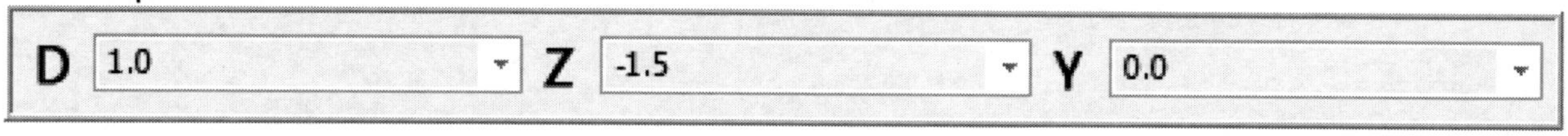

10. Click on Accept .

➲ **Create Line #3**

11. You are next prompted to **"Specify the first endpoint"**. Click on the **end of the line** that was just created as shown below:

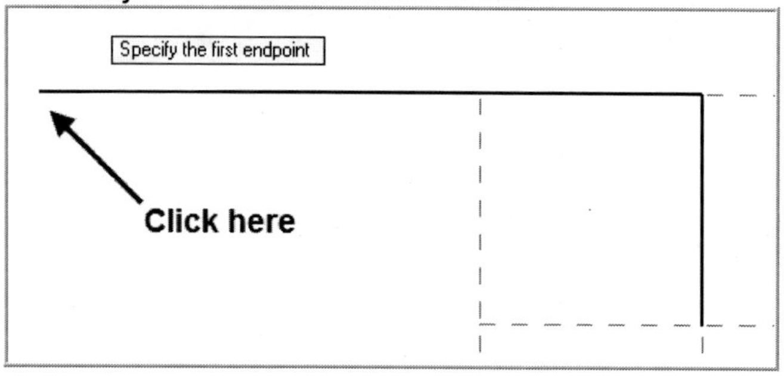

12. You are next prompted to **"Specify the second endpoint".** On the Line ribbon bar click in the **D** value space (Diameter) and enter a value of **1.45**. Hit the Enter key and enter a value of **-1.5 for the Z**. Hit the Enter key once again to complete this line.

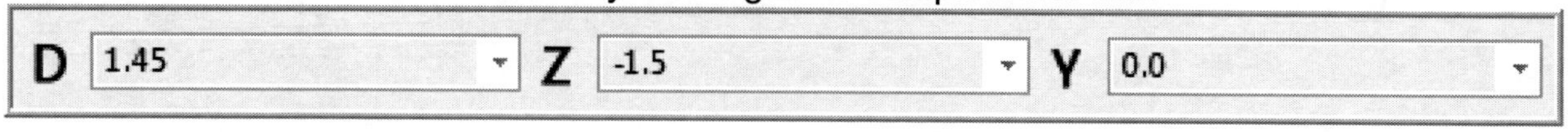

13. Click on Accept .

➲ **Create Line #4**

14. You are next prompted to **"Specify the first endpoint"**. Click on the **end of the line** that was just created as shown below:

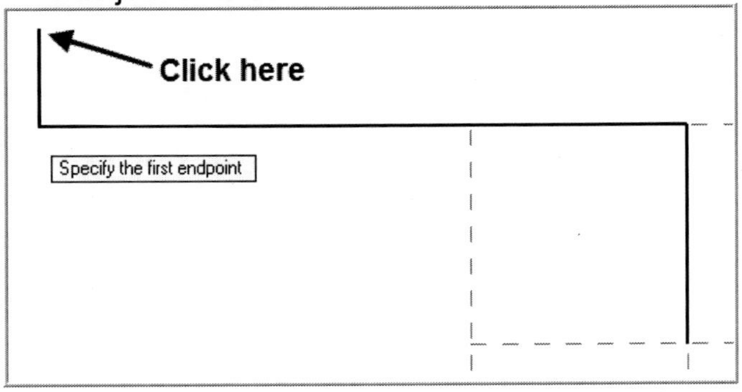

15. You are next prompted to **"Specify the second endpoint".** On the Line ribbon bar click in the **D** value space (Diameter) and enter a value of **1.45**. Hit the Enter key and enter a value of **-2.0 for the Z**. Hit the Enter key once again to complete this line.

16. Click on **Accept** .

17. Fit the image to the screen by clicking on the **Fit to Screen** icon as shown below:

18. Then by clicking on the **Un-Zoom .8** icon as shown below:

Fit
Use this function to maximize your view of visible geometry in the graphics window. When you use this function, the system positions and sizes the displayed geometry to fill as much of the graphics area as possible.

In addition to using the View menu, you can access this function from the right-click menu, from the toolbar, by pressing [Alt+F1], or by pressing the Home key on your keyboard.

Unzoom .8:
This reduces the size of the displayed geometry to 80% of its current size.

➲ Create Line #5

19. You are next prompted to **"Specify the first endpoint"**. Click on the **end of the line** that was just created as shown below:

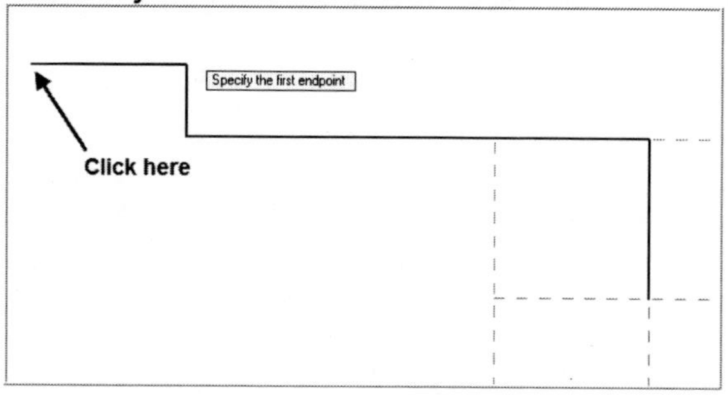

20. You are next prompted to **"Specify the second endpoint".** On the Line ribbon bar click in the **D** value space (Diameter) and enter a value of **0**. Hit the Enter key and enter a value of **-2.0 for the Z**. Hit the Enter key once again to complete this line.

21. Click on the **OK** icon  to complete this feature.
22. Select the **Screen Fit** icon to fit the part to the screen .
23. Your geometry should look like the figure below:

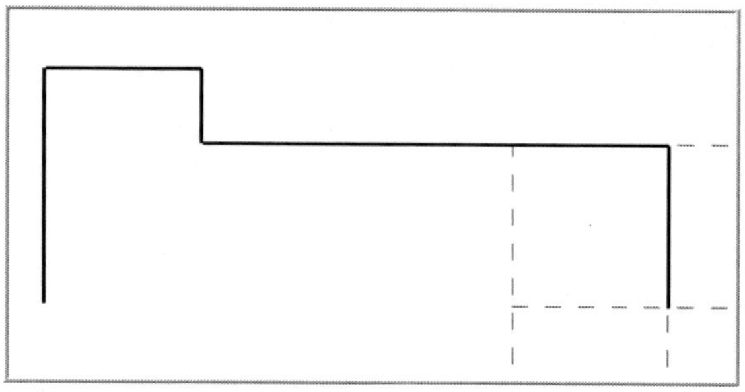

TASK 4:
CREATE THE FILLETS

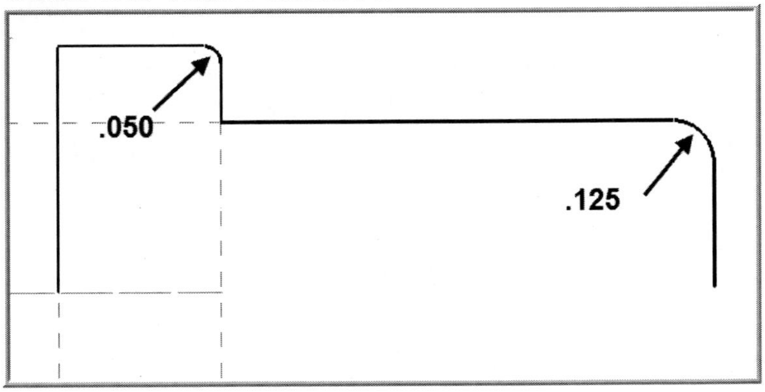

➲ **Create the .050 fillet radius.**

1. Select **CREATE>Fillet>Entities…**

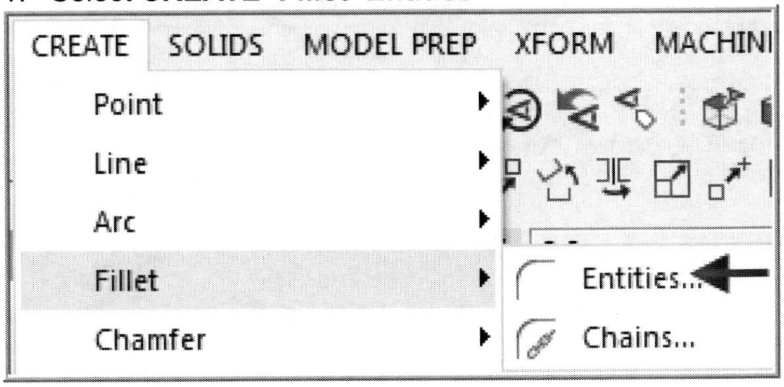

Fillet Entities
Use this ribbon bar to apply fillets to existing entities.

Before selecting the entities to fillet, choose the **fillet style** (normal, inverse, circle, clearance), and enter the desired radius value.

Then choose the first and second entities. Mastercam's auto-preview feature displays a temporary fillet at the selected location.

You can also choose to trim to the fillet or to leave the selected lines untrimmed. **Trimming is the default**, so for no trimming, select the **No Trim** button.

2. The **Fillet Entities** ribbon bar appears and you are prompted to **"Fillet: Select an entity"**.

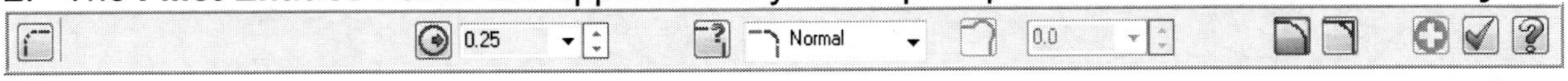

3. Click in the space for radius and input **.050** and then hit the tab key.

4. You are now transported over to the **Fillet Style field**. Click on the drop down arrow to review the various fillet radius styles and then ensure **Normal** is selected before moving on.

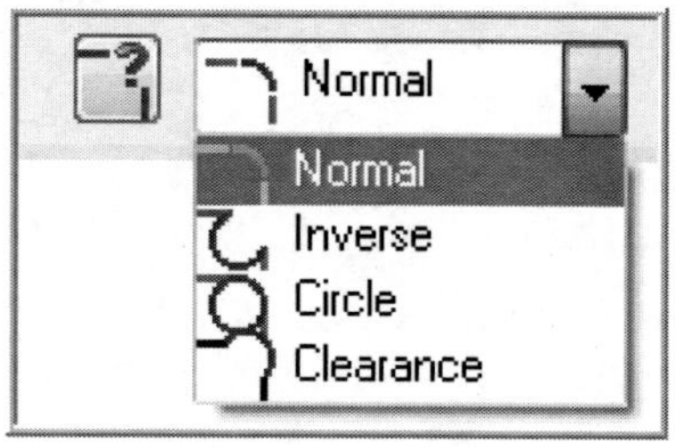

5. Ensure the **Trim** option for fillet is activated, the icon is depressed as shown below:

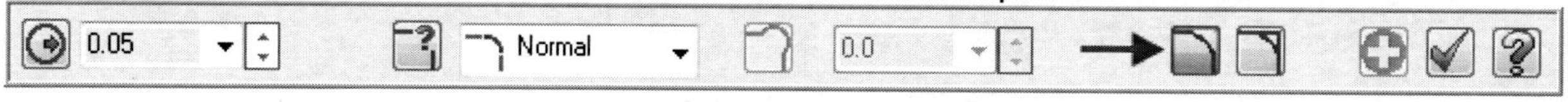

6. Click on **line 1** and then click on **Line 2** as shown below:

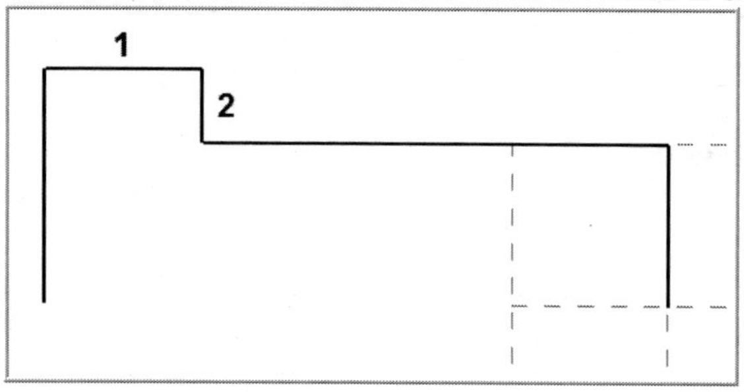

7. Click on the **OK** icon  to complete this feature.

8. The completed fillet is shown below:

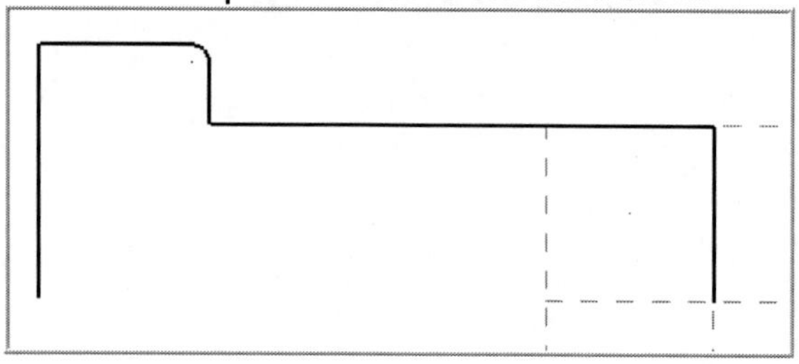

➲ **Create the .125 radius**

9. Select **CREATE>Fillet>Entities…**

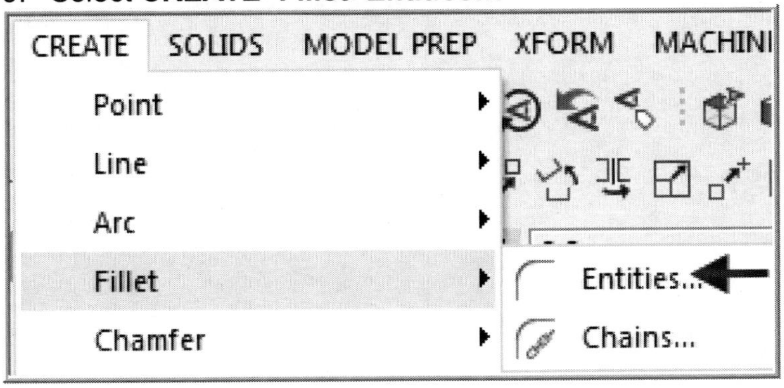

10. The **Fillet Entities** ribbon bar appears and you are prompted to **"Fillet: Select an entity".**

11. Click in the space for radius and input **.125** and then hit the tab key.

12. You are now transported over to the **Fillet Style field**. Ensure **Normal** is selected before moving on.

13. Ensure the **Trim** option for fillet is activated, the icon is depressed as shown below:

14. Click on **Line 1** and then click on **Line 2** as shown below:

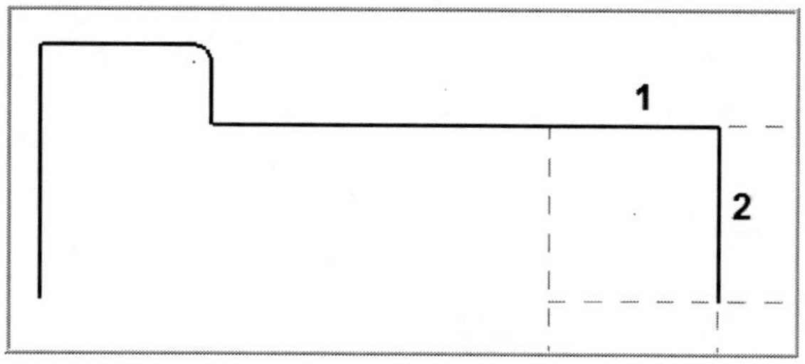

15. Click on the **OK** icon  to complete this feature.

16. The completed fillet is shown below:

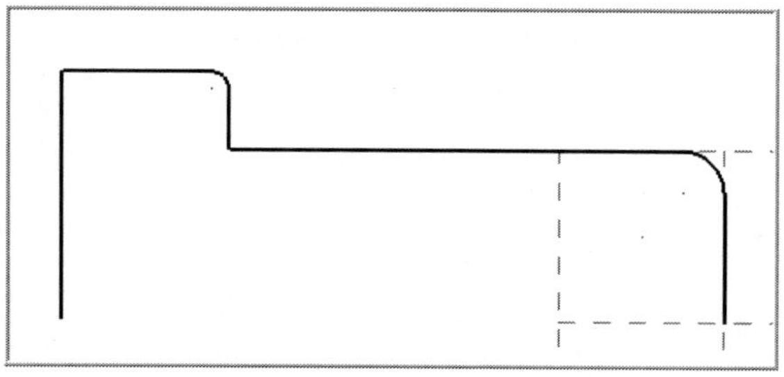

17. This completes the geometry for this part.

TASK 5:
SAVE THE DRAWING

1. Select **File.**
2. Select **Save As…**
3. In the **"File name"** box, type **Lathe-Lesson-1.**
4. Save to an appropriate location.
5. Select the Save button to save the file and complete this function.

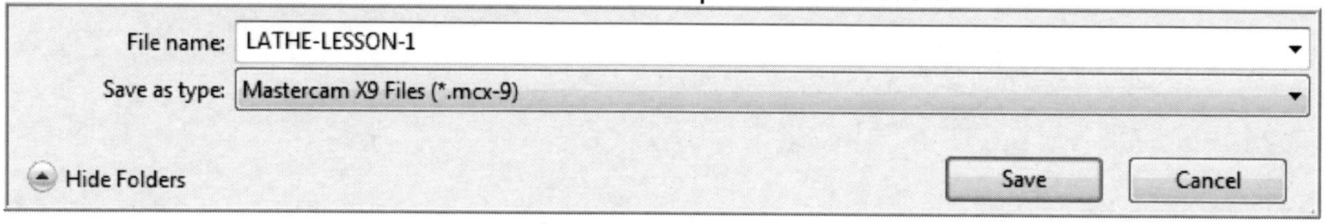

Toolpath Creation

TASK 6:
DEFINING THE STOCK AND CHUCK PARAMETERS

1. Select the **screen Fit** icon.

2. Select **Un Zoom Previous / .5**

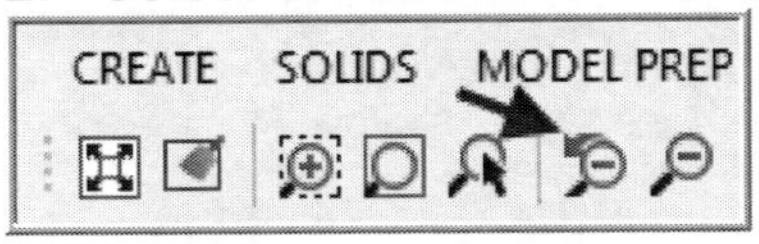

3. Ensure your screen looks like the image below:
   a. The Toolpaths Manager is open, if it is not Select Alt and O on your keyboard to open it.
   b. The properties icon displays Lathe Default. If it is not turn to the section titled **Setting the Environment** at the beginning of this book.
   c. The **Lathe - Lesson-1** Geometry is showing.

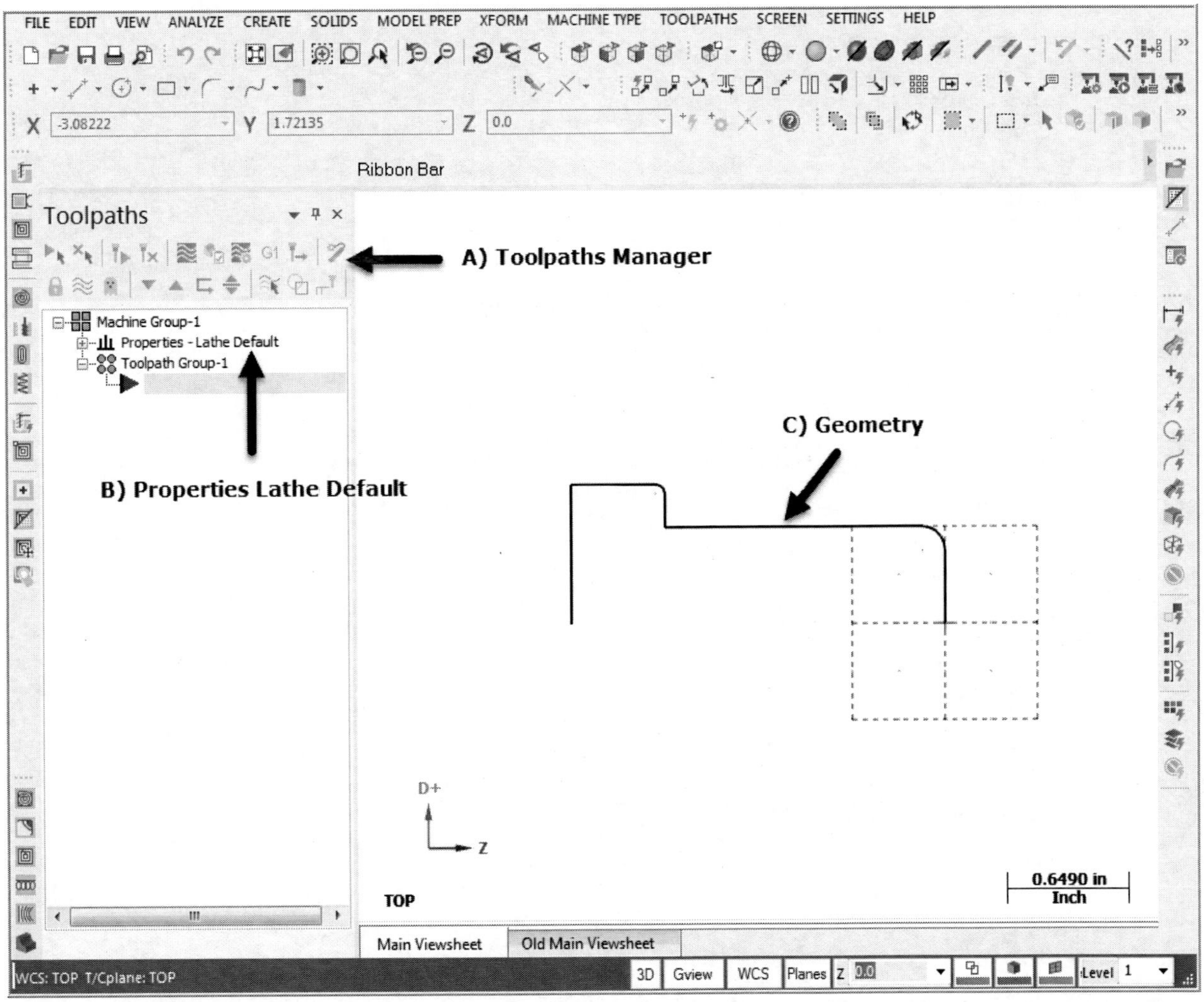

4. Select the plus in front of **Properties** to expand the Machine Group Properties.

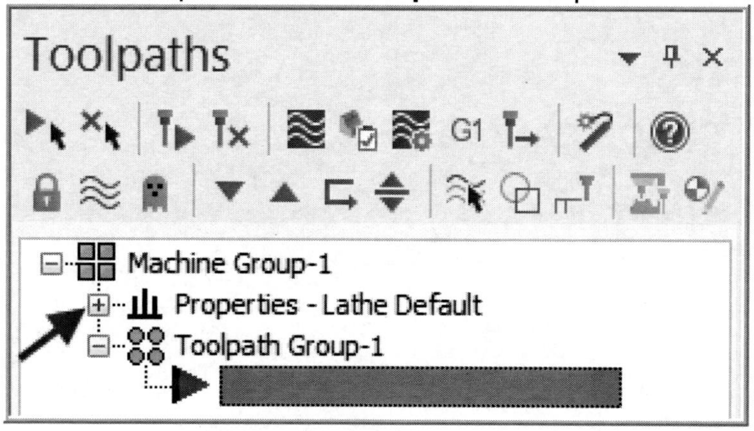

5. **This is optional** - To expand the toolpaths manager window, click on the outside of the window with the left mouse button (hold the button down) and drag it to the right.

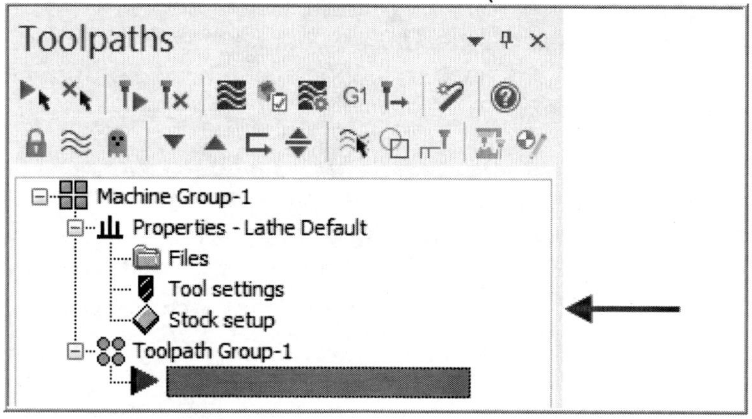

6. Select **Stock setup** in the Toolpaths Manager window.

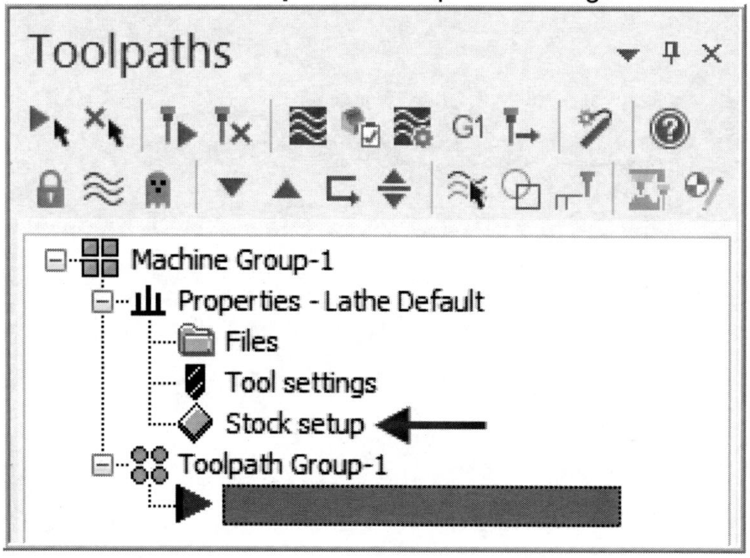

7. Select the **Stock Properties** button in the Stock Setup page as shown in the screenshot below:

Note: To learn more about Stock Setup refer to the Tips and Techniques section on the Mastercam Training Guide – Lathe DVD that accompanies this book.

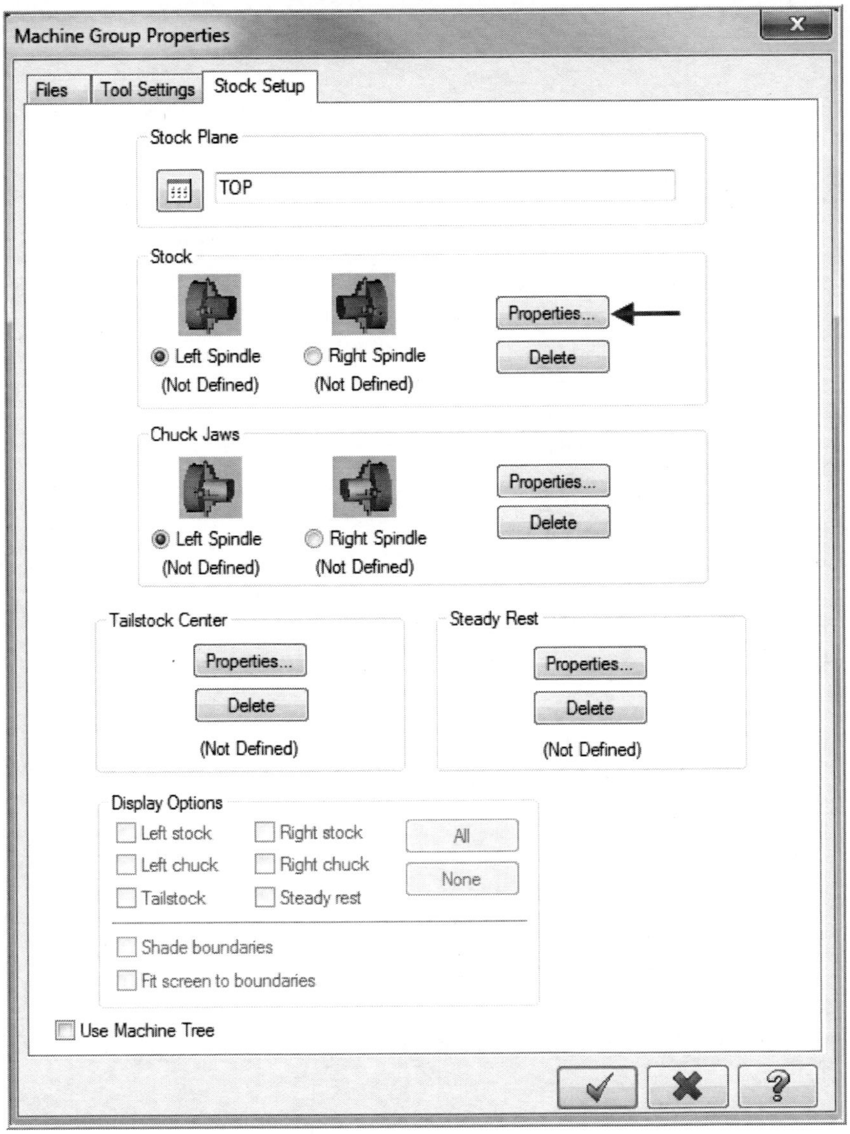

8. In the **Machine Component Manager-Stock** window click on the Geometry button and select Cylinder as shown below:

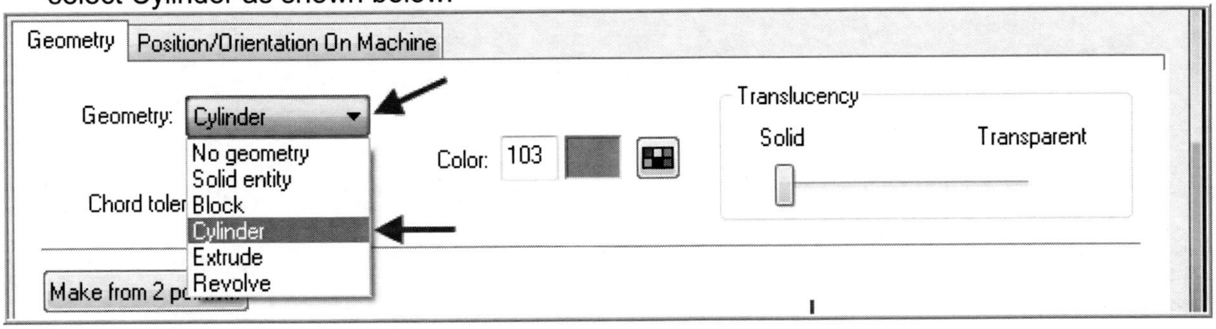

9. In the **Stock** setup activate **Use Margins** and set the values as shown below. Note that **Axis** is set to **–Z**.

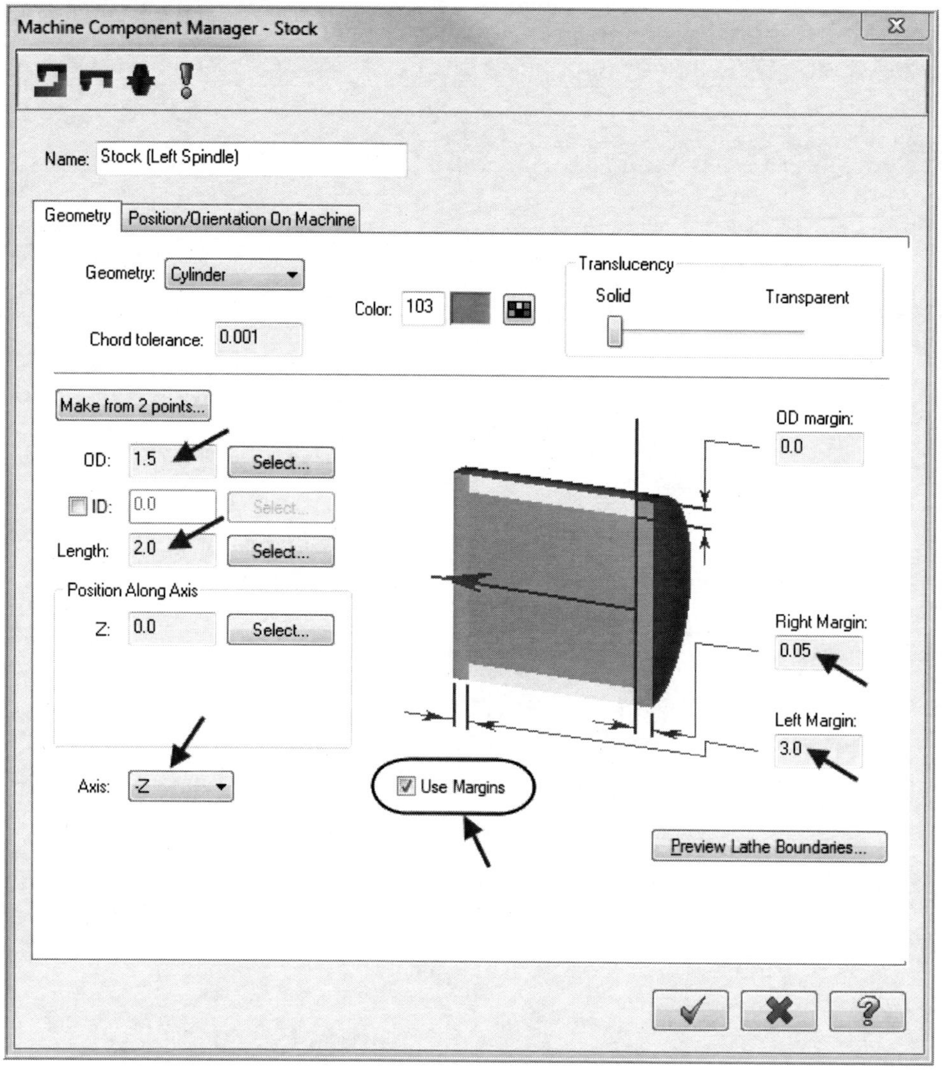

10. Click on the **OK** icon to complete this feature.
11. Still on the Stock Setup page activate **Fit screen to boundaries**.

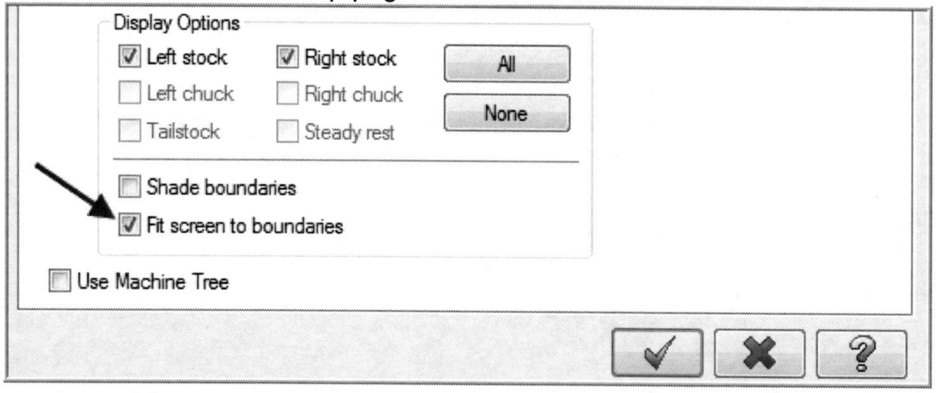

Fit screen to boundaries
Check to determine that the stock, chuck, and tailstock boundaries are included when fitting geometry to the graphics window

12. Select the **Chuck Properties** button in the Stock Setup page as shown in the screenshot below:

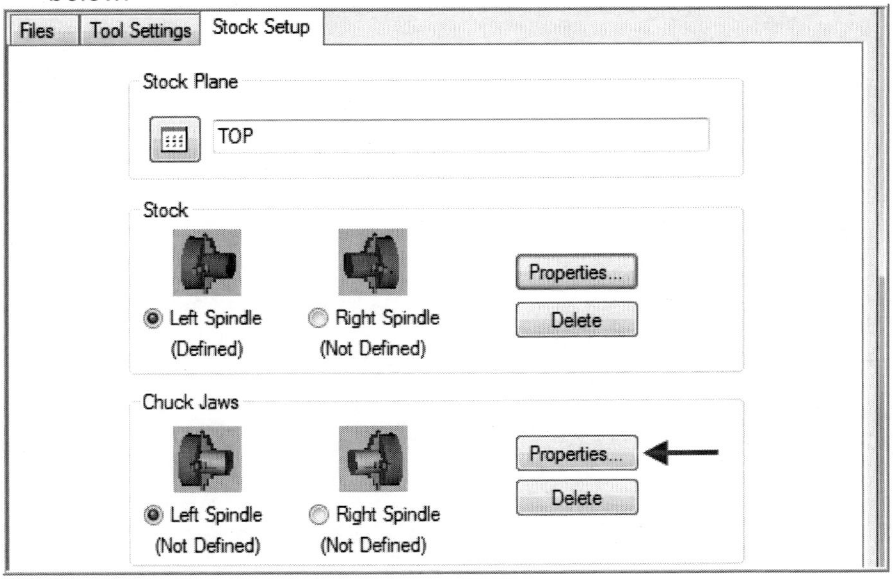

13. In the **Chuck Jaws** setup set the values as shown below:

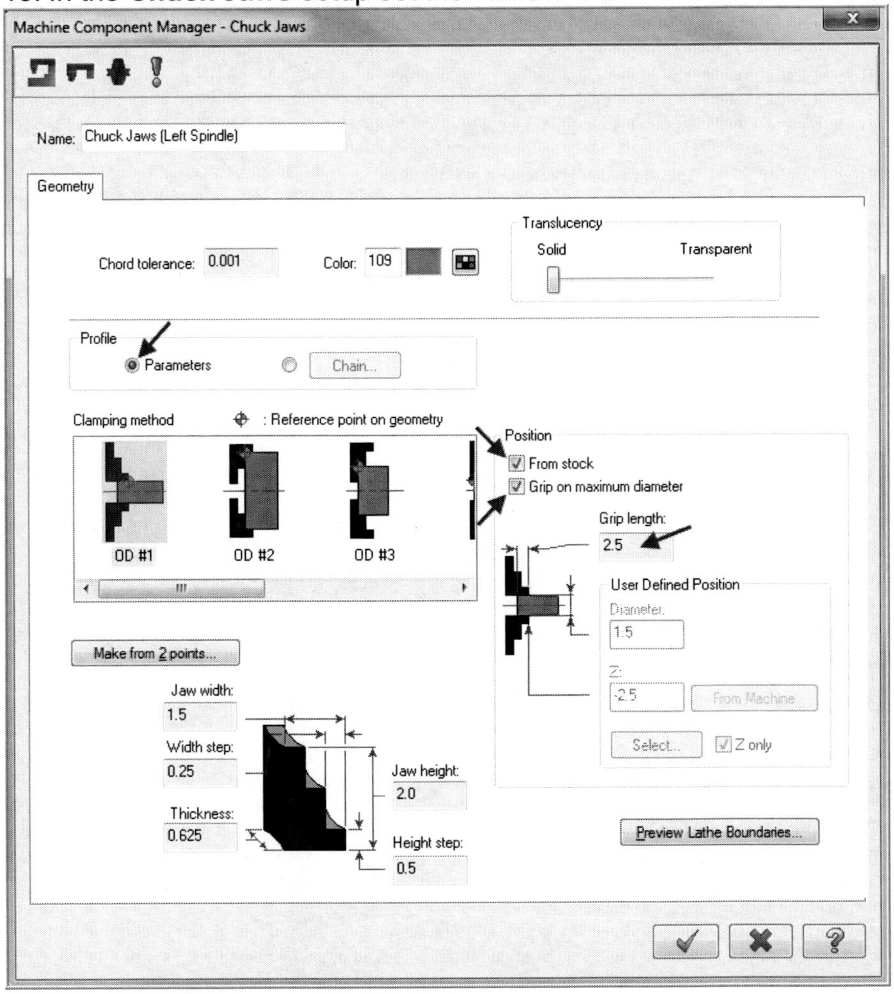

14. Click on the **OK** icon  to complete this feature.

15. Click on the **Tool Settings** page:

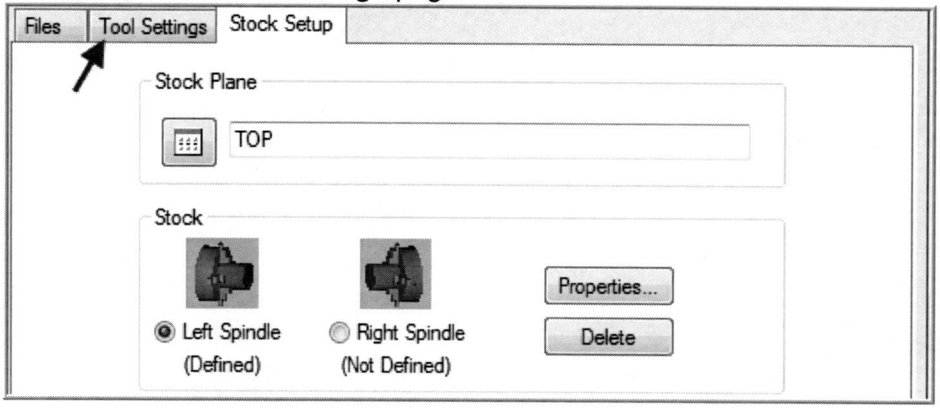

16. Make changes as shown below then click on the **Select** button:

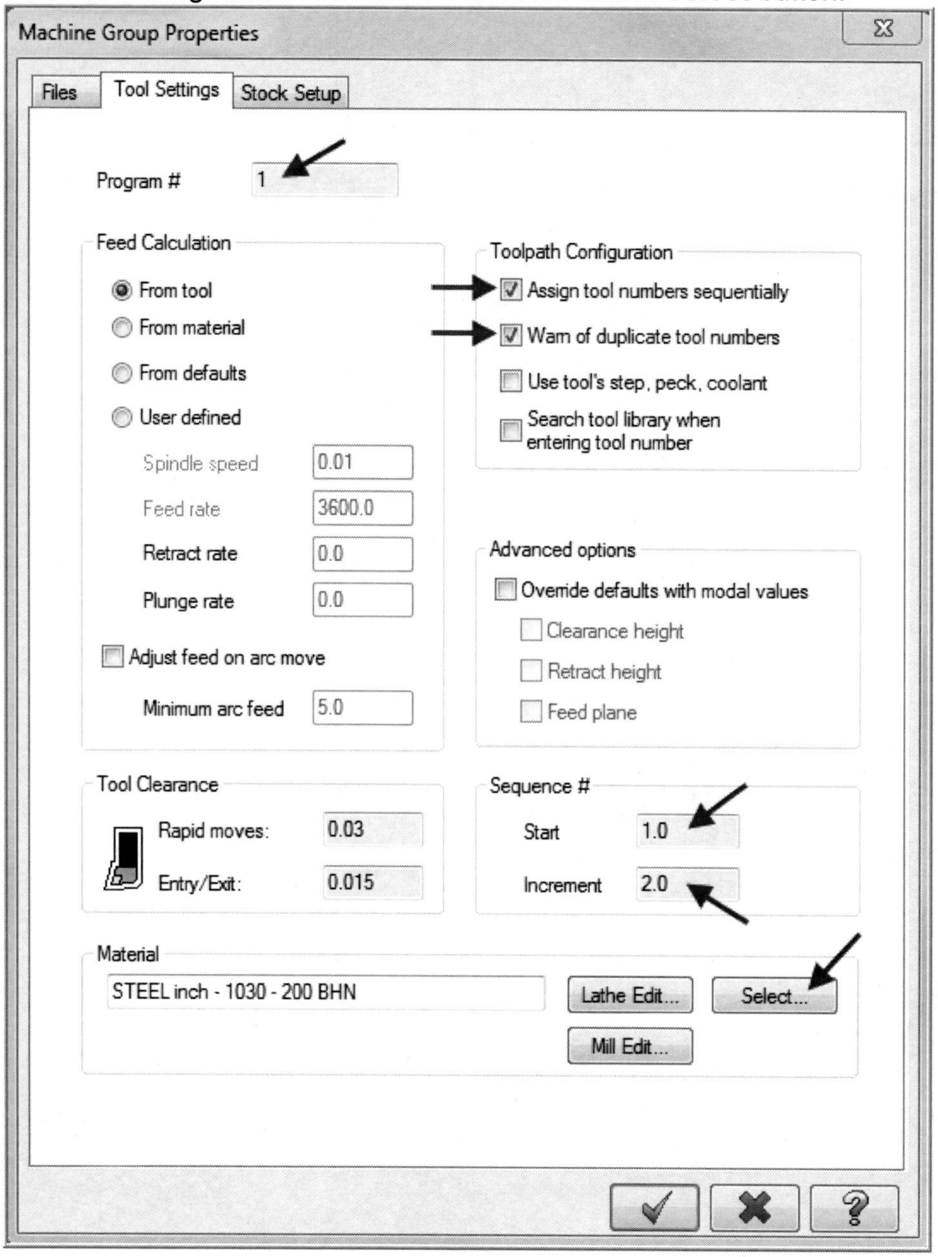

17. Select **Lathe – library** from the drop down **Material List** dialog box as shown below:

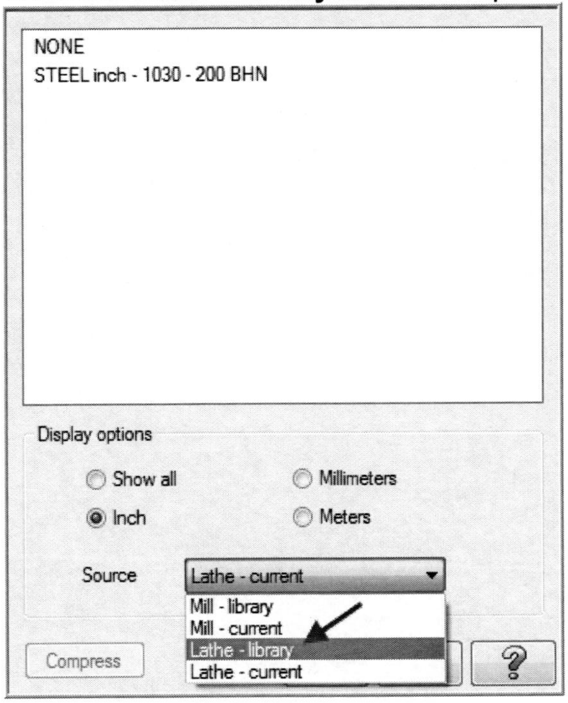

18. Select ALUMINUM inch - 6061 from the Default Materials list.

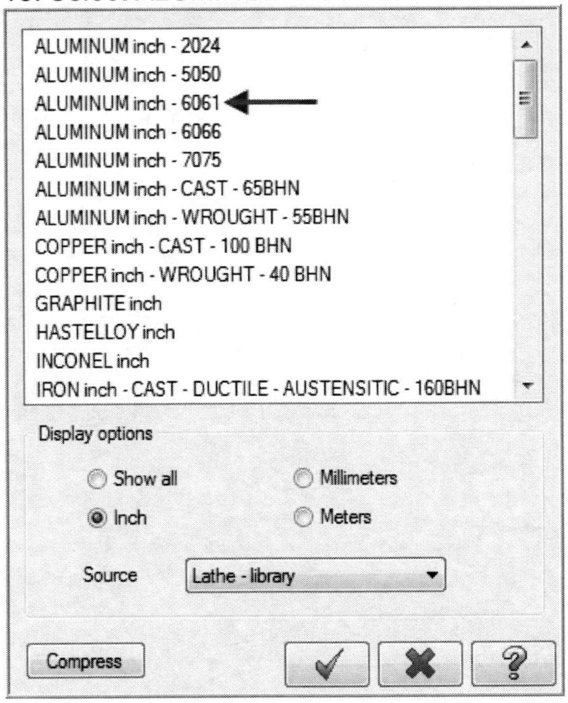

19. Select the OK button.

20. Select the OK button again to complete this Stock Setup function.

21. Select the **screen Fit** icon.

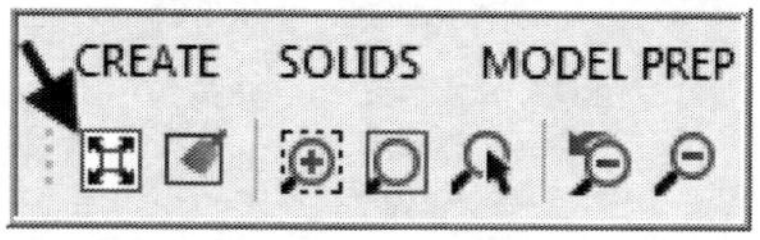

Notice the stock setup outline as indicated by broken lines as shown below:

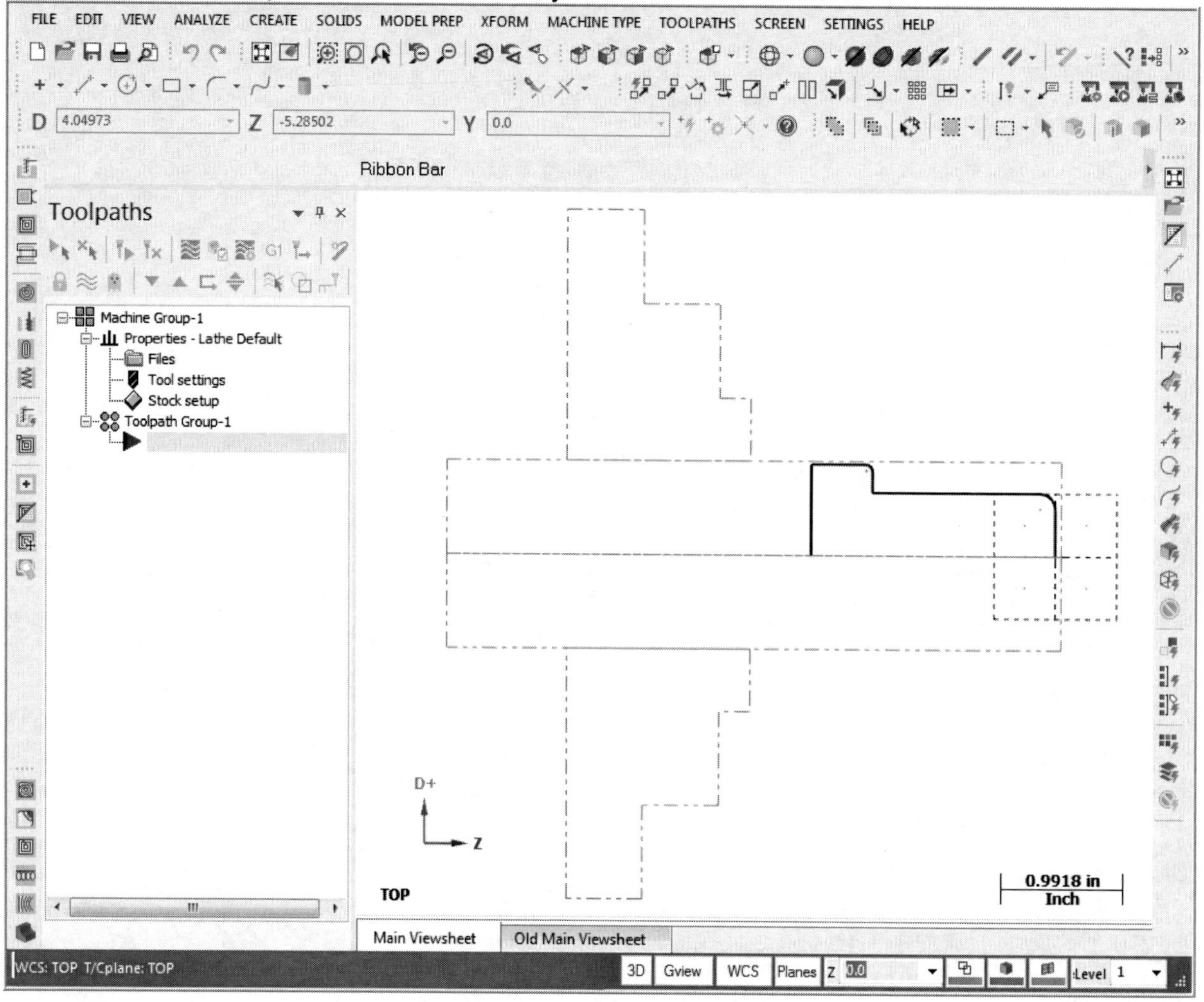

TASK 7:
FACE THE FRONT OF THE PART:

➲ In this task you will use a facing tool to face the front of the part in one cut.

1. If required select the **Fit** icon as shown:

2. From the menu bar select **TOOLPATHS>Face…**

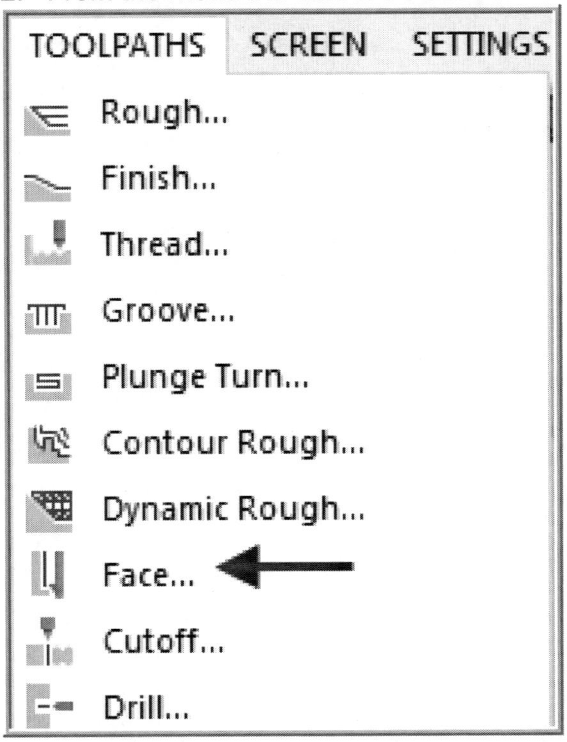

3. When prompted to **"Enter new NC name"** select the OK button  to accept LATHE-LESSON-1 as shown below:

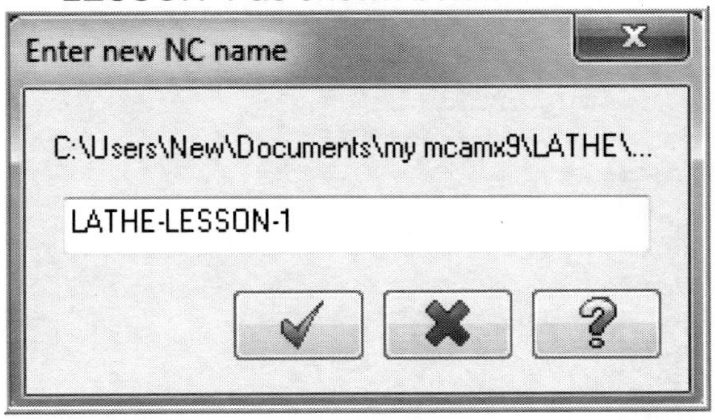

➲ After selecting the OK button you are confronted with **Toolpath parameters** page. The first task here will be to select **Tool #1 an OD Rough- Right – 80 deg.**

4. Click on **Tool #1 OD ROUGH RIGHT** and make changes in the Toolpath parameters page as shown below:

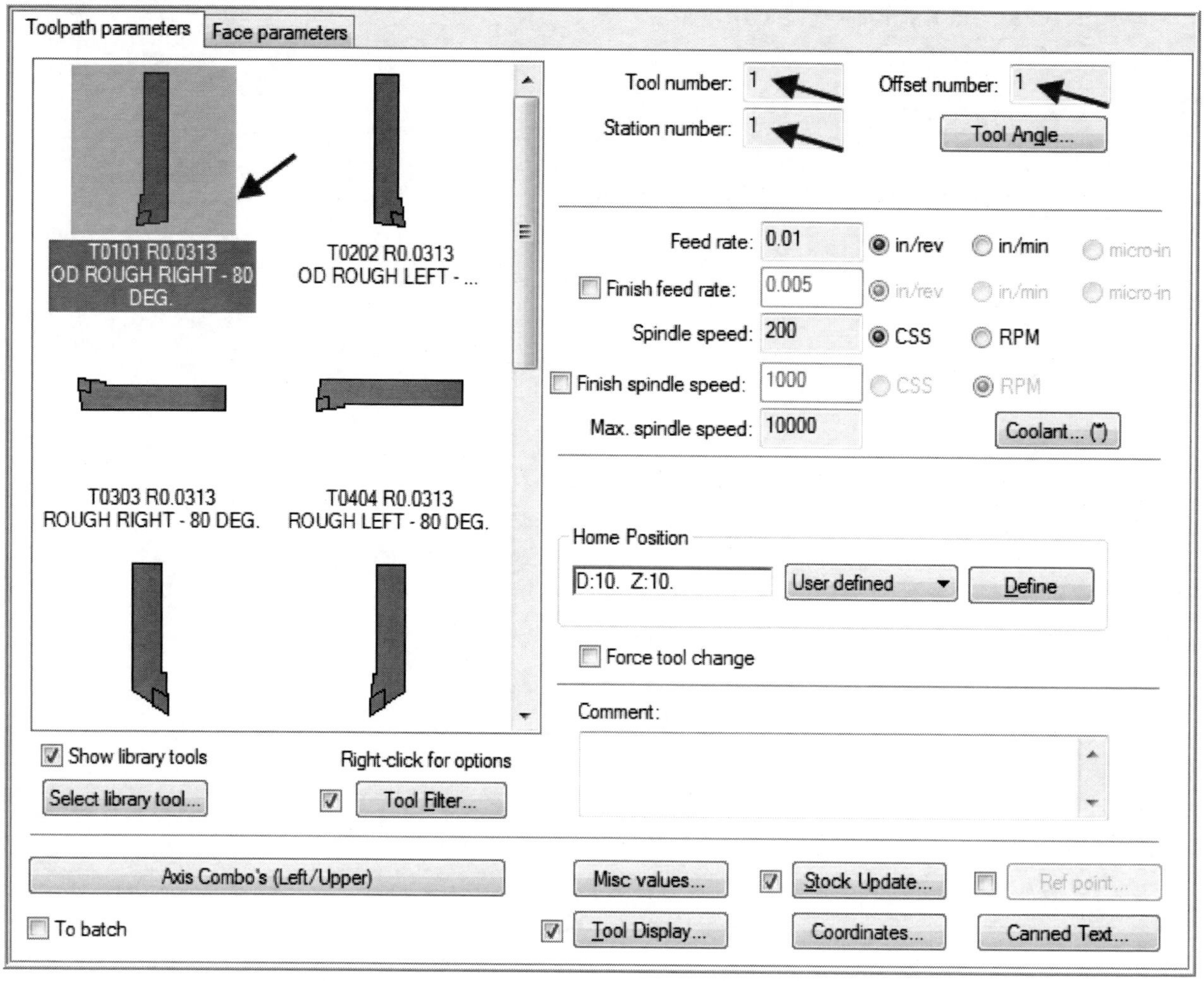

5. Select the **Face parameters** page as shown below:

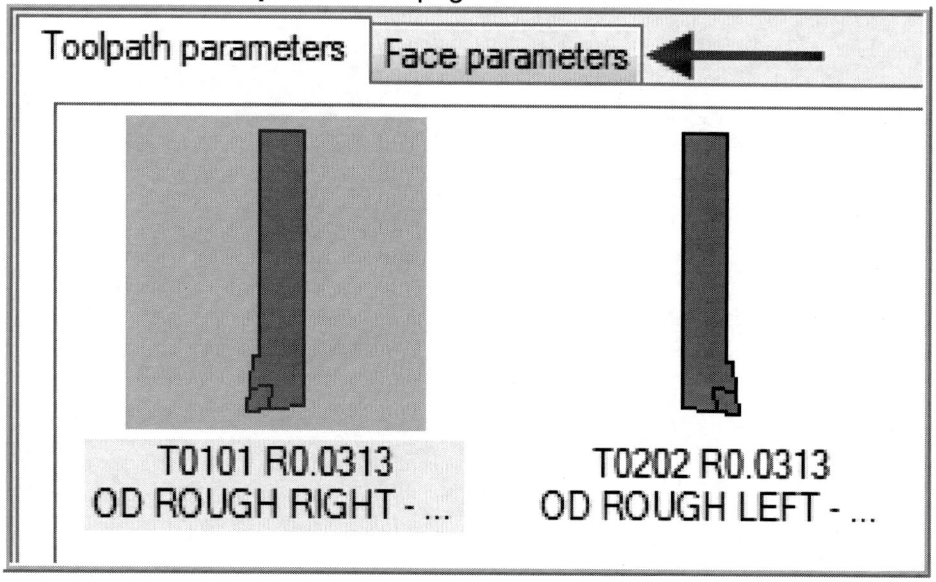

6. Make changes as shown below:

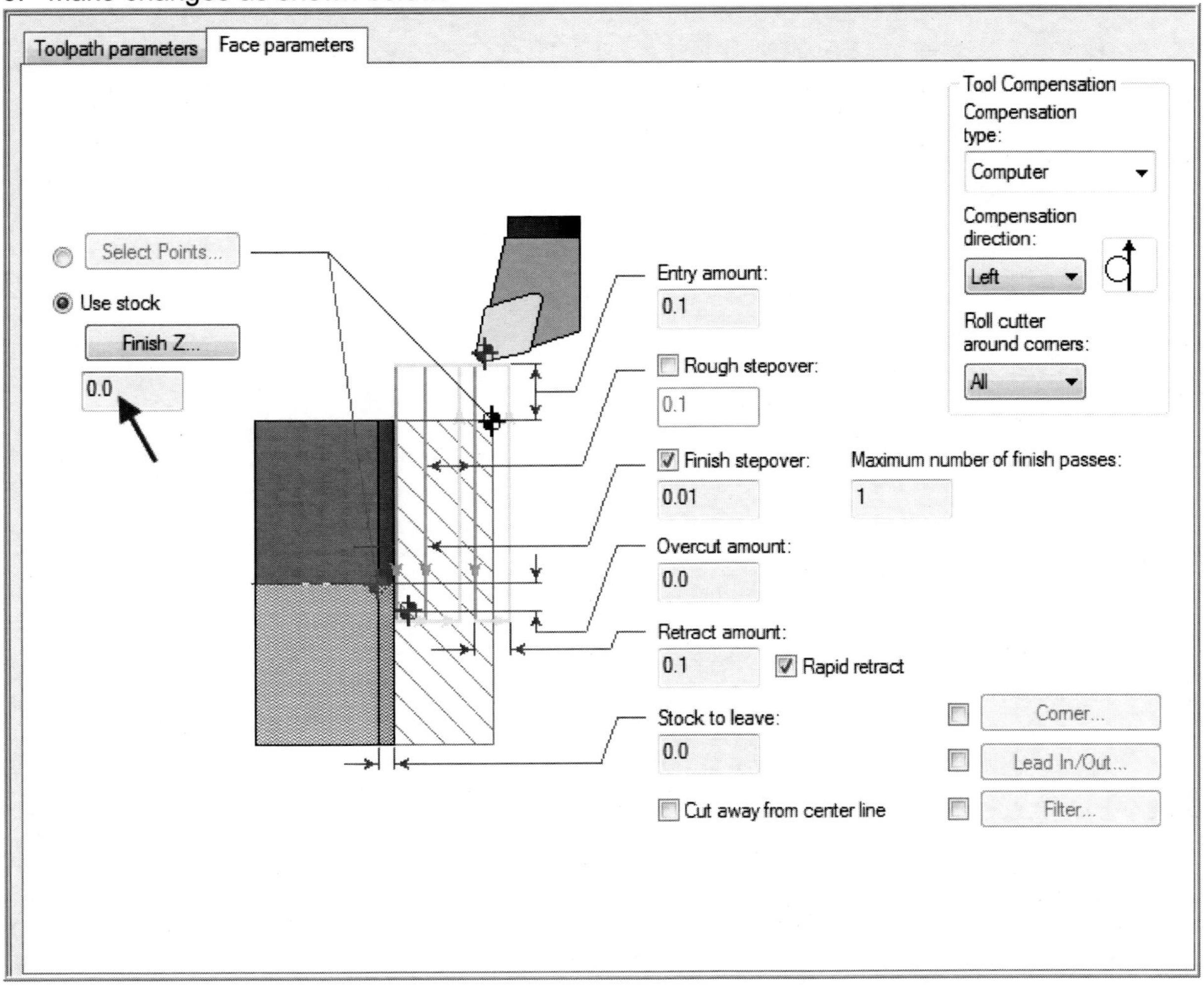

7. Select the OK button ✔ to complete this **Lathe Face** operation.

8. Your screen should look like the image below:

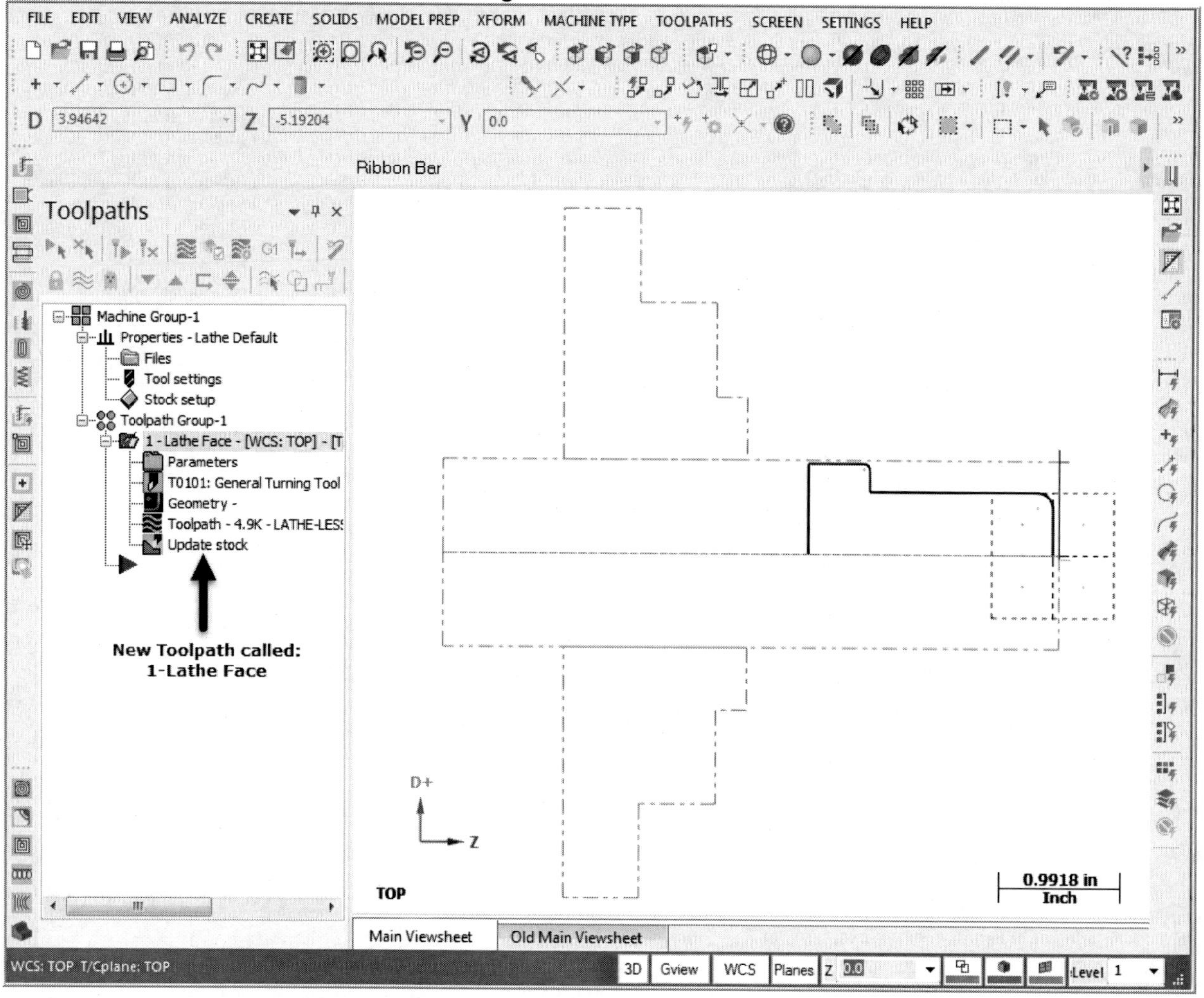

➲ Note: the new Toolpath called **1-Lathe Face**. This is where all the toolpath information is kept. If changes are required to this toolpath just click on the parameter icon 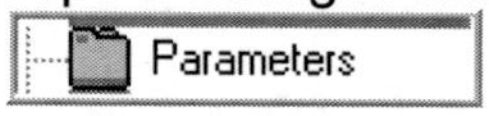

and the Screens from steps 4 through 8 will be available. This is handy in case a mistake was made in setting the toolpath parameters or in case a modification needs to be made.

9. To experience how this works, click on the **Parameters** icon 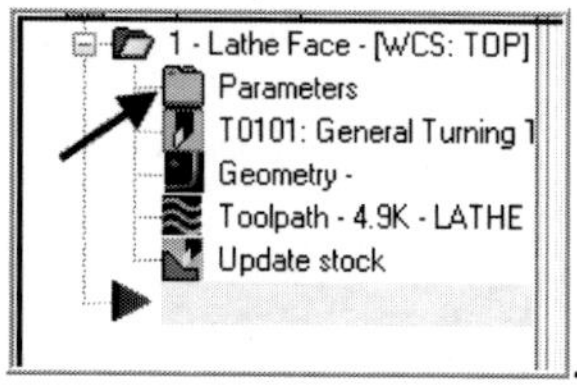

.

10. Click on the **Toolpath parameters** tab or the **Face parameters** tab as shown below:

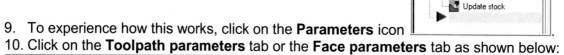

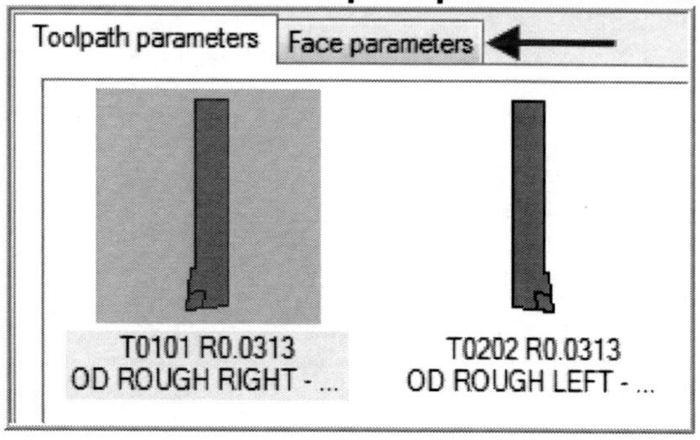

➲ As you can see, all the toolpath settings (parameters) are available in case a change or correction is required.

11. Click on the OK button  to return to the main screen.

TASK 8:
ROUGH THE OUTSIDE DIAMETERS

➲ In this task you will use the same tool as used for the previous facing operation **Tool #1 an OD Rough- Right – 80 deg.**

1. From the menu bar select **TOOLPATHS>Rough…**

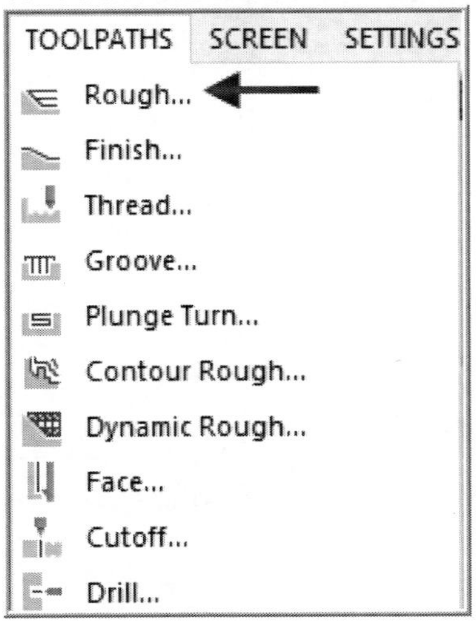

2. In the **Chaining** window Chaining mode is set to **Partial** by default.

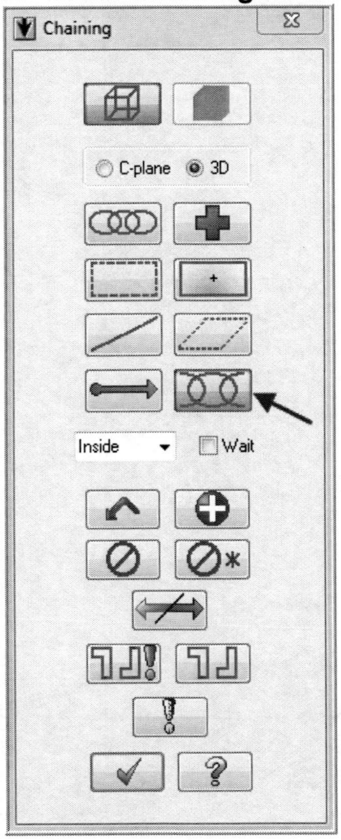

3. Select **Arc 1** as the start of the **Partial chain**.

After you have selected the arc **ensure** that the arrows are pointing up and to the left of the part

If it is not select the reverse button in the Chaining dialog box: 

4. Then select **Line 2** as the end entity in this chain.

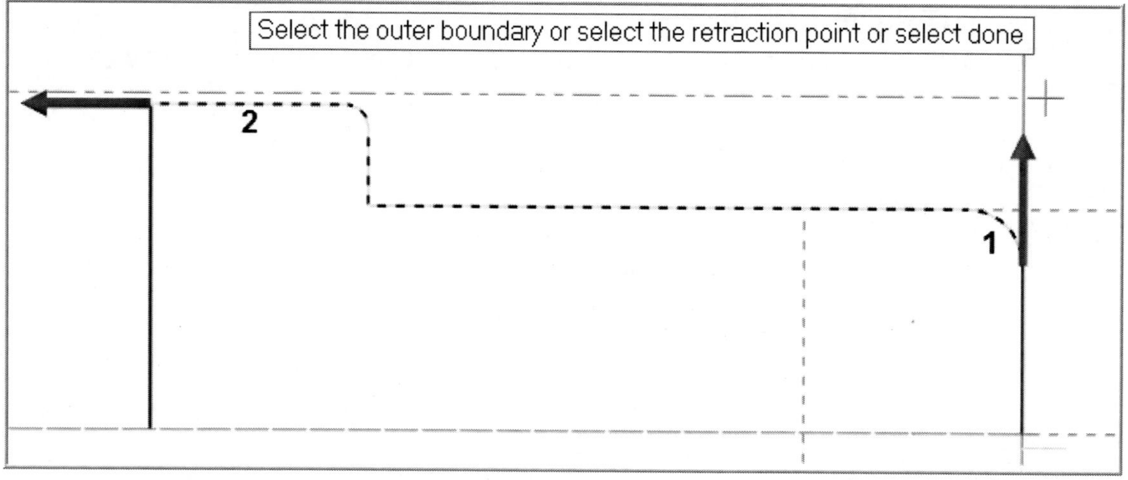

5. Select the **OK** button  to exit the Chaining dialog window.
6. In the **Toolpath parameters** page select the same tool used to face the part **Tool #1 OD ROUGH RIGHT** and make sure the settings are the same as shown below:

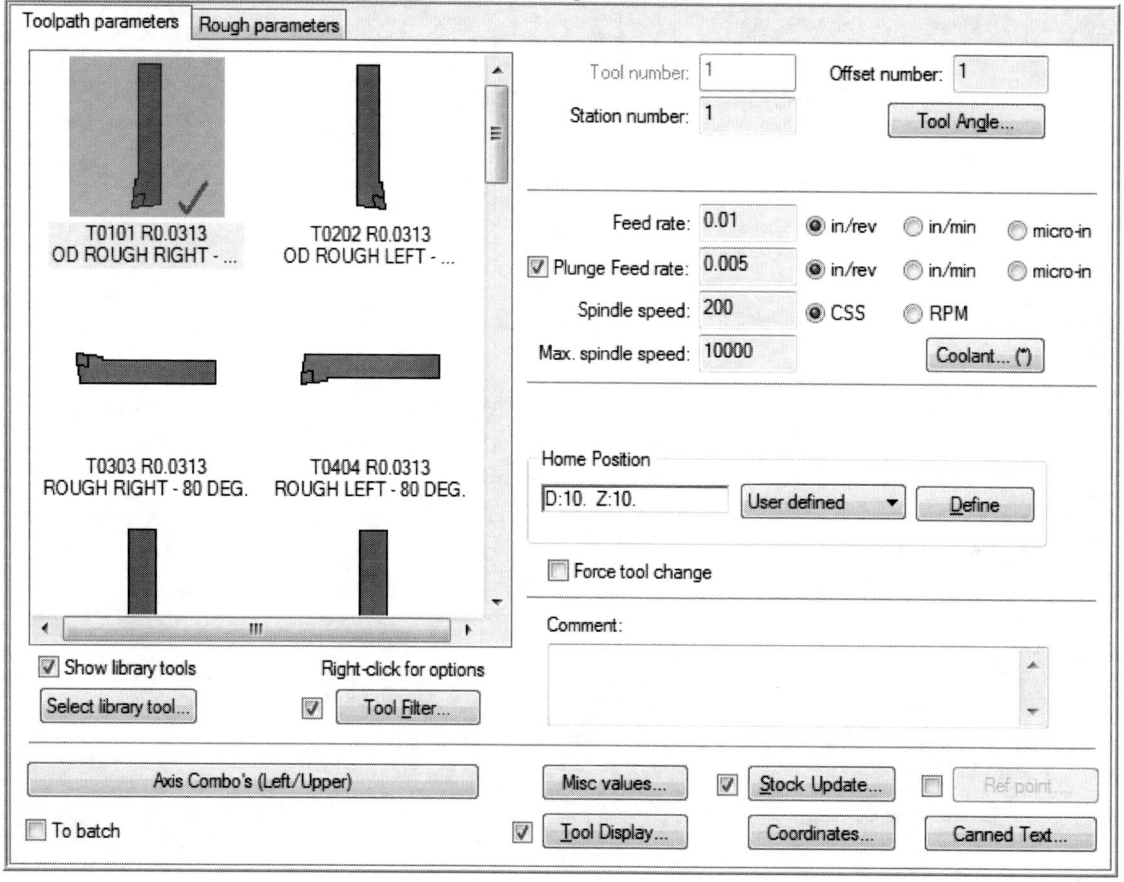

7. Select the **Rough parameters** page and make changes as shown below:

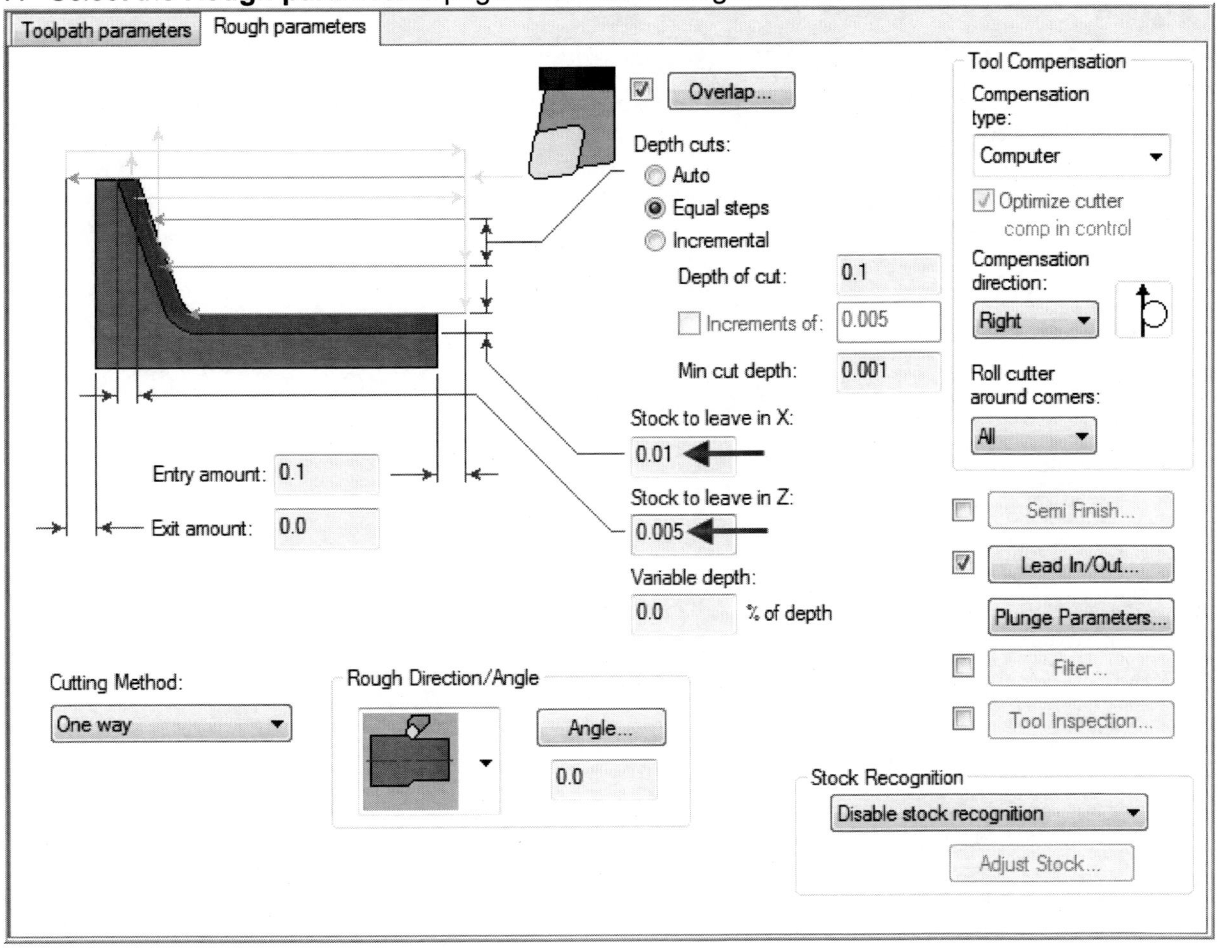

8. Select the **Lead In/Out** button select the **Lead out** page and extend the contour by **.2** as shown below:

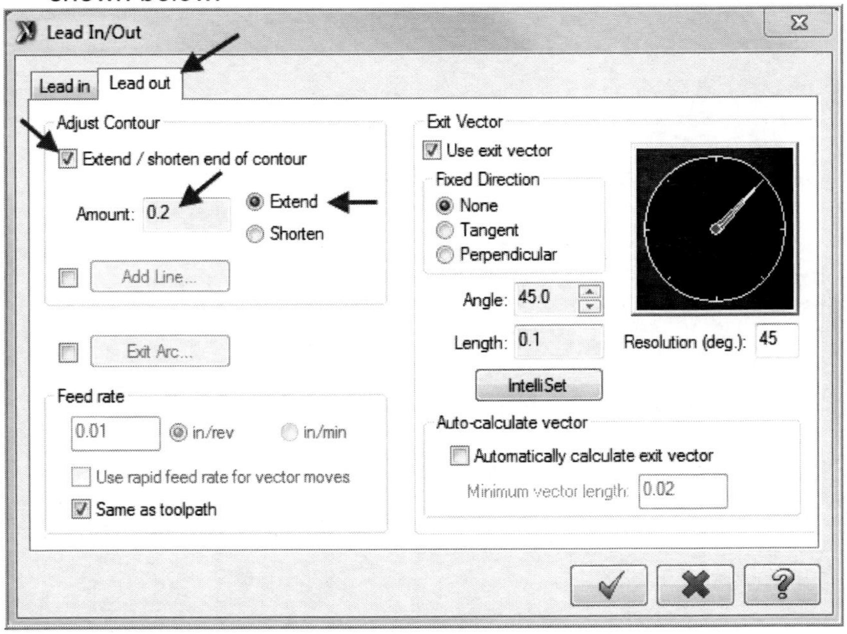

9. Select the **OK** button ✓ to exit this function.
10. Select the **OK** button ✓ to exit Rough Parameters.

TASK 9:
FINISH THE OUTSIDE DIAMETERS

➲ In this task you will finish the outside diameters in one cut using **Tool #1 an OD Rough-Right – 80 deg.**

1. From the menu bar select **TOOLPATHS>Finish…**

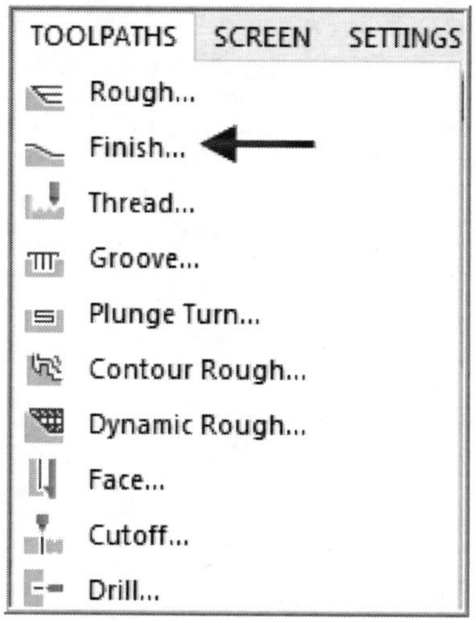

2. Select **Last** in the Chaining dialog box.

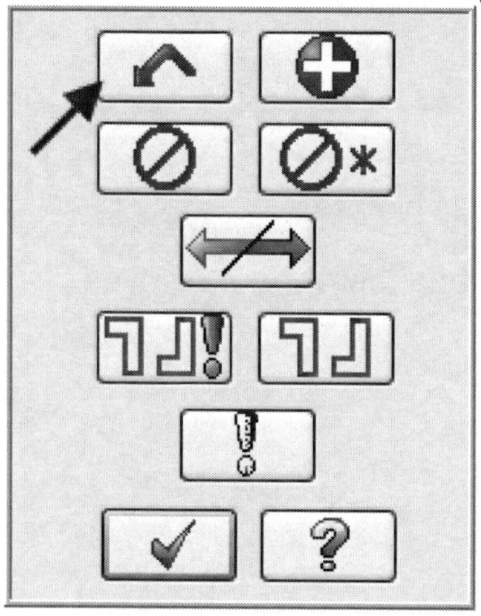

3. Select the **OK** button  to complete the selection.

4. Select the same tool used to rough the part; **Tool #1 OD Rough Right** tool from the tool list and make changes as shown below if required:

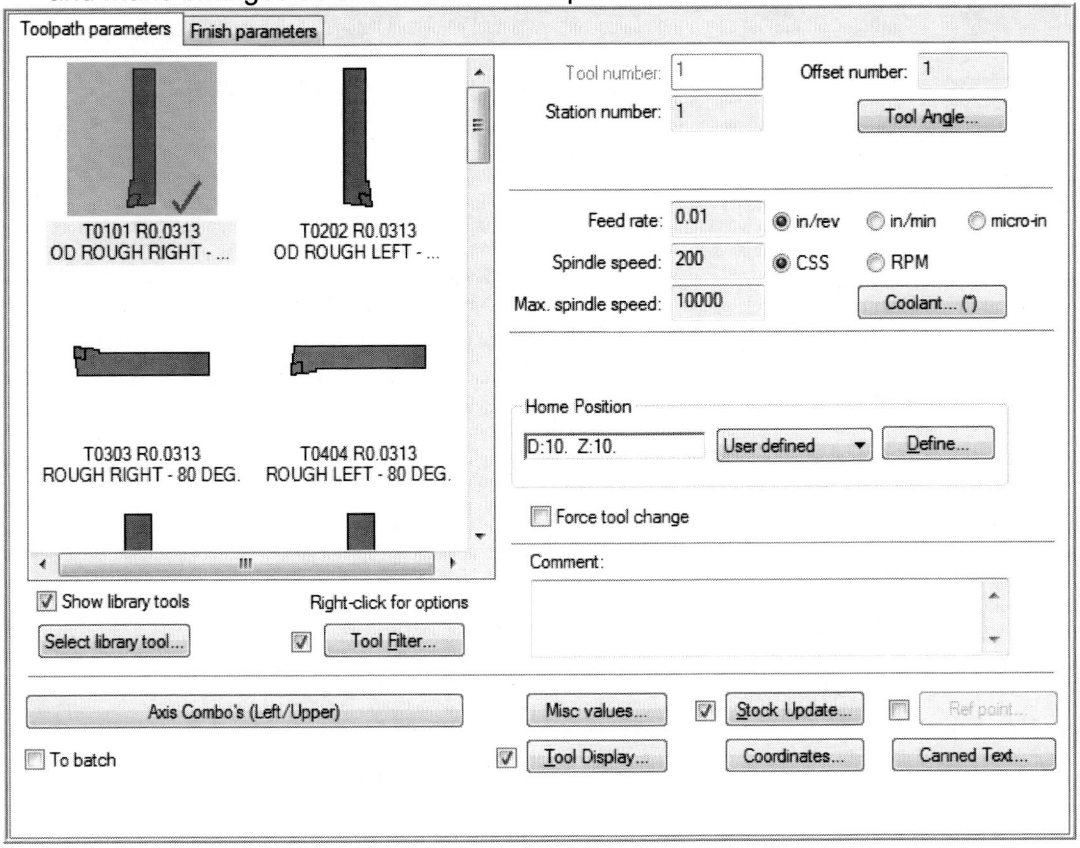

5. Select the **Finish parameters** page and make changes as shown below:

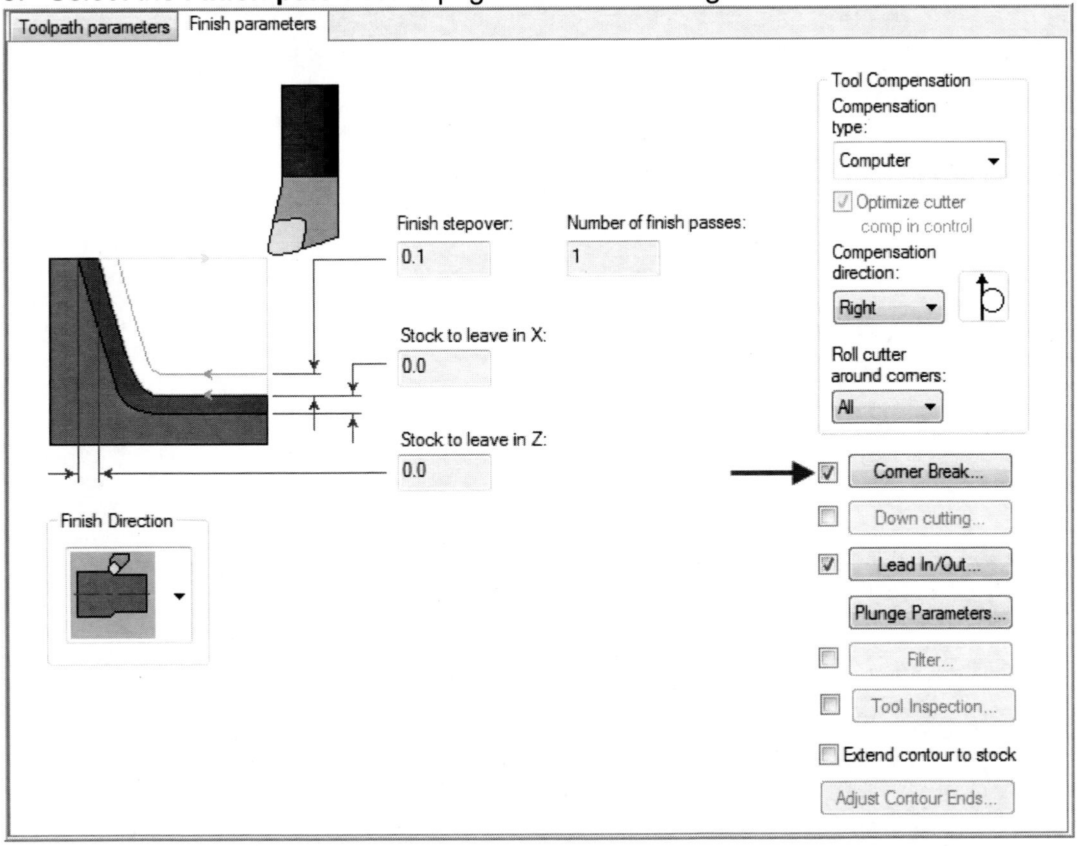

Corner Break: Select the check box to automatically create radii or chamfers on all outer corners of the toolpath. Click the button to edit the corner break settings.

6. Select the **Corner Break** button and make changes as shown below if required:

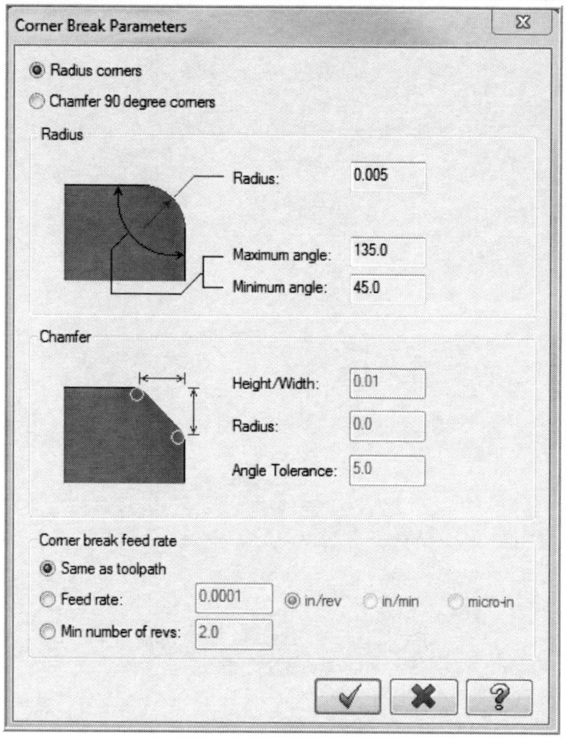

Corner Break
Use this dialog box to automatically create radii or chamfers on all outer corners of lathe finish toolpaths.
You can also set the feed rate when the tool creates the radii or chamfers.

7. Select the OK button ✓ to complete this feature.
8. Select the **Lead In/Out** button select the **Lead out** page and extend the contour by .2 as shown below:

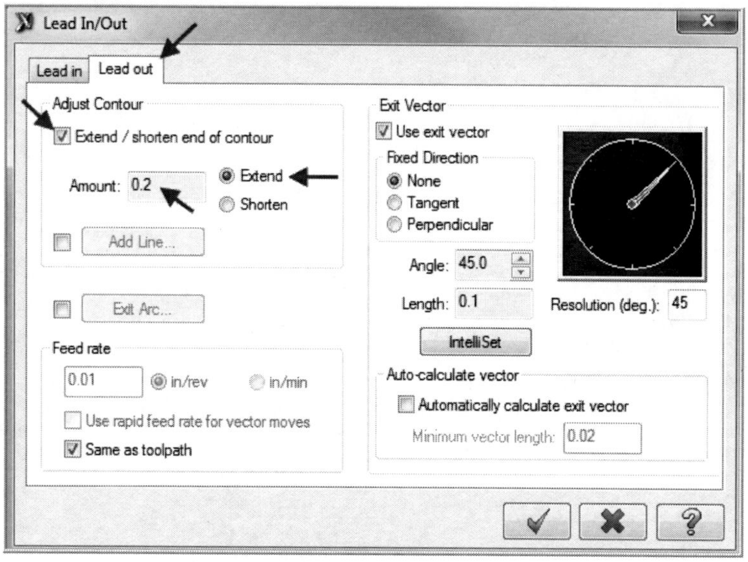

9. Select the **OK** button ✓ to exit this function.
10. Select the **OK** button ✓ to exit **Finish parameters.**

TASK 10:
CUTOFF THE PART

➲ In this task you will cutoff the part using a .125 wide cutoff tool.

1. From the menu bar select **Toolpaths>Cutoff…**

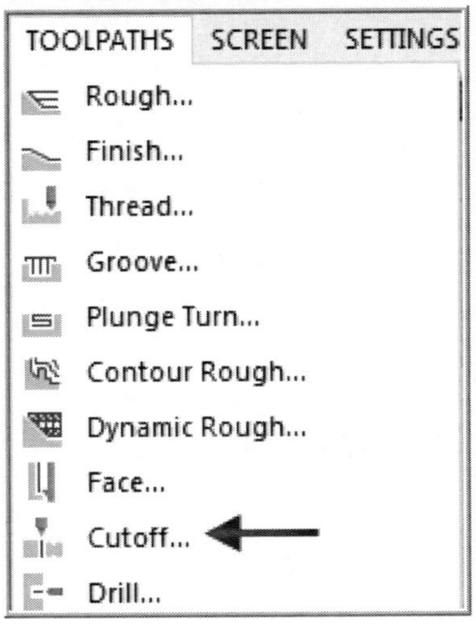

2. Select the **Alt key** and the **T** key on the keyboard to hide the toolpath lines.

Toolpath Lines visible:

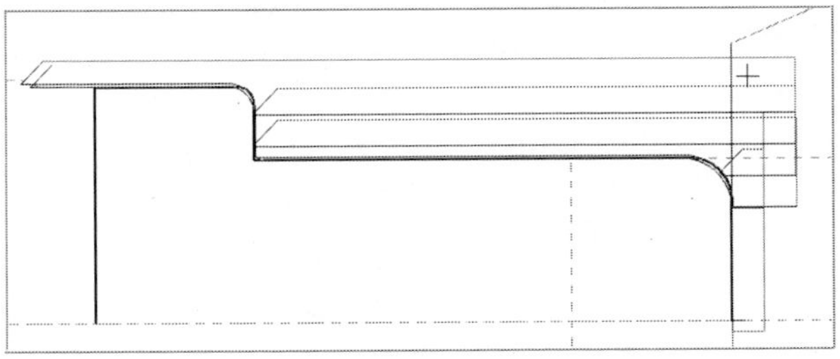

Press Alt T to hide toolpath Lines:

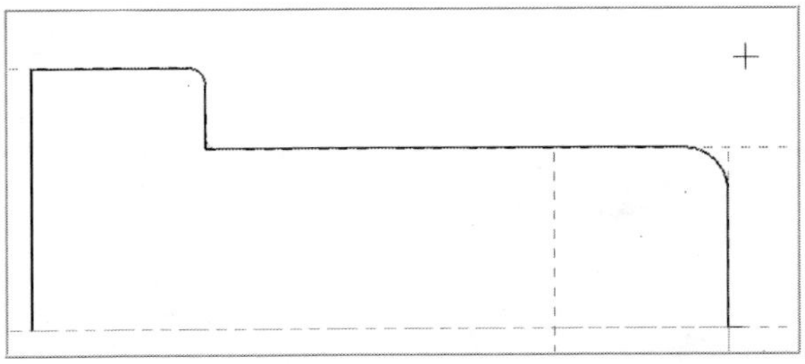

3. Move the cursor over the corner (where **Line 1** and **Line 2** meet) until the visual cue  for End point displays and then click on this point as shown below:

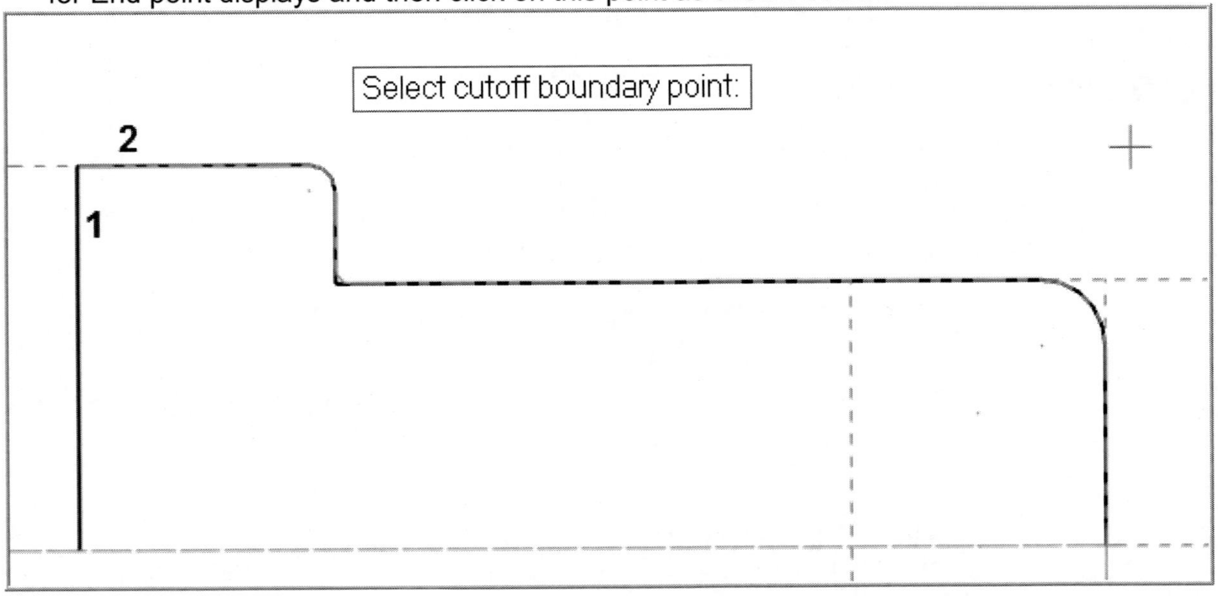

4. Scroll down if required in the tool window and select the **OD Cutoff Right Width .125** tool and make changes as shown below in the **Toolpath parameters** page:

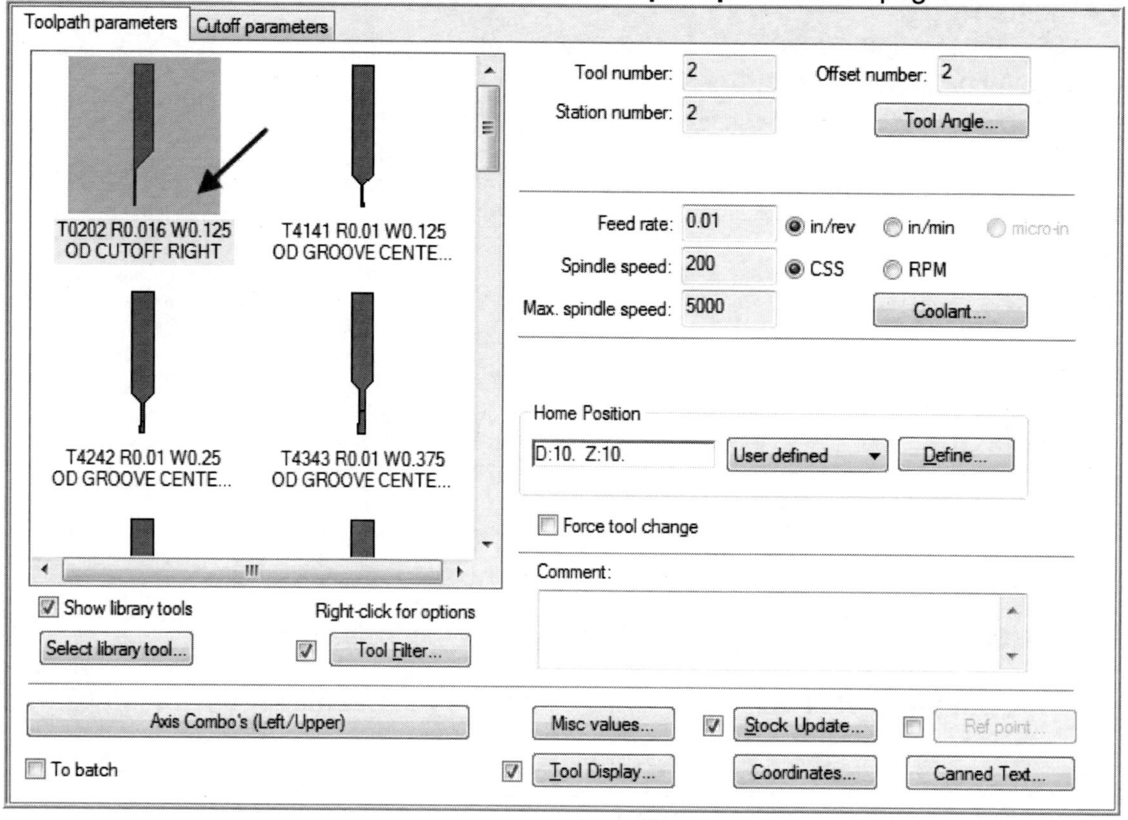

5. Select the **Cutoff parameters** page and make changes if required as shown below:

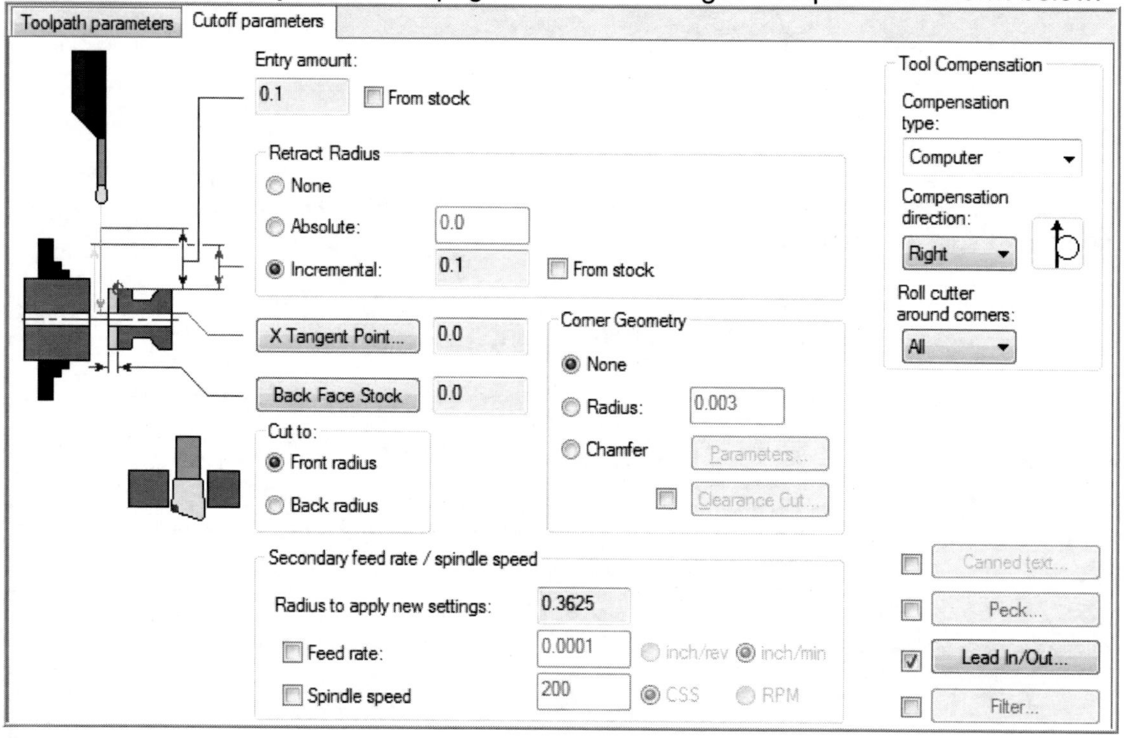

6. Select the **OK** button  to exit **Cutoff parameters.**

TASK 11:
BACKPLOT THE TOOLPATH

- ⊃ In this task you will use Mastercam's Backplot function to view the path the tools take to cut this part.
- ⊃ Backplot will enable you to review the cutting motions and identify any problem areas when cutting the part.
- ⊃ When the toolpaths are being Backplotted Mastercam displays tool path information on the right of the screen. Information such as the current tool position in X and Z coordinates.
- ⊃ **For more information on Backplot see the Tips and Techniques section on the multimedia DVD supplied with this text**.

1. To pick all the operations to backplot pick the **Select All** icon circled below:

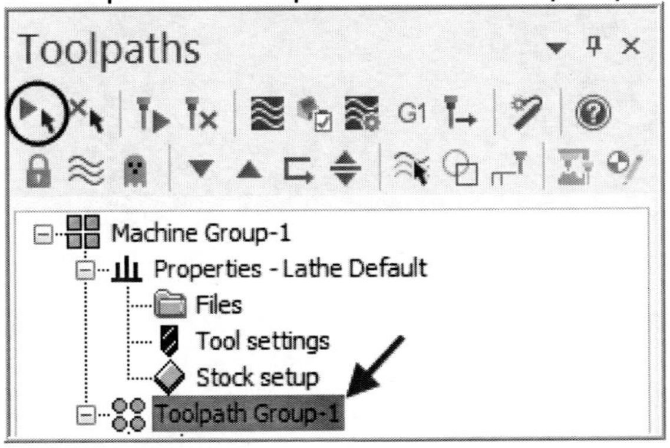

- ⊃ Another method to **Select all** the operations is by clicking on the **Toolpath Group-1** in the Toolpaths Manager as shown by the arrow above.

2. The next step is to select the **Backplot selected operations** icon shown below:

3. **Maximize** the Backplot/Verify window if required.
4. Select the **Home** Tab if required.

5. Activate the options shown below in the **Visibility** section of the Home tab.

☐ Toolpath	☑ Stock	☑ Wireframe
☑ Tool	☐ Initial Stock	☑ Gnomon
☐ Workpiece	☑ Fixtures	☑ Axes
Visibility		

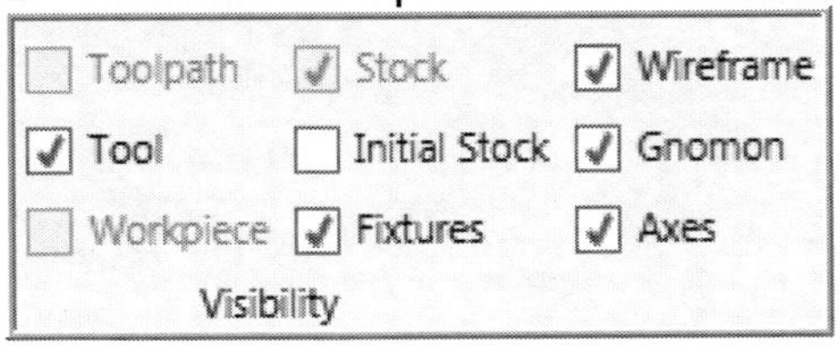

Initial Stock
This displays the stock before machining.
Click to cycle through three states:
On
Translucent
Off

Tool
This displays the tool during Backplot or Verification. Click to cycle through three states as mentioned above

6. At the top of the screen select the **View** tab, the **Isometric** icon and then select **Fit**.

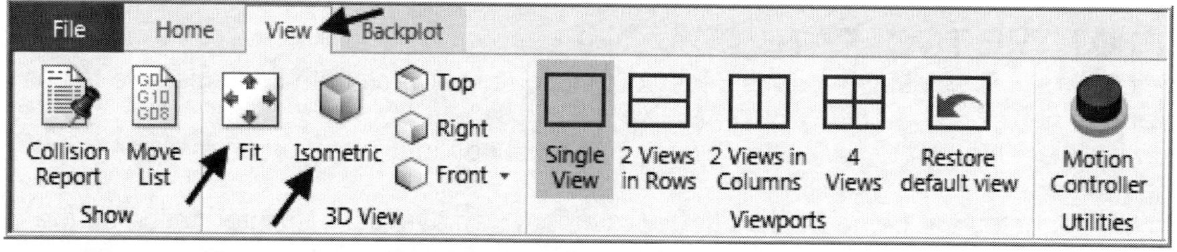

7. Click on the **Backplot** tab at the top left of the screen

8. Activate the **Both** option in the Toolpath section of the Backplot tab.

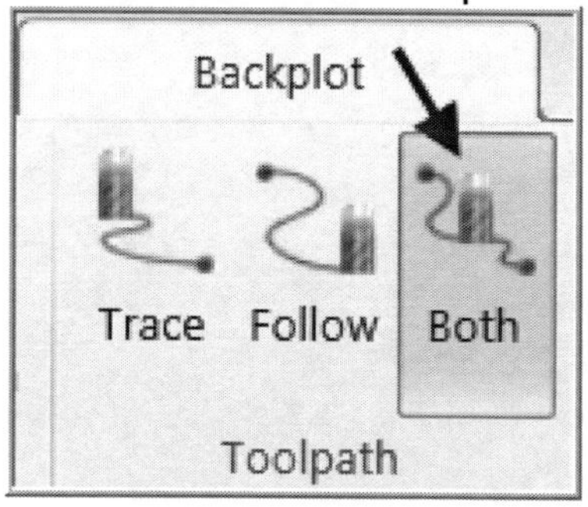

Both
This displays the entire toolpath and the tool as it travels over the displayed toolpath.

9. In the lower right corner of the screen now set the run **Speed** to slow by moving the slider bar pointer over to the left as shown below.

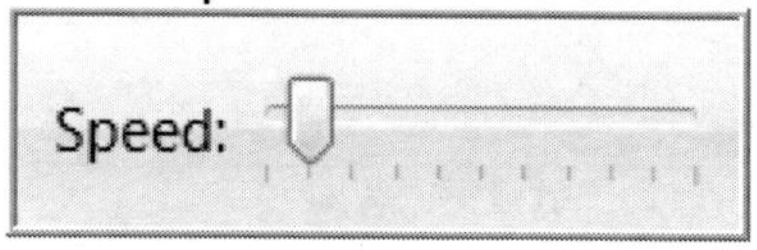

10. Now select the **Play Simulation** button to review the toolpaths.

11. Now hit the **rewind** button on the controls to move back to the **start** position.

12. After reviewing the Backplot of the toolpaths select the **Close** button 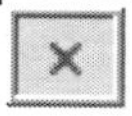 in the top right hand corner to exit Backplot.

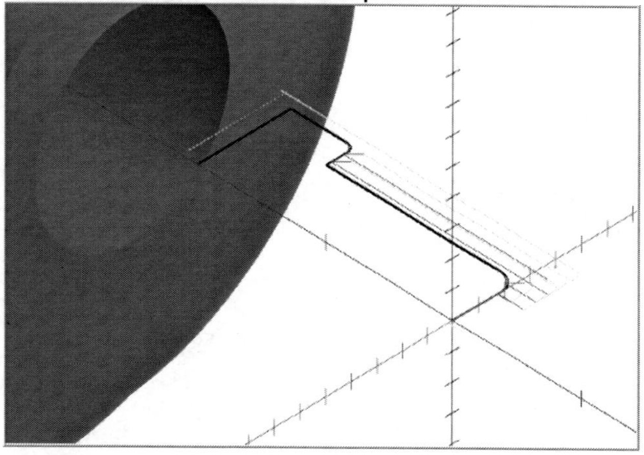

TASK 12:
VERIFY THE TOOLPATH

⊃ Mastercam's Verify utility allows you to use solid models to simulate the machining of a part. The model created by the verification represents the surface finish, and shows collisions, if any exist.

⊃ This allows you to identify and correct program errors before they reach the shop floor.

⊃ Backplot and Verify are very similar. The differences between these two functions are that Backplot offers basic simulation options. Whereas Verify offers material removal, collision checking and precision control.

⊃ **For more information on Verify see the Tips and Techniques section on the multimedia DVD supplied with this text**

1. In the **Toolpaths Manager** pick all the operations to verify by picking the **Select All** icon

.

2. Select the **Verify selected operations** icon shown below:

3. **Maximize** the Backplot/Verify window if required.
4. Now select the **Home** Tab if required.

5. Activate the options shown below in the **Visibility** section of the Home tab. **Initial Stock not activated.**

☐ Toolpath	☑ Stock	☑ Wireframe
☑ Tool	☐ Initial Stock	☑ Gnomon
☐ Workpiece	☑ Fixtures	☑ Axes
	Visibility	

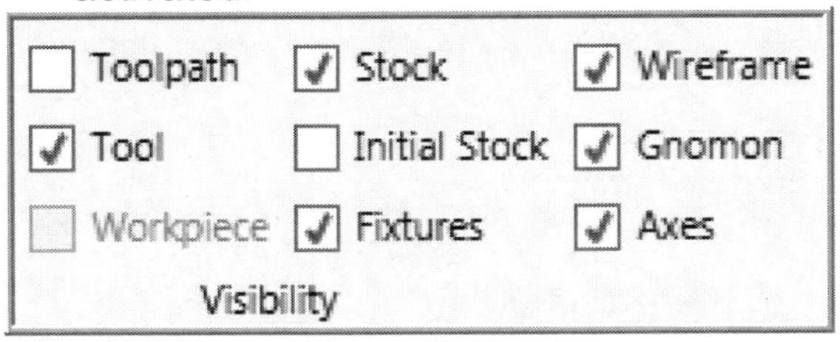

6. Activate the **Color Loop** to change the color of the tools for the verified part.

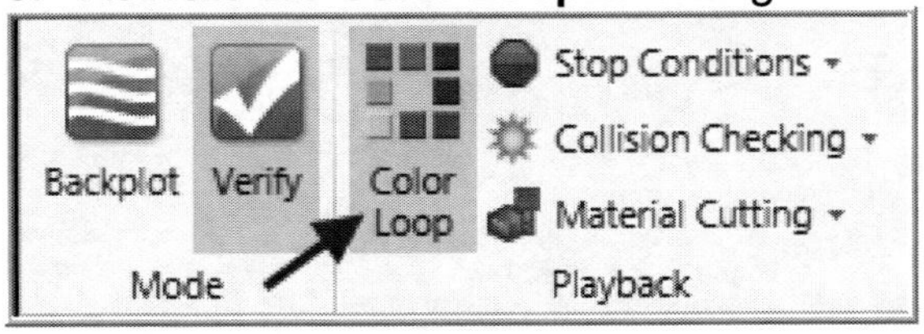

> **Color Loop**
> Changes the color of the toolpath or cut stock by operation or by tool change.
>
> Choose **File Options** to set the colors.

7. At the top of the screen select the **View** tab, the **Isometric** icon and then select **Fit**.

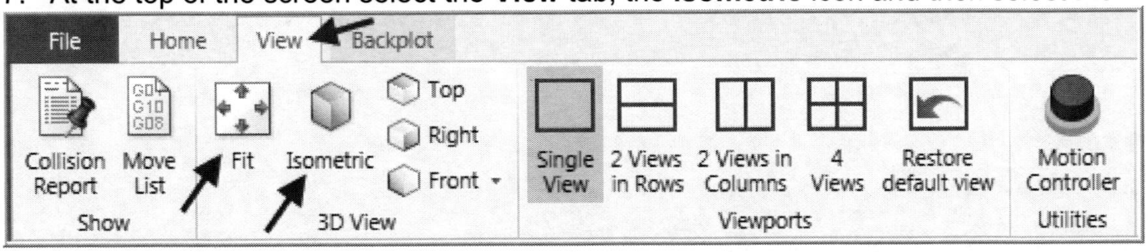

8. In the lower right corner of the screen now set the run **Speed** to slow by moving the slider bar pointer over to the left as shown below.

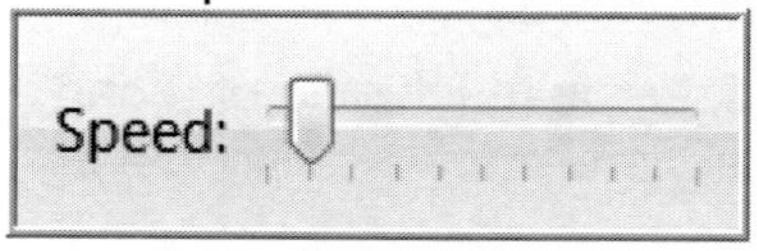

9. Now select the **Play Simulation** button to review the toolpaths.

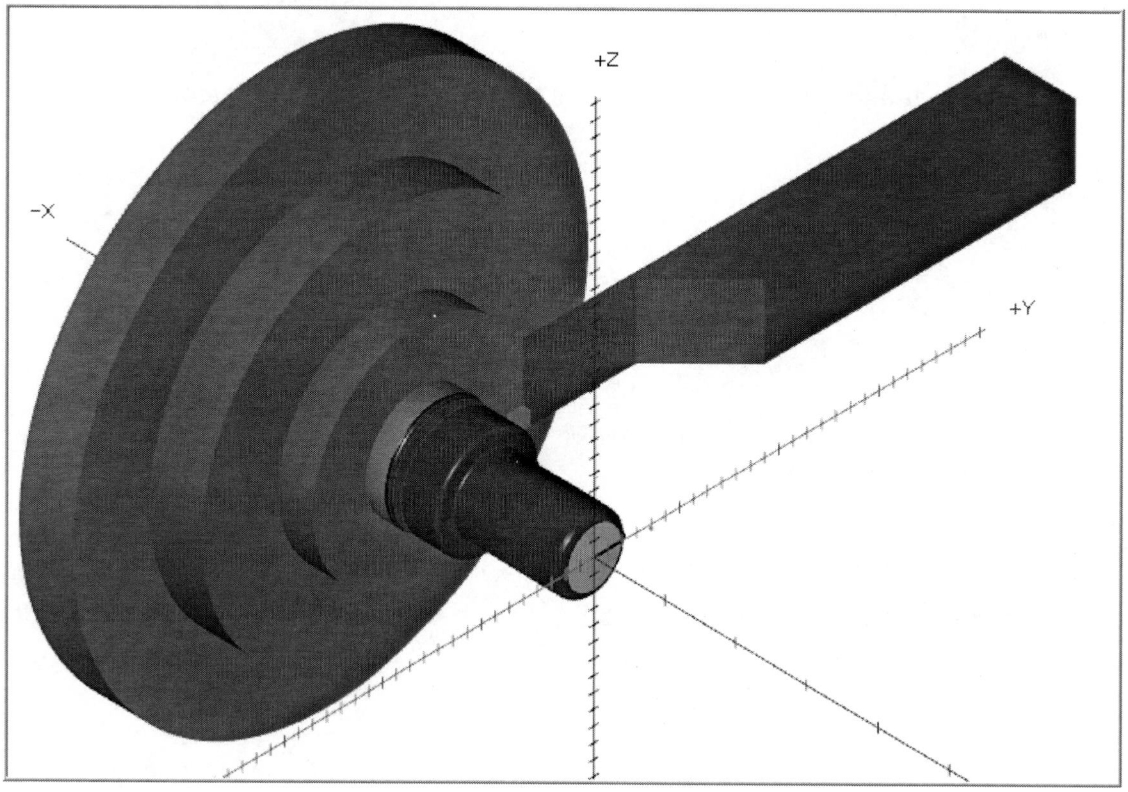

10. Select the **Close** button  in the top right hand corner to exit Verify.

TASK 13:
SAVE THE UPDATED MASTERCAM FILE

1. Select the **save** icon from the toolbar .

TASK 14:
POST AND CREATE THE CNC CODE FILE

Please Note:
Users of the Mastercam **Home Learning Edition** (HLE) will not be able to Post and Create the CNC code file.

1. Ensure all the operations are selected by picking the **Select All** icon  from the Toolpaths manager.

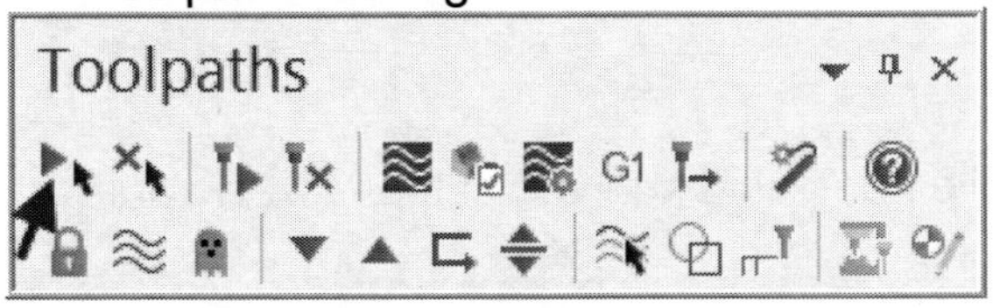

2. Select the **Post selected operations** button from the Toolpaths manager.
➲ **Please Note:** If you cannot see **G1** click on the right pane of the Toolpaths manager window and expand the window to the right.

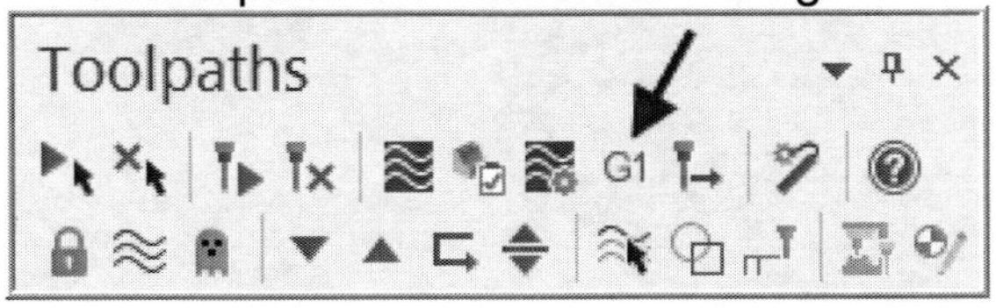

3. In the Post processing window, make the necessary changes as shown below:

About Post Processing

NC file:
Select this option to save the NC file. The file name and extension are stored in the machine group properties for the selected operation. If you are posting operations from different machine groups or Mastercam files, or batch processing, Mastercam will create several files according to the settings for each machine group.

Edit:
When checked, automatically launches the default text editor with the file displayed so that you can review or modify it.

4. Select the OK button to continue.
5. Ensure the same name as your Mastercam part file name is displayed in the **NC File name** field as shown below:

| File name: | LATHE-LESSON-1 | ▼ |
| Save as type: | NC Files (*.NC) | ▼ |

6. Select the **Save** button.
7. The CNC code file opens up in the default editor.

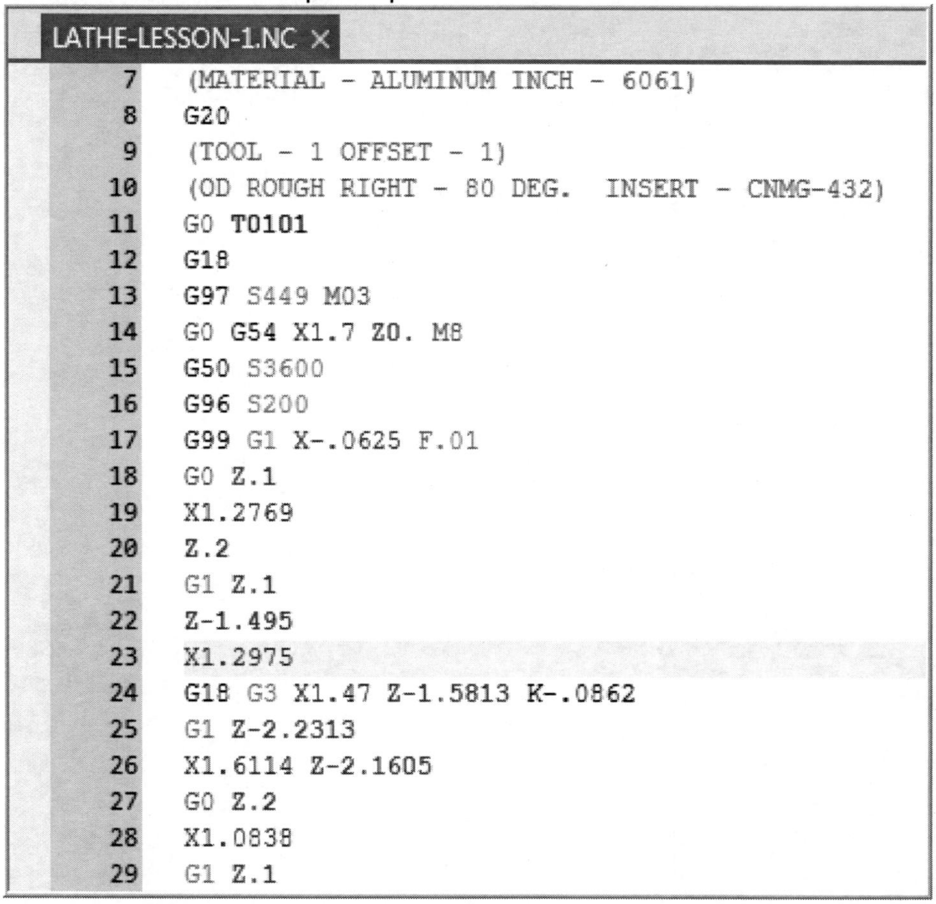

```
LATHE-LESSON-1.NC  ×
    7      (MATERIAL - ALUMINUM INCH - 6061)
    8      G20
    9      (TOOL - 1 OFFSET - 1)
   10      (OD ROUGH RIGHT - 80 DEG.  INSERT - CNMG-432)
   11      G0 T0101
   12      G18
   13      G97 S449 M03
   14      G0 G54 X1.7 Z0. M8
   15      G50 S3600
   16      G96 S200
   17      G99 G1 X-.0625 F.01
   18      G0 Z.1
   19      X1.2769
   20      Z.2
   21      G1 Z.1
   22      Z-1.495
   23      X1.2975
   24      G18 G3 X1.47 Z-1.5813 K-.0862
   25      G1 Z-2.2313
   26      X1.6114 Z-2.1605
   27      G0 Z.2
   28      X1.0838
   29      G1 Z.1
```

8. Select the ☒ in the top right corner to exit the CNC editor.
9. This completes LATHE-LESSON -1.

LATHE-LESSON-1 EXERCISE

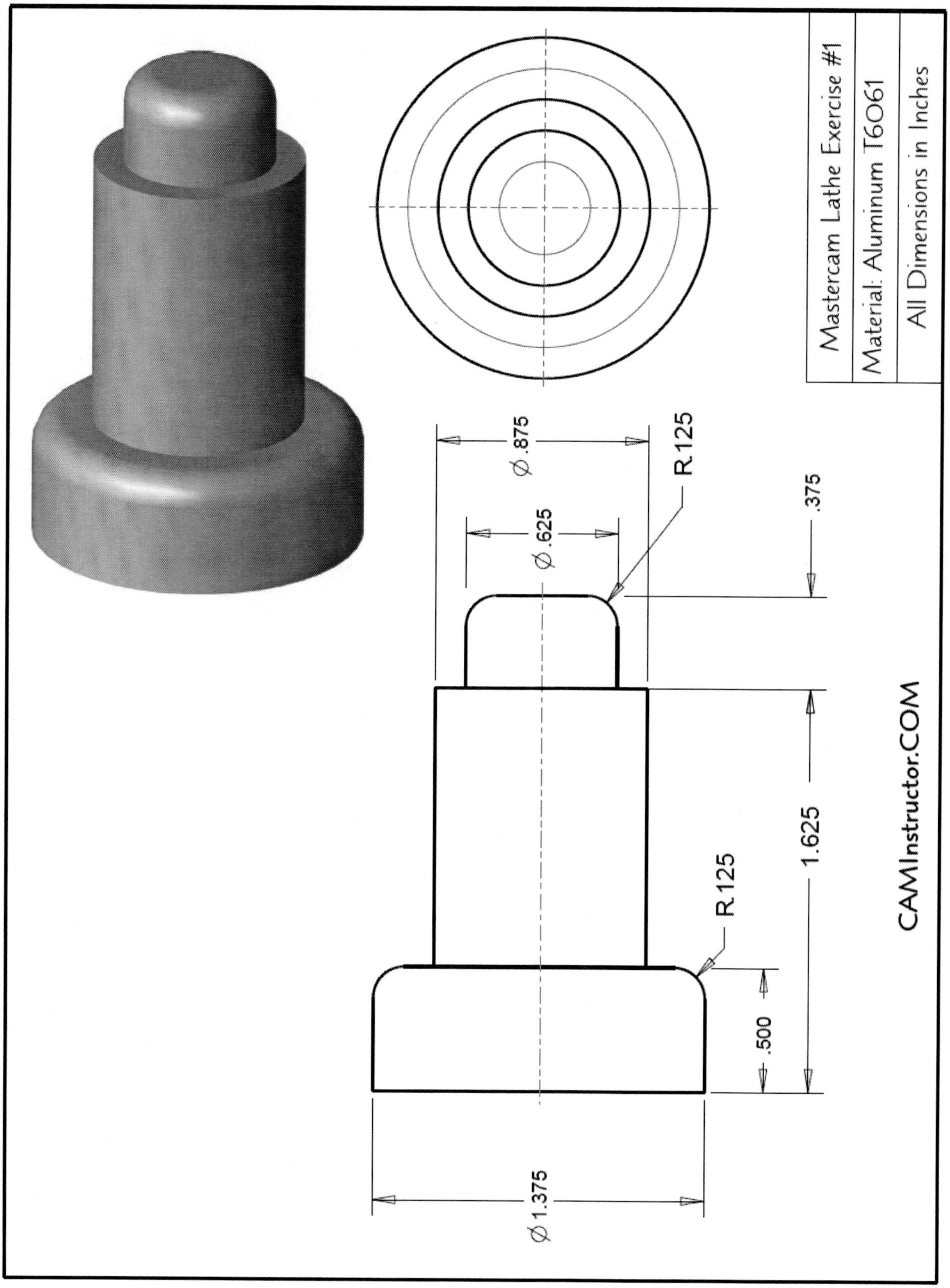

Mastercam® X⁹

TRAINING GUIDE

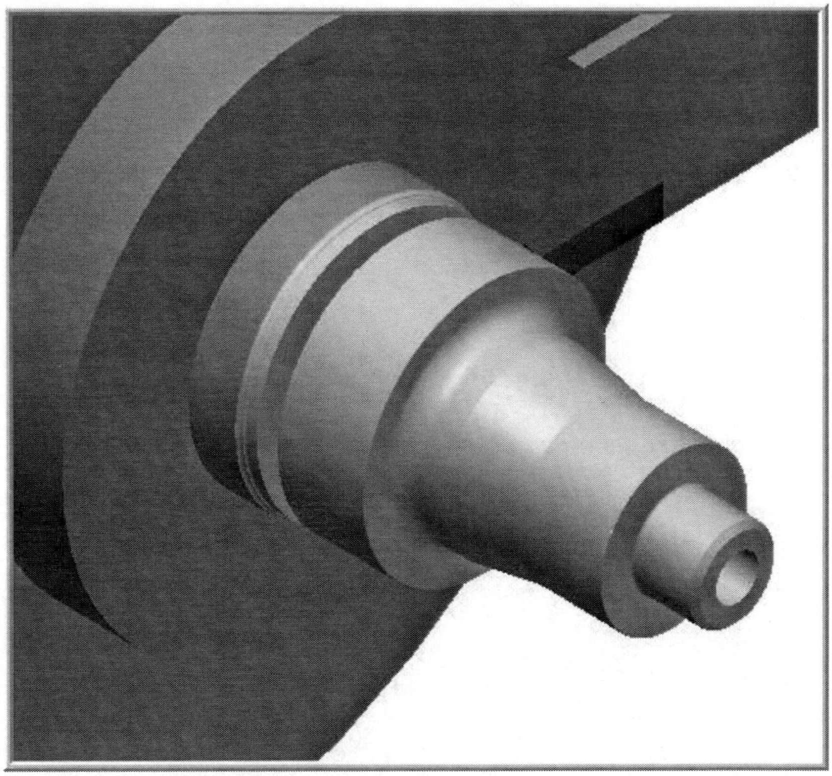

LATHE-LESSON-2

FACE, ROUGH, FINISH, DRILL AND CUTOFF

camInstructor

Objectives

You will create the geometry for Lathe Lesson 2, and then generate a toolpath to machine the part on a CNC lathe. This lesson covers the following topics:

➲ **Create a 2-dimensional drawing by:**
Creating lines.
Creating fillets.
Creating chamfers.

➲ **Establish Stock and Chuck Setup settings:**
Stock size.
Chuck Configuration.
Material for the part.
Feed calculation.

➲ **Generate a 2-dimensional lathe toolpath consisting of:**
Lathe Face.
Lathe Rough.
Lathe Finish.
Lathe Drill.
Lathe Cutoff.

➲ **Inspect the toolpath using Mastercam's Verify and Backplot by:**
Launching the Verify function to machine the part on the screen.
Using Backplot to identify the accuracy of the toolpaths.
Generating the NC- code.

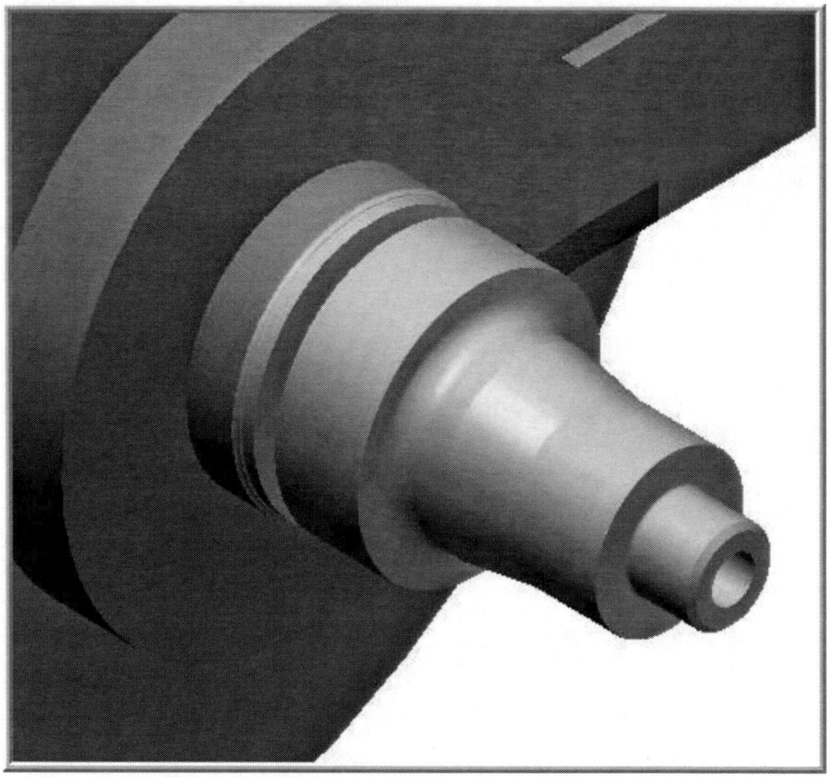

LATHE - LESSON - 2 DRAWING

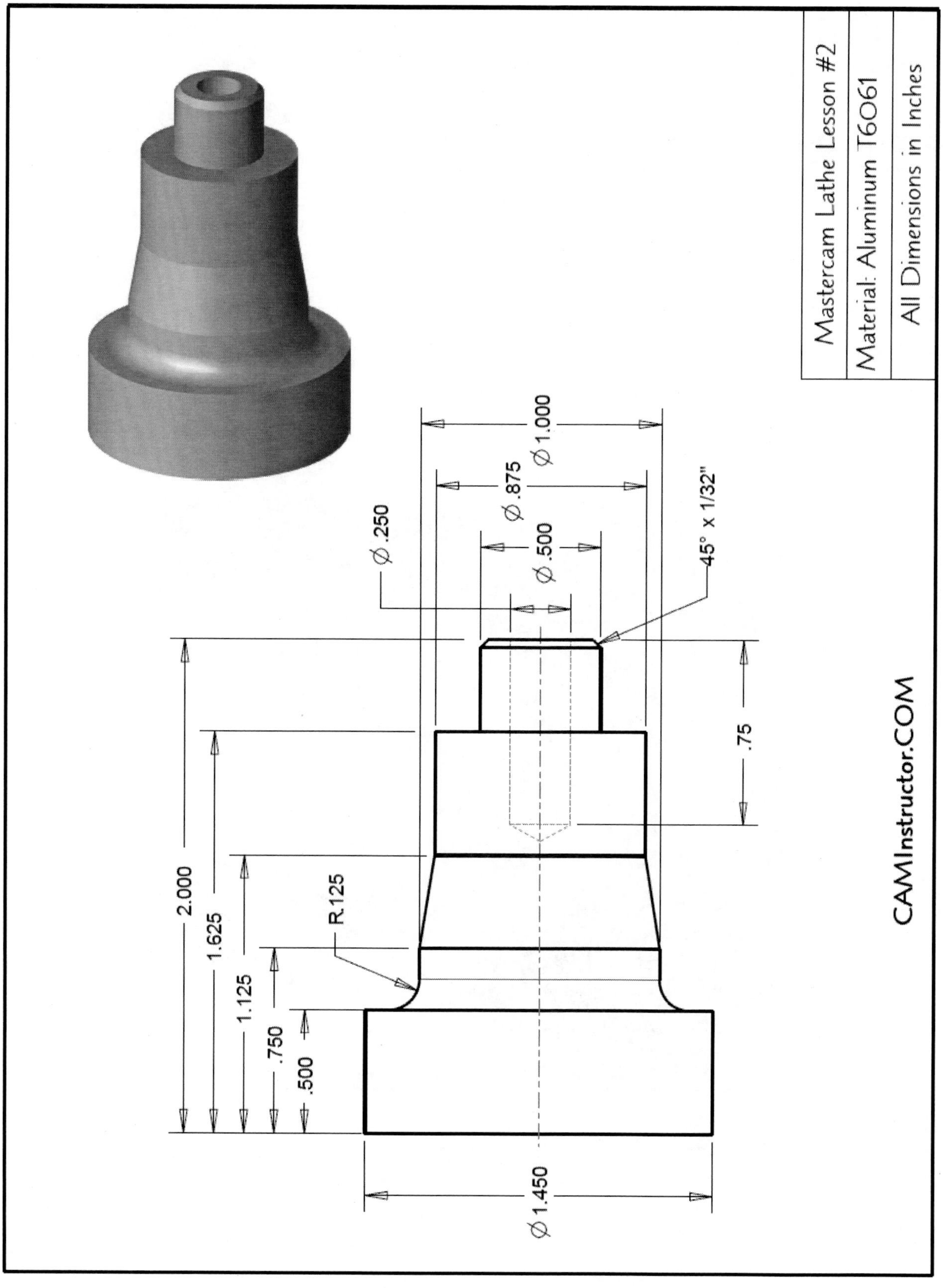

TOOL LIST

Five tools will be used to create this part.

➲ **Tool #1 Face and Rough the outside diameters**
Holder: Outside Diameter Rough Right Hand - DCGNR-164D.
Insert: 80 Degree Diamond Insert – CNMG-432.

➲ **Tool #2 Finish the outside diameters**
Holder: Outside Diameter Finish Right Hand - MVJNR-164D.
Insert: 35 Degree Diamond Insert – VNMG-431.

➲ **Tool #3 Centre drill the hole**
Centre Drill – body diameter 0.250”

➲ **Tool #4 Drill the .25 diameter hole**
Drill 0.25” diameter

➲ **Tool #5 Cutoff the part**
Holder: Outside Diameter Cut-off Right Hand.
Insert: 0.125” Wide.

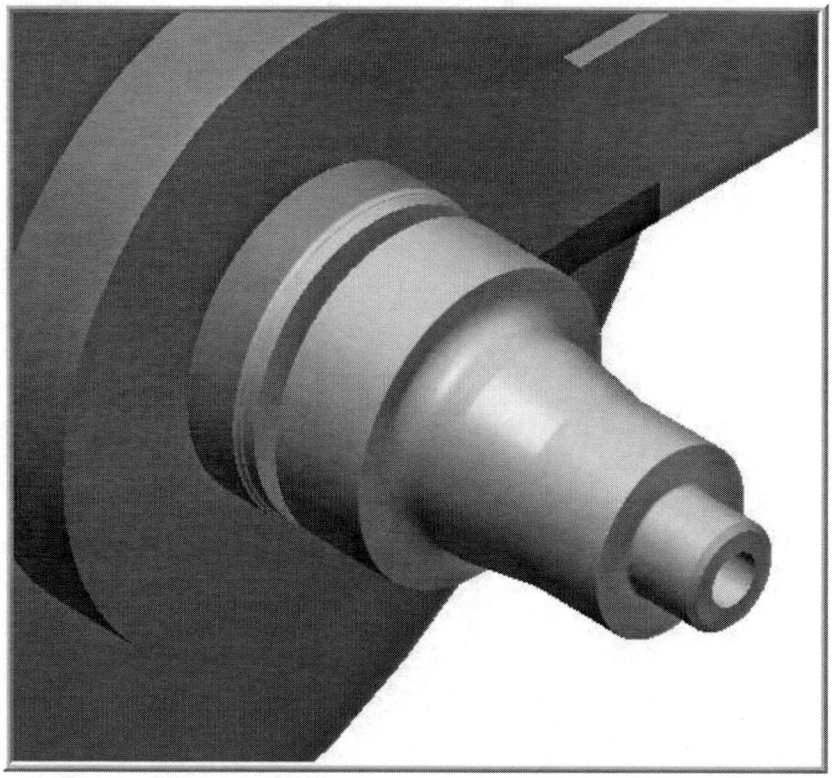

LESSON #2 - THE PROCESS

Geometry Creation

TASK 1: Setting the Environment
TASK 2: Setting the Construction Planes
TASK 3: Create the Geometry
TASK 4: Create the.125 Fillet radius and 45° x 1/32" –Chamfer
TASK 5: Save the Drawing

Toolpath Creation

TASK 6: Define the Stock and Chuck parameters
TASK 7: Face the Front of the Part
TASK 8: Rough the Outside Diameters
TASK 9: Finish the Outside Diameters
TASK 10: Center Drill the .25" Hole
TASK 11: Drill the .25" Hole
TASK 12: Cut off the Part
TASK 13: Backplot the Toolpath
TASK 14: Verify the Toolpath
TASK 15: Save the Updated Mastercam File
TASK 16: Post and Create the CNC Code File

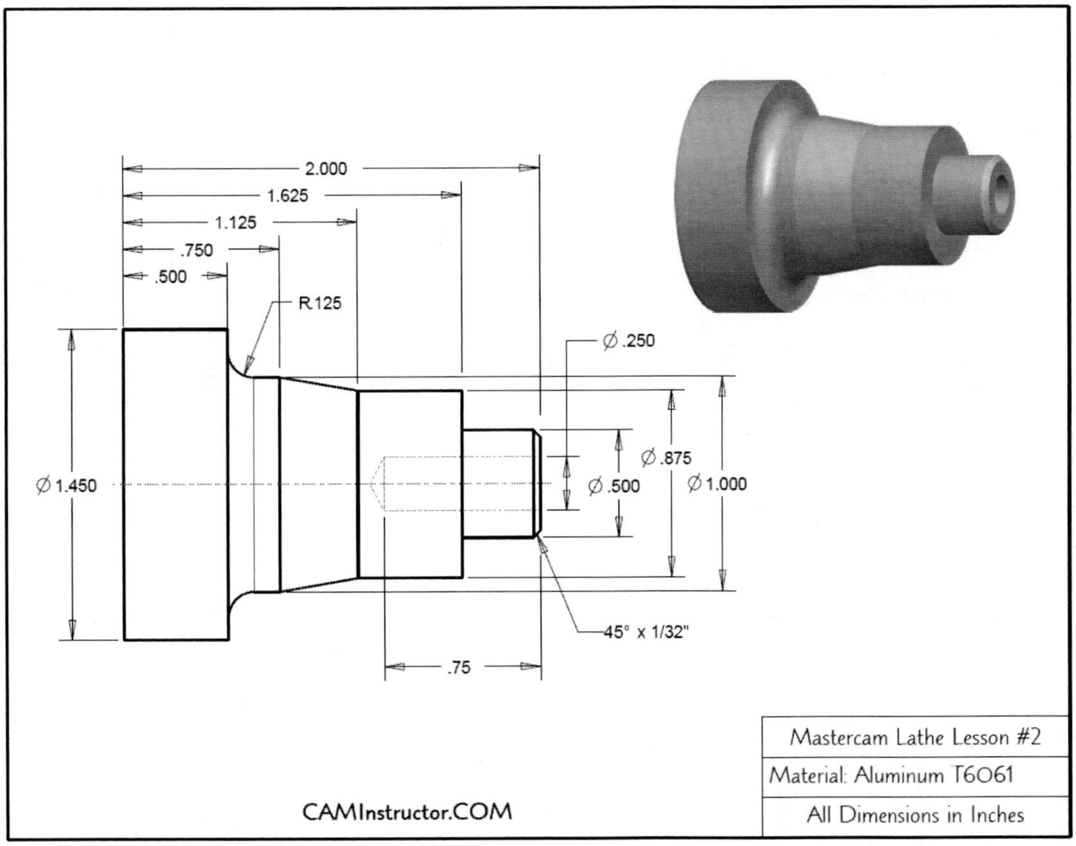

Geometry Creation

TASK 1:
SETTING THE ENVIRONMENT

Before starting the geometry creation you should set up the grid and toolbars as outlined in the **Setting the Environment** section at the beginning of this text:
1. Set up the **Grid**. This will help identify the location of the origin.
2. Load the Workspace – **SETTINGS>Load Workspace>Lathe** to machine a part on the Lathe.
3. Set the **MACHINE TYPE** to the **Lathe Default**.

TASK 2:
SETTING THE CONSTRUCTION PLANES:

➲ **Set the Construction Plane to Lathe diameter +D +Z (WCS).**
1. Click on **Planes** at the bottom of the screen as shown below:

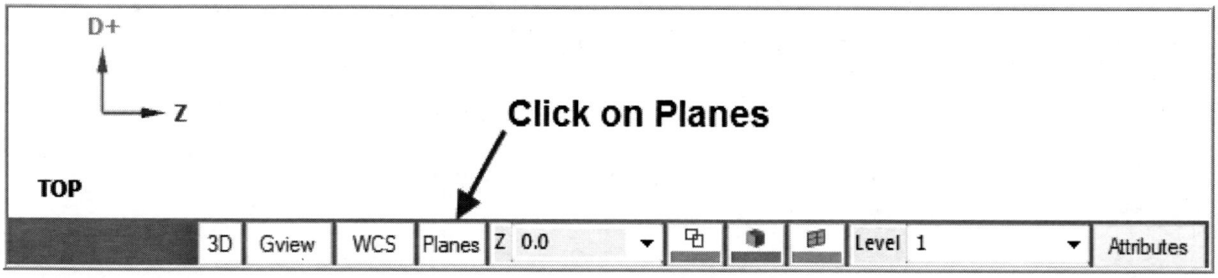

2. Click on **Lathe diameter>+D +Z (WCS)** as shown below:

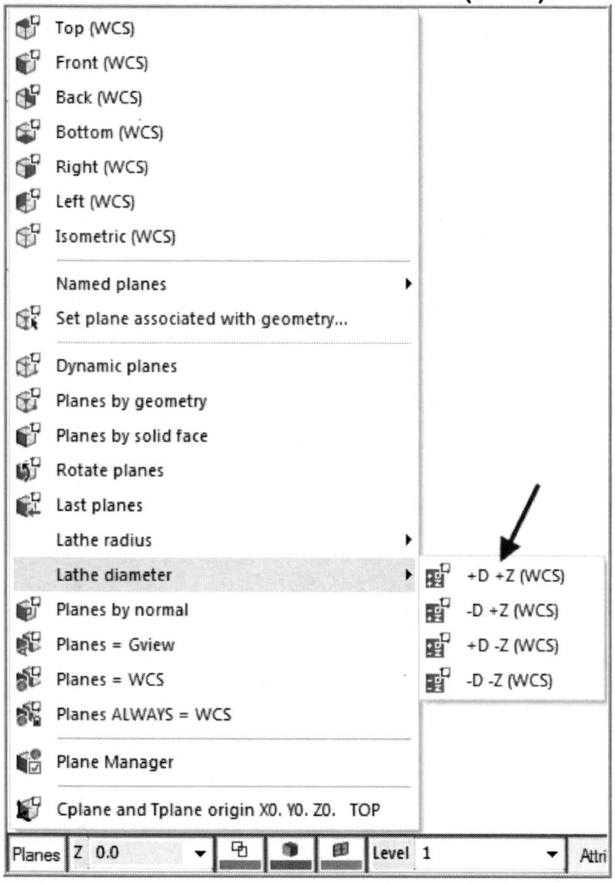

Lathe Cplanes
Once your machine is set up, Mastercam includes special lathe construction planes that let you work in radius or diameter coordinates.

For conventional 2D turning applications, use the Planes menu on the status bar to select the desired coordinate system.

Choose to use either radius or diameter coordinates, then choose the desired X/D and Z directions

TASK 3:
CREATE THE GEOMETRY – THE LEFT HAND FACE IS AT Z0

- This task explains how to create the geometry of this part. In this lathe part you only need to create **half of the geometry**, the geometry above the center line.
- Lines 1 through 9 will be created first and then the fillet and chamfer will be created.

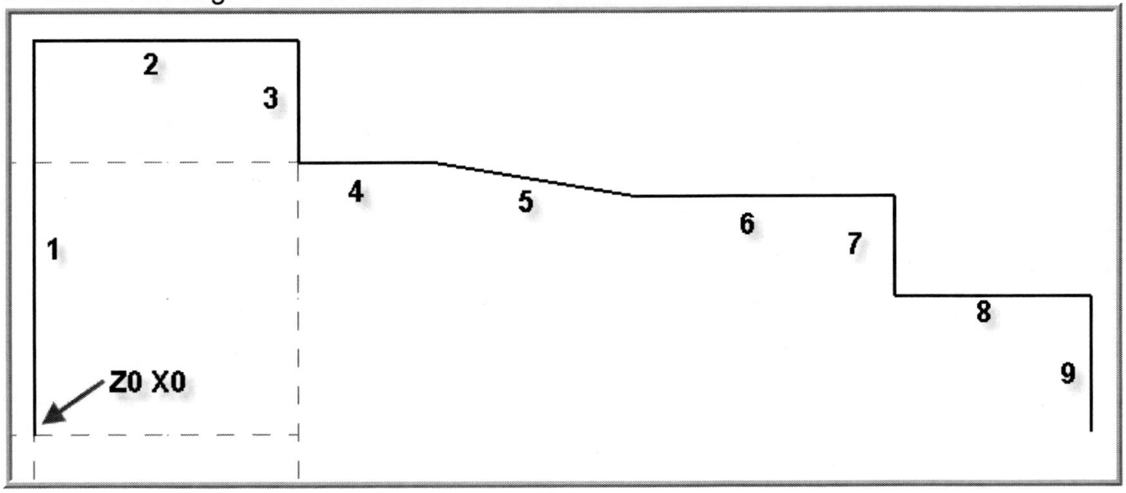

- **Create Line #1**

1. Select from the pull down menu **CREATE>Line>Endpoint…**

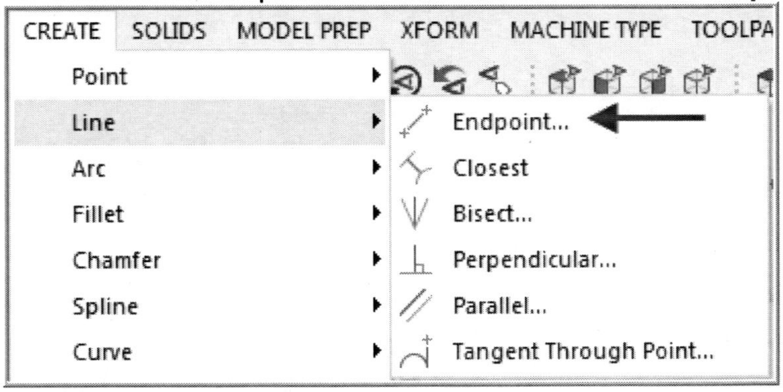

2. The **Line ribbon bar** appears.

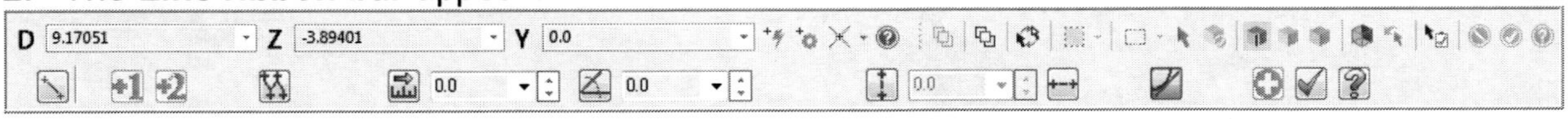

3. Move the cursor over the **center of the grid** and as you get close to the origin a visual cue appears.  This is the cue that will allow you to snap to the **origin**. With this visual cue highlighted click on the **origin.**

> **AutoCursor:**
> Visual Cues detects and highlights endpoints and midpoints of curves, lines, arc center points, and point entities.
>
> In addition, AutoCursor can snap to angle, nearest, tangent, perpendicular, horizontal, and vertical conditions.

➲ The following are Mastercam Visual Cues:

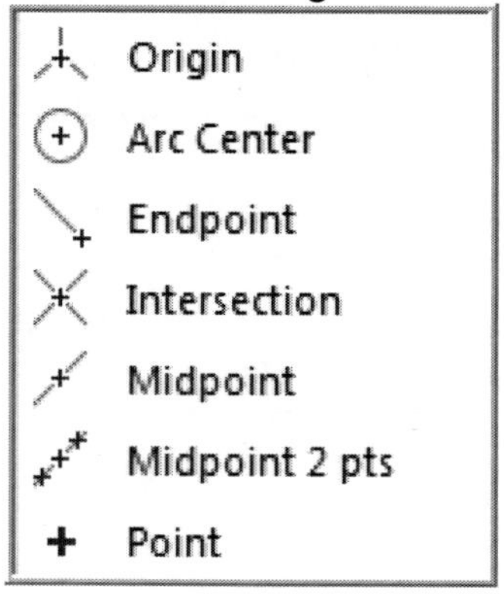

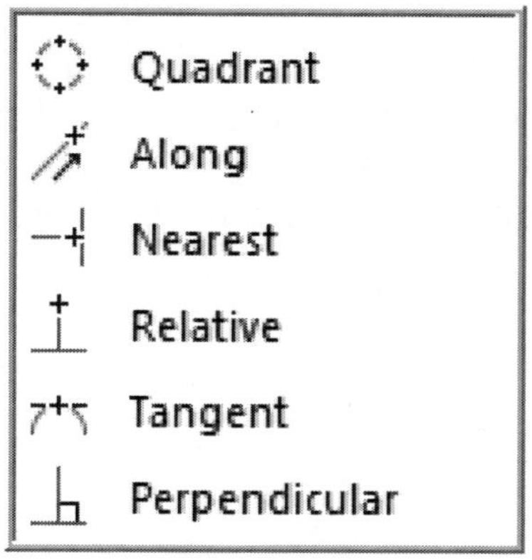

4. You are next prompted to **"Specify the second endpoint".** On the left hand side of the Line ribbon bar click on the **Multi-Line** button to activate it as shown below by the arrow:

5. Click in the **D** value space (Diameter) (as shown by the arrow below) and enter a value of **1.45**. Hit the Enter key and enter a value of **0 for the Z**, hit the Enter key again. **Note** the value of Y is set to **Zero**, this does not need to be input.

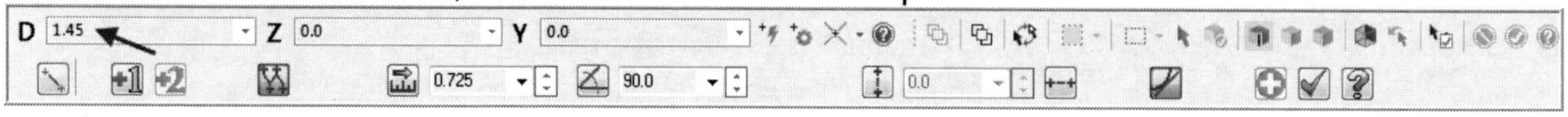

6. A vertical line should be visible as shown below:

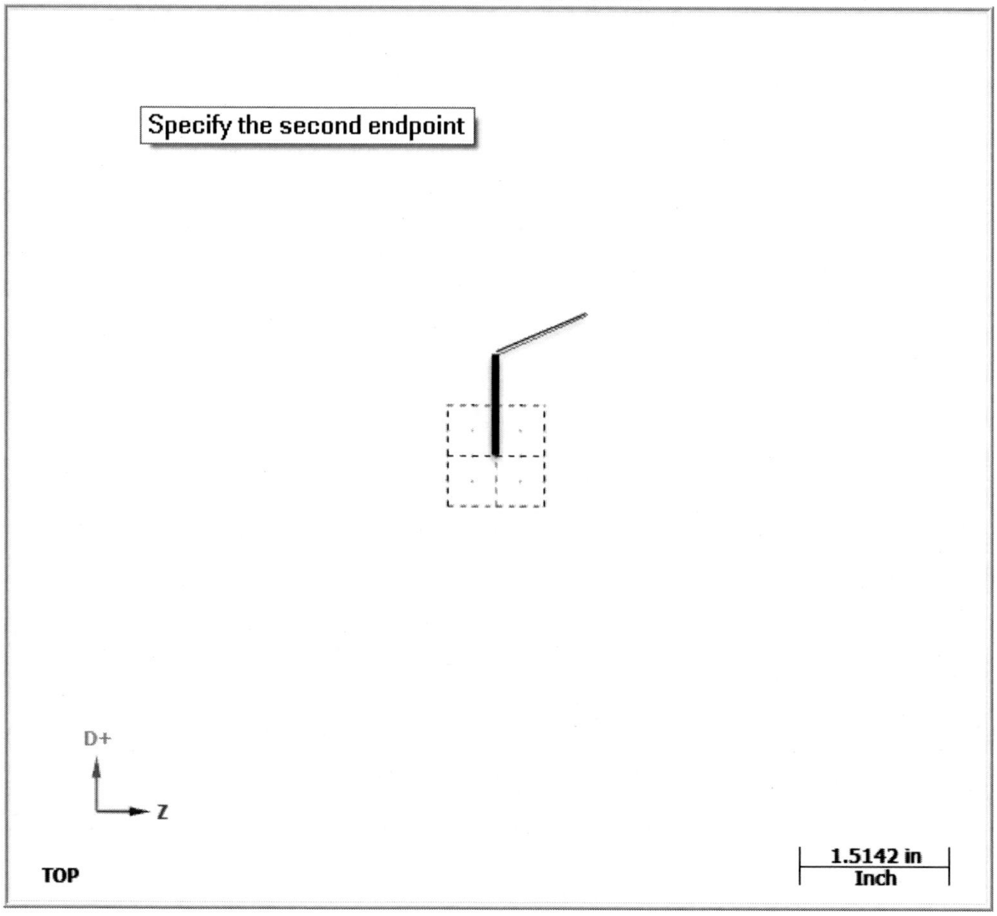

NOTE: If you make a mistake creating lines, click on the **Accept** icon and click on the **Undo** icon . Then redo the Line.

➲ **Create Line #2**

7. **"Specify the second endpoint";** Type in **1.45 in D** hit Enter, type in **0.5 in Z. Note** the value of Y is set to **Zero**, this does not need to be input. Hit the Enter key once again to complete this line.

➲ **Create Line #3**

8. **"Specify the second endpoint";** Type in **1.0 in D** hit Enter, type in **0.5 in Z.** Hit the Enter key once again to complete this line.

➲ **Create Line #4**

9. **"Specify the second endpoint";** Type in **1.0 in D** hit Enter, type in **0.75 in Z.** Hit the Enter key once again to complete this line.

➲ **Create Line #5**

10. **"Specify the second endpoint";** Type in **0.875 in D** hit Enter, type in **1.125 in Z.** Hit the Enter key once again to complete this line.

➲ **Create Line #6**

11. **"Specify the second endpoint";** Type in **0.875 in D** hit Enter, type in **1.625 in Z.** Hit the Enter key once again to complete this line.

12. Fit the image to the screen by clicking on the **Fit to Screen** icon as shown below:

13. Then unzoom by clicking on the **Un-Zoom Previous/ .5** icon as shown below:

➲ **Create Line #7**

14. **"Specify the second endpoint";** Type in **0.5 in D** hit Enter, type in **1.625 in Z.** Hit the Enter key once again to complete this line.

➲ **Create Line #8**

15. **"Specify the second endpoint";** Type in **0.5 in D** hit Enter, type in **2.0 in Z.** Hit the Enter key once again to complete this line.

➲ **Create Line #9**

16. **"Specify the second endpoint";** Type in **0.0 in D** hit Enter, type in **2.0 in Z.** Hit the Enter key once again to complete this line.

17. Click on the **OK** icon to complete this feature.
18. Select the **Screen Fit** icon to fit the part to the screen.
19. Your geometry should look like the figure below:

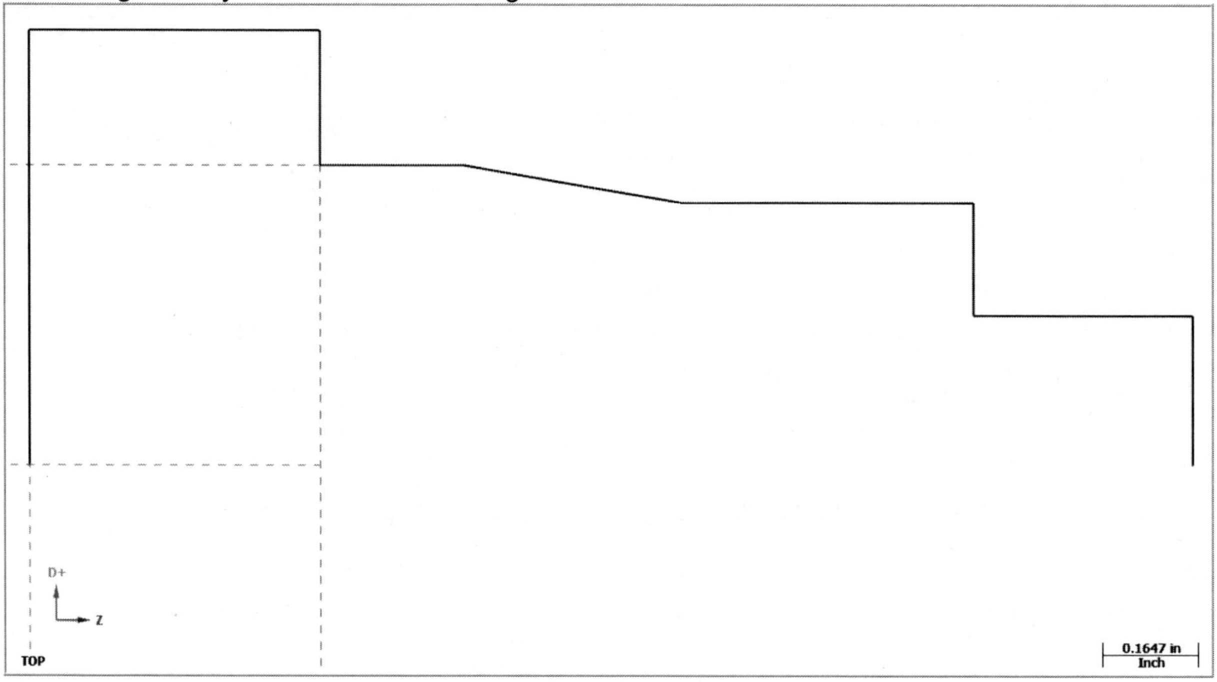

TASK 4:
CREATE THE .125 FILLET RADIUS AND 45° X 1/32" –CHAMFER

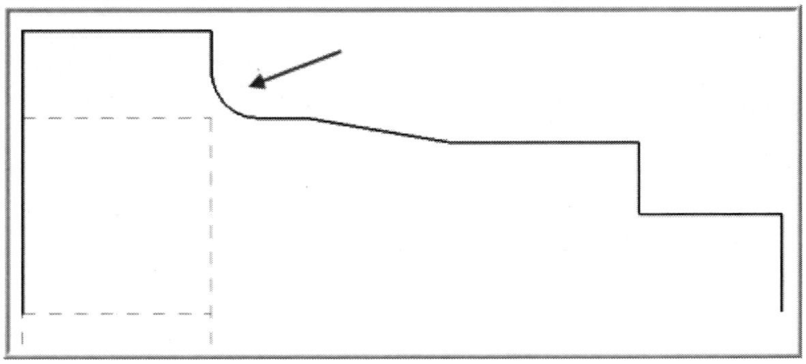

➲ **Create the .125 fillet radius.**

1. Select **CREATE>Fillet>Entities…**

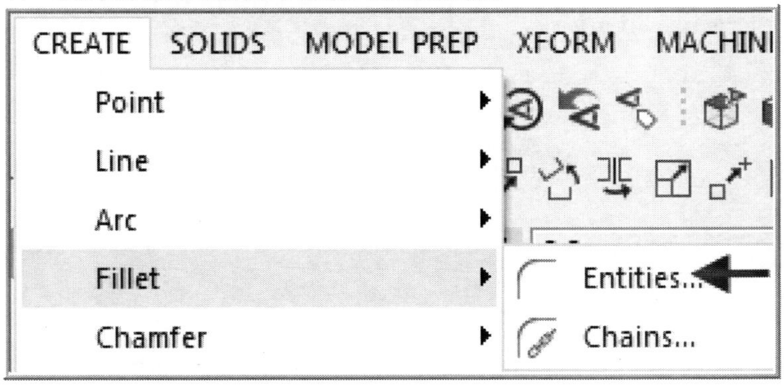

2. The Fillet Entities ribbon bar appears and you are prompted to **"Fillet: Select an entity".**

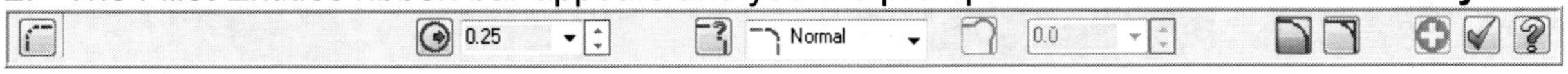

3. Click in the space for radius (shown below), and input **.125** and then hit the tab key.

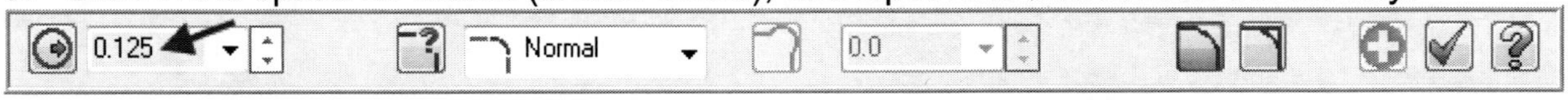

4. You are now transported over to the **Fillet Style field** (shown below). Click on the drop down arrow to review the various fillet radius styles and then ensure **Normal** is selected before moving on.

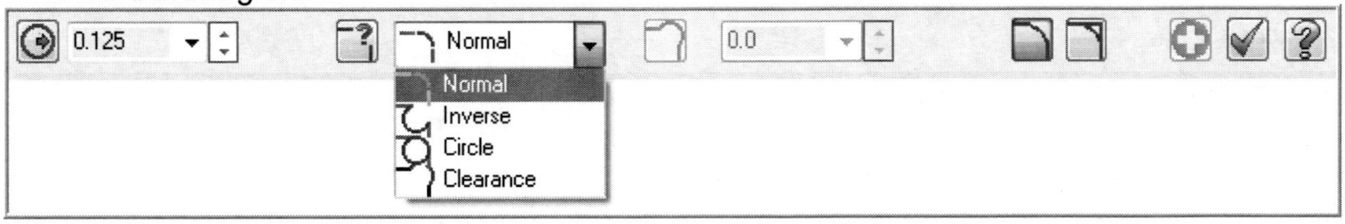

Style Field: Sets the fillet style to be created. The following styles are available from the drop down list:
Normal = creates normal fillets on the corners of a contour, resulting in rounded corners.
Inverse = creates inverted arcs on the corners of a contour.
Circle = creates full circles in each of the corners of a contour.
Clearance = creates fillets on inside corners of a contour so that the tool will reach completely into the corner to remove material.

5. Ensure the **Trim** option for fillet is activated, the icon is depressed as shown below:

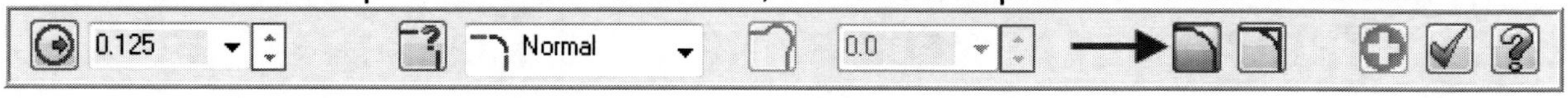

6. Move over to the graphic screen and for the prompt **"Fillet: Select an entity"** click on **Line 1** and then for the prompt **"Fillet: Select another entity"** click on **Line 2** as shown below:

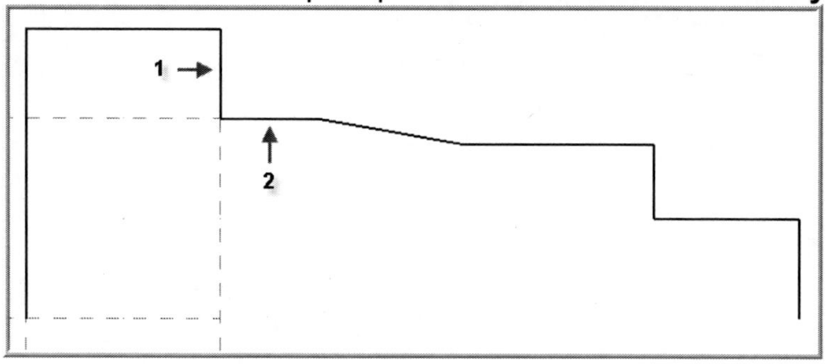

7. Click on the **OK** icon  to complete this feature.

The completed fillet is shown below:

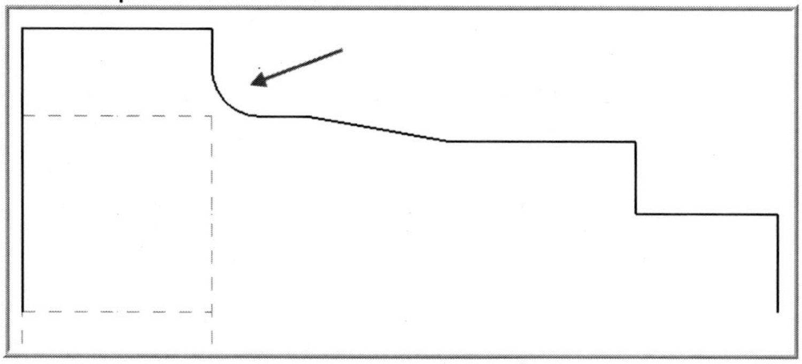

➲ **Create the 45° x 1/32" (.03125) Chamfer.**

8. Select **CREATE>Chamfer>Entities…**

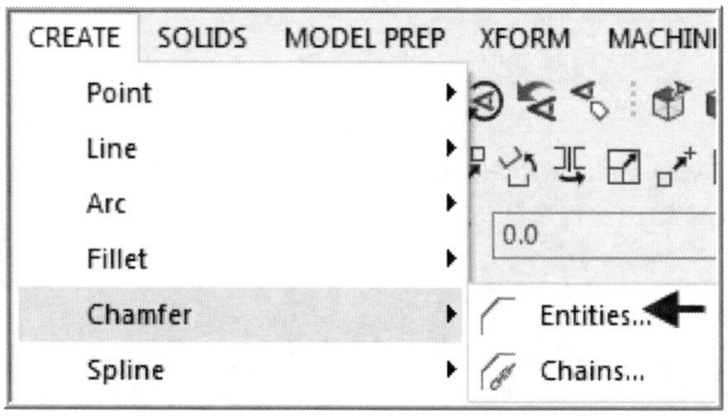

9. The **Chamfer Entities** ribbon bar appears.

10. Click in the space for **distance 1** and input **1/32** and then hit the tab key.

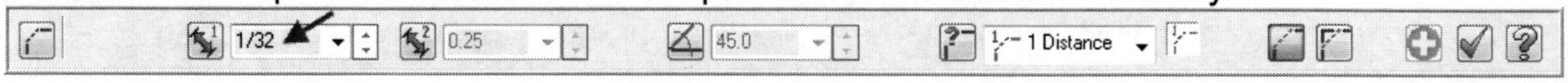

11. This fractional 1/32 will then be converted to a decimal **0.03125** when you hit the tab key.

12. You are moved into the **Chamfer Style** options as shown below:

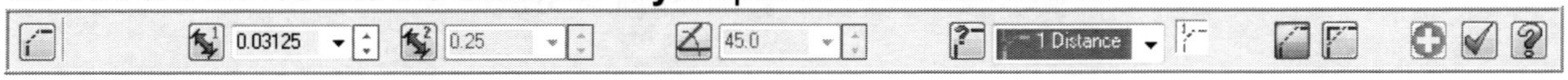

13. Ensure **1 Distance** is selected as shown below:

14. Ensure the **Trim** option for Chamfer is activated, the icon is depressed as shown below:

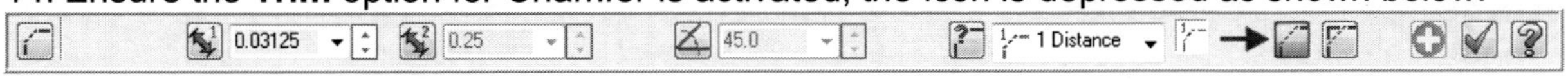

15. Click on **Line 1** and then click on **Line 2** as shown below:

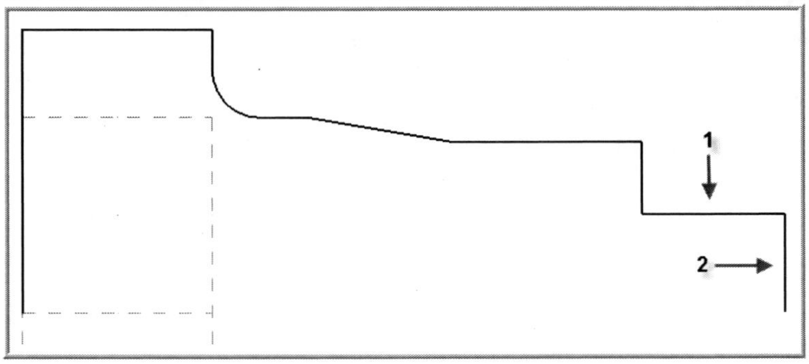

16. Click on the **OK** icon  to complete this feature.
17. The Chamfer should look like the figure below:

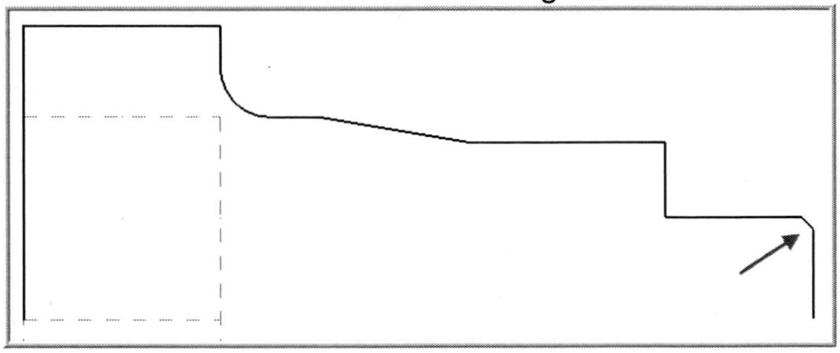

18. This completes the geometry for this part.

TASK 5:
SAVE THE DRAWING

1. Select **File.**
2. Select **Save As…**
3. In the **"File name"** box, type **"Lathe-Lesson-2".**
4. Save to an appropriate location.

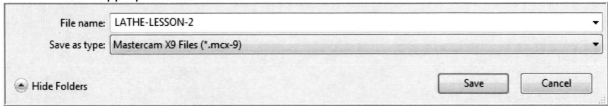

5. Select the **Save** button to save the file and complete this function.

Toolpath Creation

TASK 6:
DEFINING THE STOCK AND CHUCK PARAMETERS

1. Select the screen fit icon as shown to the right to display the geometry:

2. Ensure your screen looks like the image below:
   a. The Toolpaths Manager is open, if it is not Select Alt and O on your keyboard to open it.
   b. The properties icon displays Lathe Default. If it is not refer to **Setting the Environment** chapter at the beginning of the book.
   c. The **Lathe Lesson-2** Geometry is showing.

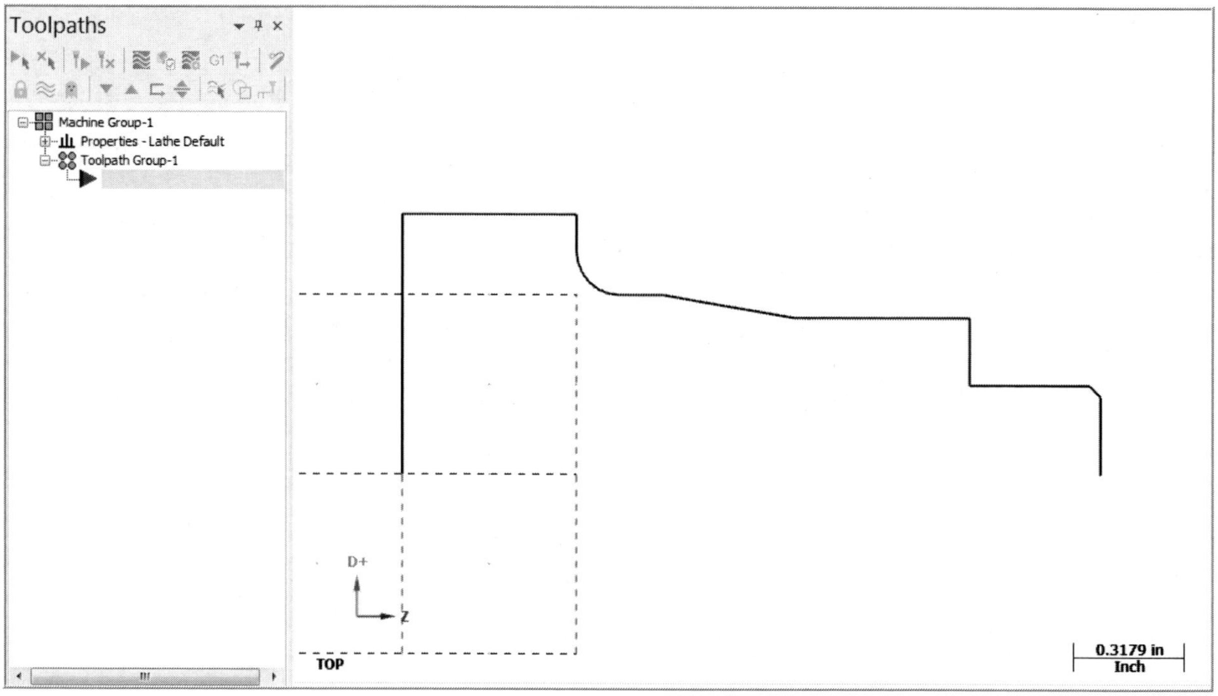

3. Click on the plus in front of **Properties** to expand the Machine Group Properties.

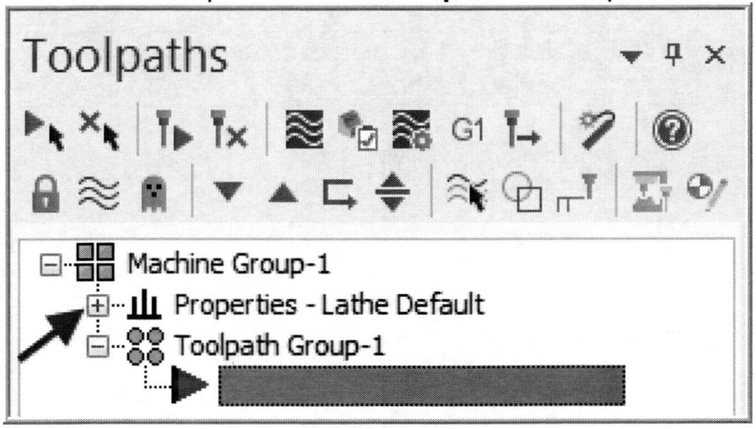

4. **This is Optional -** To expand the toolpaths manager window, click on the outside of the window with the left mouse button (hold the button down) and drag it to the right.

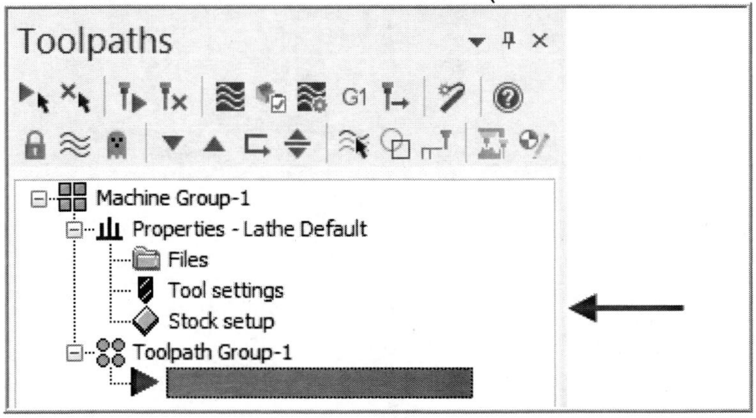

5. Click on **Stock setup** in the Toolpaths Manager window.

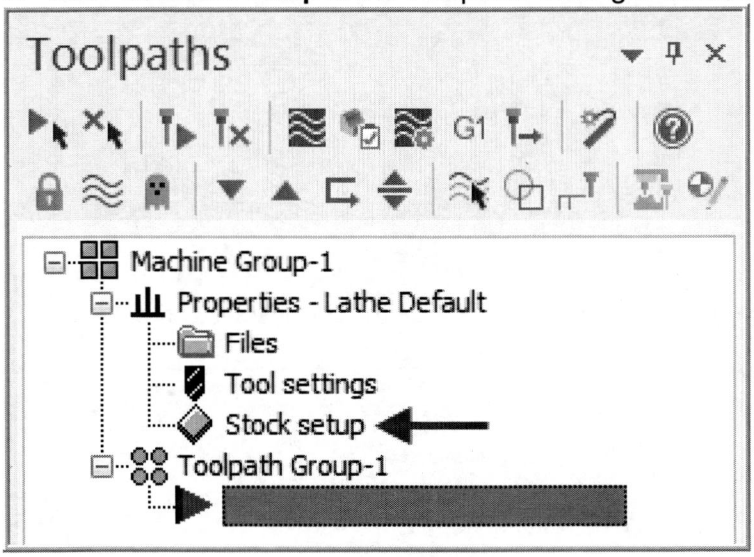

6. Select the **Stock Properties** button in the **Stock Setup** page as shown in the screenshot below:

Note: To learn more about Stock Setup refer to the Tips and Techniques section on the Mastercam Training Guide – Lathe DVD that accompanies this book.

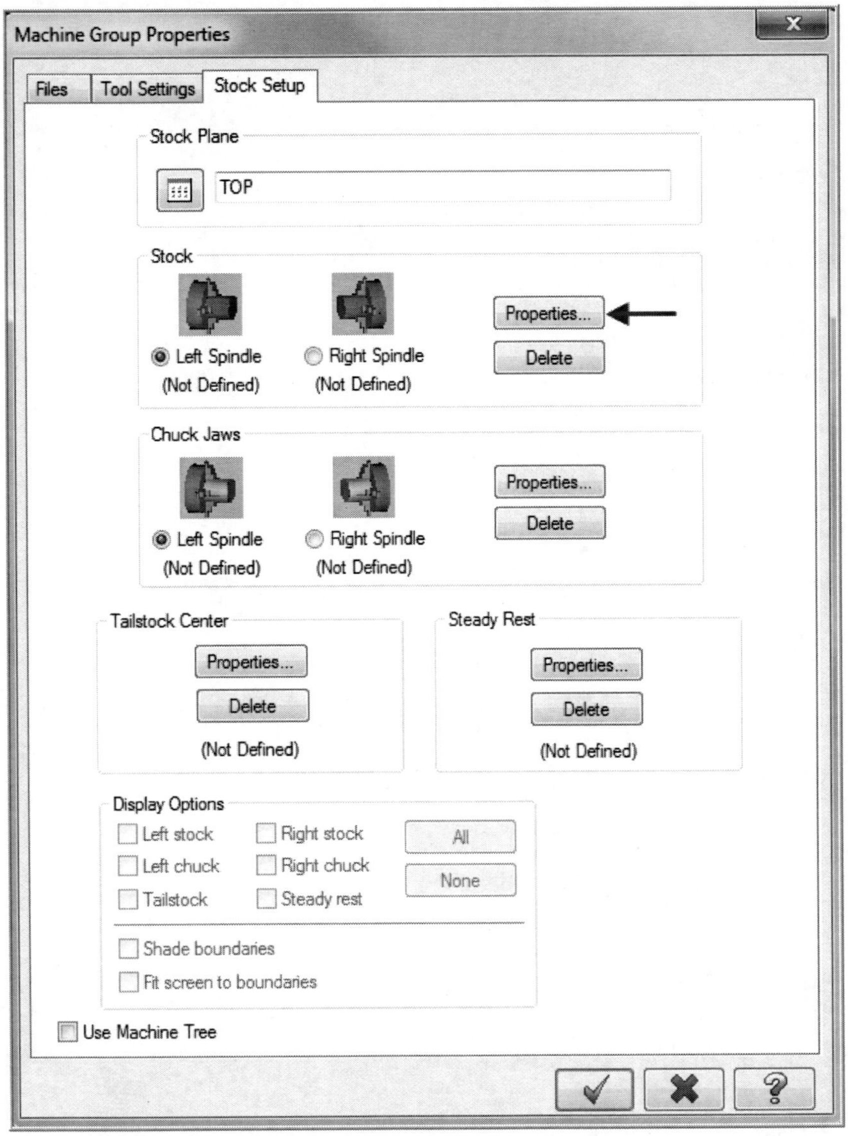

7. In the **Machine Component Manager-Stock** window click on the **Geometry** button and select **Cylinder** as shown below:

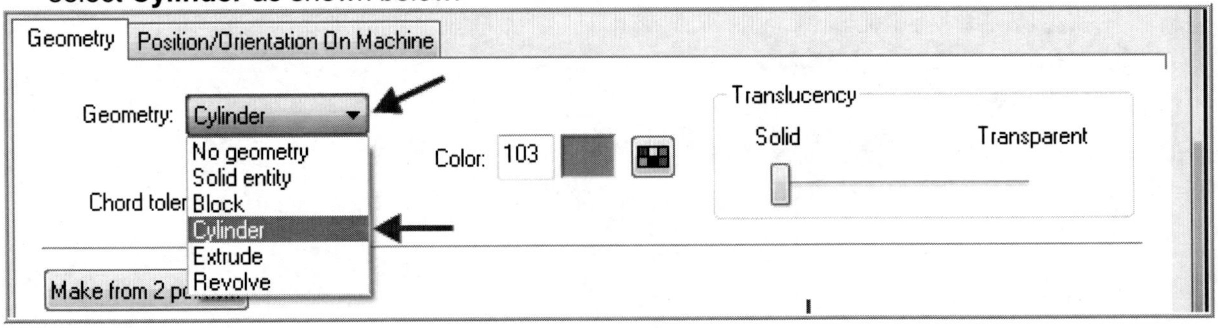

8. In the **Stock setup** set the values as shown below. **Axis is set to +Z**.

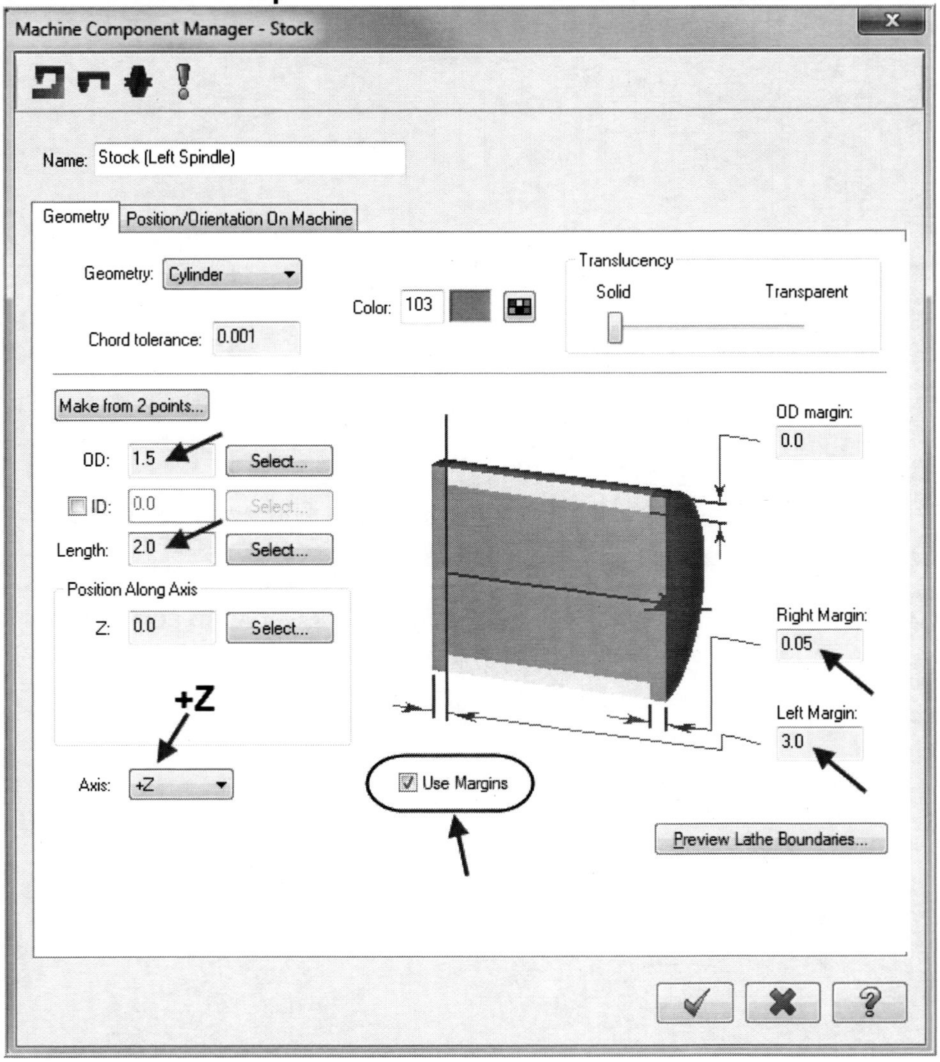

Use Margins Select this option to use stock margins. This is an extra safety feature; Mastercam will add the margin to the stock boundary when calculating the Tool Clearance warnings.

Axis Select the orientation and direction in which the cylinder will be generated relative to the Base Point.
Please note that these axis labels represent 3D world coordinates, not 2D lathe part coordinates. This means that to create stock aligned with a lathe Z axis for a typical turning application, you would choose either +X or -X.

OD Enter the value of the outer diameter, or click the Select button to choose a point from the graphic window.

Length Enter the length of the stock.

Position Along Axis Enter the location of the base point of the stock model or component or click the Select button to choose a point from the graphic window.
For a lathe stock model, this is typically a Z-axis position that represents either the left or right face of the stock.

9. Click on the OK icon  to complete this feature.
10. Still on the Stock Setup page activate **Fit screen to boundaries**.

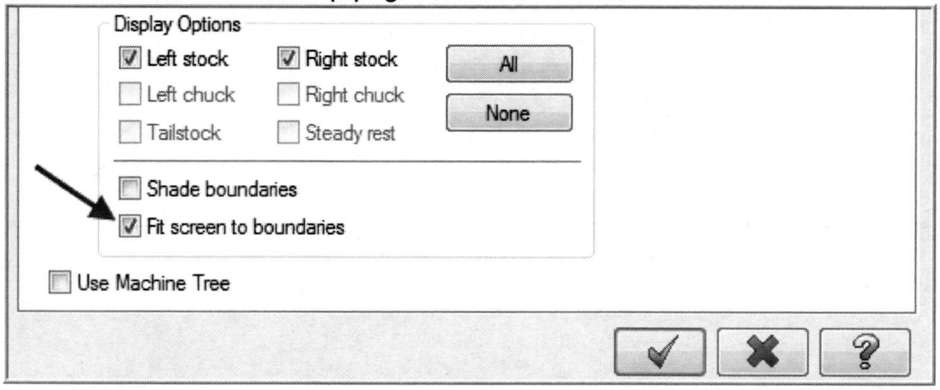

Fit screen to boundaries
Check to determine that the stock, chuck, and tailstock boundaries are included when fitting geometry to the graphics window

11. Select the **Chuck Properties** button in the **Stock Setup** page as shown in the screenshot below:

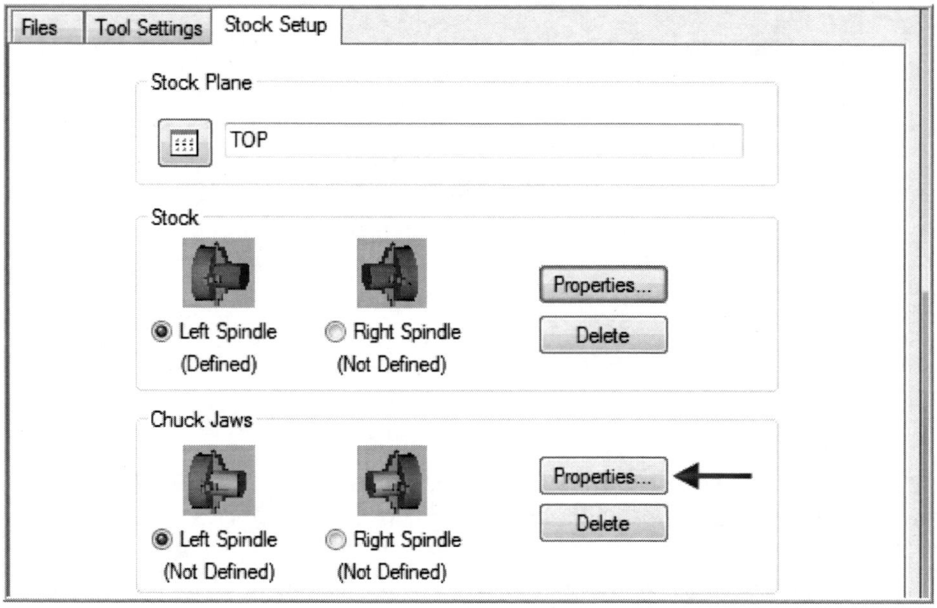

12. In the **Chuck Jaws** setup set the values as shown below:

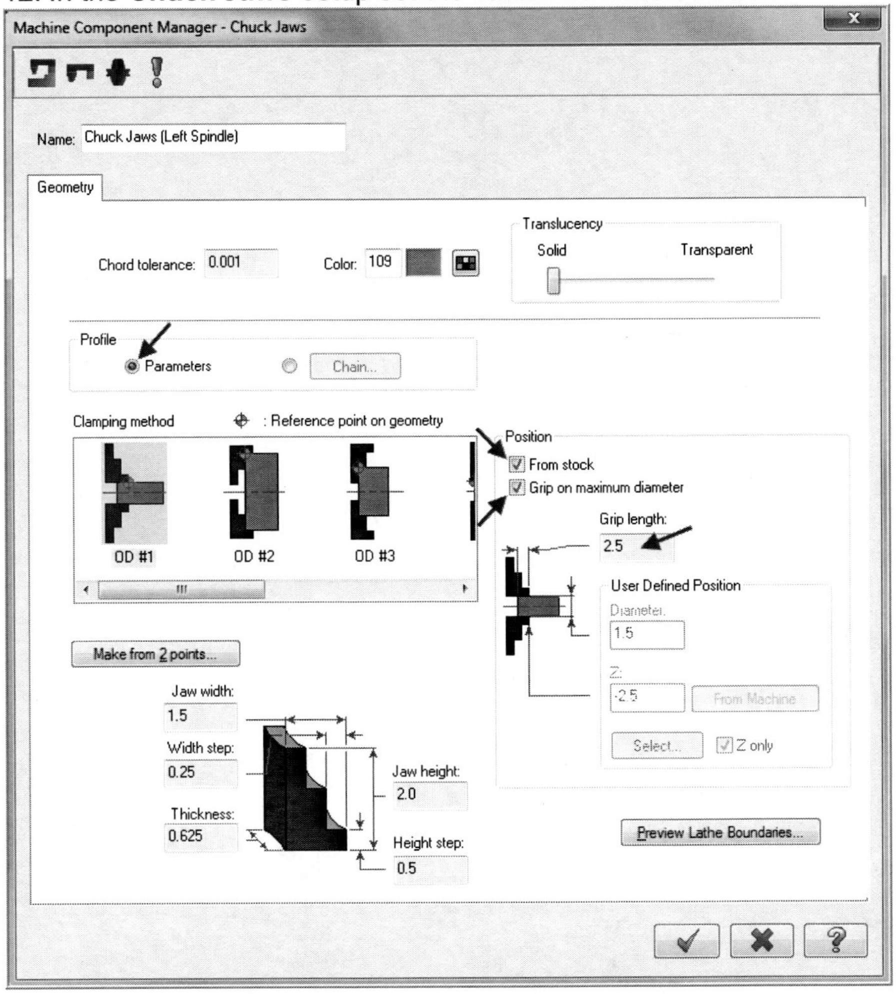

Chuck Jaws Geometry tab

Use this tab to define a set of chuck jaws for a machining operation. This locates the chuck in relation to the part and ensures that the tool will not make a move into the chuck.

To define the chuck jaw you need to:

Define the chuck jaw's shape
Select a clamping method
Tell Mastercam where the chuck is located

Clamping method

Choose the picture which best represents how your chuck clamps the stock. The reference point is the point that represents the chuck position that is defined in the Position section of this dialog box and should be where the chuck clamps the stock.

Position - From stock

Check to have the system calculate the chuck jaw's position in space using the defined stock. You must have stock defined on the screen for this option to be enabled.

Grip on maximum diameter

Check to have the chuck jaw hold the stock at its maximum diameter. If cleared, the system calculates the chuck holding the stock at its minimum diameter. You must have stock defined on the screen for this option to be enabled.

Grip length

Enter a value to determine how much stock is being held by the chuck jaw.

13. Click on the **OK** icon  to complete this feature.

14. Click on the **Tool Settings** page and make changes as shown below:

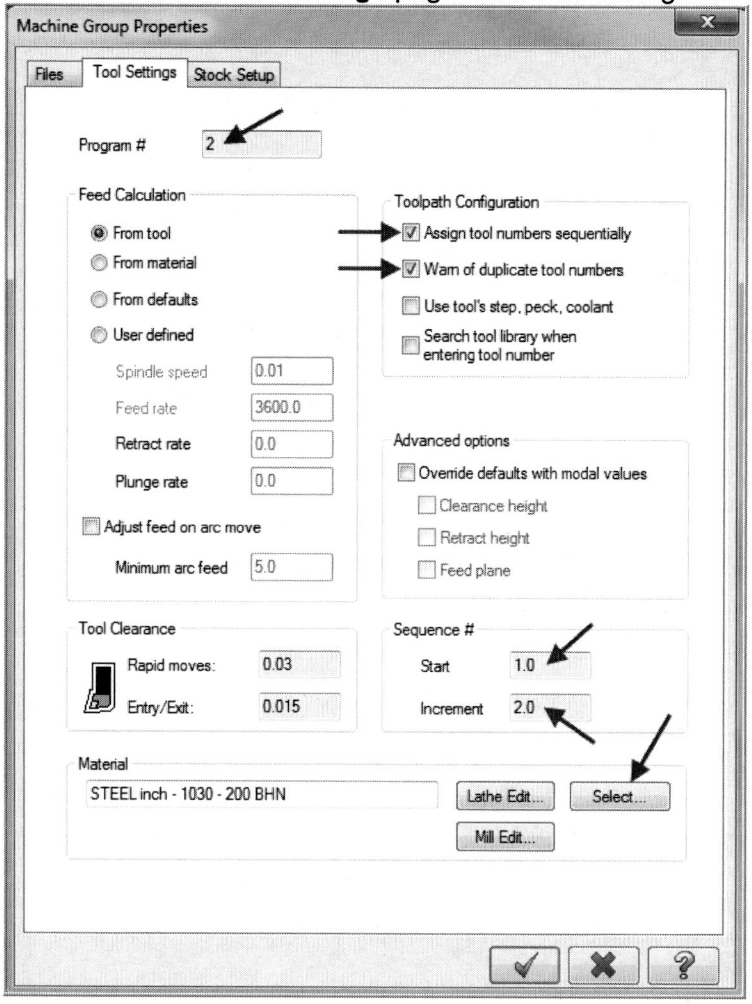

Tool Settings tab
Use this tab to control how Mastercam assigns tool numbers, tool offset numbers, and default values for feeds, speeds, coolant, and other toolpath parameters.

Program # The post processor will use this field if your machine tool requires a number for a program name.
From tool Uses the feed rate, plunge rate, retract rate, and spindle speed directly from the tool definition.
Assign tool numbers sequentially Assigns the next available tool number for new tools created or selected from the tool library. If you select this option, Mastercam overwrites the tool numbers stored in the tool definition with a sequential number.
Warn of duplicate tool numbers Informs you when duplicate tool numbers are entered and displays a description of the duplicate tool.
Sequence # (For the NC Code File) Enter the starting sequence number and the increment in the proper fields. The default values and specific format for these fields is determined by the **NC Output** section of the control definition.

15. To change the **Material** type to Aluminum 6061 now pick the **Select** button at the bottom of the Tool Settings page.

16. At the **Material List** dialog box open the Source drop down list and click on **Lathe–library.**

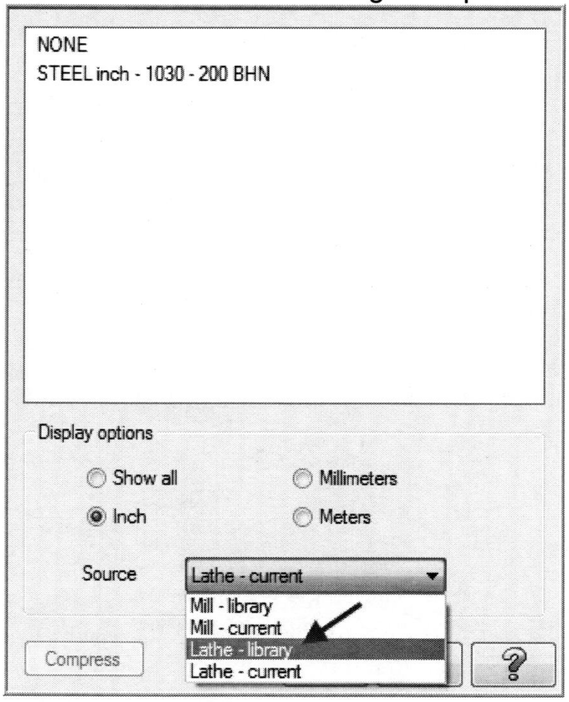

17. From the **Default Materials** list click on **ALUMINUM inch - 6061** and then click on .

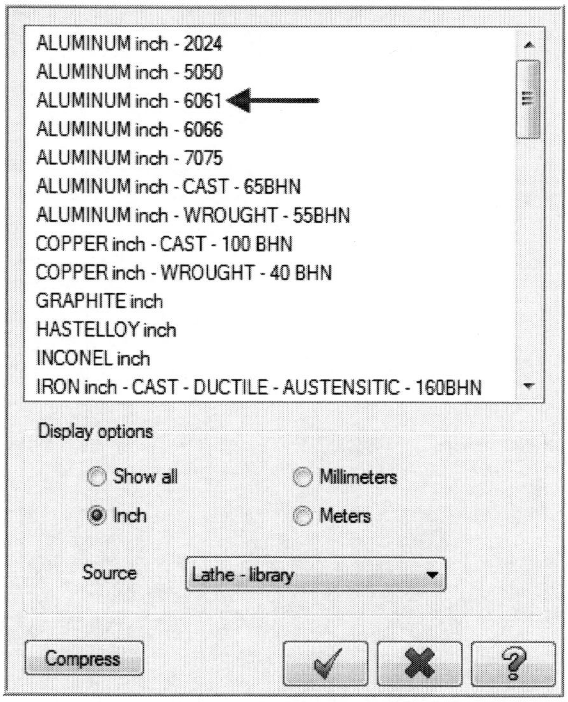

Material List dialog box
Use this dialog box to select materials and manage the materials list.

Right-click in the main window or on a material definition to see a menu of options.

These let you edit a material definition, create a new material, select different material libraries, and view the contents of a material library in different text formats.

Use the options in the **Source** list to display materials in the current part file or from a material library.

The **Compress** option reads a selected material library file and removes any deleted library entities. This decreases the size of the library file for more efficient storage.

18. Click on the OK button  again to complete this Stock Setup function.

19. Select the **screen Fit** icon.

Notice the stock setup outline as indicated by broken lines as shown below:

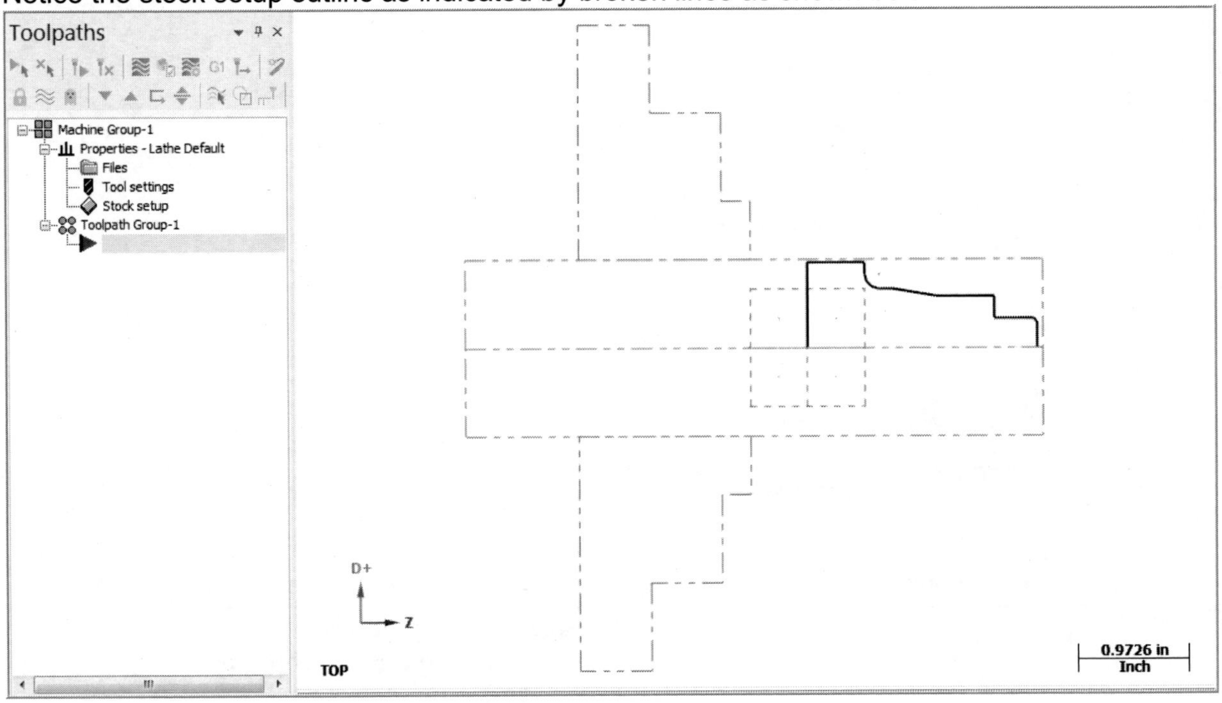

TASK 7:
FACE THE FRONT OF THE PART:

➲ In this task you will use a facing tool to face the front of the part in one cut.

1. If required select the **Fit** icon as shown:

2. From the menu bar select **TOOLPATHS>Face…**

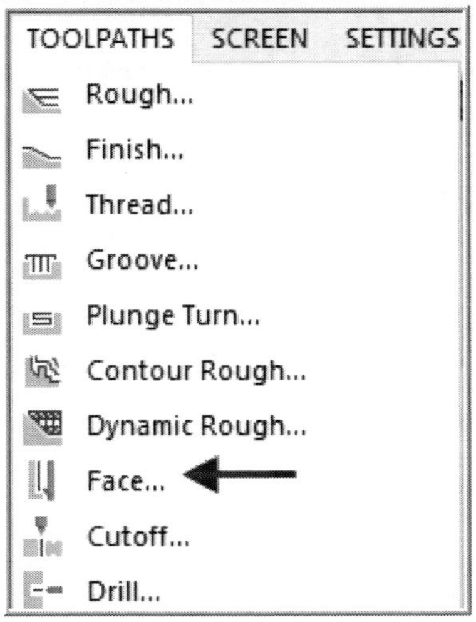

Face toolpaths
Face toolpaths prepare the face of the part for further machining. Once the face of the part is clean, you can use it to set tools or determine tool offsets.

You do not need to chain any geometry to create the toolpath. Instead, the Face Parameters tab gives you **two ways** to specify how much stock to remove:
Choose **Select Points** to return to the graphic window and select two points which represent opposite corners of a rectangle.

Use the **stock boundary**. If you do so, **you must enter the Z coordinate of the finished face** of the part in the Finish Z text box. This option is available only if you have defined the stock boundary in Job Setup.

3. When prompted to **"Enter new NC name"** ensure **Lathe-Lesson-2** is entered as shown below and then select the OK button ✓.

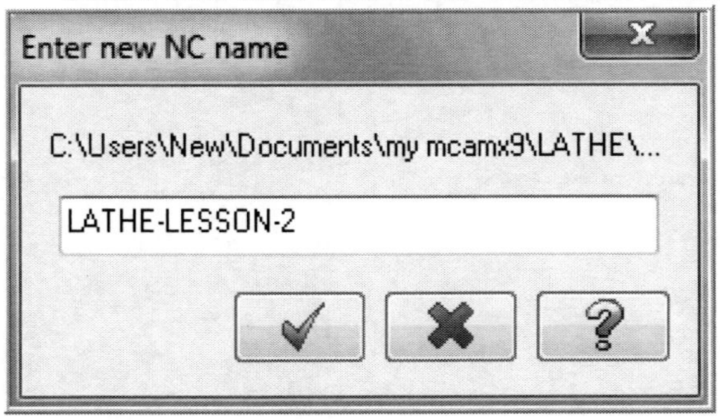

➲ After selecting the OK button you are confronted with **Toolpath parameters** page. The first task here will be to select **Tool #1 an OD Rough- Right – 80 deg.**

4. Click on **Tool #1** and make changes in the Toolpath parameters page as shown below:

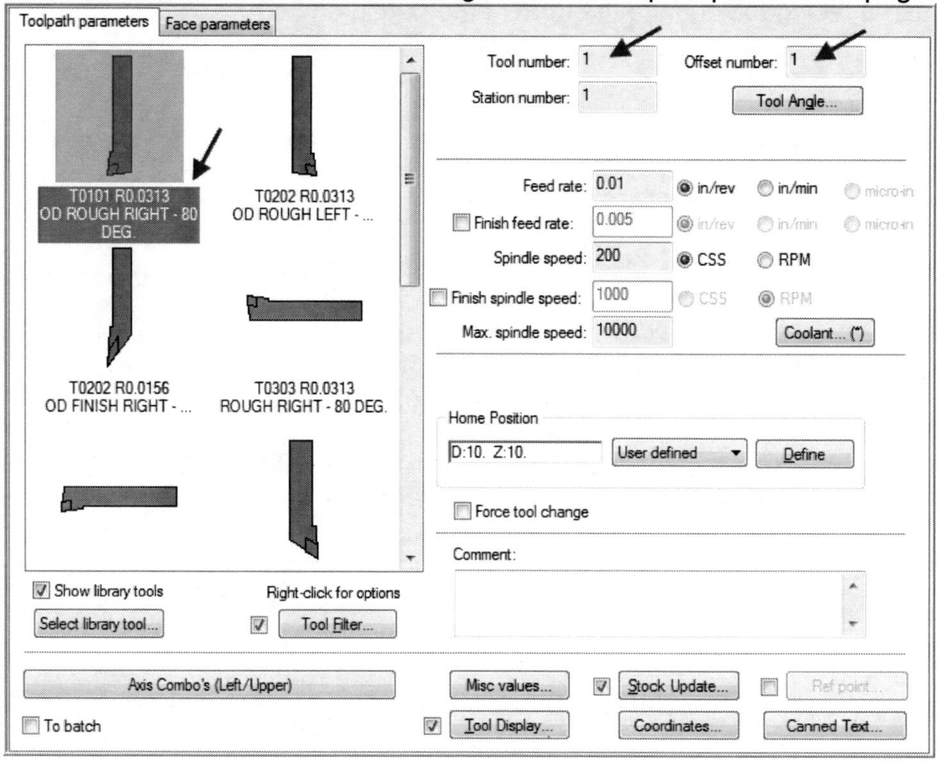

Use the Toolpath parameters tab to: Select a tool, set feeds and speeds, and set other general toolpath parameters.

This tab is very similar for most Lathe toolpaths.

5. Select the **Face parameters** page and make changes as shown below:

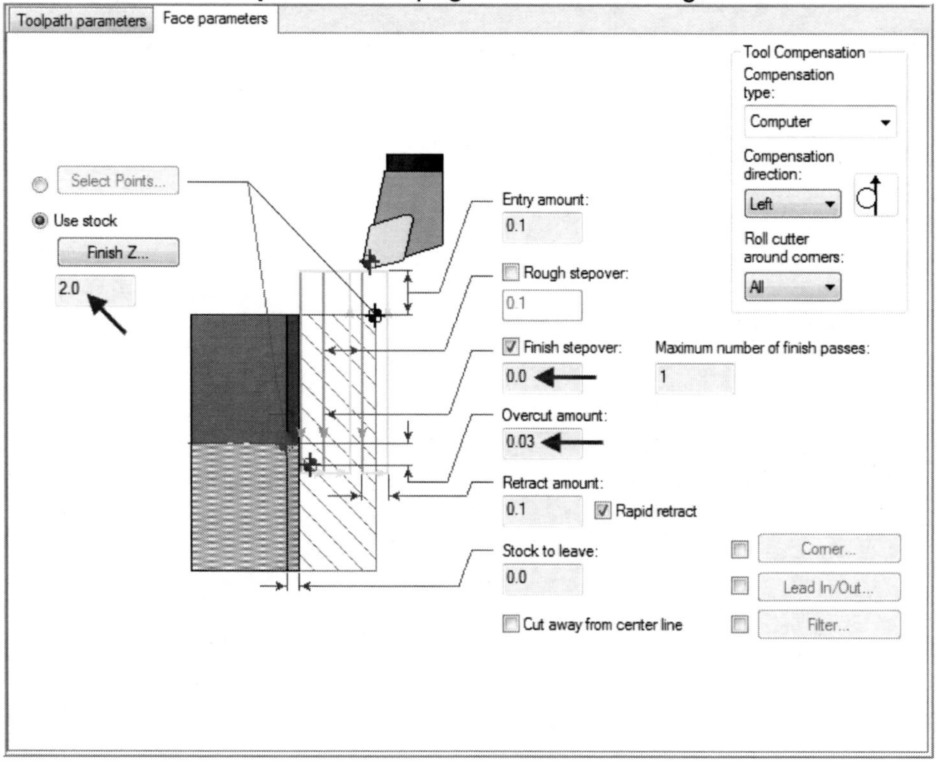

Finish stepover
Select this option to create one or more finish passes. Enter a stepover distance to define how much stock gets removed during each finish cut.

Overcut amount
A rectangle is used to define the material removed by the facing toolpath. The overcut amount determines how far past the rectangle the tool will cut. Typically this is a small distance that the **tool cuts past the part centerline**.

6. Select the OK button ✓ to complete this **Lathe Face** operation.

7. A new Toolpath called **1-Lathe Face** should be displayed as shown below:

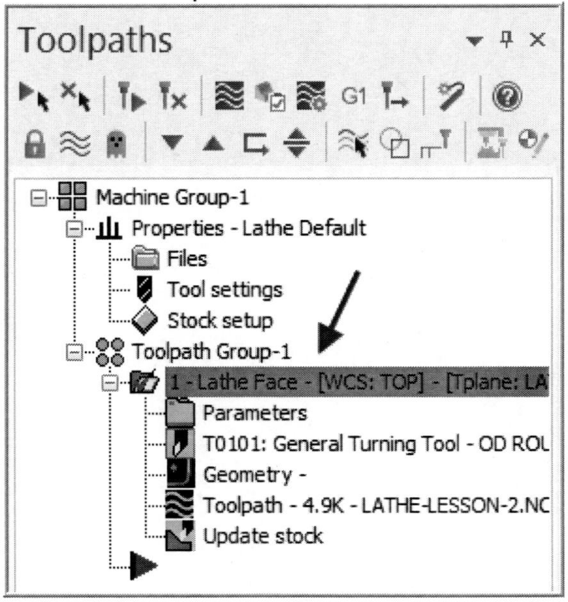

➲ Note: the new Toolpath called 1-Lathe Face. This is where all the toolpath information is kept. If changes are required to this toolpath just click on the parameter icon 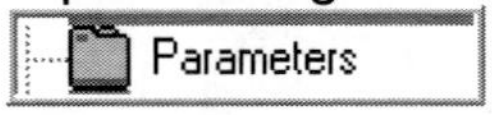

and the Screens from steps 4 and 5 will be available. This is handy in case a mistake was made in setting the toolpath parameters or in case a modification needs to be made.

TASK 8:
ROUGH THE OUTSIDE DIAMETERS

➲ In this task you will use the same tool as used for the previous facing operation **Tool #1 an OD Rough- Right – 80 deg.**

1. From the menu bar select **TOOLPATHS>Rough…**

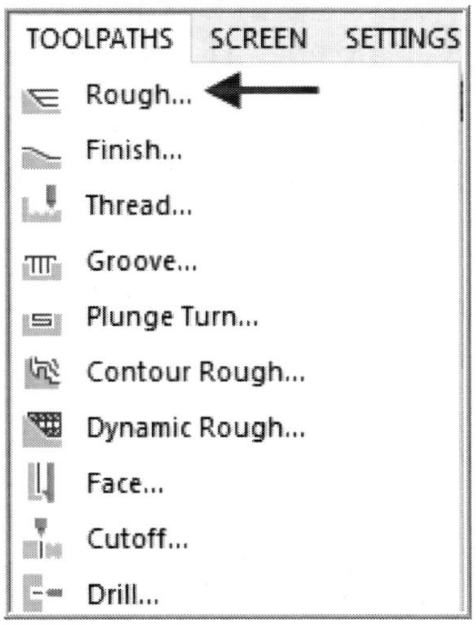

Rough toolpaths
Use rough toolpaths to quickly remove large amounts of stock in preparation for a finish pass. Roughing passes are typically straight cuts parallel to the Z-axis; however, you can set options for plunging into undercut areas. Standard rough toolpaths also include a semi-finish option, in which the roughing tool makes a final pass which follows the part contour, like a finish pass.
Mastercam includes several types of roughing toolpaths:
Standard rough toolpaths, which let you access all of Mastercam's roughing options.
Quick rough toolpaths, which let you quickly create simple rough toolpaths with fewer options.
Canned rough toolpaths, which use your machine tool's canned cycles to create the most efficient code (however, these do not offer as many options as the standard rough toolpaths).
Canned pattern repeat toolpaths, which create roughing passes in the shape of the part contour, rather than cutting parallel to the Z-axis.

2. In the **Chaining** window Chaining mode is set to **Partial** by default.

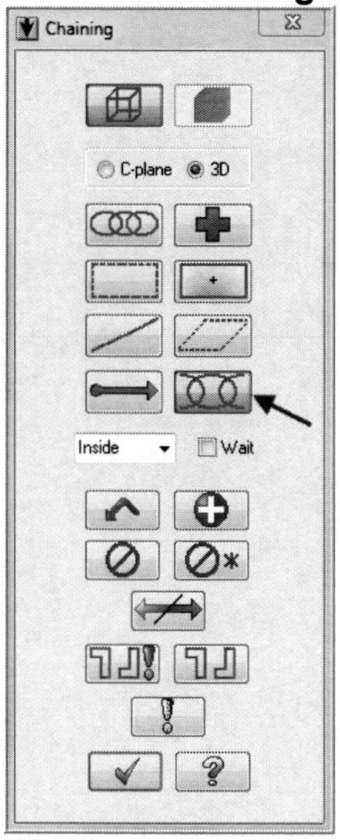

3. Click on **chamfer** as shown below:

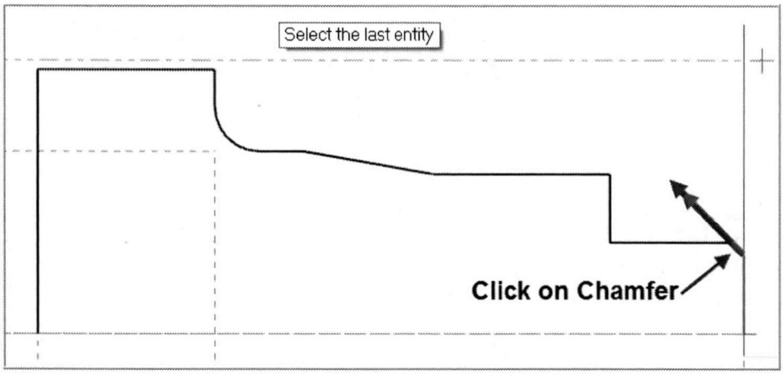

After you have selected the chamfer **ensure** that the arrows are pointing up and to the left of the part. If it is not select the reverse button in the Chaining dialog box.

4. Then select the Line shown below as the end entity in this chain.

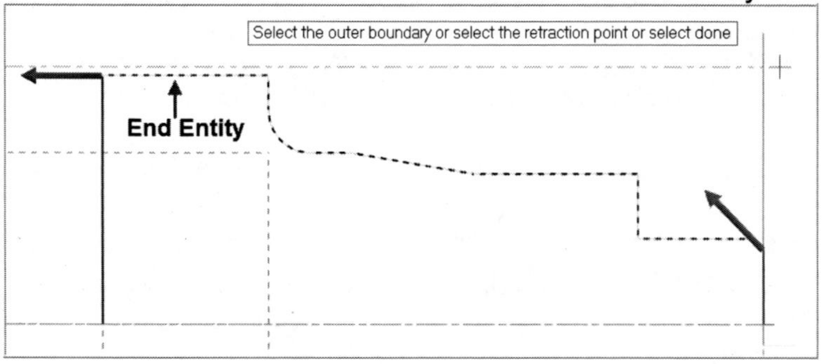

5. Select the OK button  to exit the Chaining dialog window.

6. In the **Toolpath parameters** page select the same tool used to face the part **Tool #1 an OD Rough- Right – 80 deg** and make changes as shown below:

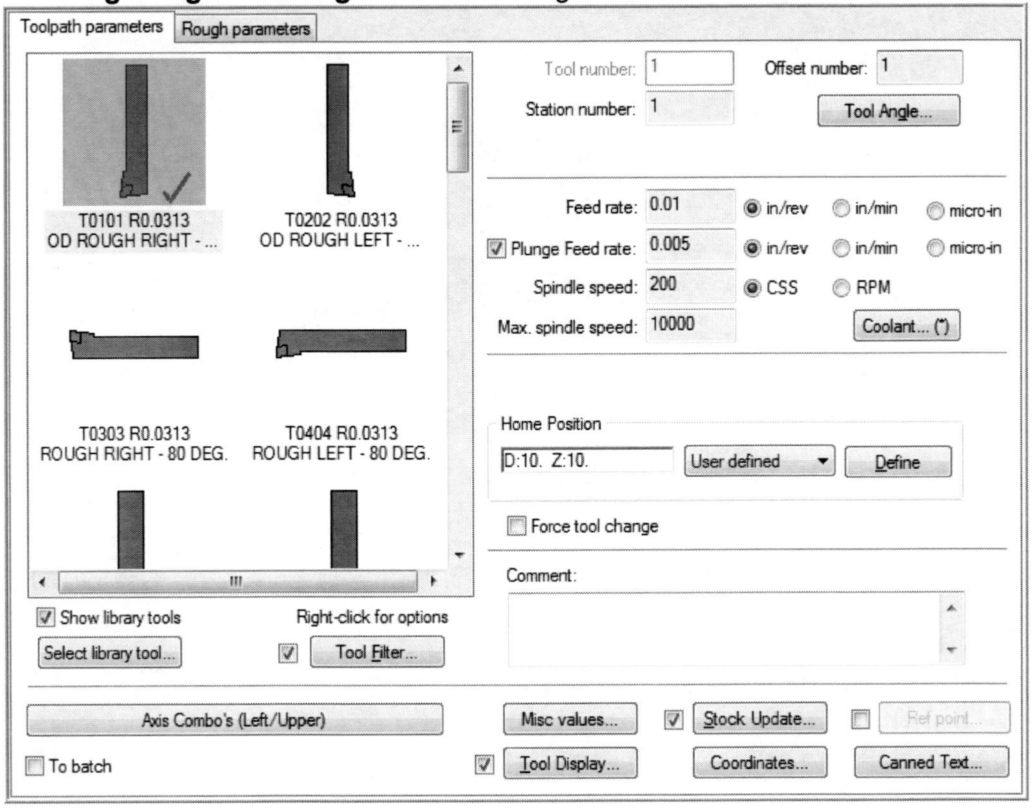

7. Select the **Rough parameters** page and make changes as shown below:

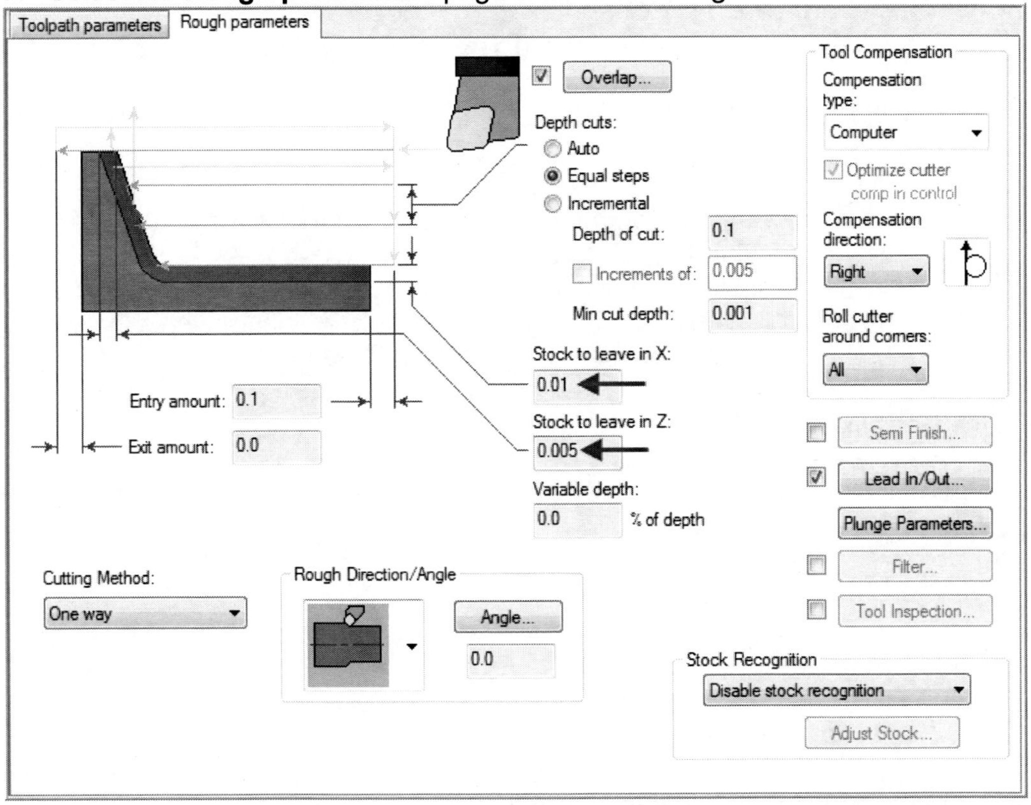

8. Select the **Lead In/Out** button select the **Lead out** page and extend the contour by .2 as shown below:

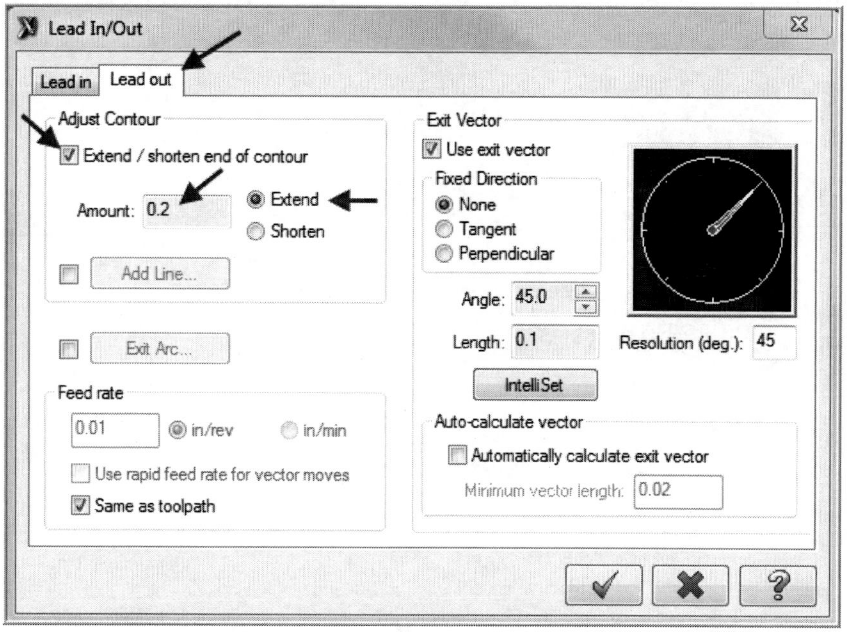

9. Select the OK button  to exit this function.

10. Select the OK button  to exit Rough Parameters.

TASK 9:
FINISH THE OUTSIDE DIAMETERS

➲ You will finish the outside diameters in one cut using **Tool #2 OD Finish Right – 35 DEG.**

1. From the menu bar select **TOOLPATHS>Finish…**

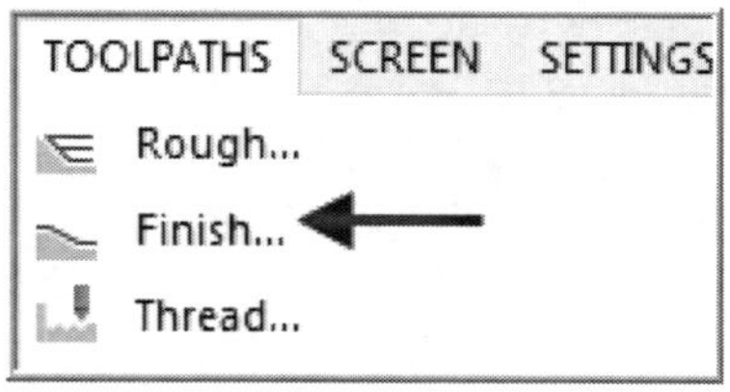

Finish toolpaths
Use finish toolpaths to have the tool follow the contour of chained geometry.
Typically, a finish toolpath follows a roughing toolpath, but this is not required. You can create a finish toolpath even if no roughing operation has been created.

2. Select **Last** in the Chaining dialog box.

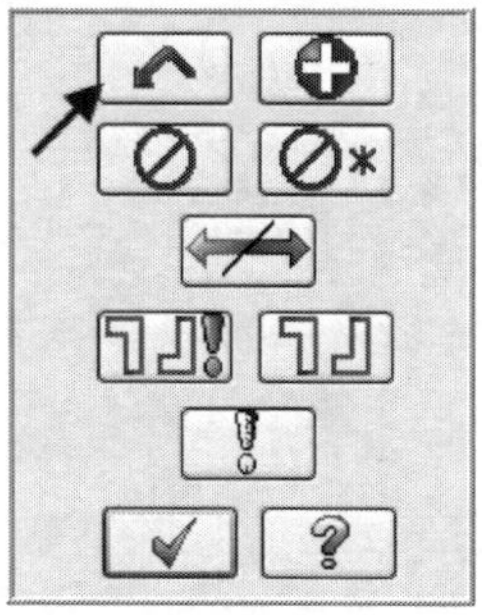

3. Select the OK button  to complete the selection.

4. Select **Tool #2 OD Finish Right – 35 DEG** tool from the tool list and make changes as shown below:

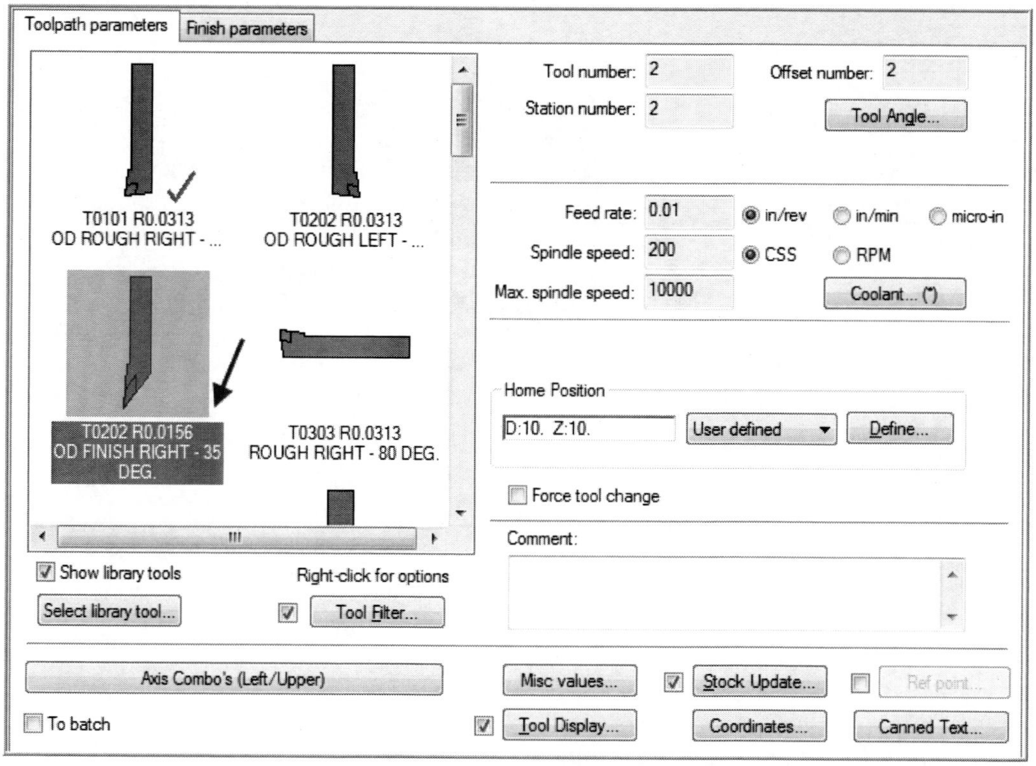

5. Select the **Finish parameters** page and make changes as shown below. Activate Corner Break.

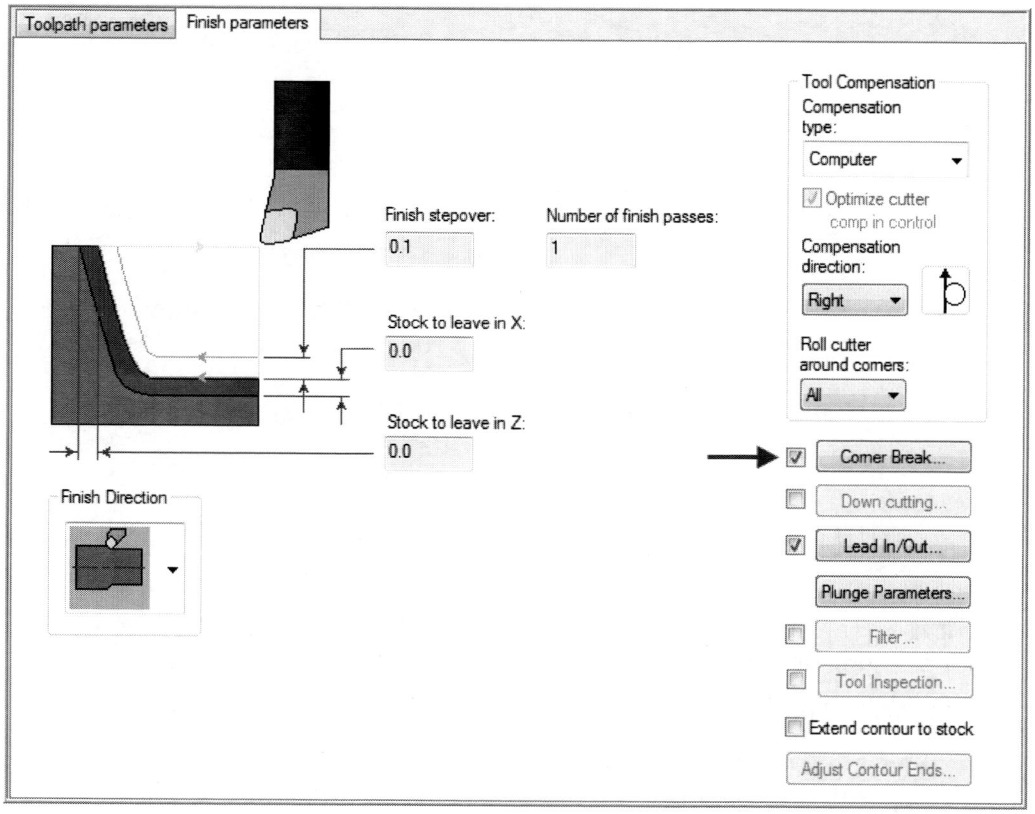

6. Select the Corner Break button and make changes as shown below if required:

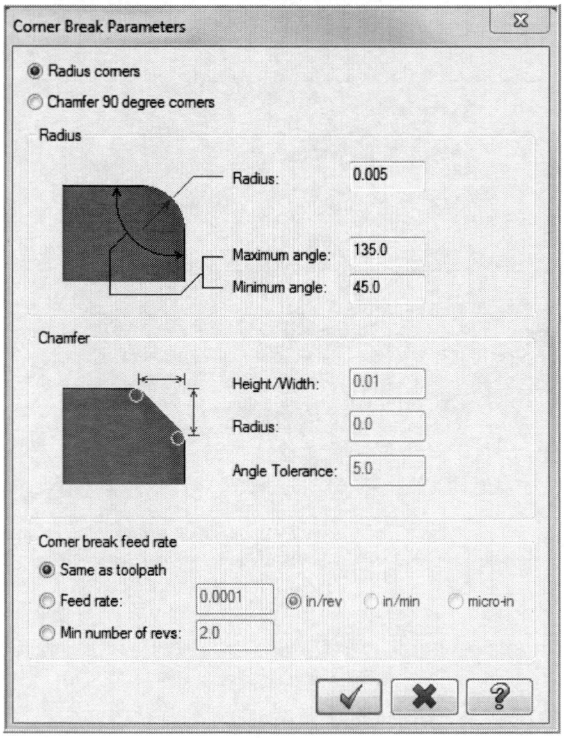

Corner Break
Use this dialog box to automatically create radii or chamfers on all outer corners of lathe finish toolpaths.

You can also set the feed rate when the tool creates the radii or chamfers.

7. Select the OK button to complete this feature.

8. Select the **Lead In/Out** button select the **Lead in** page and change the **Fixed Direction** to **Tangent** as shown below:

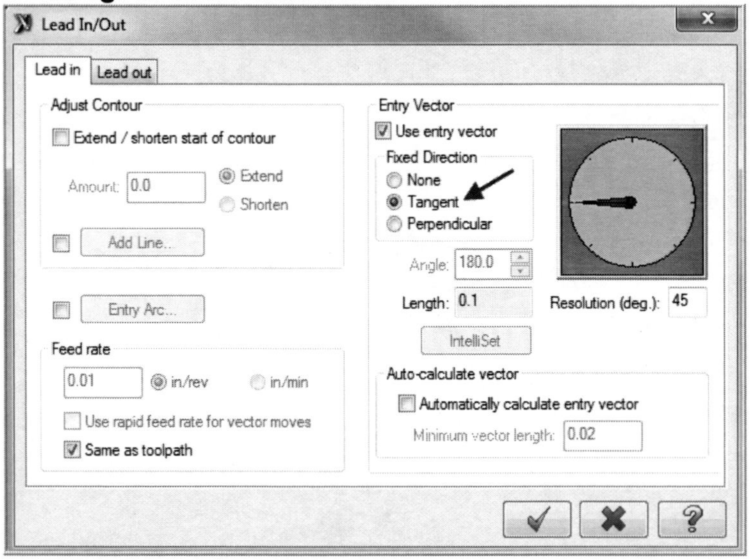

Lead In/Out dialog box
Use this dialog box to control how the tool approaches or retracts from the part for each pass in the toolpath. This eliminates the need to create extra geometry for this purpose

Fixed Direction Tangent
Force the vector to be tangent to either the first move in the toolpath, or the entry arc, if one is defined.

Lead In/Out dialog box
Use any of the following techniques:
extend/shorten the geometry in the chained contour
add a line to the start of the chained contour
create a tangent arc move to the start of the toolpath
manually define an entry/exit vector, or let the system calculate a vector for you.
The Lead In and Lead Out tabs have identical options for creating entry and exit moves, letting you set different values for each move.

9. **Select** the **Lead out** page and **extend** the contour by .2 as shown below:

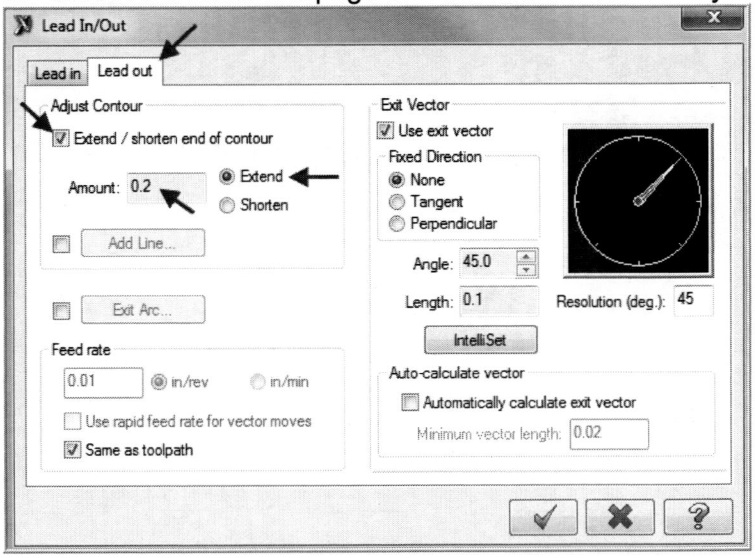

Lead In/Out dialog box
You can also combine different types of moves.

For example, you can extend a contour and lead in to it with a tangent arc.

10. Select the OK button to exit **Lead In/Out.**

11. Select the OK button to exit **Finish parameters.**

TASK 10:
CENTER DRILL THE .25" HOLE

➲ In this task you will center drill .2" depth using **Tool #3 Centre Drill - .25 diameter.**

1. From the menu bar select **TOOLPATHS>Drill...**

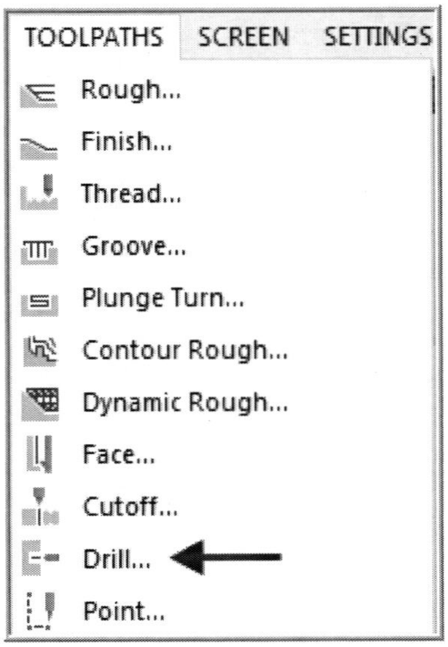

Lathe Drill Toolpaths
Mastercam Lathe offers several different types of drill cycles for drill toolpaths.

Lathe drill toolpaths typically drill into the face of the part along the centerline.

To drill off-center, in the side of the part, or in a different plane, use one of Mastercam's C-axis toolpaths.

You do not need to have any geometry or drill points in the graphics window to create a drill toolpath. Mastercam creates the toolpath entirely from parameters which you specify.

2. Select the **Centre Drill .25 diameter** tool from the tool list and make changes as shown below:

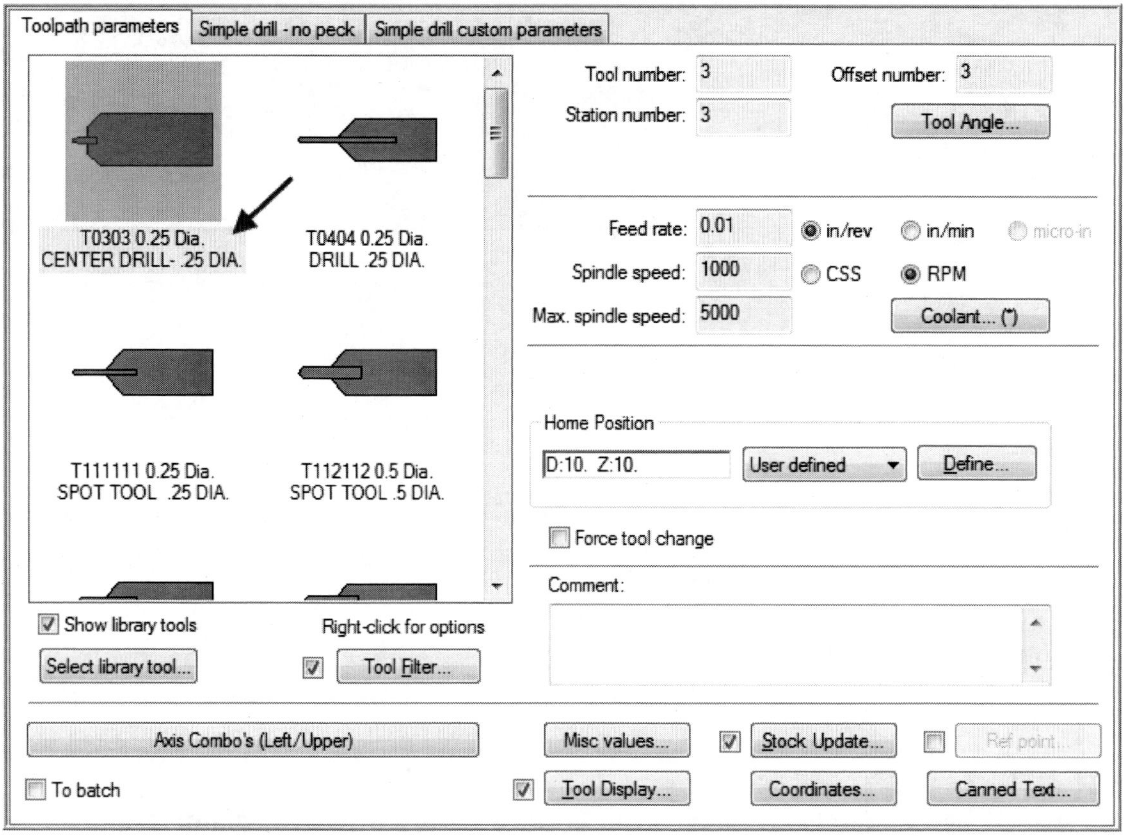

3. Select the **Simple drill – no peck** page and make changes as shown below:

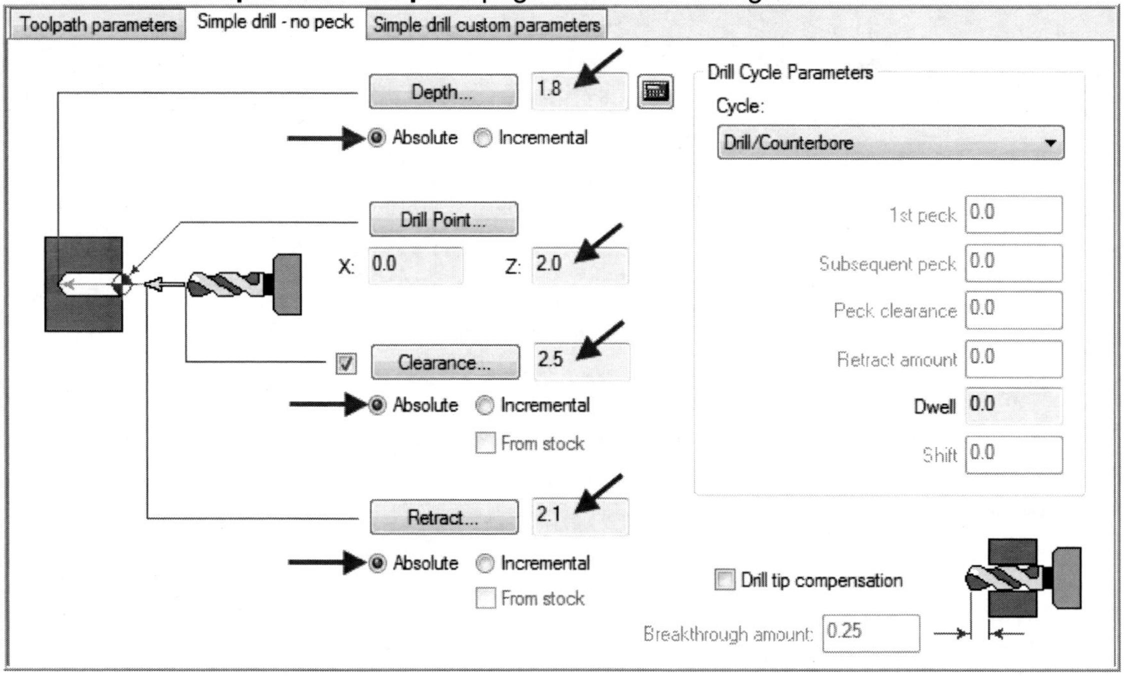

4. Select the OK button ✓ to exit **Simple drill – no peck.**

TASK 11:
DRILL THE .25" HOLE

➲ In this task you will drill the .25" hole .75" depth using **Tool #4 Drill - .25 diameter.**

1. From the menu bar select **TOOLPATHS>Drill…**

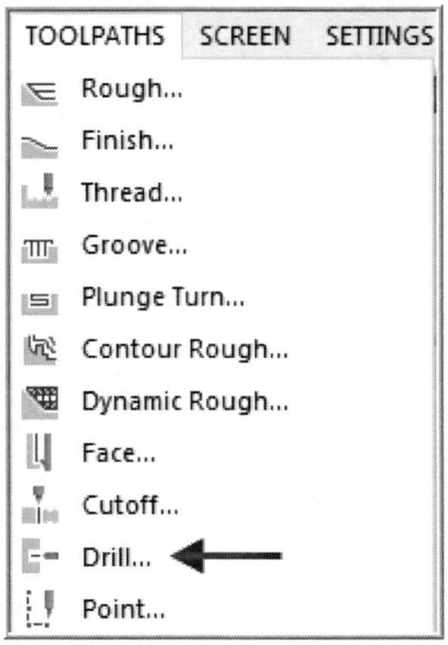

2. Scroll down and select the **Drill - .25 diameter** tool from the tool list and make changes as shown below:

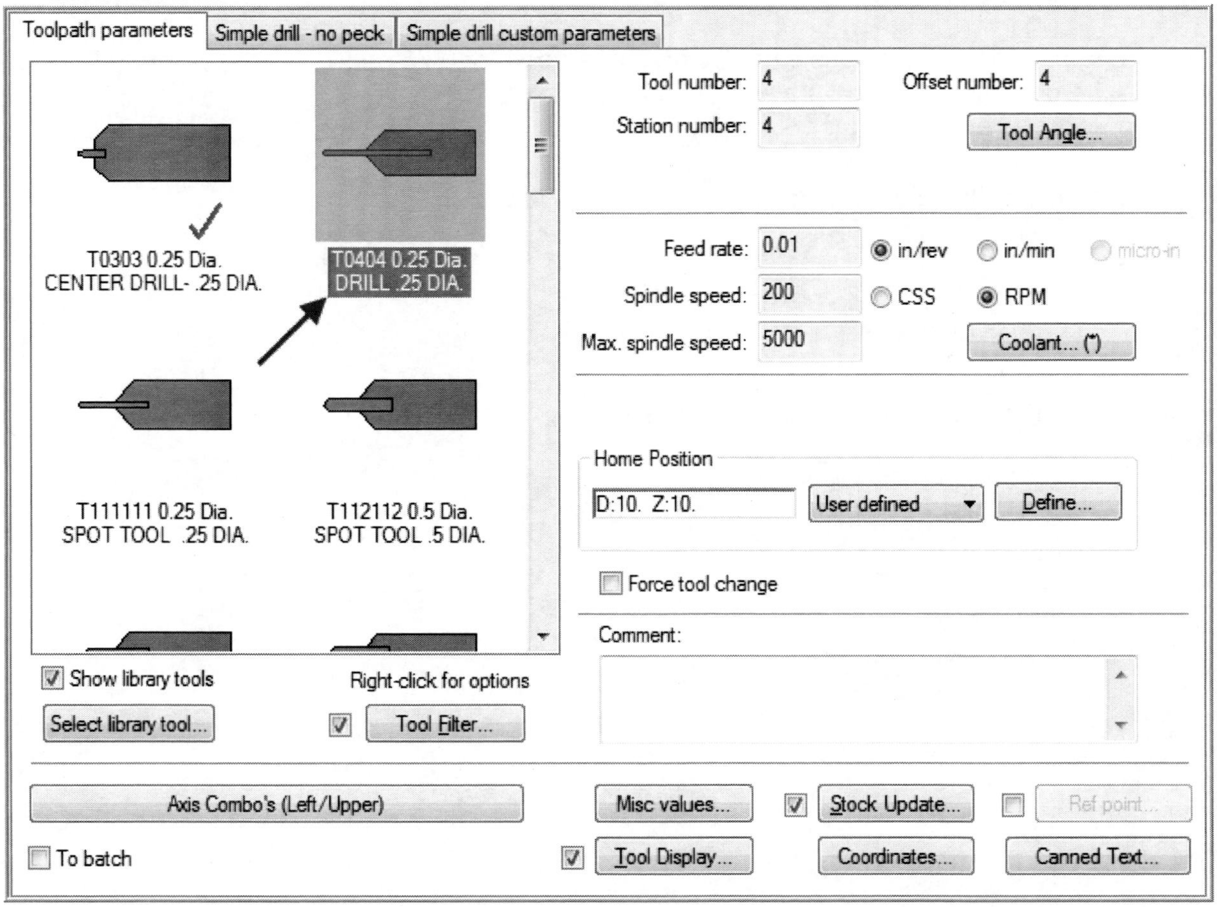

3. Select the **Single drill – no peck** page and make changes as shown below. This hole will be **peck drilled**. The **depth of the hole is .75 from the front face** so click in the space for depth and type in **1.25** and hit the enter key. Make changes as shown below:

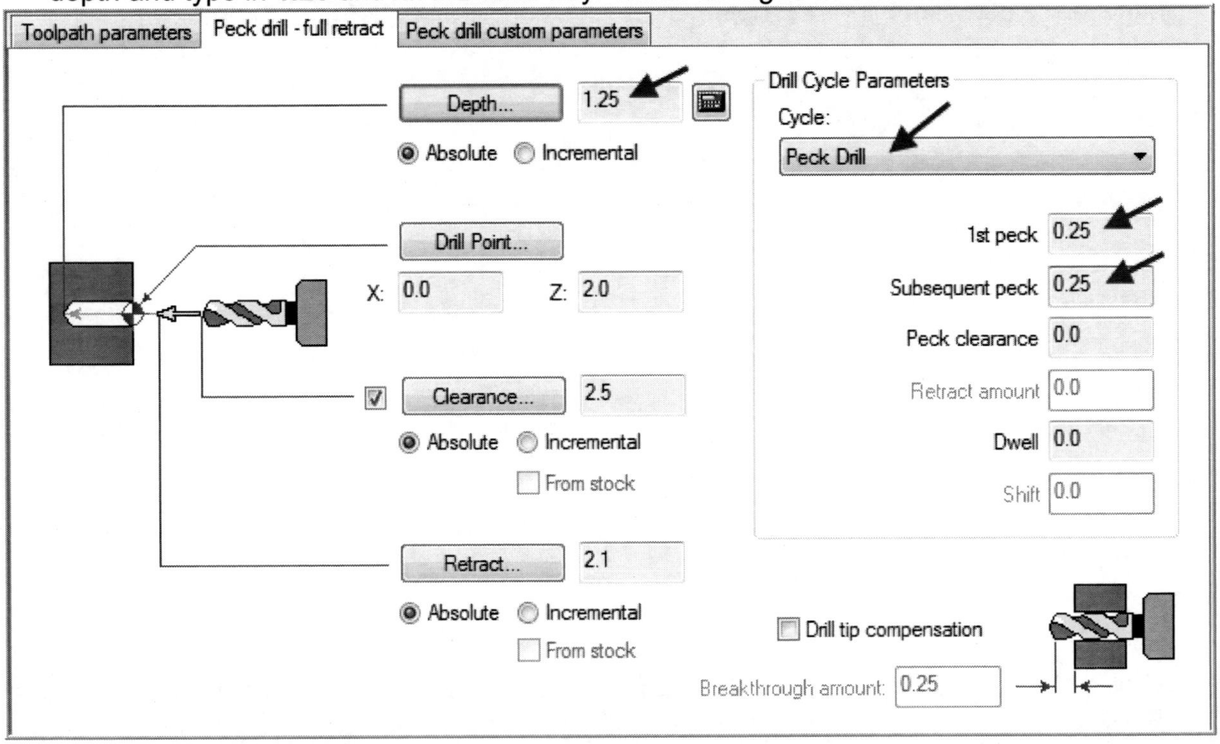

The hole depth on the drawing is dimensioned to .a depth of 0.75" at the full diameter of the hole. So the point of the drill will have to go deeper than 0.75"
You can use the depth calculator button to figure out the correct depth.

4. Select the **Depth Calculator** icon.

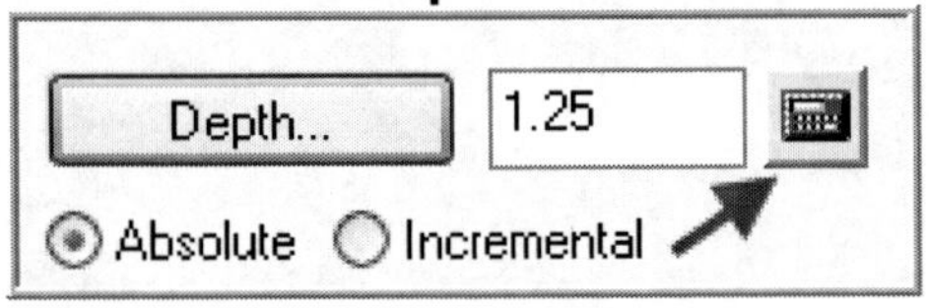

5. Make changes to the **Depth Calculator** as shown below:

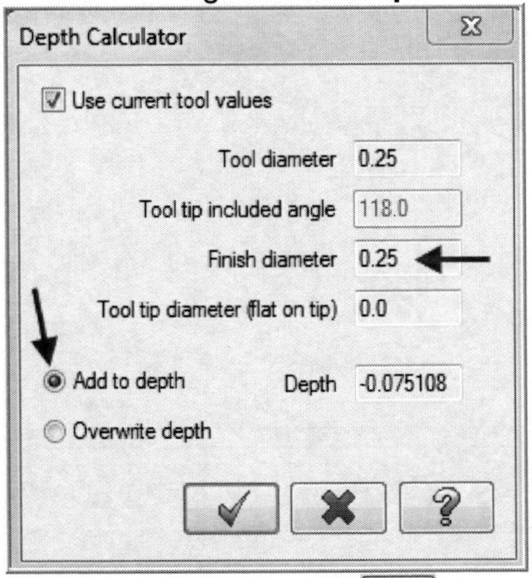

6. Select the **OK** button  to exit **the Depth Calculator.**

7. The depth has now been updated.

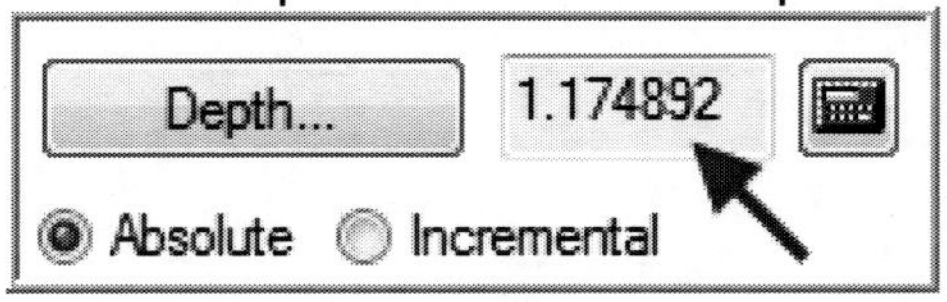

8. Select the **OK** button  to exit **Peck drill – full retract.**

TASK 12:
CUTOFF THE PART

➲ In this task you will cutoff the part using a .125 wide cutoff tool.

1. From the menu bar select **TOOLPATHS>Cutoff…**

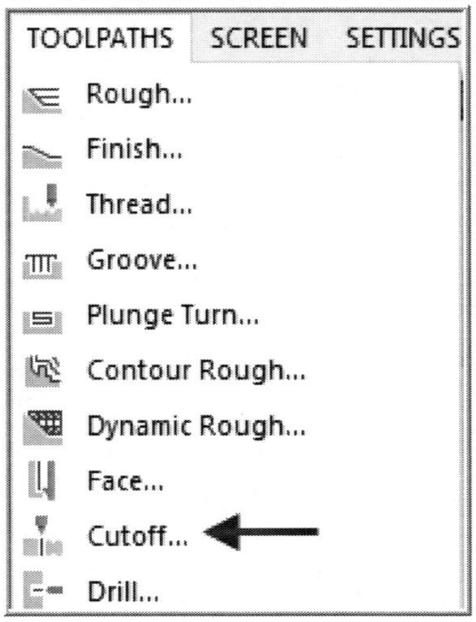

2. Select the Alt key and the T key on the keyboard to hide the toolpath lines.

Toolpath Lines visible:

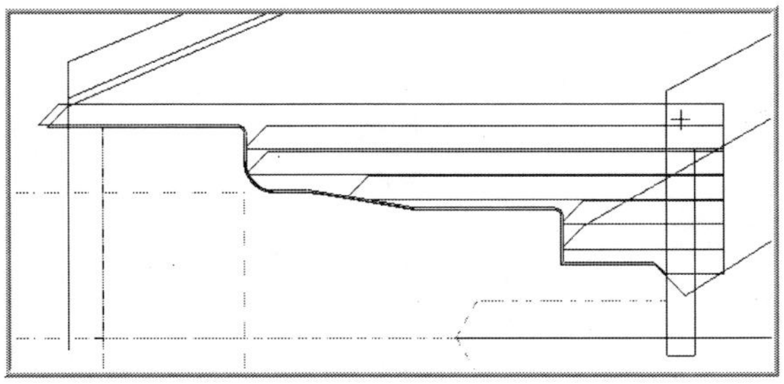

Press Alt T to hide toolpath Lines:

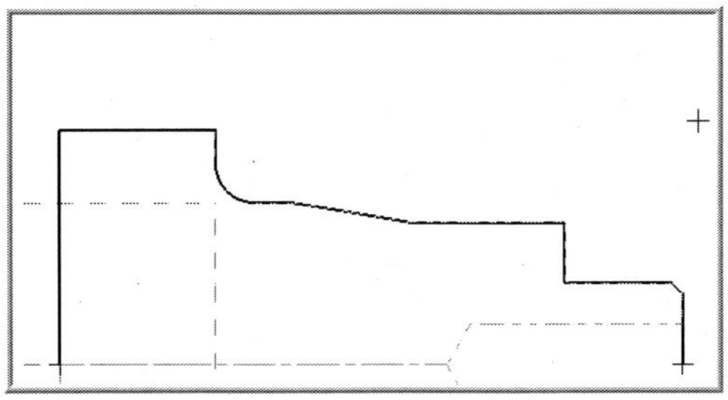

3. Pick where **Line 1 and Line 2** meet as shown below: (Move the cursor over the corner until the visual cue 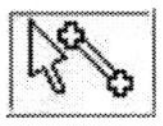 for End point displays and then click on this point.)

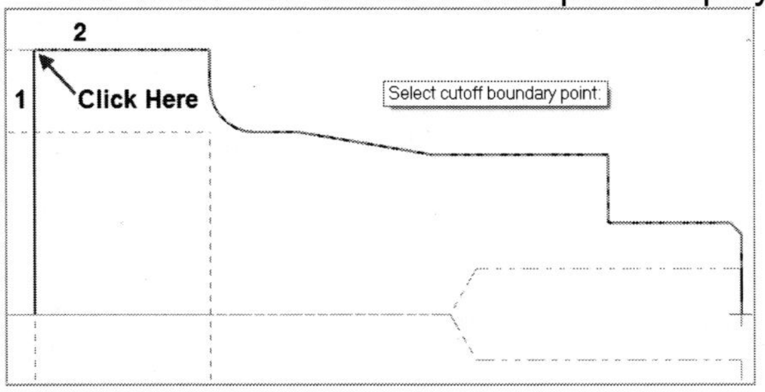

4. Scroll down the tool window and select the **OD Cutoff Right Width .125** tool and make changes as shown below in the **Toolpath parameters** page.

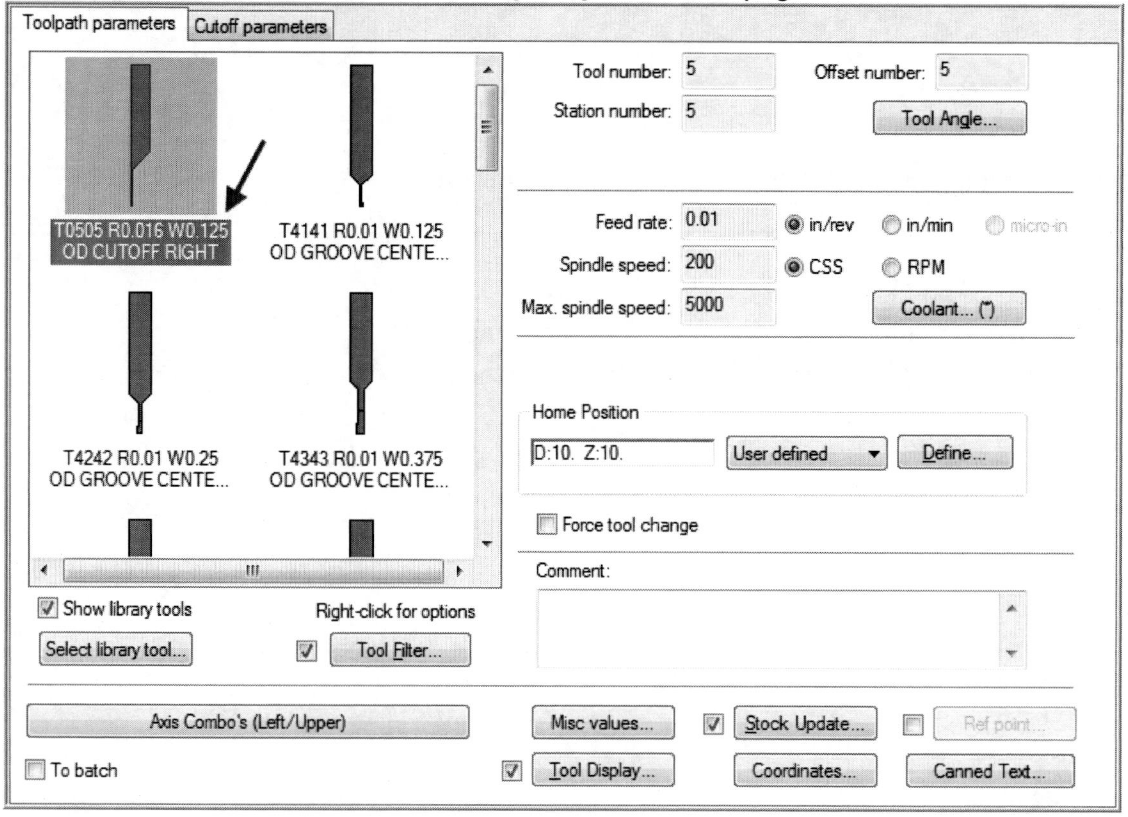

5. Select the **Cutoff parameters** page and make sure the settings are as shown below:

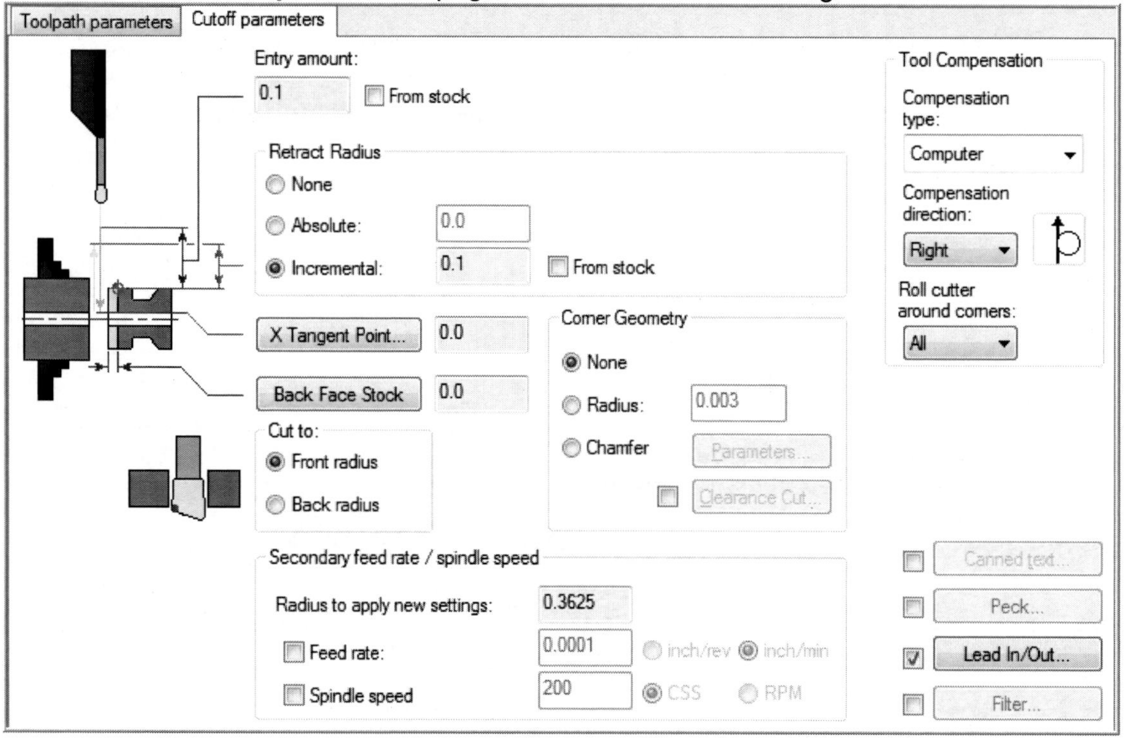

6. Select the OK button ✓ to exit **Cutoff parameters.**

TASK 13:
BACKPLOT THE TOOLPATH

- ➲ In this task you will use Mastercam's Backplot function to view the path the tools take to cut this part.
- ➲ Backplot will enable us to review the cutting motions and identify any problem areas when cutting the part.

1. Fit the image to the screen by clicking on the **Fit to Screen** icon as shown below:

2. To pick all the operations to Backplot pick the **Select All** icon .

3. The next step is to select the **Backplot selected operations** icon shown below:

4. **Maximize** the Backplot/Verify window if required.
5. Select the **Home** Tab if required.

6. Activate the options shown below in the **Visibility** section of the Home tab.

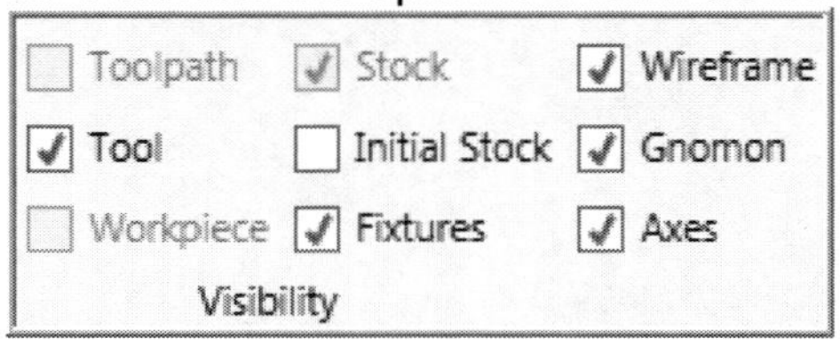

Initial Stock
This displays the stock before machining.
Click to cycle through three states:
On
Translucent
Off

Tool
This displays the tool during Backplot or Verification. Click to cycle through three states as mentioned above

7. At the top of the screen select the **View** tab, the **Isometric** icon and then select **Fit.**

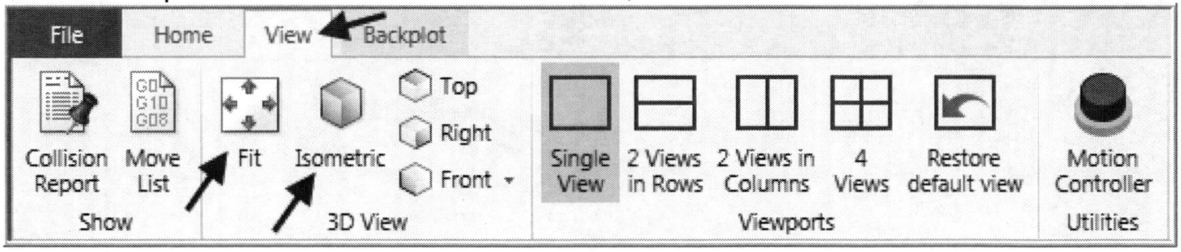

8. Click on the **Backplot** tab at the top left of the screen

9. Activate the **Both** option in the Toolpath section of the Backplot tab.

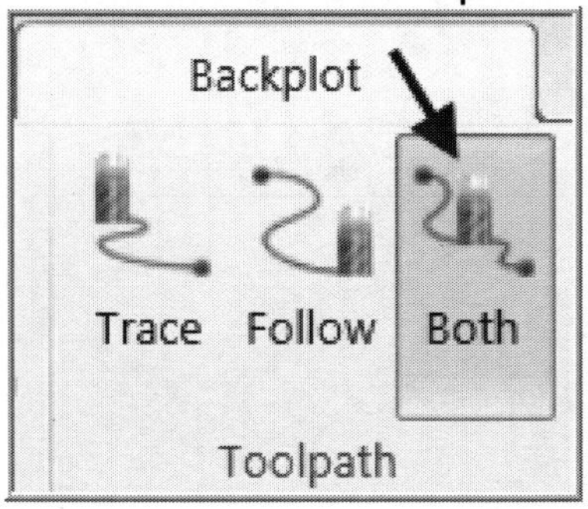

Both
This displays the entire toolpath and the tool as it travels over the displayed toolpath.

10. In the lower right corner of the screen now set the run **Speed** to slow by moving the slider bar pointer over to the left as shown below.

11. Now select the **Play Simulation** button to review the toolpaths.

12. After reviewing the Backplot of the toolpaths select the Close button 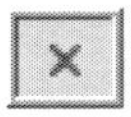 to exit Backplot.

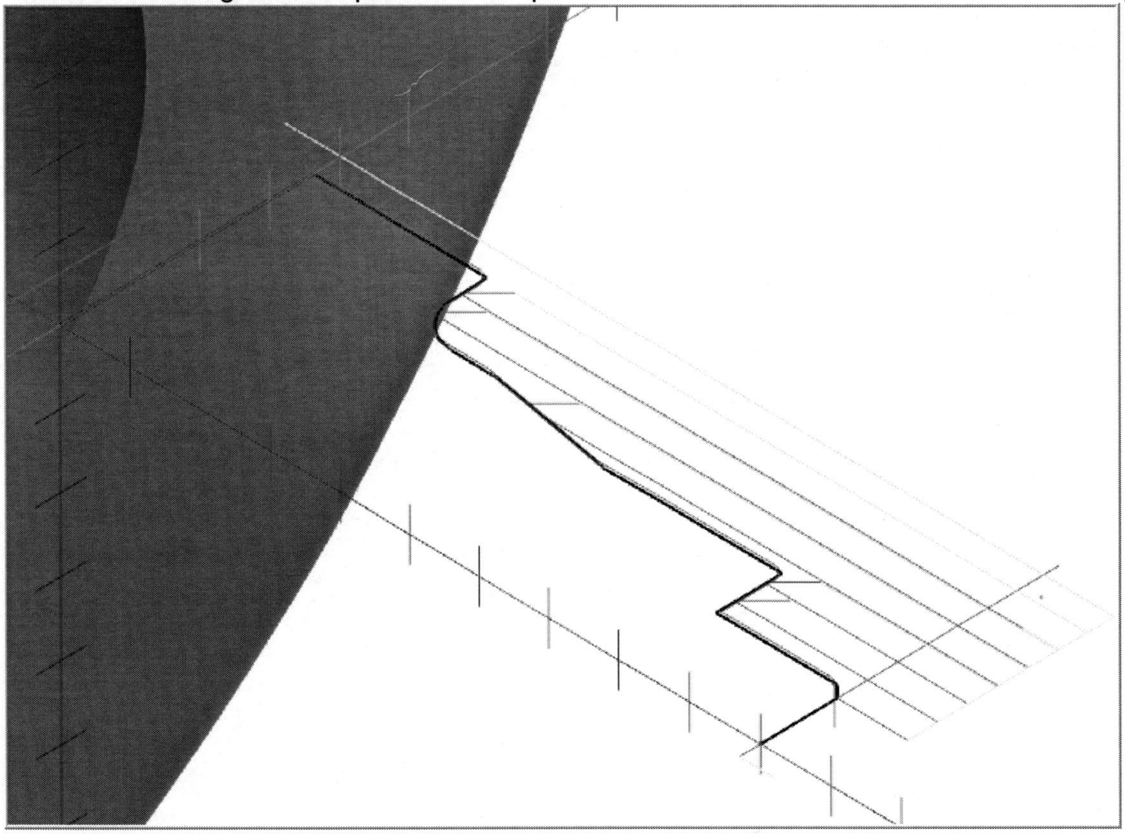

TASK 14:
VERIFY THE TOOLPATH

- Mastercam's Verify utility allows you to use solid models to simulate the machining of a part. The model created by the verification represents the surface finish, and shows collisions, if any exist.
- This allows you to identify and correct program errors before they reach the shop floor.
- Backplot and Verify are very similar. The differences between these two functions are that Backplot offers basic simulation options. Whereas Verify offers material removal, collision checking and precision control.
- **For more information on Verify see the Tips and Techniques section on the multimedia DVD supplied with this text**

1. In the Toolpaths Manager pick all the operations to Verify by clicking the **Select All** icon .
2. Select the **Verify selected operations** icon shown below:

3. **Maximize** the Backplot/Verify window if required.
4. Now select the **Home** Tab if required.

5. Activate the options shown below in the **Visibility** section of the Home tab. **Initial Stock** not activated.

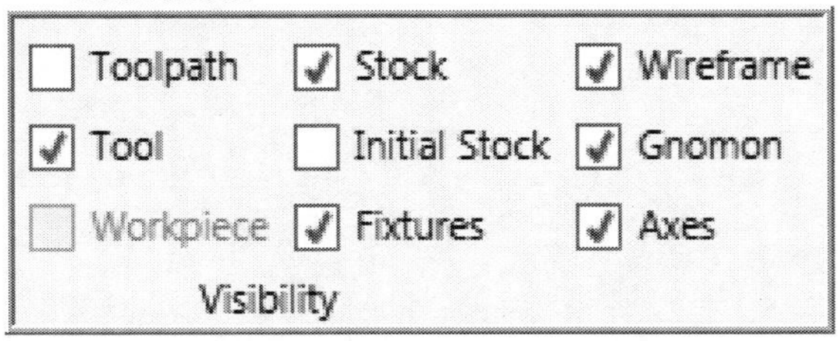

6. Activate the **Color Loop** to change the color of the tools for the verified part.

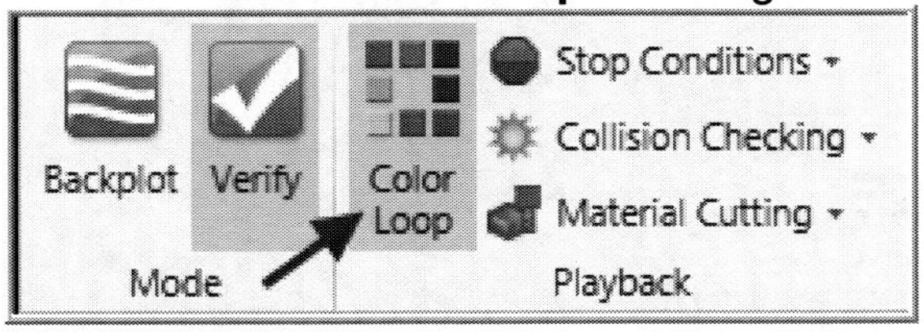

Color Loop
Changes the color of the toolpath or cut stock by operation or by tool change.

Choose **File Options** to set the colors.

7. At the top of the screen select the **View** tab, the **Isometric** icon and then select **Fit**.

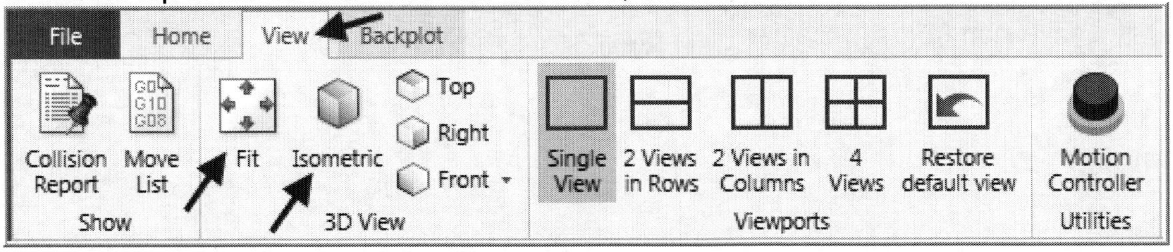

8. In the lower right corner of the screen now set the run **Speed** to slow by moving the slider bar pointer over to the left as shown below.

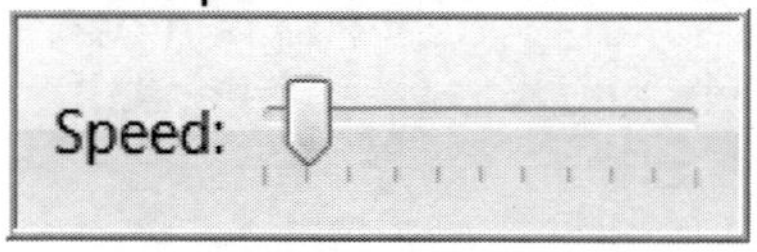

9. Now select the **Play Simulation** button to review the toolpaths.

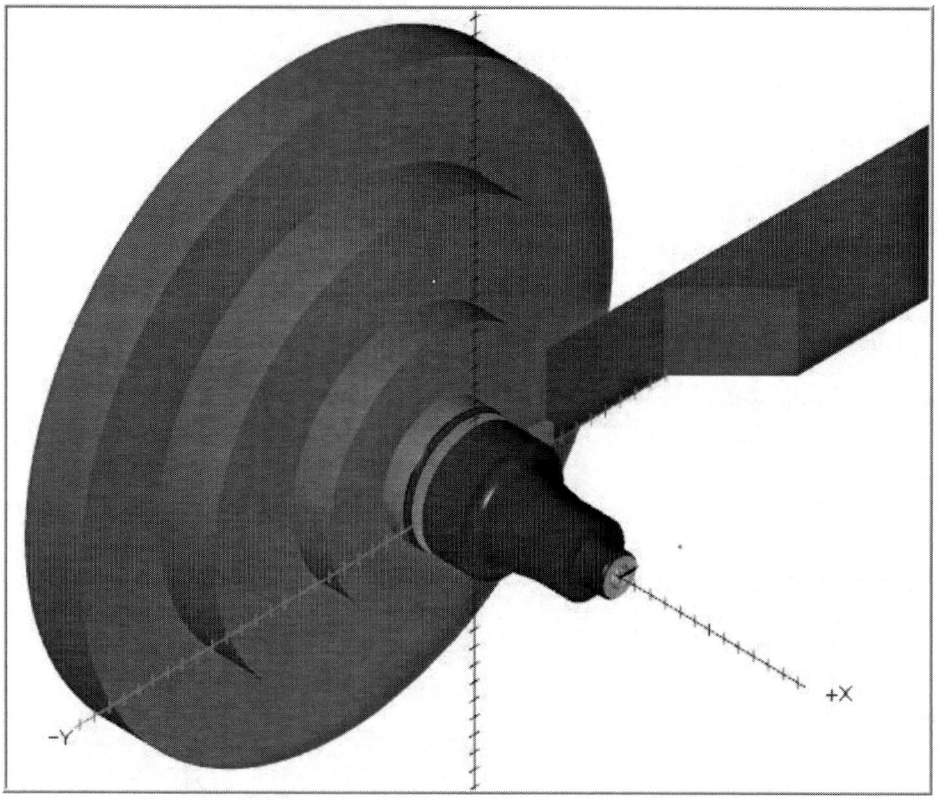

10. Select the **Close** button  in the top right hand corner to exit Verify.

TASK 15:
SAVE THE UPDATED MASTERCAM FILE

1. Select the save icon from the toolbar 

.

TASK 16:
POST AND CREATE THE CNC CODE FILE

1. Ensure all the operations are selected by picking the **Select All** icon  from the Toolpaths manager.

2. Select the **Post selected operations** button from the Toolpaths manager.

➲ **Please Note:** If you cannot see **G1** click on the right pane of the Toolpaths manager window and expand the window to the right.

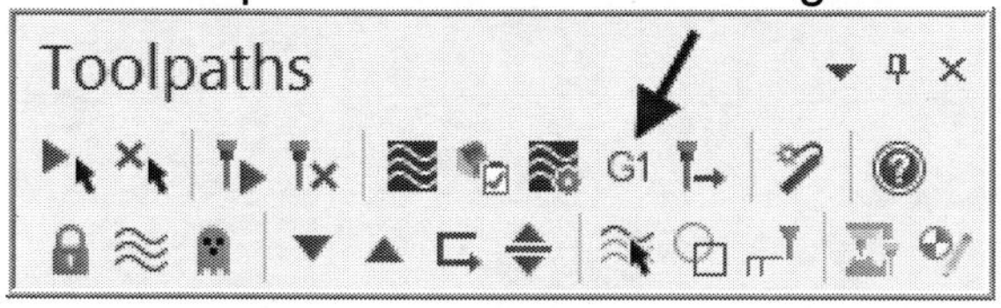

3. In the Post processing window, make the necessary changes as shown below:

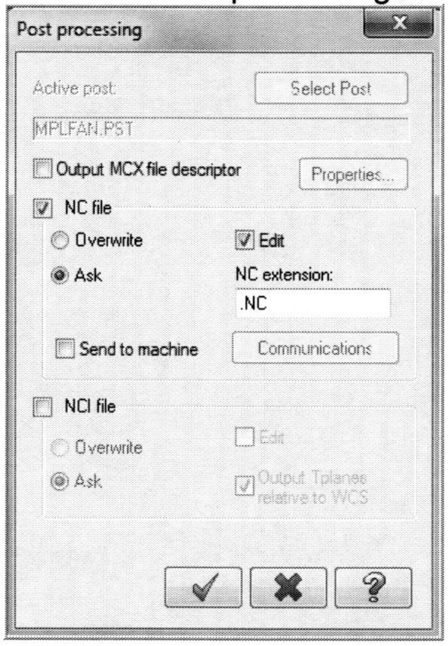

About Post Processing

NC file:
Select this option to save the NC file. The file name and extension are stored in the machine group properties for the selected operation. If you are posting operations from different machine groups or Mastercam files, or batch processing, Mastercam will create several files according to the settings for each machine group.

Edit:
When checked, automatically launches the default text editor with the file displayed so that you can review or modify it.

4. Select the OK button  to continue.

5. Ensure the same name as your Mastercam part file name is displayed in the **NC File name** field as shown below:

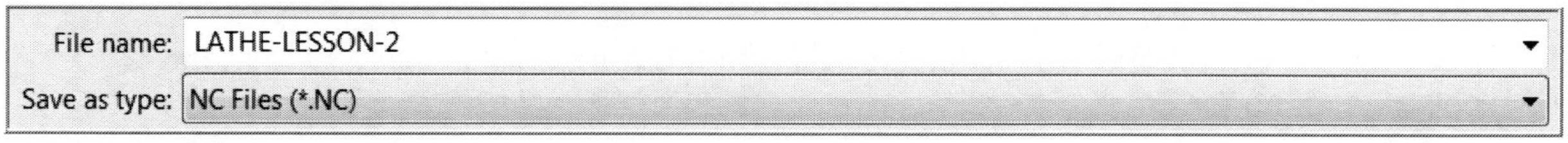

6. Select the **Save** button.
7. The CNC code file opens up in the default editor.

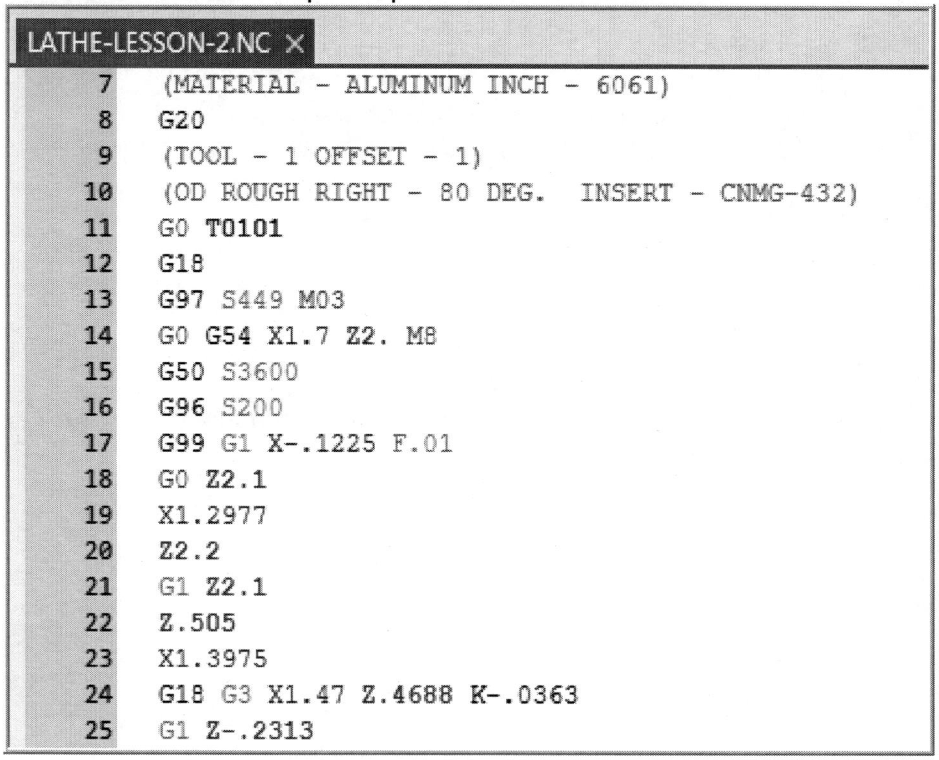

8. Select the × in the top right corner to exit the CNC editor.

9. This completes LATHE-LESSON-2.

LATHE-LESSON-2 EXERCISE

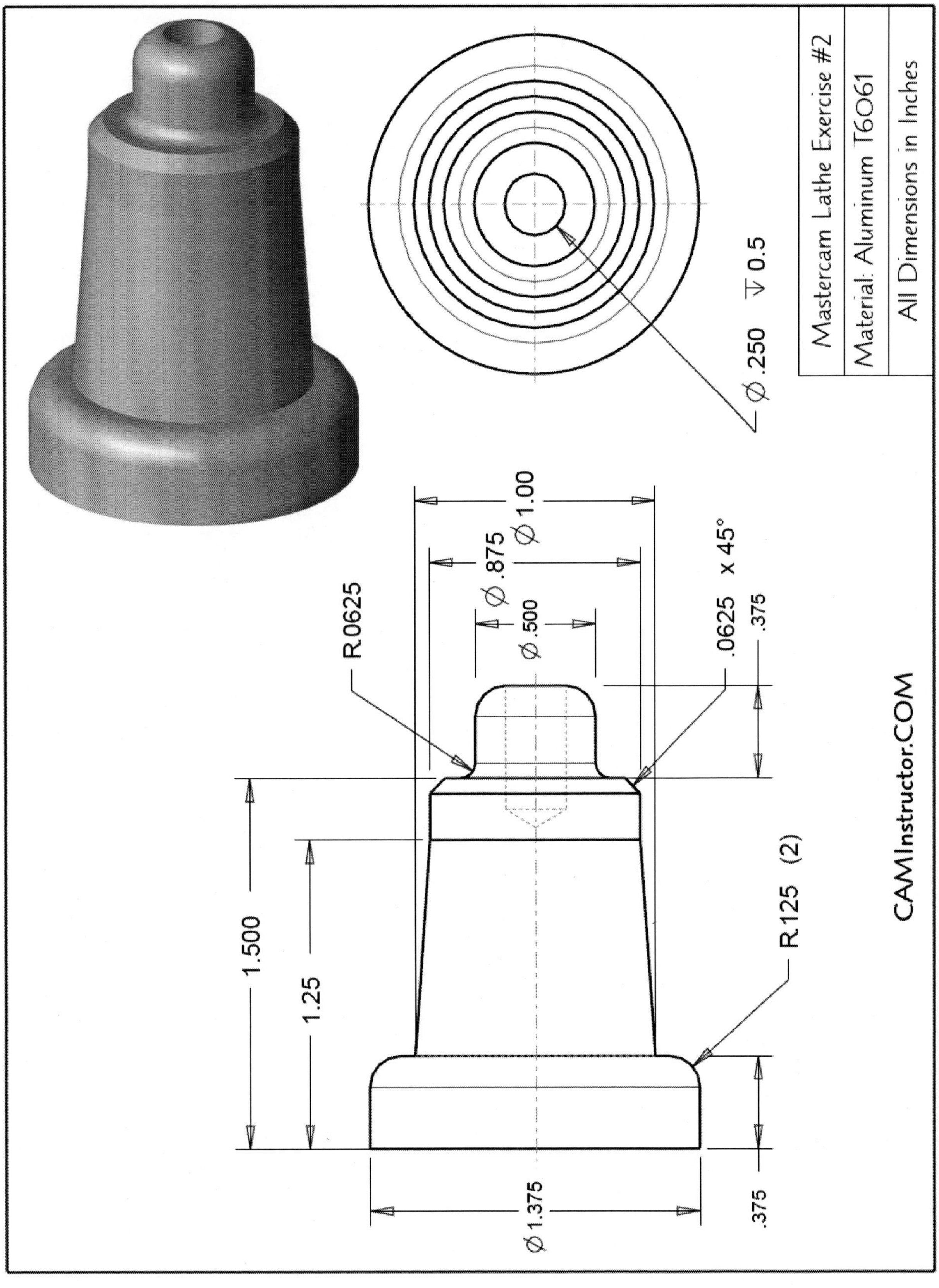

Mastercam® X9

Training Guide

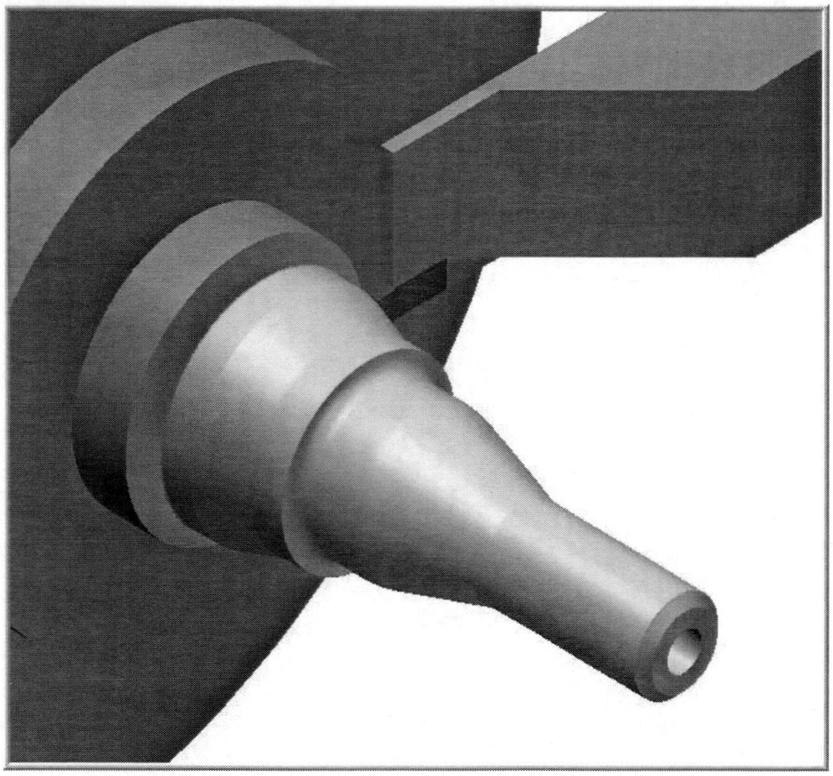

Lathe-Lesson-3

Face, Rough, Finish, Drill, Internal Thread and Cutoff

camInstructor

Objectives

You will create the geometry for Lathe Lesson 3, and then generate a toolpath to machine the part on a CNC lathe. This lesson covers the following topics:

➲ **Create a 2-dimensional drawing by:**
Creating lines.
Creating fillets.
Creating chamfers.

➲ **Establish Stock and Chuck Setup settings:**
Stock size.
Chuck Configuration.
Material for the part.
Feed calculation.

➲ **Generate a 2-dimensional lathe toolpath consisting of:**
Lathe Face.
Lathe Rough.
Lathe Finish.
Lathe Drill and Thread.
Lathe Cutoff.

➲ **Inspect the toolpath using Mastercam's Verify and Backplot by:**
Launching the Verify function to machine the part on the screen.
Generating the NC- code.

LATHE - LESSON - 3 DRAWING

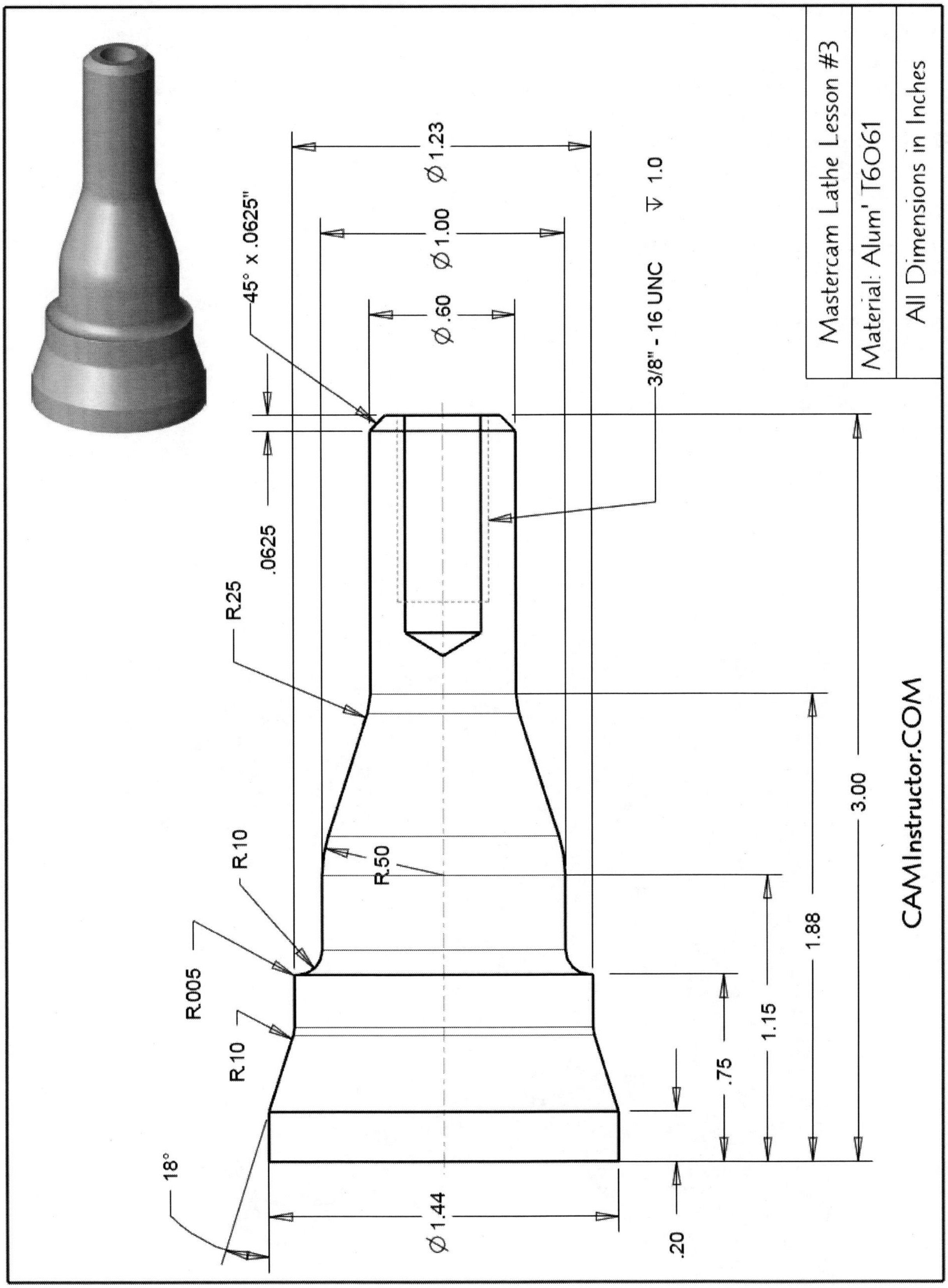

TOOL LIST

Six tools will be used to create this part.

- **Tool #1 Face and Rough the outside diameters**
  Holder: Outside Diameter Rough Right Hand - DCGNR-164D.
  Insert: 80 Degree Diamond Insert – CNMG-432

- **Tool #2 Finish the outside diameters**
  Holder: Outside Diameter Finish Right Hand - MVJNR-164D.
  Insert: 35 Degree Diamond Insert – VNMG-431.

- **Tool #3 Centre drill the hole**
  Centre Drill – body diameter 0.250”

- **Tool #4 Tap Drill the .3125 diameter hole**
  Drill 0.3125” diameter

- **Tool #5 Tap the .375-16 hole**
  Right Hand Tap 3/8”-16UNC

- **Tool #6 Cutoff the part**
  Holder: Outside Diameter Cut-off Right Hand.
  Insert: 0.125” Wide.

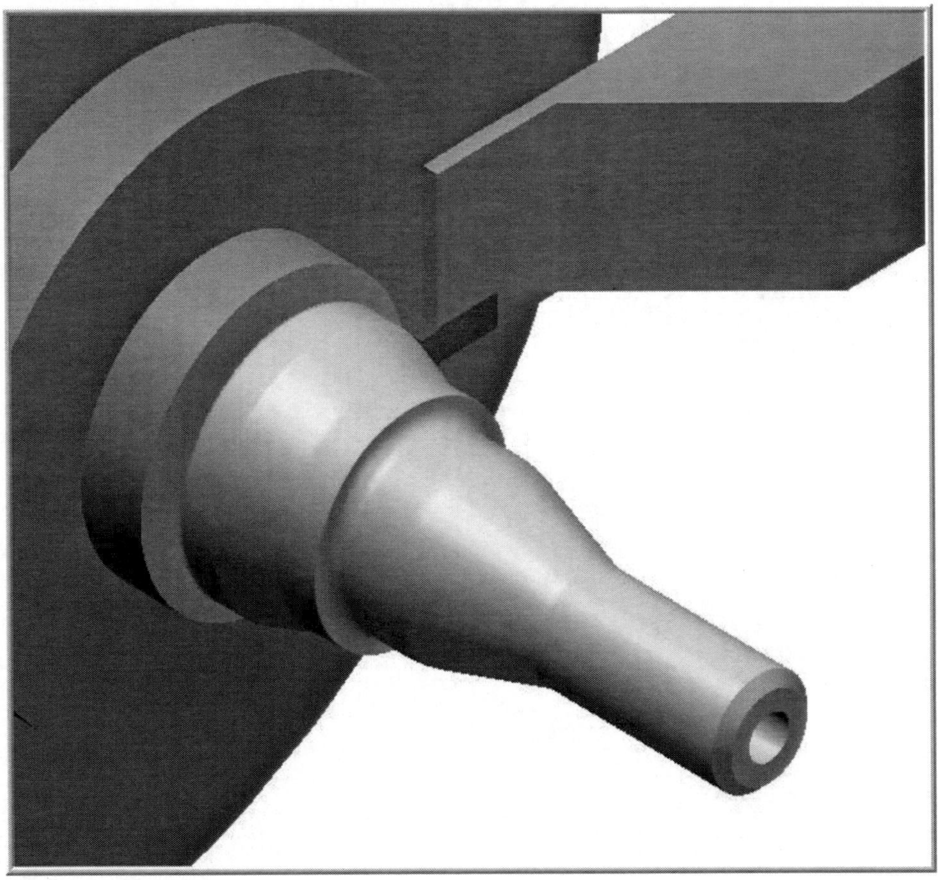

LESSON - 3 - THE PROCESS

Geometry Creation

TASK 1: Setting the Environment
TASK 2: Setting the Construction Planes
TASK 3: Create the Geometry
TASK 4: Create the 18 Degree Angle
TASK 5: Create the Fillets (Radius)
TASK 6: Create the Chamfer
TASK 7: Save the Drawing

Toolpath Creation

TASK 8: Define the Stock and Chuck Parameters
TASK 9: Face the Front of the Part
TASK 10: Rough the Outside Diameters
TASK 11: Finish the Outside Diameters
TASK 12: Center Drill the 5/16" Hole
TASK 13: Drill the 5/16" Hole
TASK 14: Tap the 3/8"-16 Hole
TASK 15: Cut off the Part
TASK 16: Verify the Toolpath
TASK 17: Save the Updated Mastercam File
TASK 18: Post and Create the CNC Code File

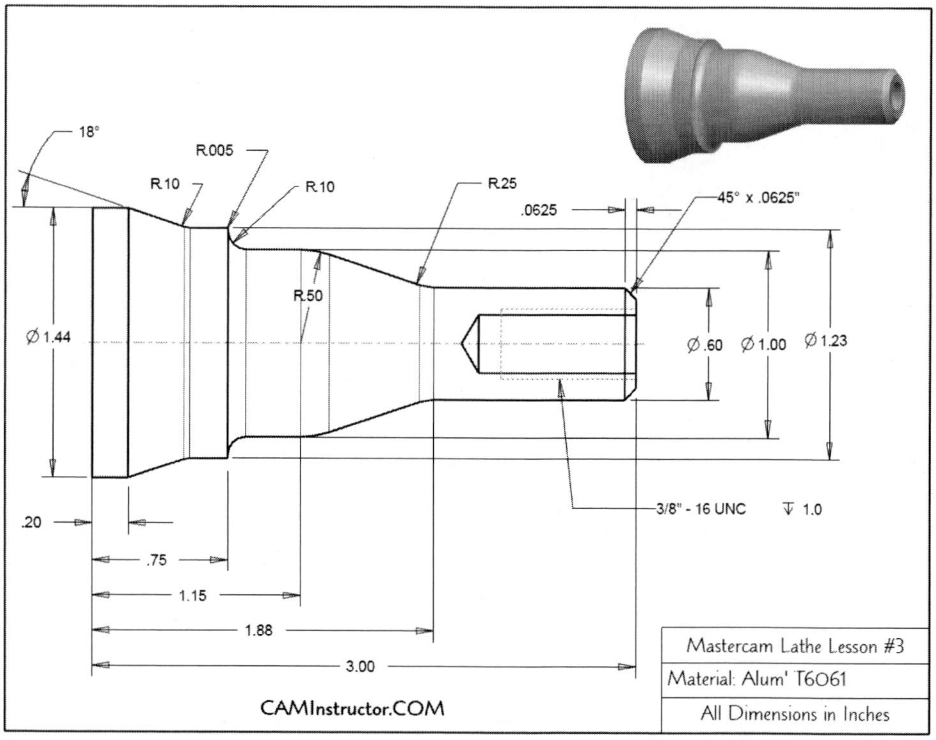

Geometry Creation

TASK 1:
SETTING THE ENVIRONMENT

Before starting the geometry creation you should set up the grid and toolbars as outlined in the **Setting the Environment** section at the beginning of this text:

1. Set up the Grid. This will help identify the location of the origin.
2. Load the Workspace – **SETTINGS>Load Workspace>Lathe** to machine a part on the Lathe.
3. Set the machine type to the default Lathe.

TASK 2:
SETTING THE CONSTRUCTION PLANES:

➲ **Set the Construction Plane to Lathe diameter +D +Z (WCS)**

1. Click on Planes at the bottom of the screen as shown below:

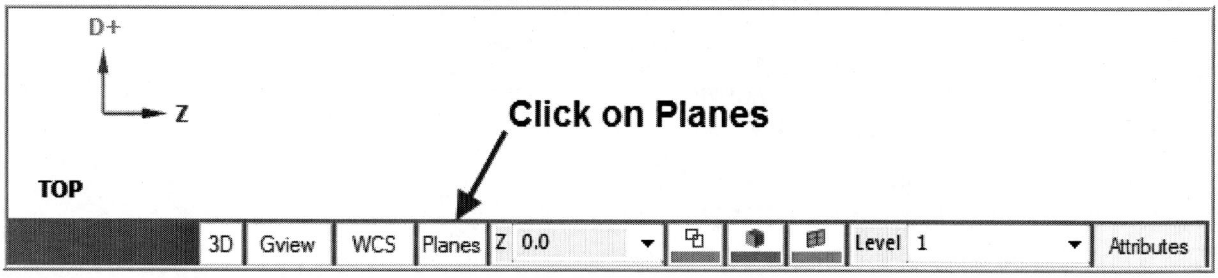

2. Click on **Lathe diameter>+D +Z (WCS)** as shown below:

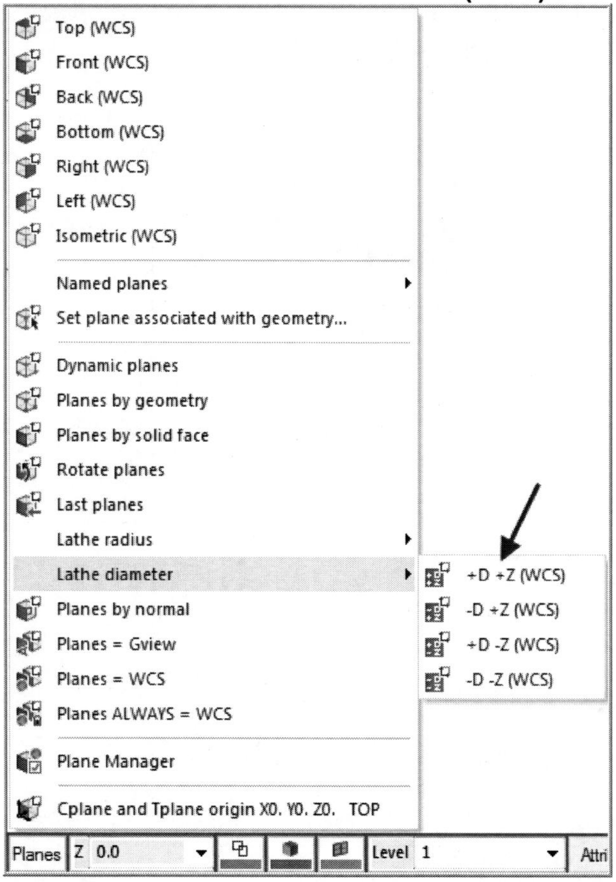

TASK 3:
CREATE THE GEOMETRY

- This task explains how to create the geometry of this part. In this lathe part you only need to create **half of the geometry**, the geometry above the center line.
- Lines 1 through 9 will be created first and then the fillet and chamfer will be created.

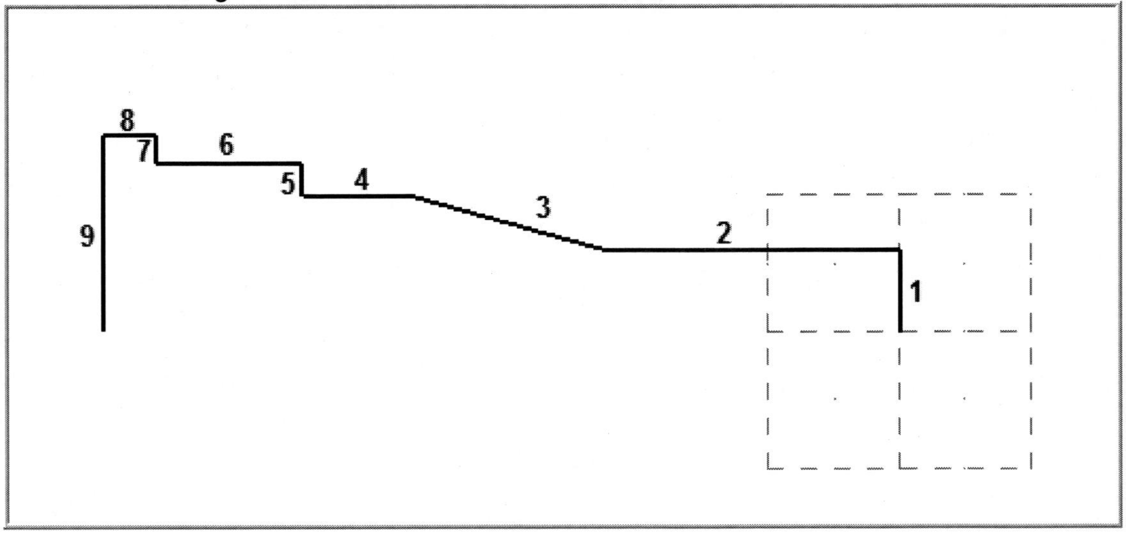

- **Create Line #1**

1. Select from the pull down menu **CREATE>Line>Endpoint…**

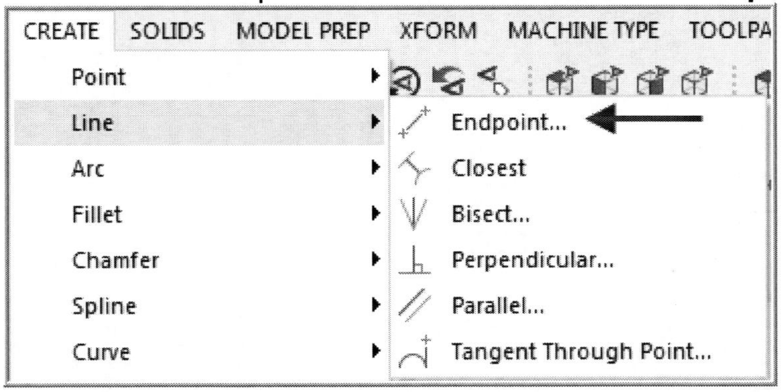

2. The Line ribbon bar appears

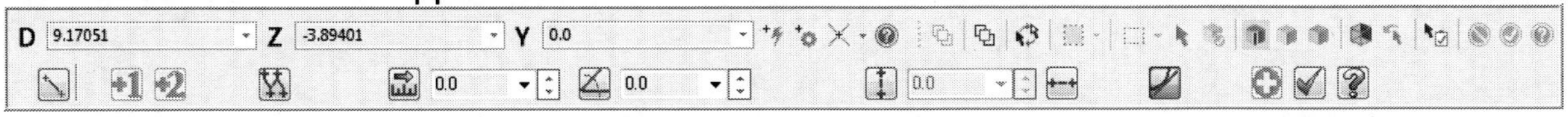

3. Move the cursor over the **center of the grid** and as you get close to the origin a visual cue appears.  This is the cue that will allow you to snap to the **origin**. With this visual cue highlighted pick the **origin.**

> **AutoCursor:** Visual Cues detects and highlights endpoints and midpoints of curves, lines, arc center points, and point entities.
>
> In addition, AutoCursor can snap to angle, nearest, tangent, perpendicular, horizontal, and vertical conditions.

➲ The following are Mastercam Visual Cues:

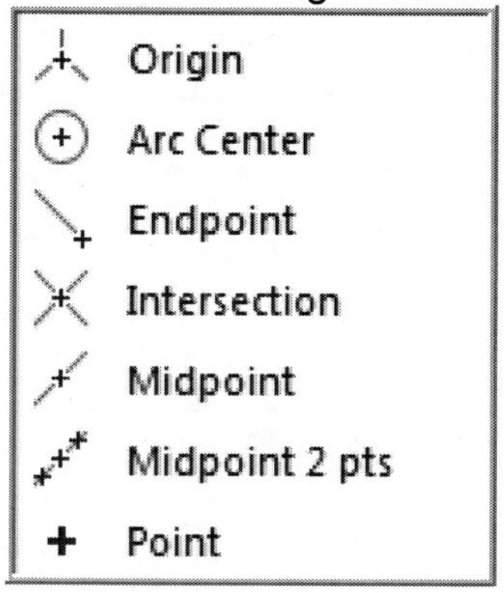

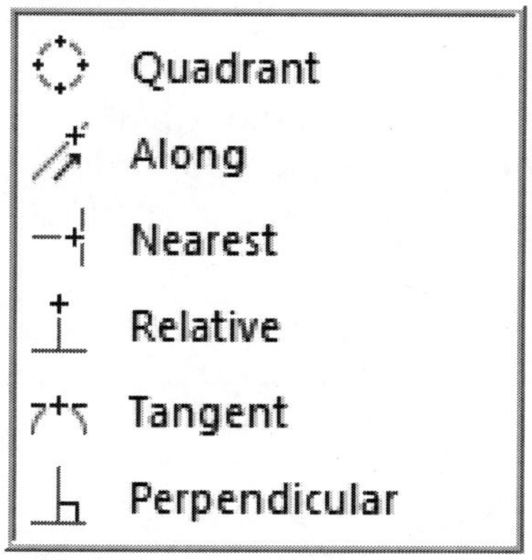

4. You are next prompted to **"Specify the second endpoint".** On the left hand side of the Line ribbon bar click on the **Multi-Line** button to activate it as shown below by the arrow:

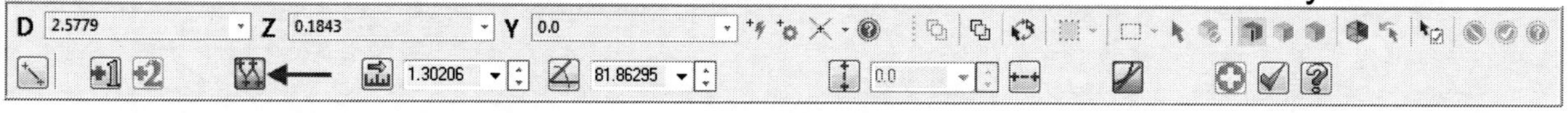

5. Click in the **D** value space (Diameter) (as shown by the arrow below) and enter a value of **0.6**. Hit the Enter key and enter a value of **0 for the Z**, hit the enter key again. **Note** the value of Y is set to **Zero**, this does not need to be input.

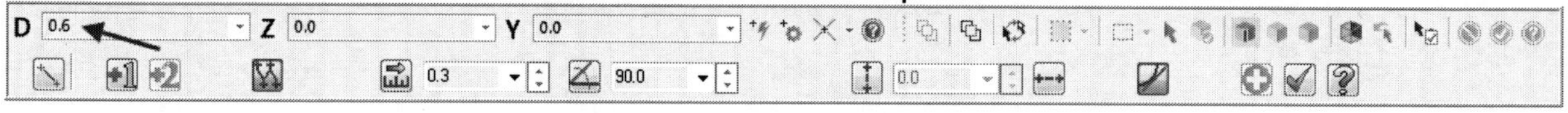

6. A vertical line should be visible as shown below:

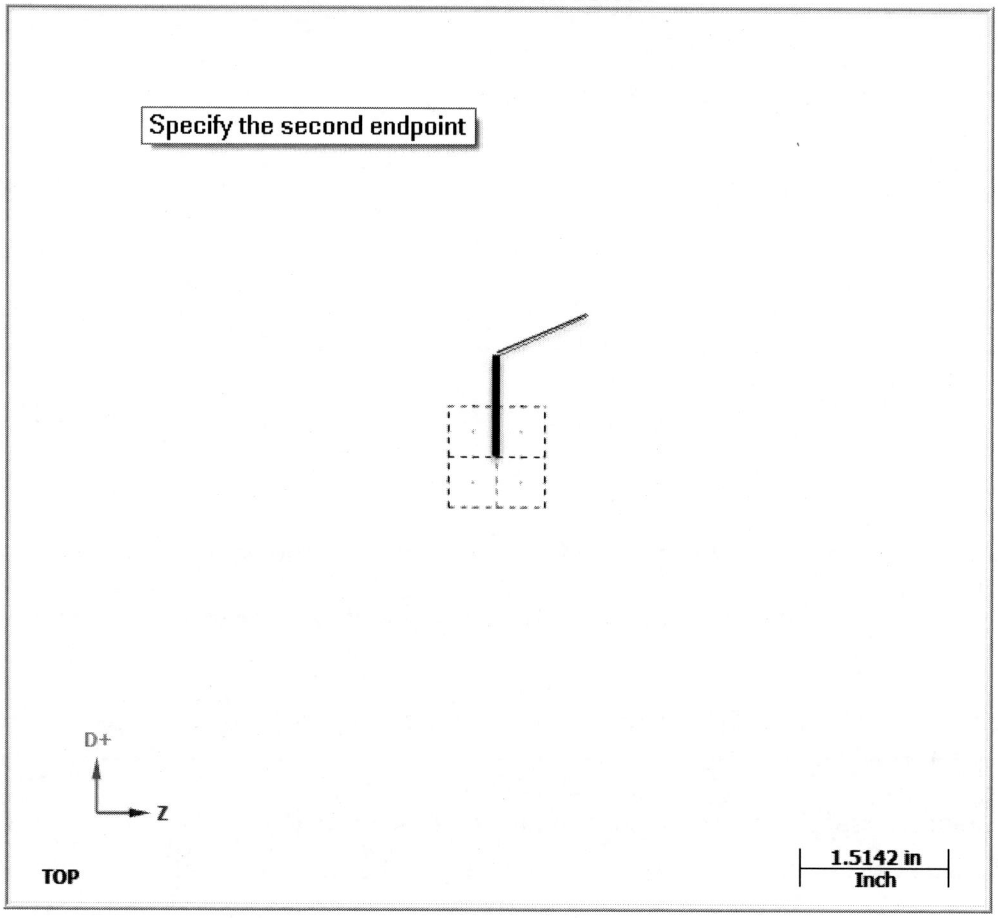

➲ **Create Line #2**

7. **"Specify the second endpoint";** Type in **0.6 in D** hit Enter, type in **-1.12 in Z. Note** the value of Y is set to **Zero**, this does not need to be input. Hit the Enter key once again to complete this line.

➲ **Create Line #3**

8. **"Specify the second endpoint";** Type in **1.0 in D** hit Enter, type in **-1.85 in Z.** Hit the Enter key once again to complete this line.

➲ **Create Line #4**

9. **"Specify the second endpoint";** Type in **1.0 in D** hit Enter, type in **-2.25 in Z.** Hit the Enter key once again to complete this line.

➲ **Create Line #5**

10. **"Specify the second endpoint";** Type in **1.23 in D** hit Enter, type in **-2.25 in Z.** Hit the Enter key once again to complete this line.

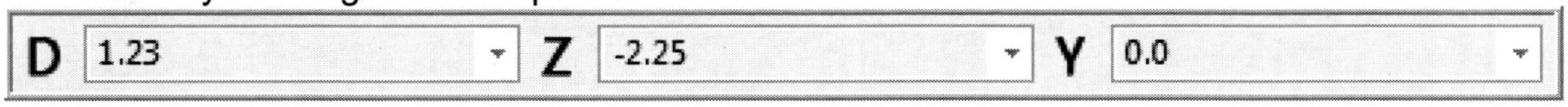

➲ **Create Line #6**

11. **"Specify the second endpoint";** Type in **1.23 in D** hit Enter, type in **-2.8 in Z.** Hit the Enter key once again to complete this line.

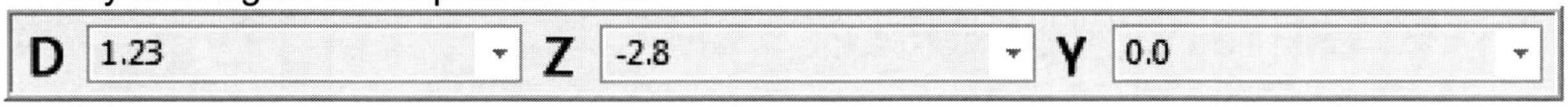

12. Fit the image to the screen by clicking on the **Fit** icon as shown below:

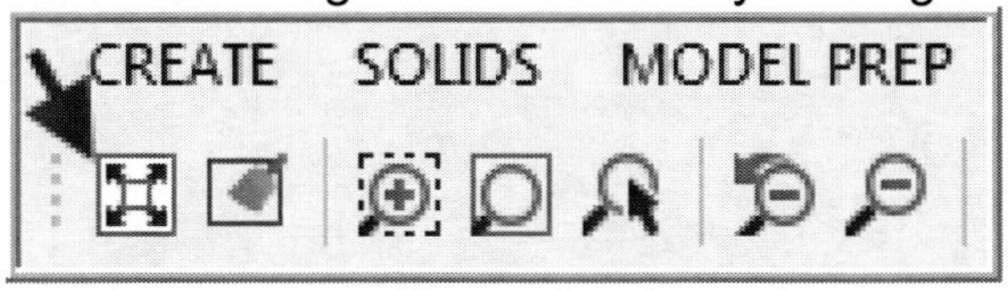

13. Then unzoom by clicking on the **Un-Zoom Previous / .5** icon as shown below:

➲ **Create Line #7**

14. **"Specify the second endpoint";** Type in **1.44 in D** hit Enter, type in **-2.8 in Z.** Hit the Enter key once again to complete this line.

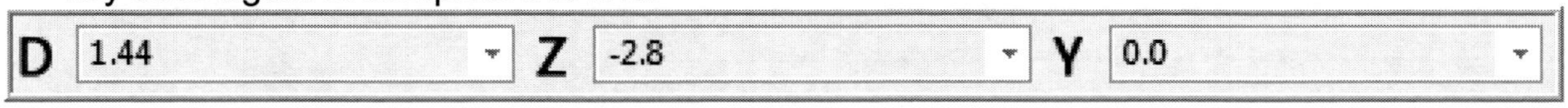

➲ **Create Line #8**

15. **"Specify the second endpoint";** Type in **1.44 in D** hit Enter, type in **-3.00 in Z.** Hit the Enter key once again to complete this line.

➲ **Create Line #9**

16. **"Specify the second endpoint";** Type in **0.0 in D** hit Enter, type in **-3.0 in Z.** Hit the Enter key once again to complete this line.

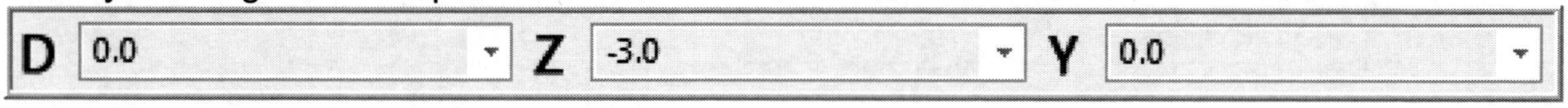

17. Click on the **OK** icon  to complete this feature.
18. Select the **Screen Fit** icon to fit the part to the screen .
19. Your geometry should look like the figure below.

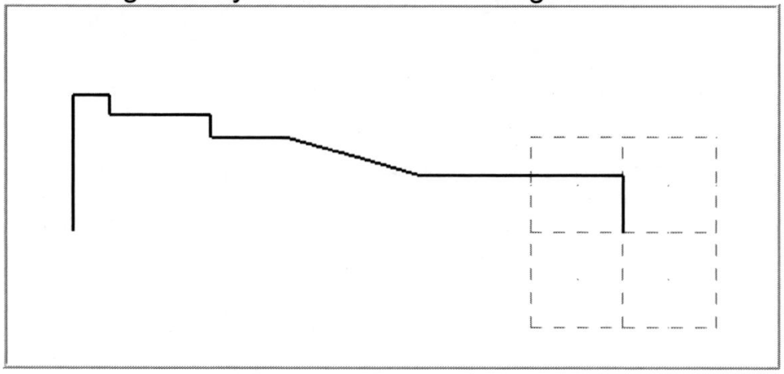

TASK 4:
CREATE THE 18 DEGREE ANGLE

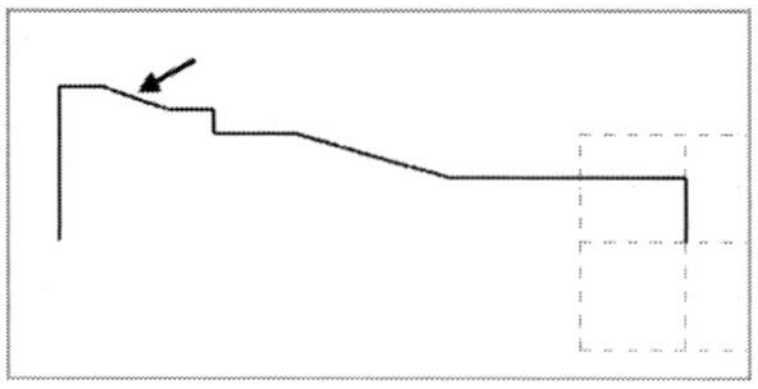

Create the 18 Degree Angle.

1. Select **CREATE>Line>Endpoint…**

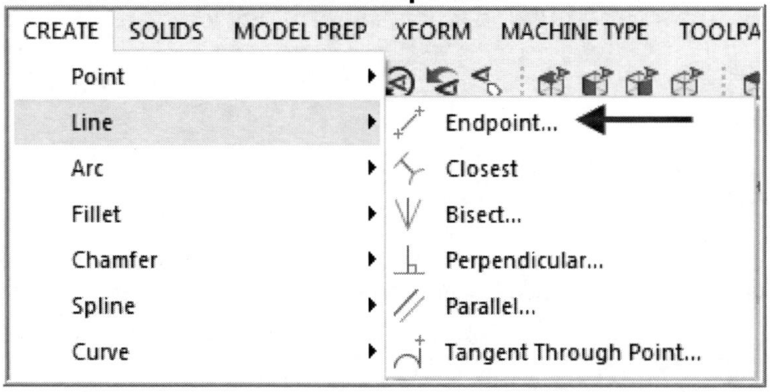

2. The Create Line ribbon bar appears and you are prompted to **"Specify the first endpoint".**

3. Click on the end of line 8 as shown below:

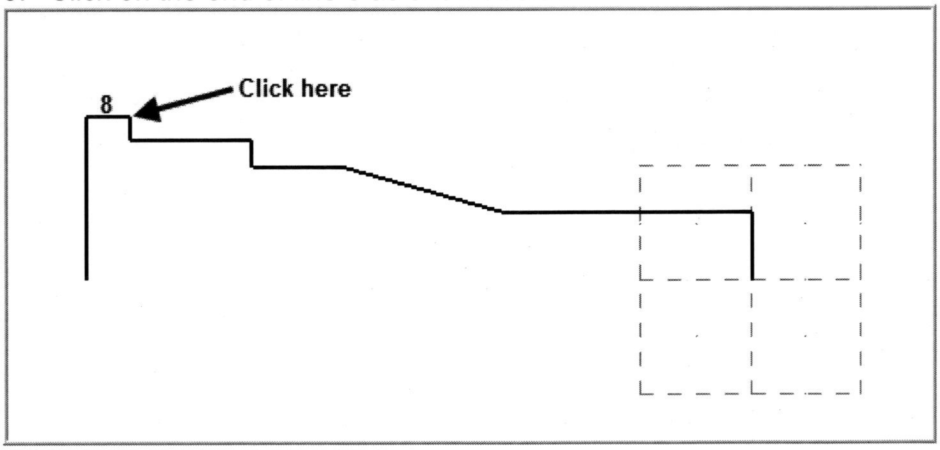

4. Click in the space for Length (#1 below) and input **-1.0** and then hit the tab key. Enter **180-18** (#2 below) and hit Enter.

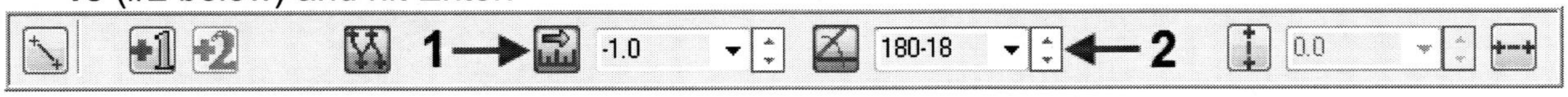

5. A new line is drawn as shown below:

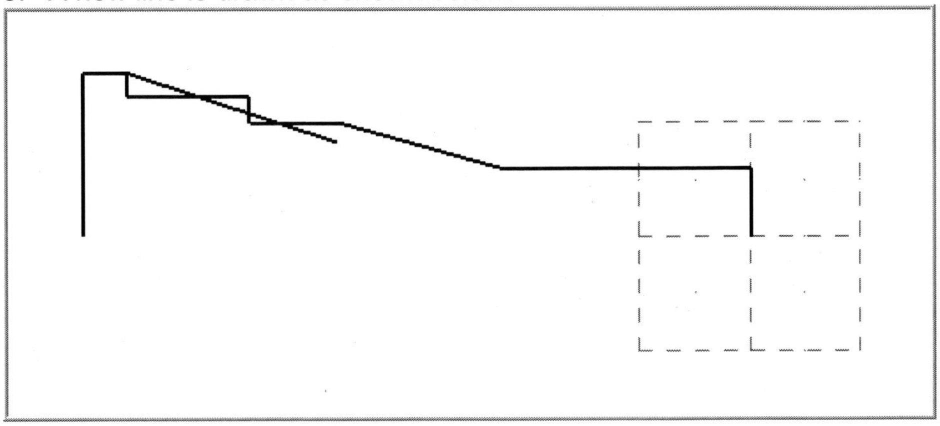

6. Click on the OK icon  to complete this feature.
7. Select **EDIT>Trim/Break>Trim/Break/Extend**.

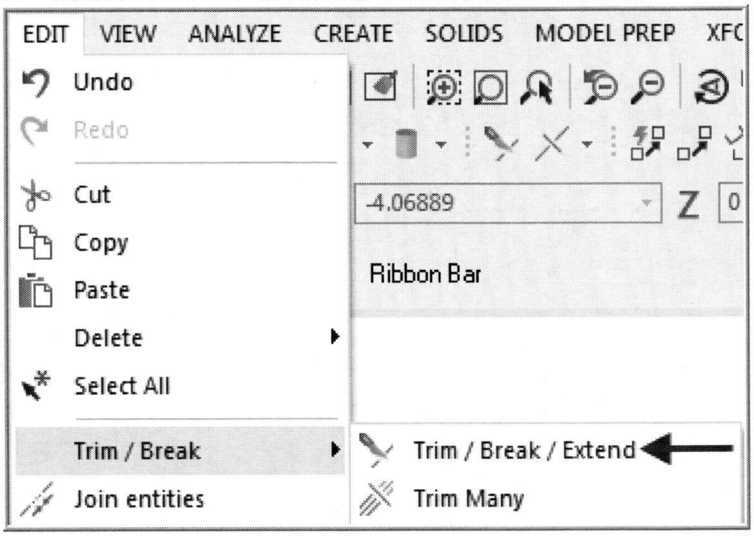

8. Click on the Trim 2 Entity Icon as shown below:

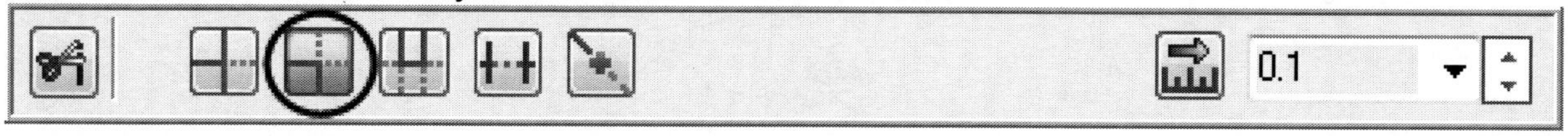

9. Click on line 1 and then line 2 as shown below:

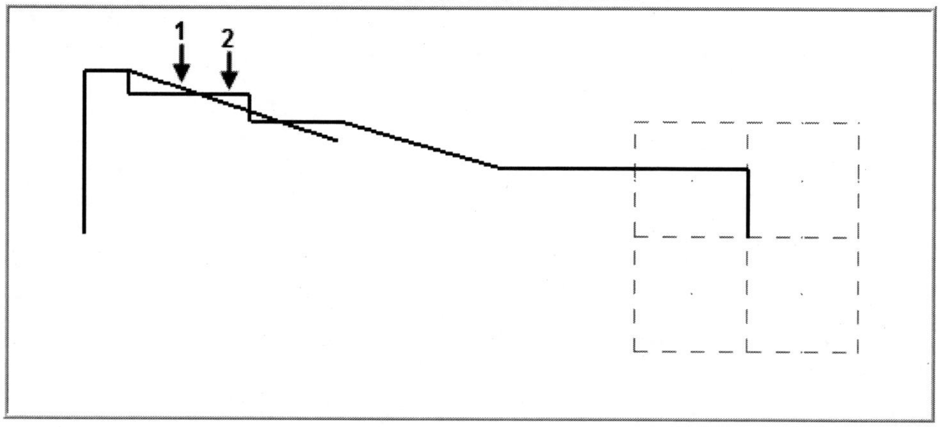

10. The line is trimmed as shown below:

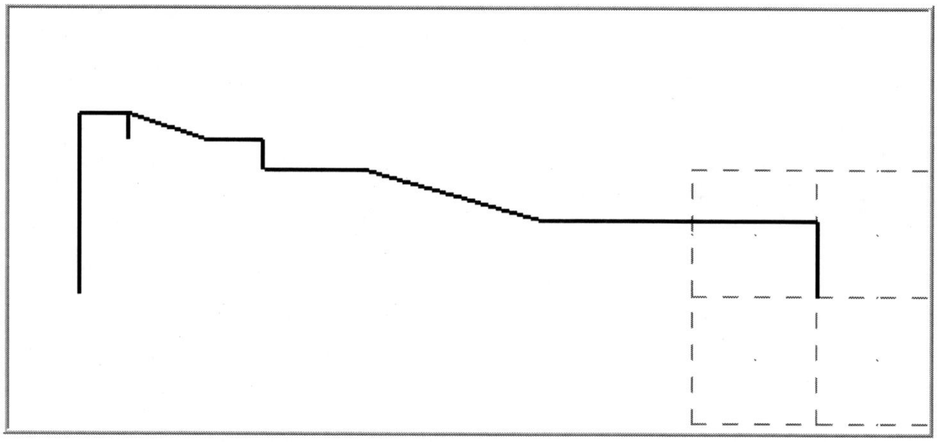

11. Click on the **OK** icon  to complete this feature.
12. Click on the line as shown below and hit the **Delete** key on your computer keyboard.

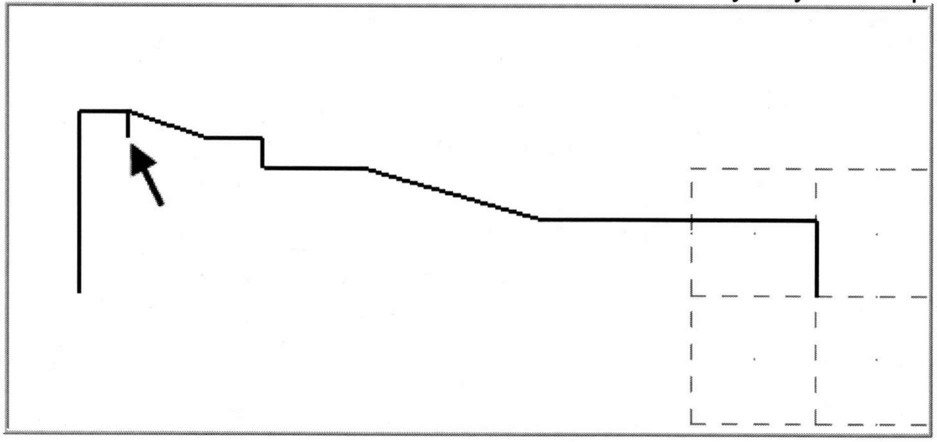

TASK 5:
CREATE THE FILLETS (RADIUS)

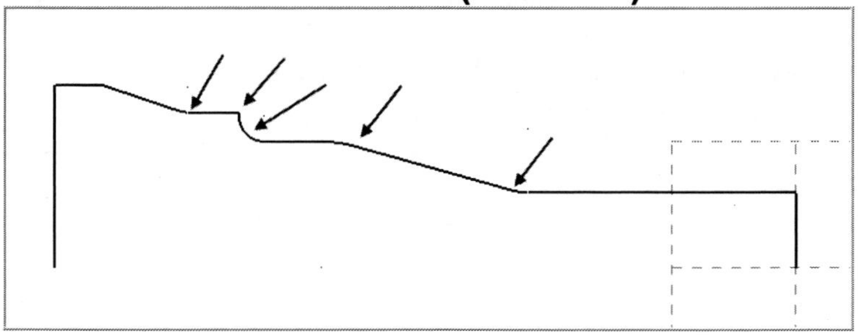

1. Select **CREATE>Fillet>Entities…**

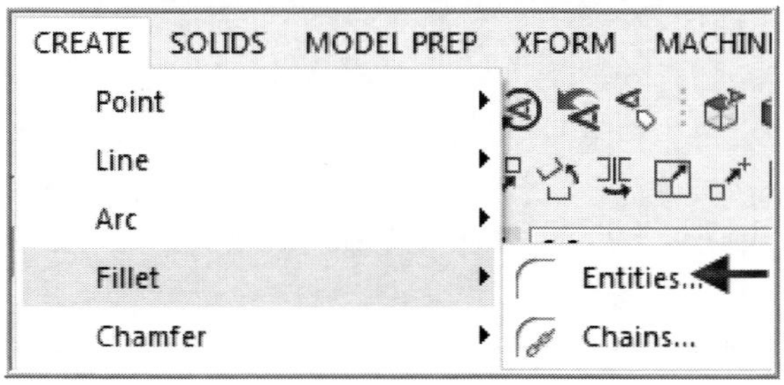

2. Click in the space for radius (shown below), and input **.10** and then hit the tab key.

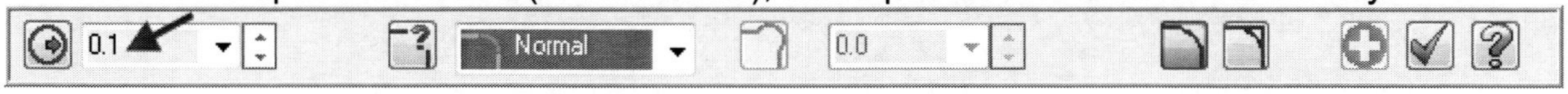

3. You are now transported over to the **Fillet Style field** (shown below). Click on the drop down arrow to review the various fillet radius styles and then ensure **Normal** is selected before moving on.

4. Ensure the **Trim** option for fillet is activated, the icon is depressed as shown below:

5. Move over to the graphic screen and for the prompt **"Fillet: Select an entity"** click on **Line 1** and then for the prompt **"Fillet: Select another entity"** click on **Line 2** as shown below:

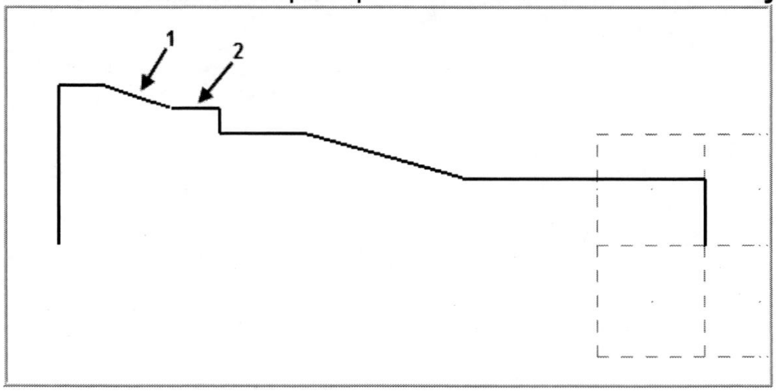

6. Click on the **Apply**  icon to complete this feature.

7. Click in the space for radius (shown below), and input **0.005** and then hit the tab key.

8. For the prompt **"Fillet: Select an entity"** click on **Line 1** and then for the prompt **"Fillet: Select another entity"** click on **Line 2** as shown below:

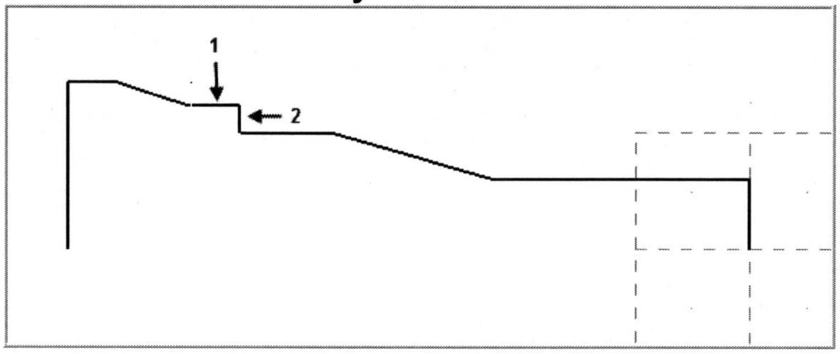

9. Click on the **Apply**  icon to complete this feature.
10. Click in the space for radius (shown below), and input **0.10** and then hit the tab key.

11. For the prompt **"Fillet: Select an entity"** click on **Line 1** and then for the prompt **"Fillet: Select another entity"** click on **Line 2** as shown below:

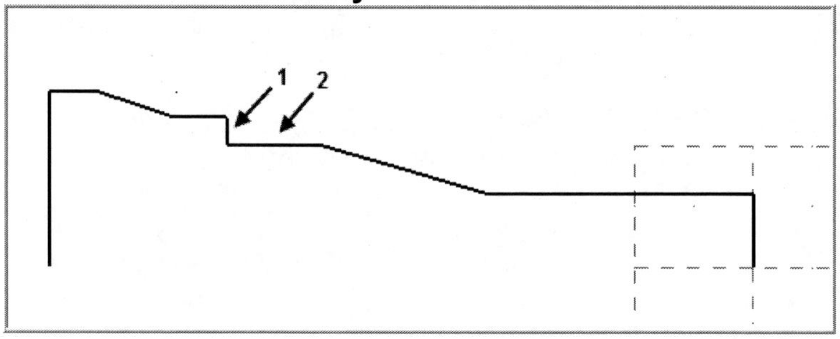

12. Click on the **Apply**  icon to complete this feature.
13. Click in the space for radius (shown below), and input **0.50** and then hit the tab key.

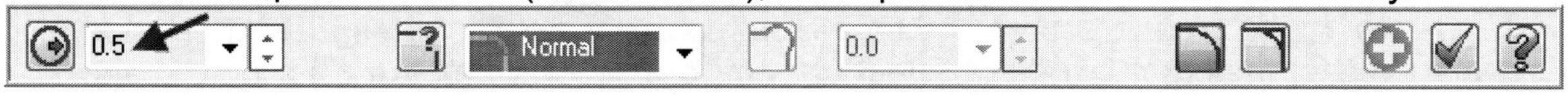

14. For the prompt **"Fillet: Select an entity"** click on **Line 1** and then for the prompt **"Fillet: Select another entity"** click on **Line 2** as shown below:

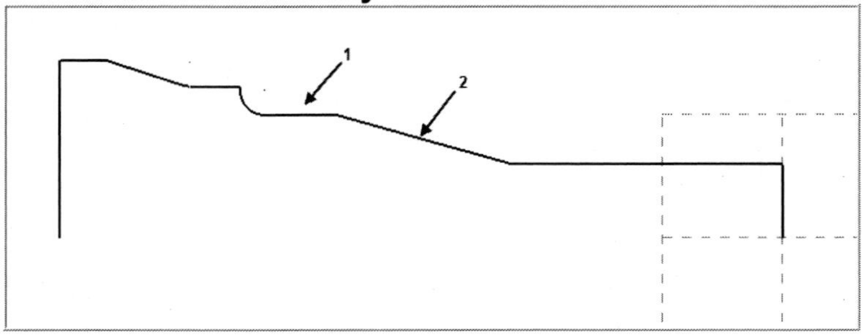

15. Click on the **Apply**  icon to complete this feature.
16. Click in the space for radius (shown below), and input **0.25** and then hit the tab key.

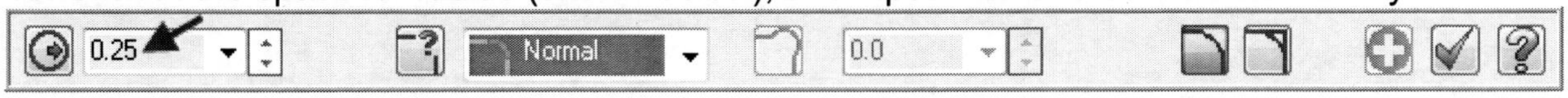

17. For the prompt **"Fillet: Select an entity"** click on **Line 1** and then for the prompt **"Fillet: Select another entity"** click on **Line 2** as shown below:

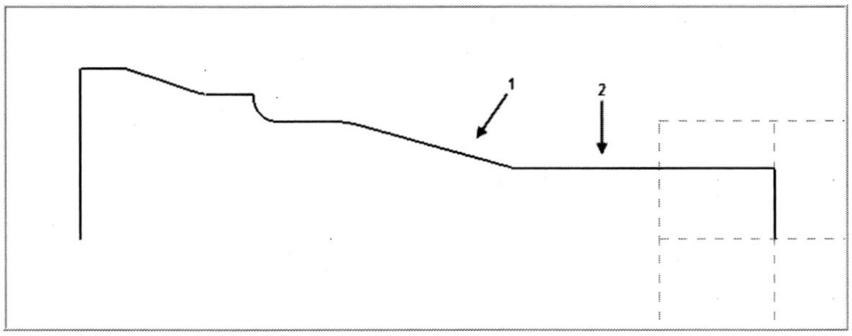

18. Click on the **OK** icon  to complete this feature.

19. The completed fillet is shown below:

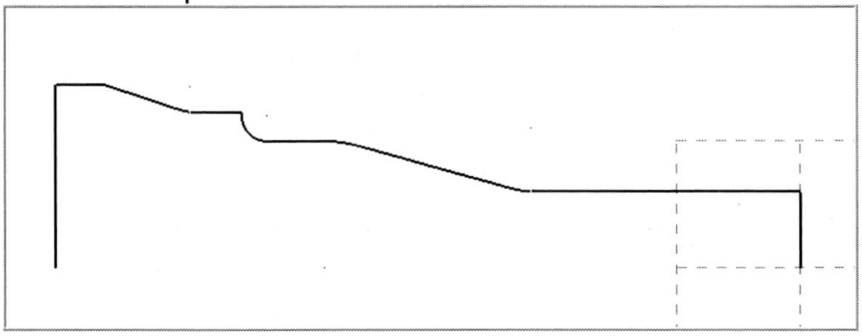

TASK 6:
CREATE THE CHAMFER

1. Select **CREATE>Chamfer>Entities…**

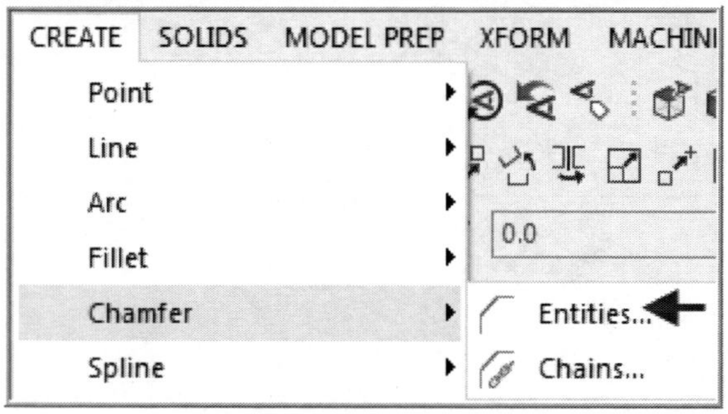

Chamfer ribbon bar:
Use this ribbon bar to chamfer existing entities. Before you select the entities to chamfer, choose the chamfer method, and enter the necessary distance and angle values. Then choose the first and second entities.

Mastercam's auto-preview feature displays a temporary fillet at the selected location. You can also choose to trim to the chamfer or to leave the selected lines untrimmed.

Trimming is the default, so for no trimming, select the No Trim button.

2. The **Chamfer Entities** ribbon bar appears.

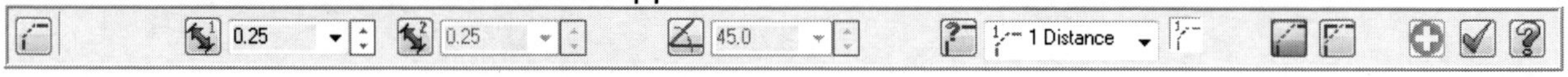

3. Click in the space for **distance 1** and input **.0625** and then hit the tab key.

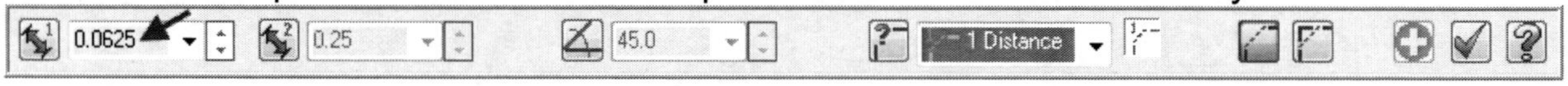

4. Ensure the 1 Distance option for **Chamfer Style** is selected as shown below:

5. Ensure the **Trim** option for Chamfer is activated, the icon is depressed as shown below:

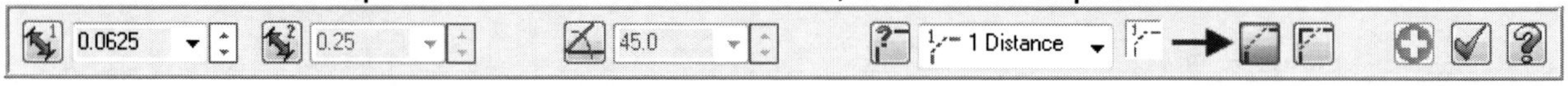

6. Move over to the graphic screen and for the prompt **"Select Line or arc"** click on **Line 1** and then for the prompt **"Select Line or arc"** click on **Line 2** as shown below:

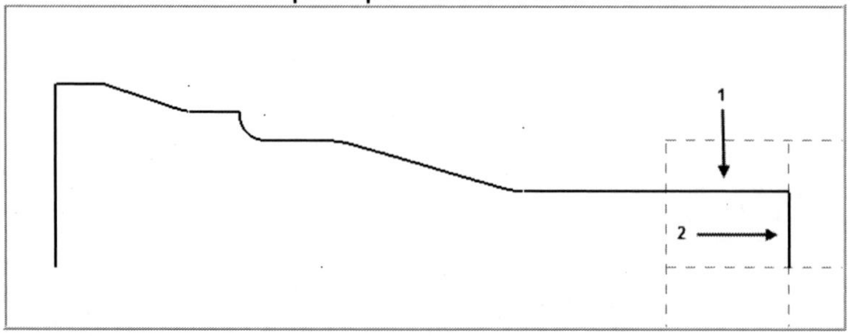

7. Click on the **OK** icon  to complete this feature.

8. The Chamfer should look like the figure below:

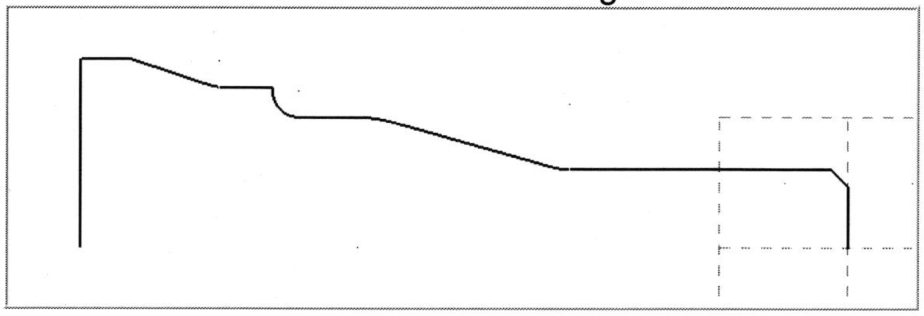

9. This completes the geometry for this part.

TASK 7:
SAVE THE DRAWING

1. Select **File.**
2. Select **Save as**.
3. In the “File name” box, type “Lathe-Lesson-3”.
4. Save to an appropriate location.
5. Select the Save button to save the file and complete this function.

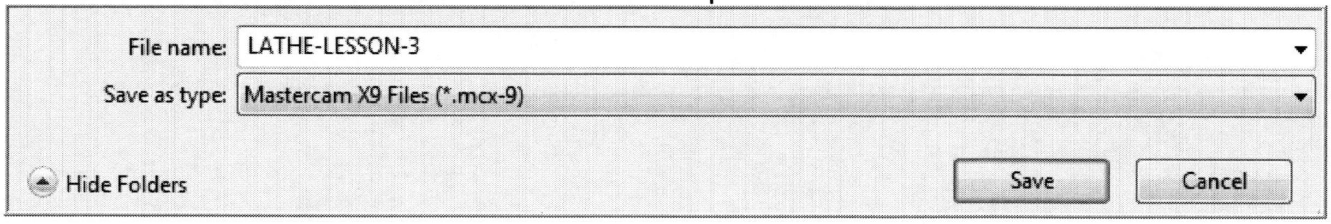

Toolpath Creation

TASK 8:
DEFINE THE STOCK AND CHUCK PARAMETERS

1. Ensure your screen looks like the image below:
   a. The Toolpath Manager is open, if it is not Select Alt and O on your keyboard to open it.
   b. The properties icon displays Lathe Default. If it is not refer to **Setting the Environment** chapter at the beginning of the book.
   c. The Lathe Lesson-3 Geometry is showing.
2. Select the screen **Fit** icon as shown below to display the geometry:

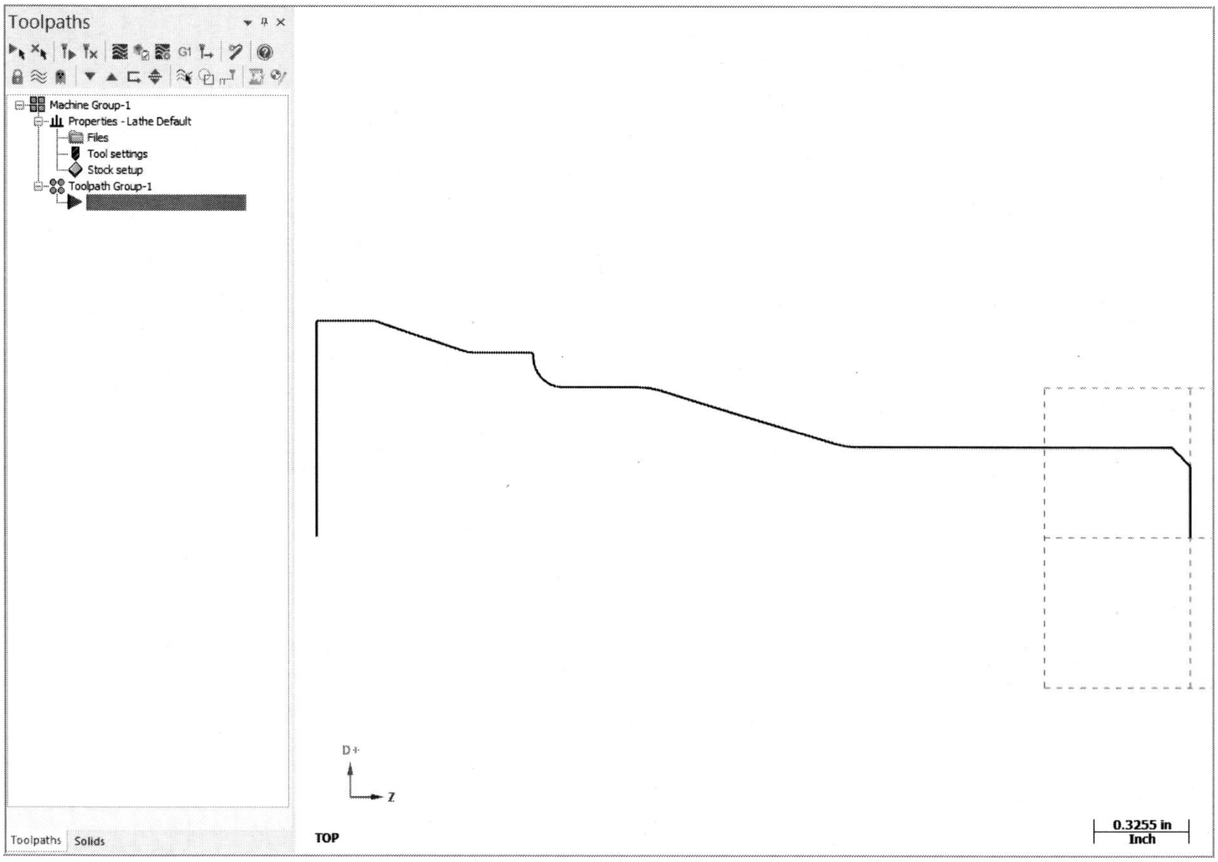

3. Select the plus in front of **Properties** to expand the Machine Group Properties.

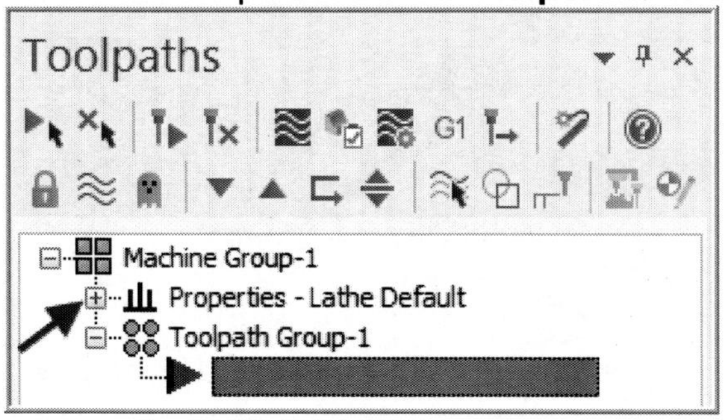

4. Select **Stock setup** in the toolpath manager window.

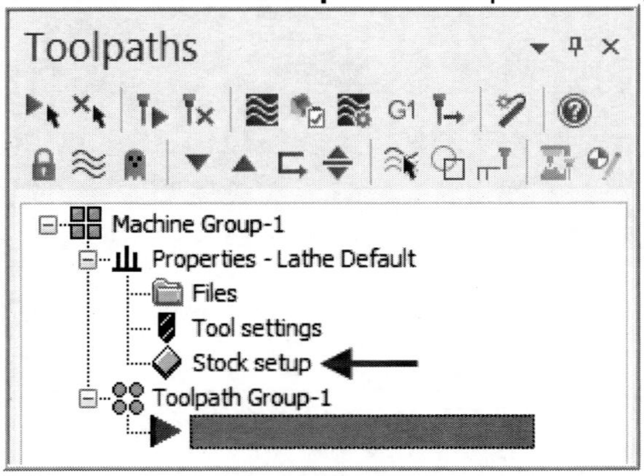

5. Select the **Stock Properties** button in the **Stock Setup** page as shown in the screenshot below:

Note: To learn more about Stock Setup refer to the Tips and Techniques section on the Mastercam Training Guide – Lathe DVD that accompanies this book.

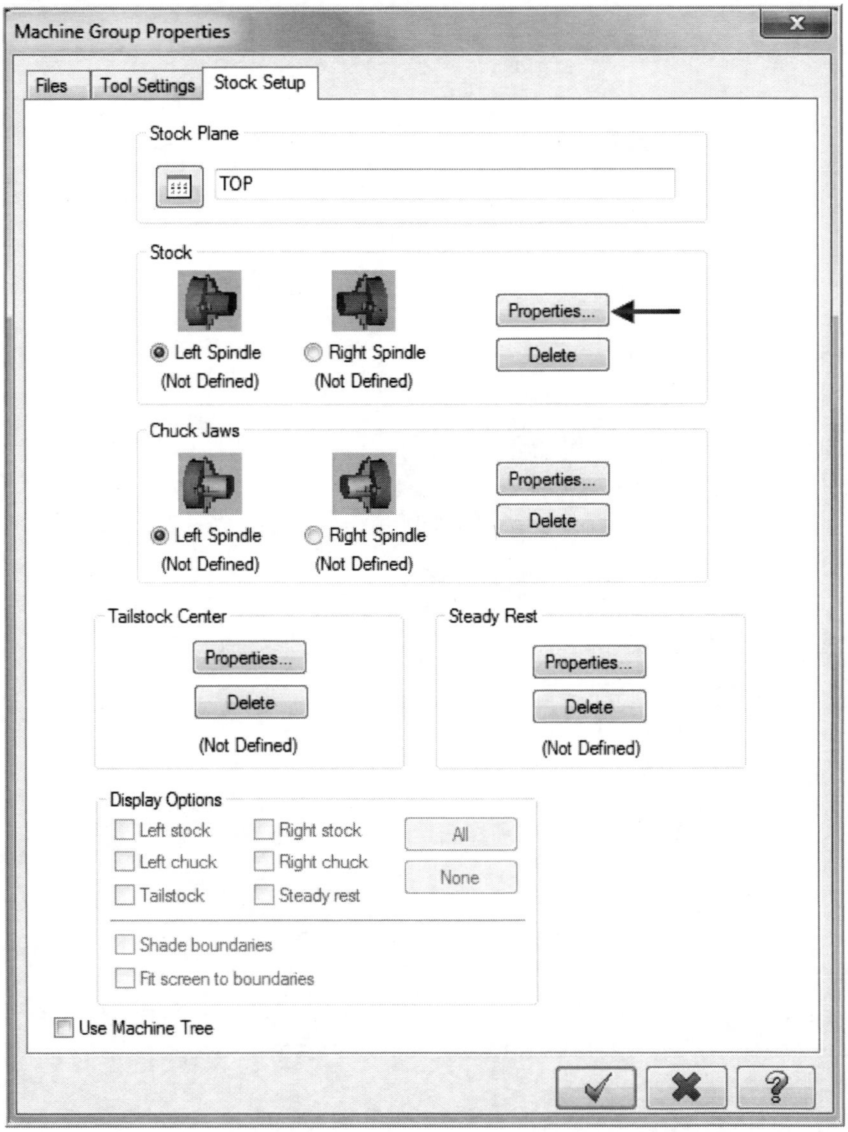

6. In the **Machine Component Manager-Stock** window click on the **Geometry** button and select **Cylinder** as shown below:

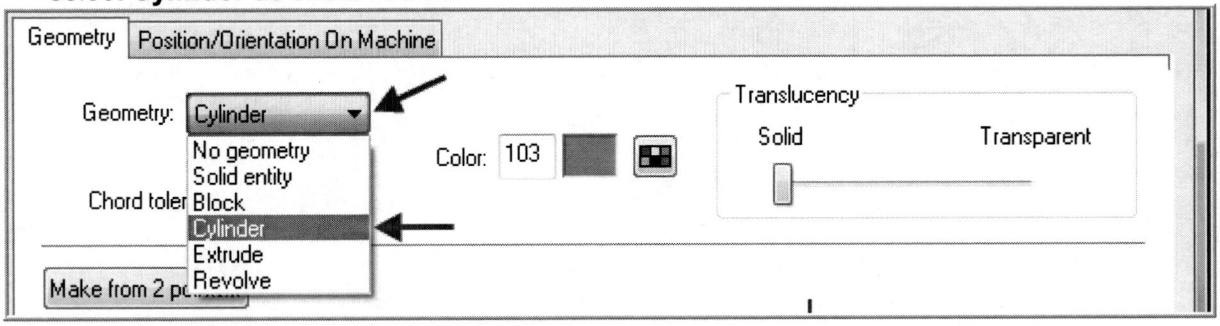

7. In the **Stock setup** set the values as shown below. **Axis is set to -Z**.

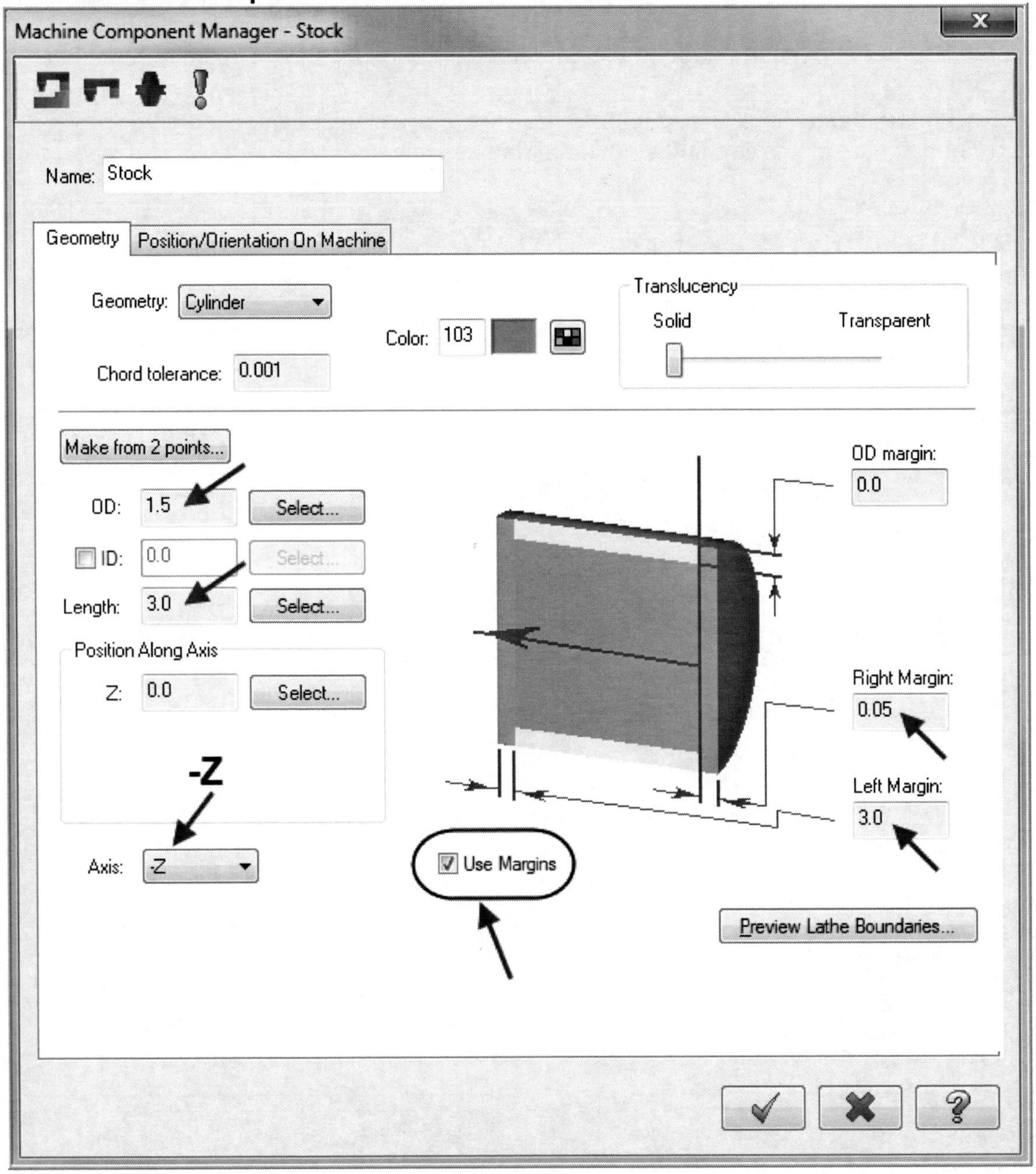

8. Click on the OK icon ✔ to complete this feature.

9. Still on the Stock Setup page activate **Fit screen to boundaries**.

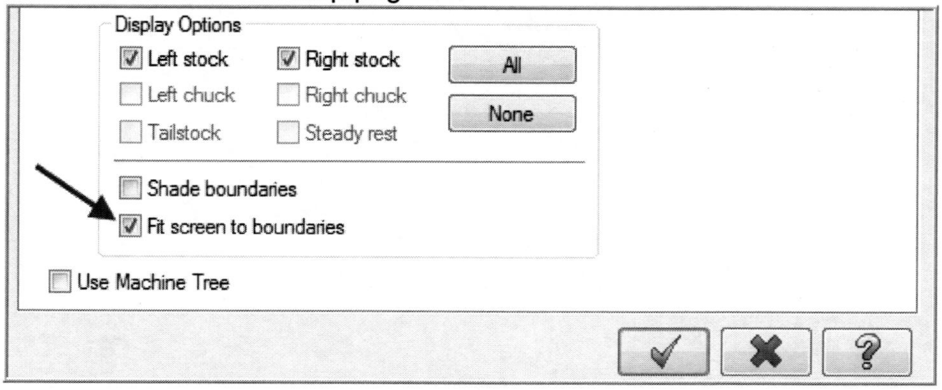

10. Select the **Chuck Properties** button in the **Stock Setup** page as shown in the screenshot below:

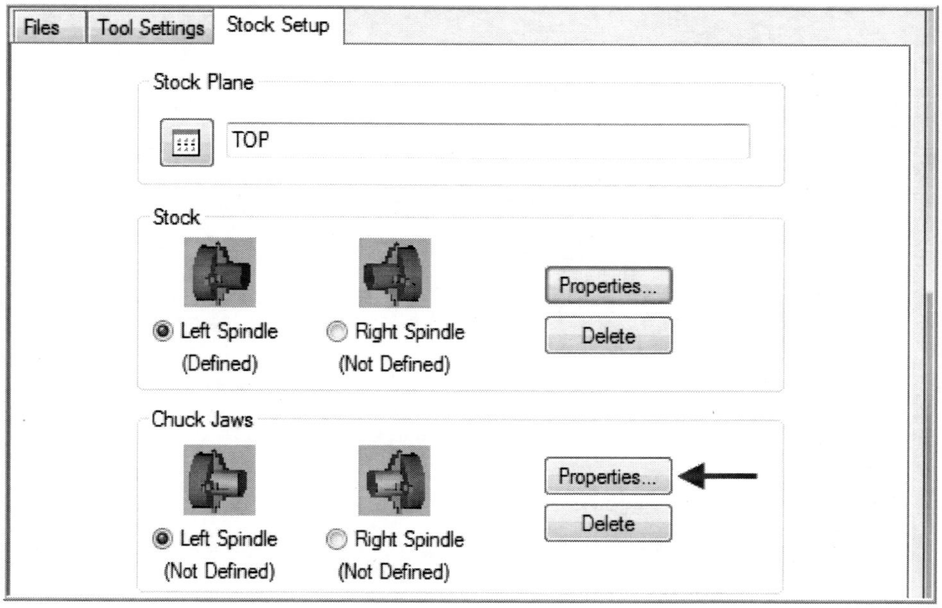

11. In the **Chuck Jaws** setup set the values as shown below:

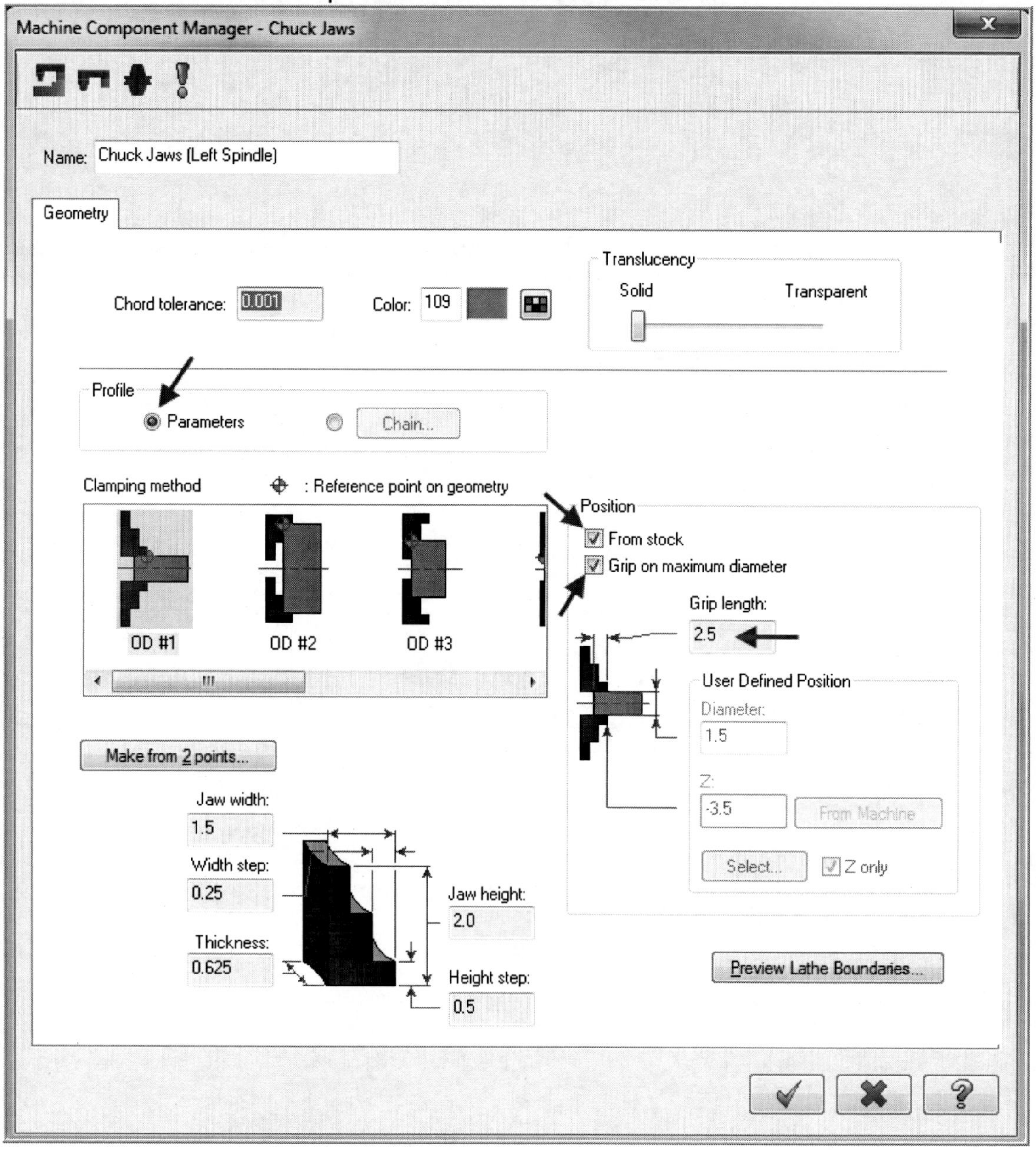

12. Click on the OK icon  to complete this feature.

13. Click on the **Tool Settings** page and make changes as shown below:

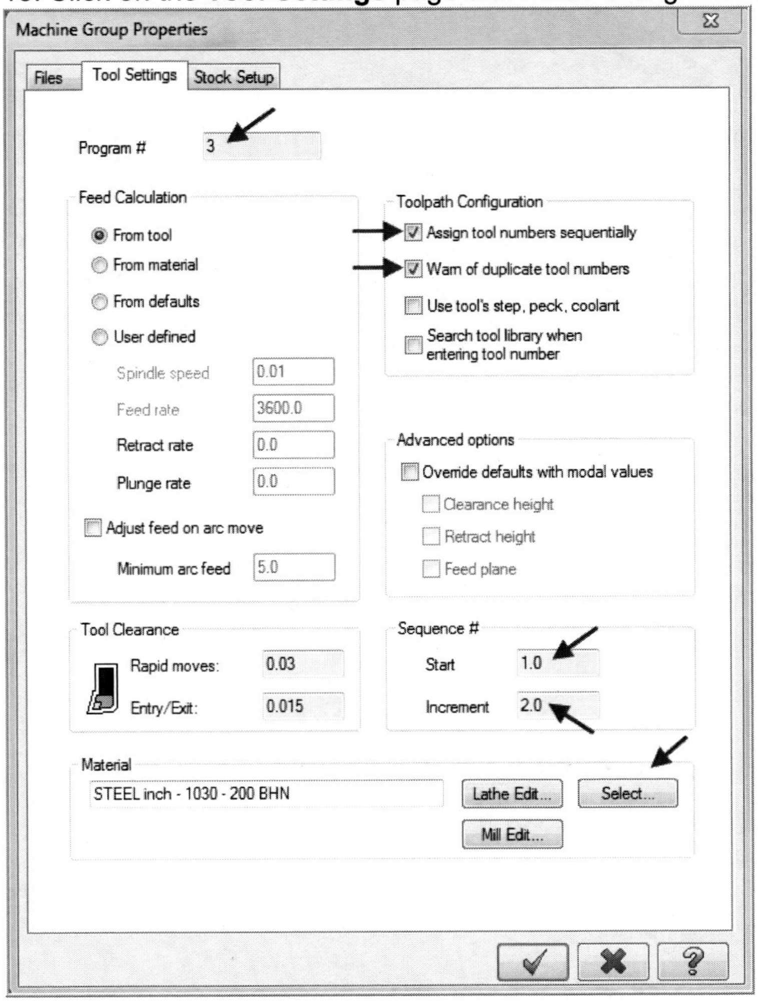

14. To change the **Material** type to Aluminum 6061 click on the **Select** button at the bottom of the Tool Settings page.
15. At the **Material List** dialog box open the Source drop down list and select **Lathe – library.**

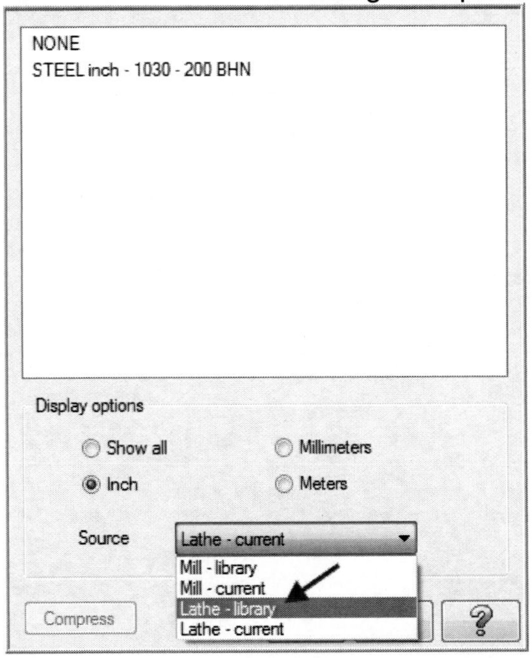

16. From the **Default Materials** list select **ALUMINUM inch - 6061** and then select .

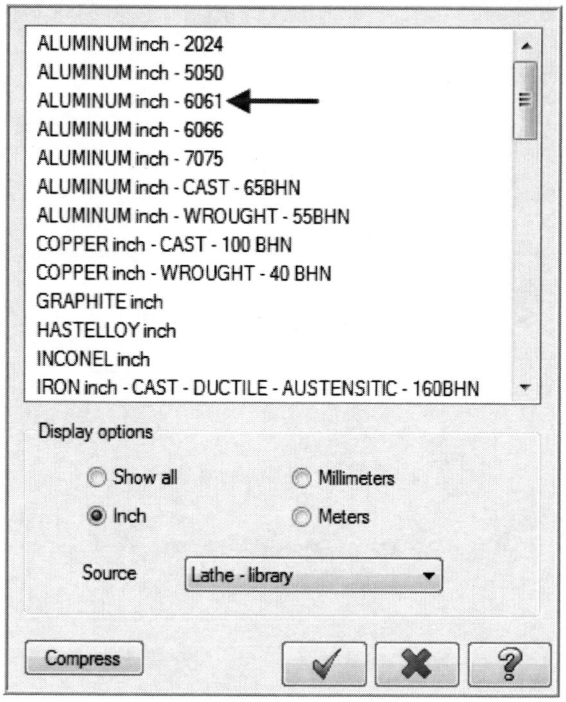

17. Select the OK button again to complete this Stock Setup function.

18. Select the **Screen Fit** icon to fit the part to the screen .
Notice the stock setup outline as indicated by broken lines as shown below:

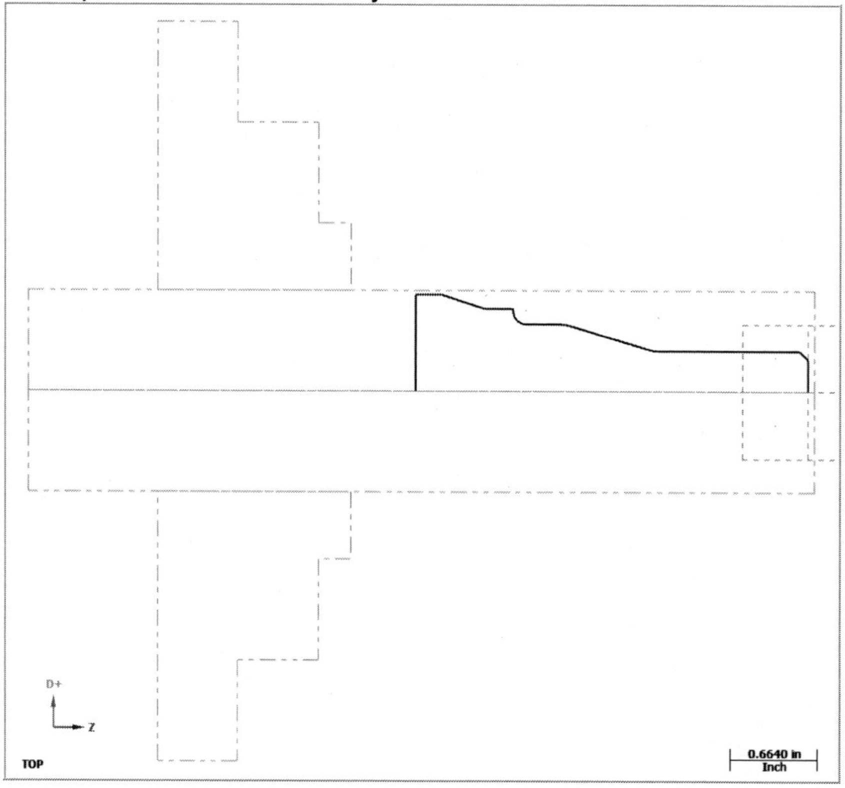

TASK 9:
FACE THE FRONT OF THE PART:

➲ In this task you will use a facing tool to face the front of the part in one cut.

1. Select the **Screen Fit** icon to fit the part to the screen if required.
2. From the menu bar select **Toolpaths>Face…**

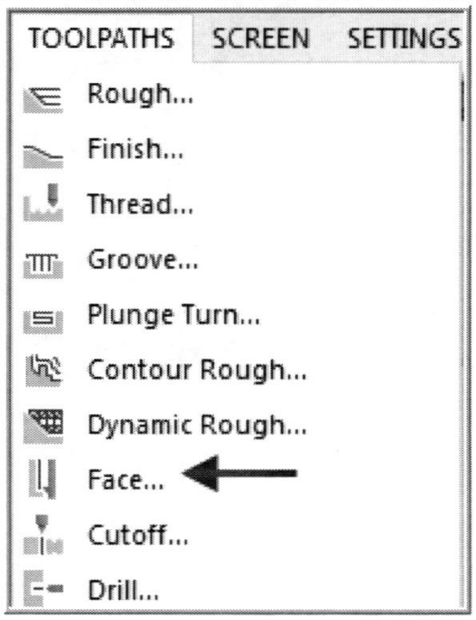

3. When prompted to **"Enter new NC name"** Ensure **Lathe-Lesson-3** is entered as shown below and then select the OK button .

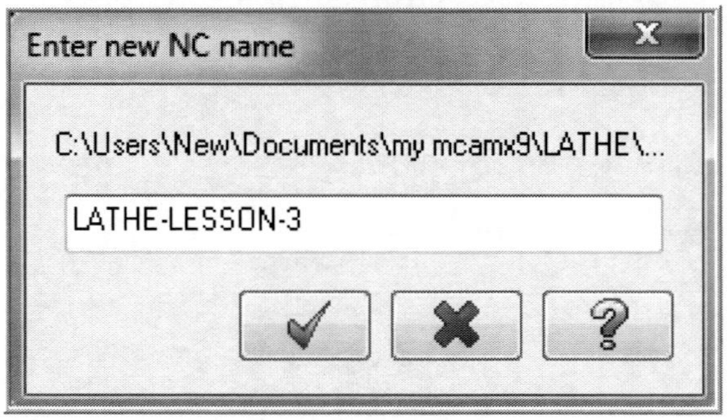

➲ After selecting the OK button you are confronted with **Toolpath parameters** page. The first task here will be to select **Tool #1 an OD Rough- Right – 80 deg.**

4. Click on **Tool #1** and make changes in the Toolpath parameters page as shown below:

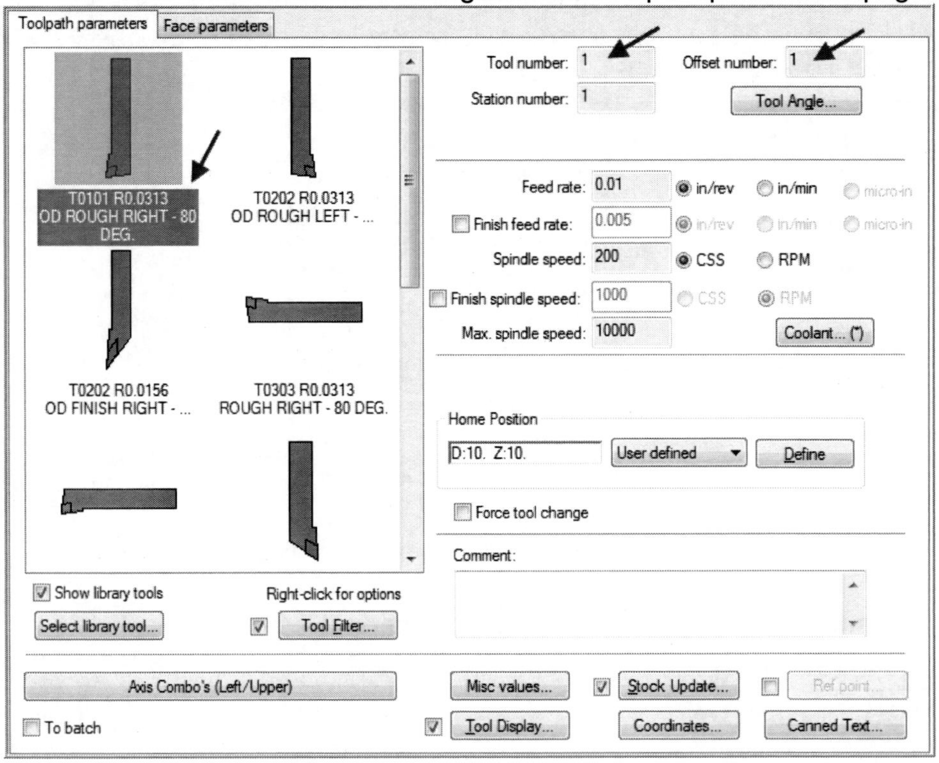

Use the Toolpath parameters tab to: Select a tool, set feeds and speeds, and set other general toolpath parameters.

This tab is very similar for most Lathe toolpaths.

5. Select the **Face parameters** page and make changes as shown below:

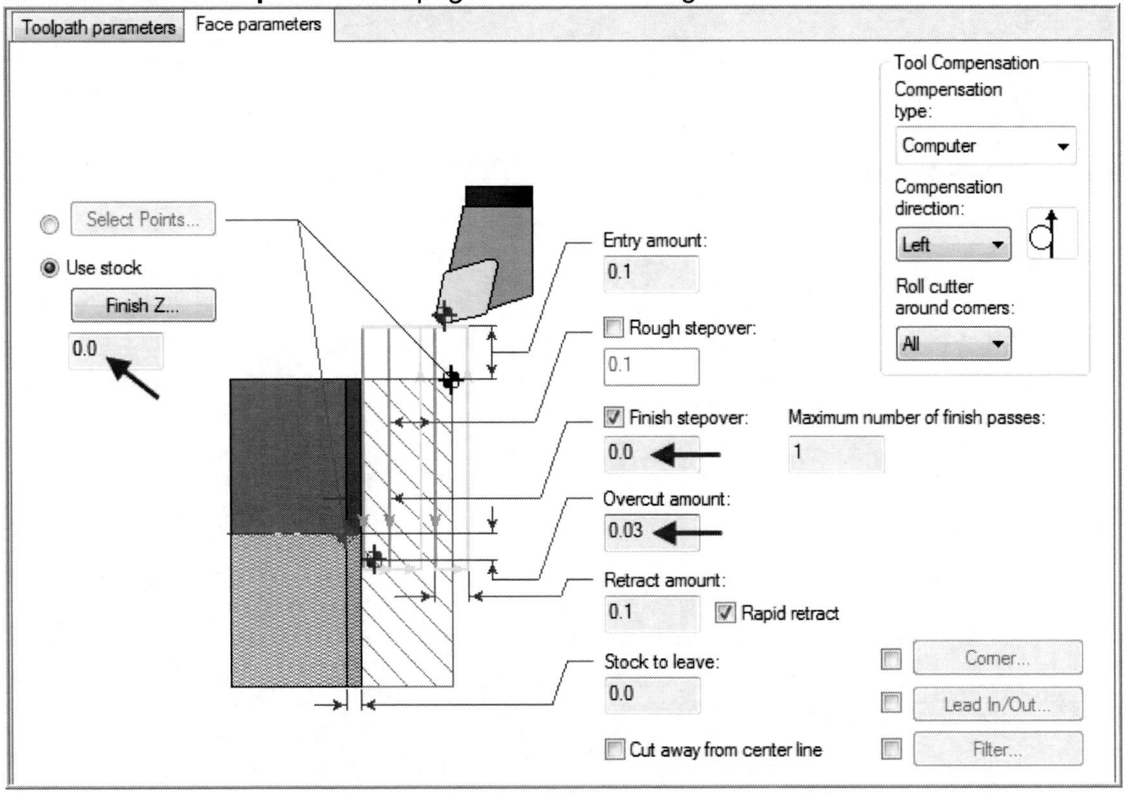

6. Select the OK button ✔ to complete this **Lathe Face** operation.

TASK 10:
ROUGH THE OUTSIDE DIAMETERS

- In this task you will use a new Lathe toolpath called Lathe Quick Toolpaths.
- In this task you will use the same tool as used for the previous facing operation **Tool #1 an OD Rough- Right – 80 deg.**

1. From the menu bar select **Toolpaths>Quick>Rough…**

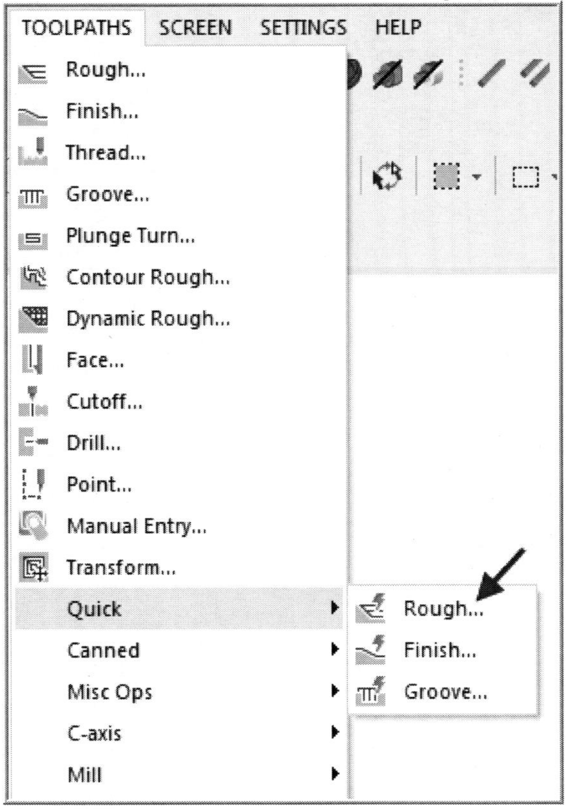

Quick rough toolpaths coarsely cut the part geometry in preparation for a finish toolpath.

Use this toolpath when you need to quickly create a simple roughing operation and don't need Mastercam's more advanced roughing features.

In addition, you have fewer options for creating entry and exit passes.

2. In the **Chaining** window chaining mode is set to **Partial** by default.

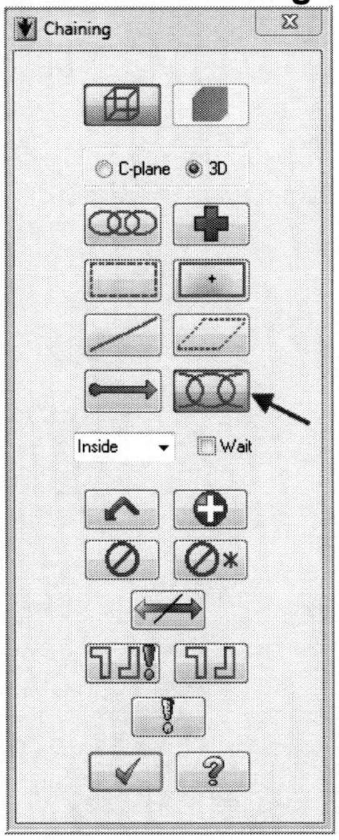

3. Select the chamfer, Line 1 as the start of the **Partial chain**.

After you have selected the chamfer **ensure** that the arrows are pointing up and to the left of the part. If it is not select the reverse button in the Chaining dialog box.

4. Then select Line 2 as the end entity in this chain.

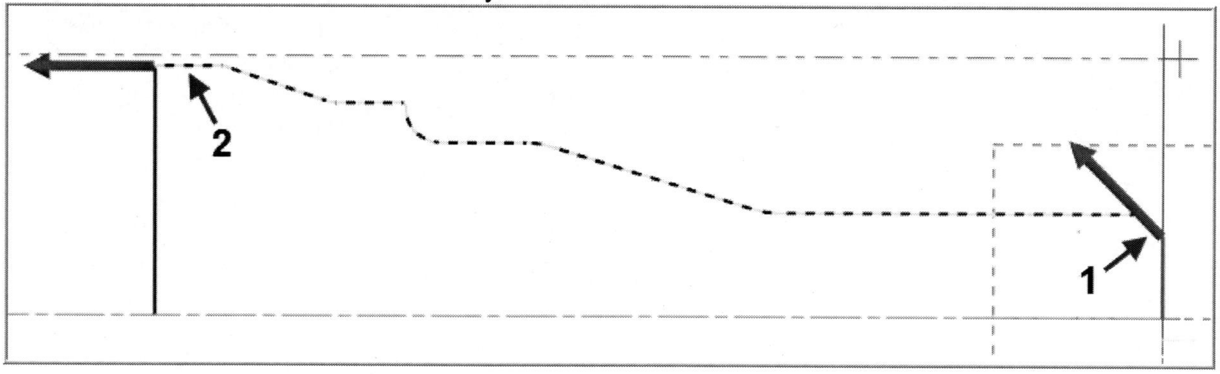

5. Select the OK button to exit the Chaining dialog window.
6. In the **Toolpath parameters** page select the same tool used to face the part **Tool #1 an OD Rough- Right – 80 deg** and make any necessary changes as shown below:

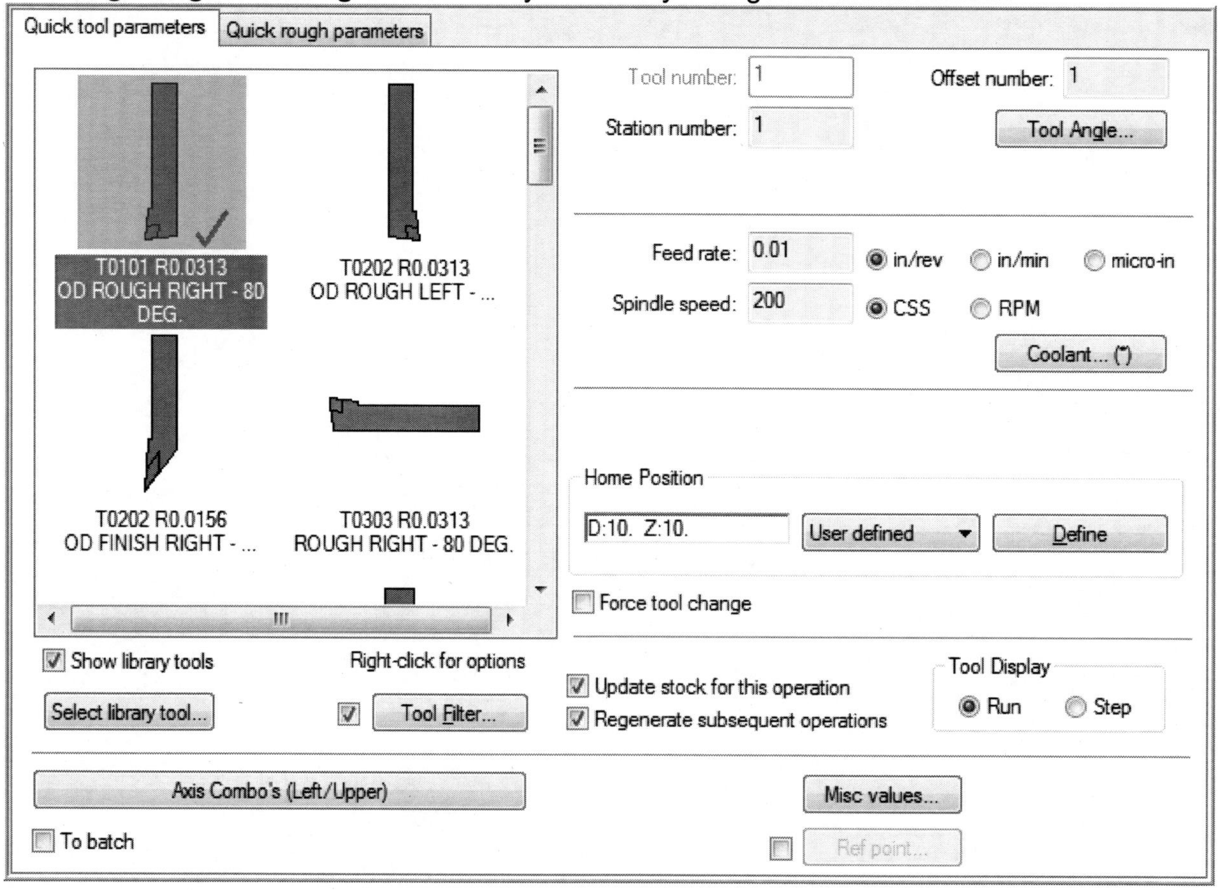

7. Select the **Rough parameters** page and make any necessary changes as shown below:

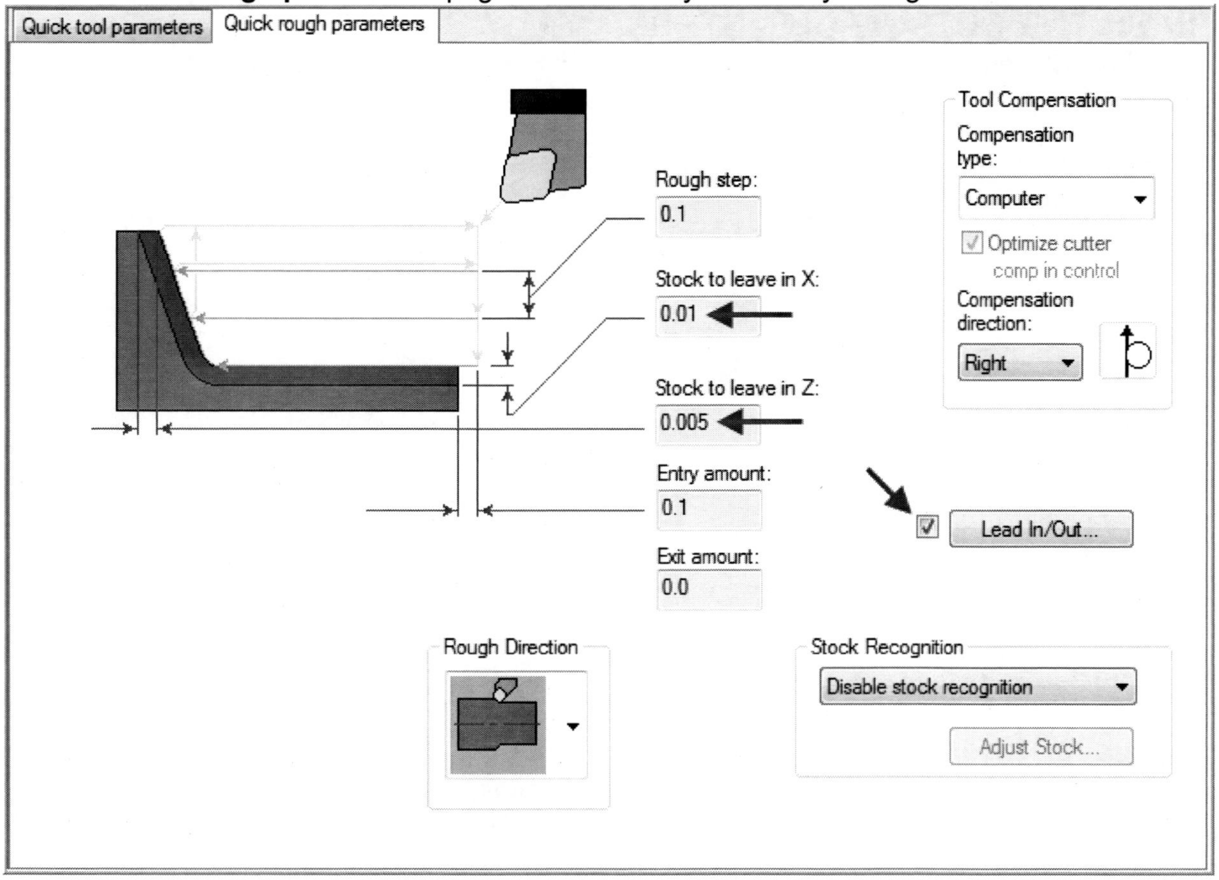

8. Select the **Lead In/Out** button select the **Lead out** page and extend the contour by .2 as shown below:

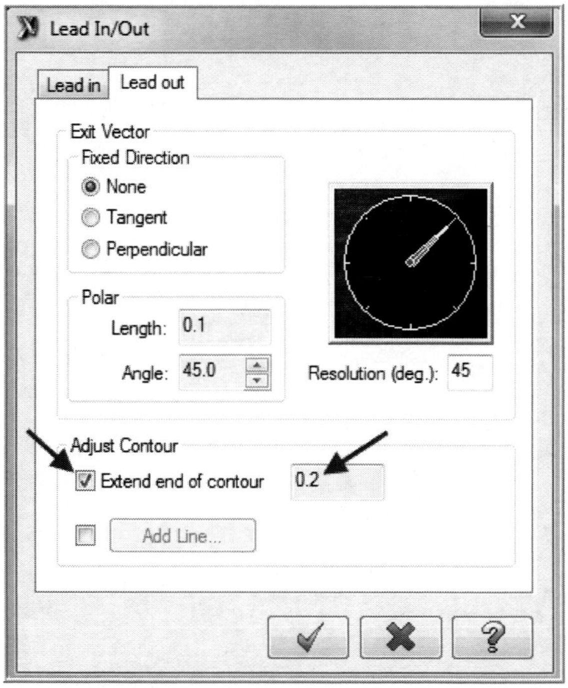

9. Select the OK button [✓] to exit this function.

10. **Select the OK button** [✓] to exit Rough Parameters.

TASK 11:
FINISH THE OUTSIDE DIAMETERS

➲ In this task you will finish the outside diameters in one cut using **Tool #2 OD Finish Right – 35 DEG.**

1. From the menu bar select **Toolpaths>Quick>Finish…**

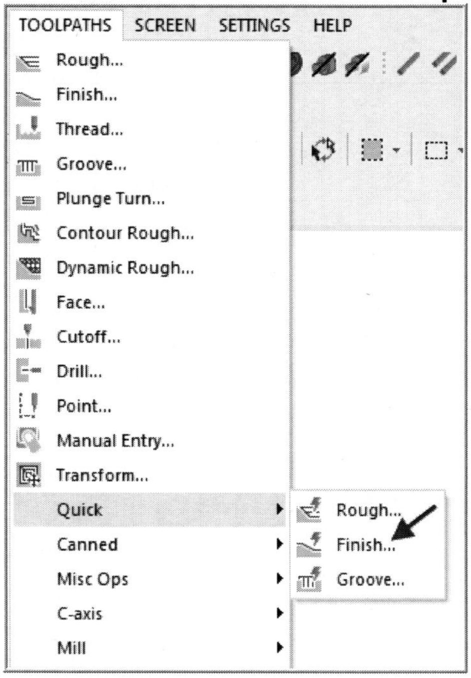

2. Select **Tool #2 OD Finish Right – 35 DEG** tool from the tool list and make any necessary changes as shown below:

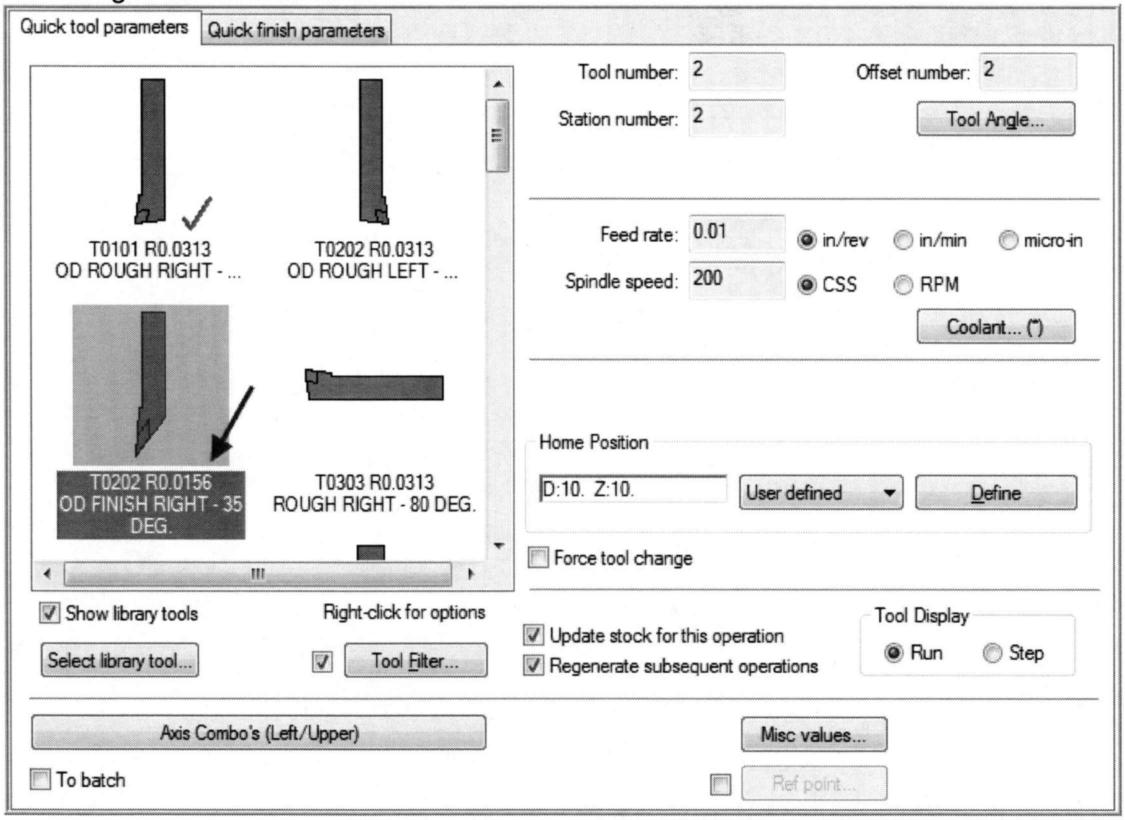

3. Select the **Finish parameters** page and make changes as shown below:

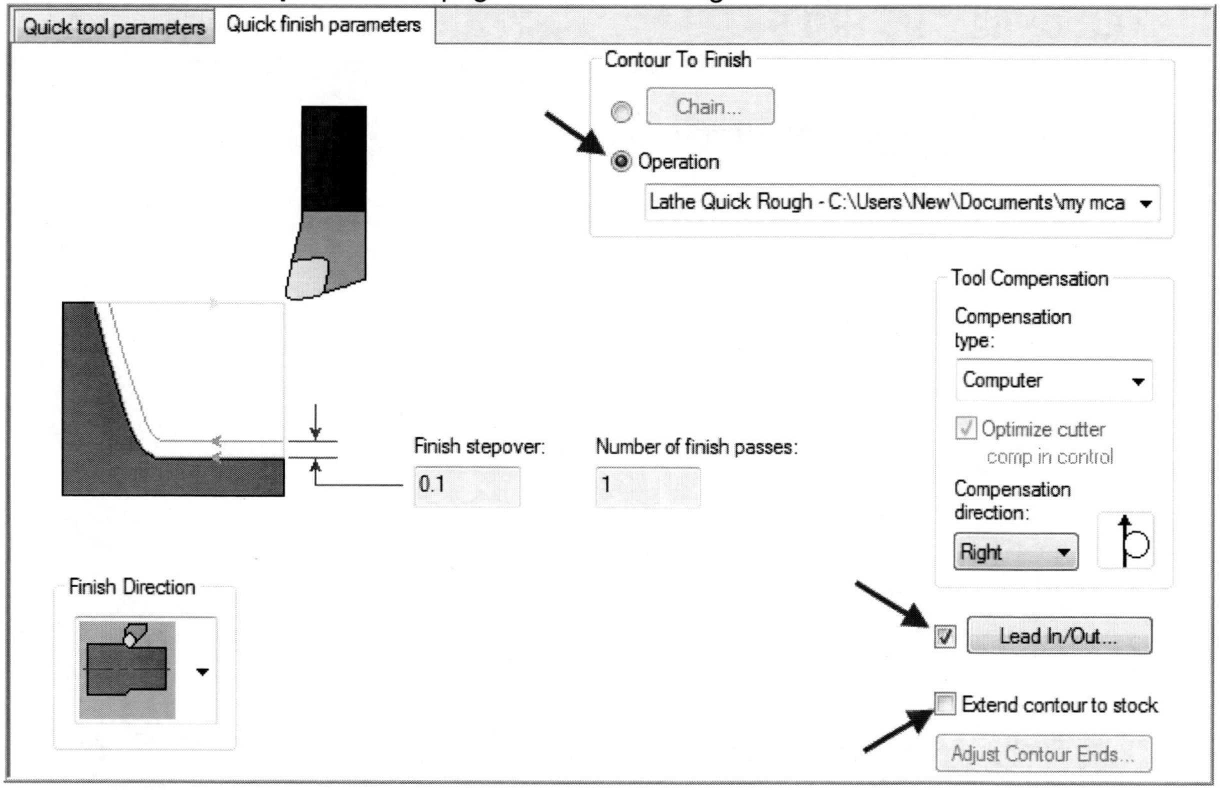

4. Select the **Lead In/Out** button select the **Lead out** page and extend the contour by .2 as shown below:

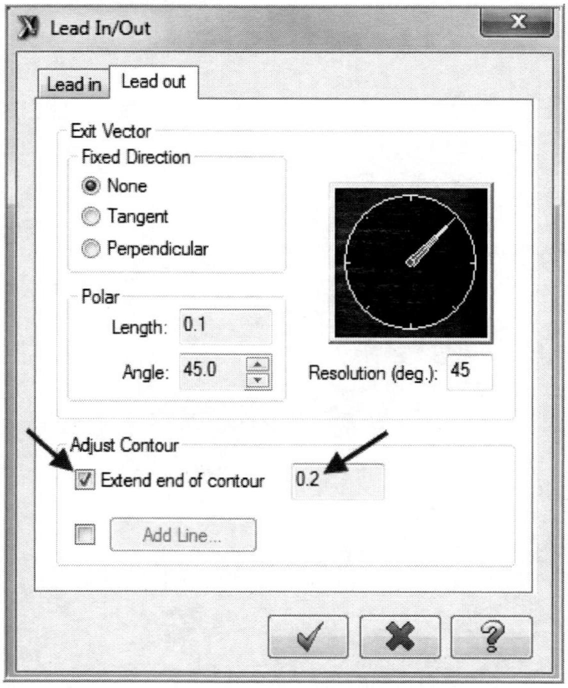

5. Select the OK button  to exit this function.
6. Select the OK button  to exit this function.

TASK 12:
CENTER DRILL THE HOLE

➲ In this task you will center drill .2" depth using **Tool #3 Centre Drill - .25 diameter.**

1. From the menu bar select **Toolpaths>Drill…**

2. Select the **CENTER DRILL .25 DIAMETER** tool from the tool list and make changes as shown below:

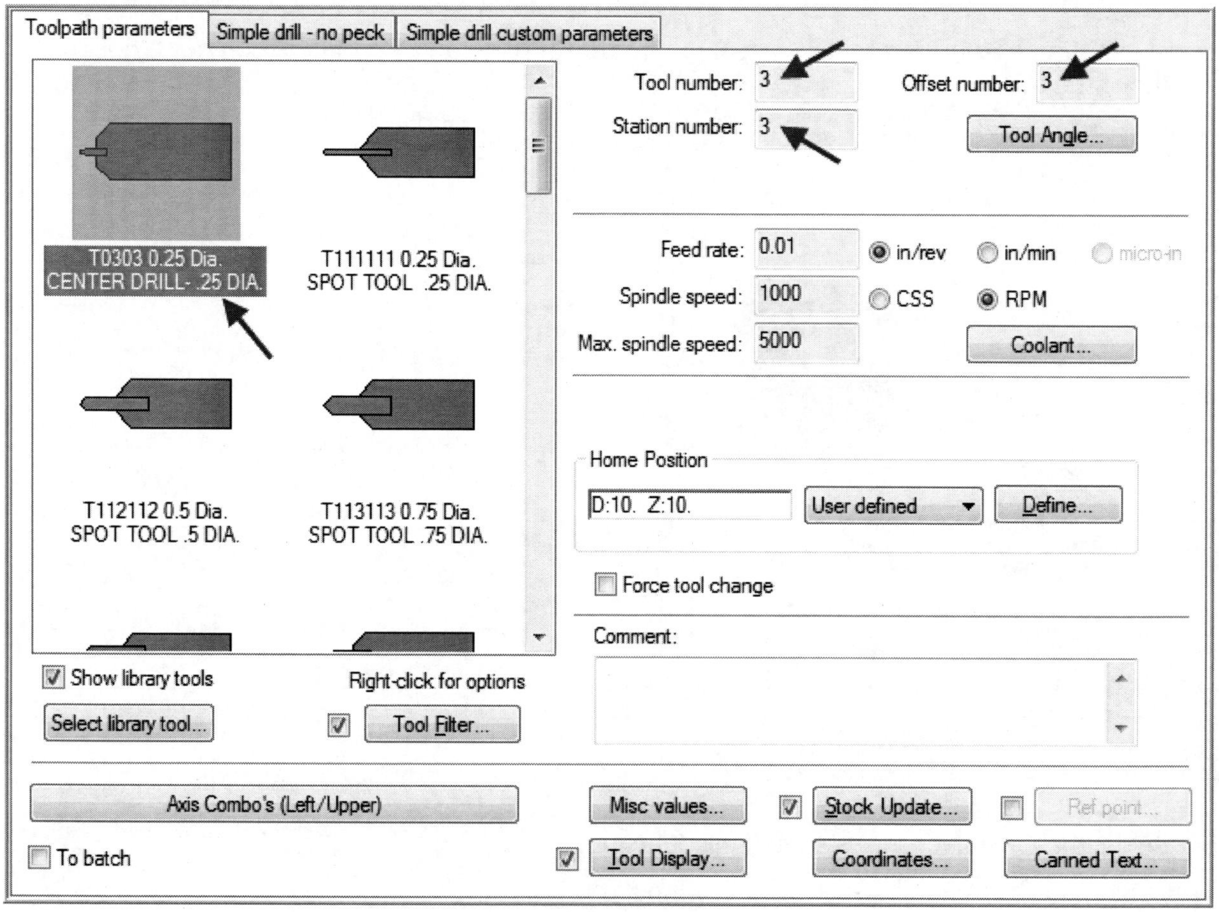

3. Select the **Simple drill – no peck** page and make changes as shown below:

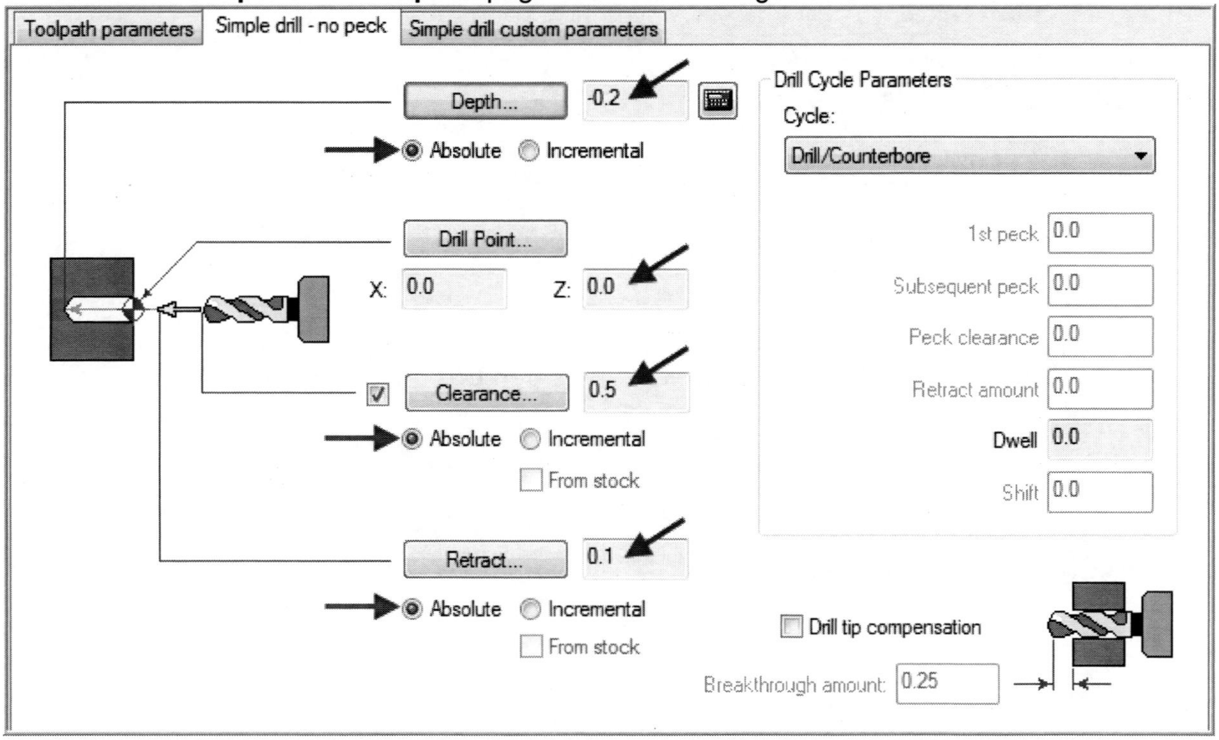

4. Select the OK button ✓ to exit **Simple drill – no peck.**

TASK 13:
TAP DRILL THE 5/16" HOLE

➲ In this task you will drill the 5/16" hole .75" depth using a **0.3125 (5/16") Drill.**

1. From the menu bar select **Toolpaths> Drill…**

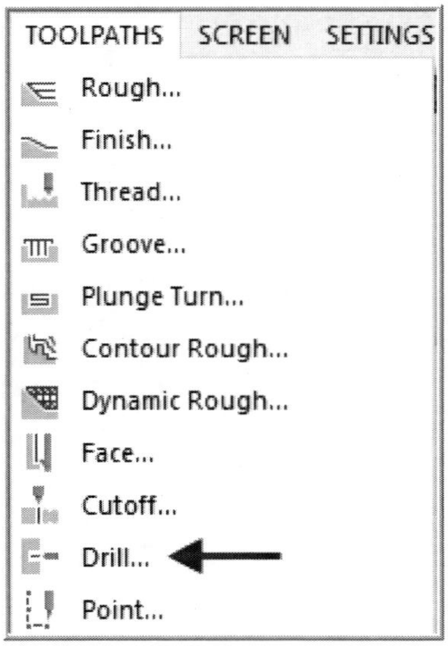

2. Click on the **Select library tool…** button in the lower left corner of the Toolpath parameters page as shown below:

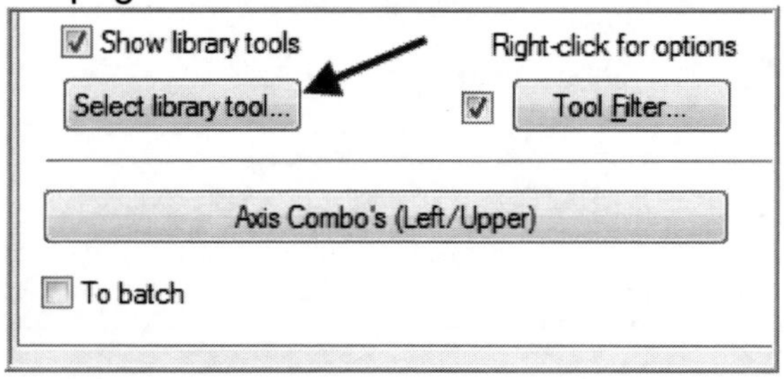

3. At the top left of this dialog box open up the Select new folder icon  to show the library tools list and select **LDRILLS.** Now click on the **Open button** to select **LDRILLS**.

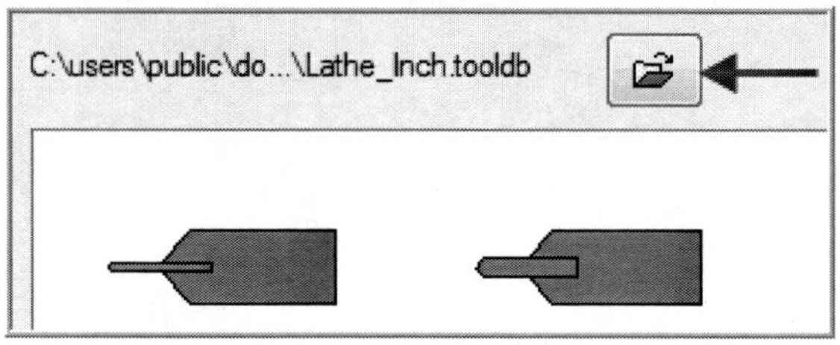

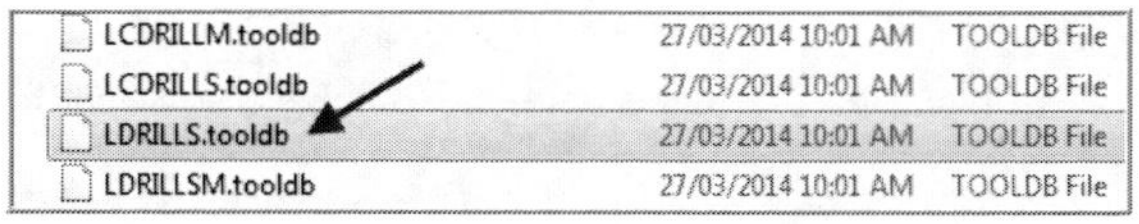

4. Scroll down and select the **0.3125 Dia. 5/16" DRILL** from the list.

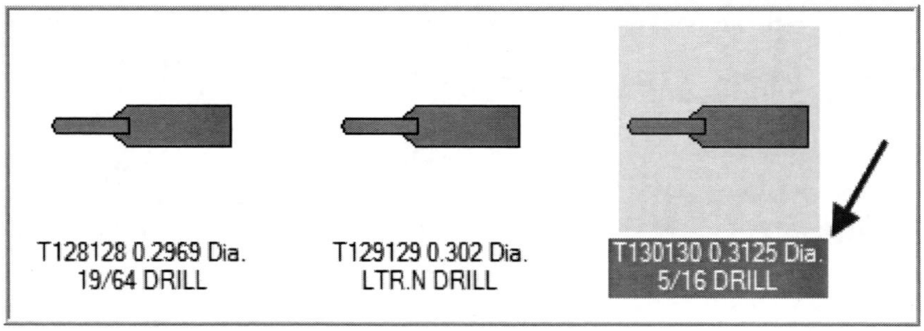

5. Select the OK button .

6. Ensure settings are as shown below:

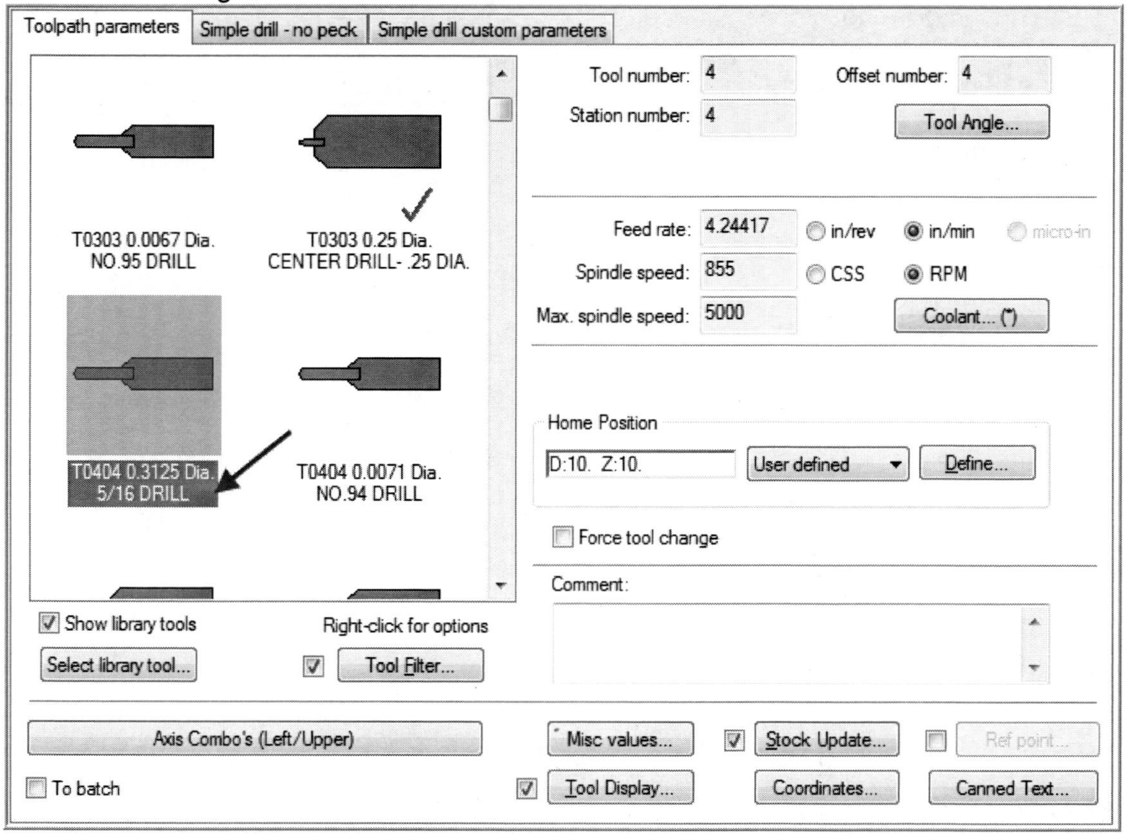

7. Select the **Simple drill – no peck** page and make changes as shown below. This hole will be **peck drilled**. The **depth of the hole is 1.00" from the front face** so click in the space for depth and type in **-1.0** and hit the tab key, Mastercam figures out the value for you. Make changes as shown below:

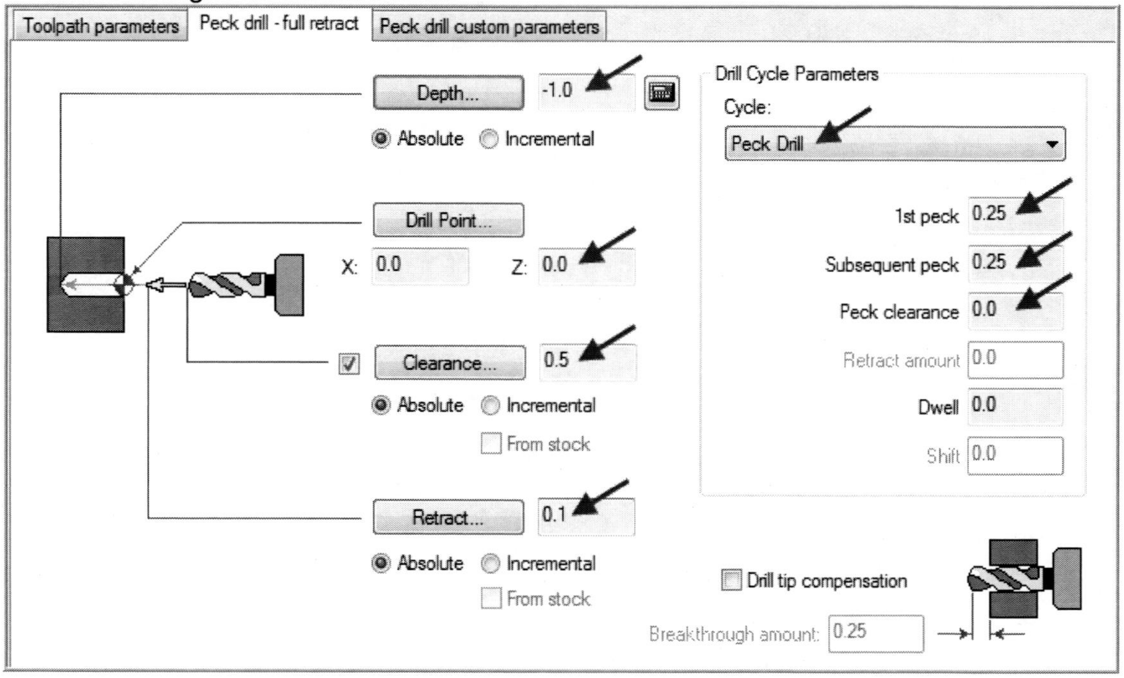

The hole depth on the drawing is dimensioned to .a depth of 1.0" at the full diameter of the hole. So the point of the drill will have to go deeper than 1.0"
You can use the depth calculator button to figure out the correct depth.

8. Select the **Depth Calculator** icon.

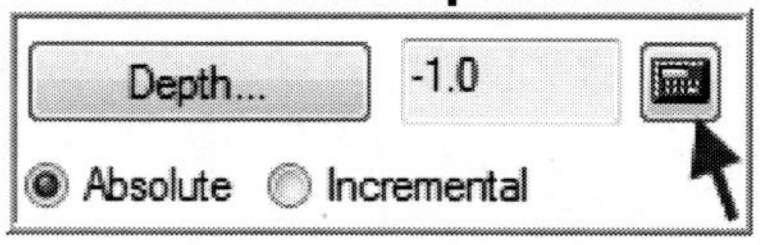

9. Make changes to the **Depth Calculator** as shown below:

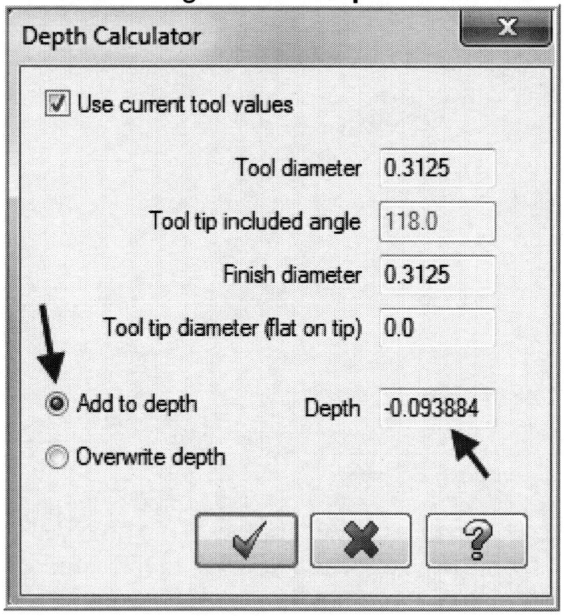

10. Select the OK button to exit **the Depth Calculator.**
11. The depth has now been updated.

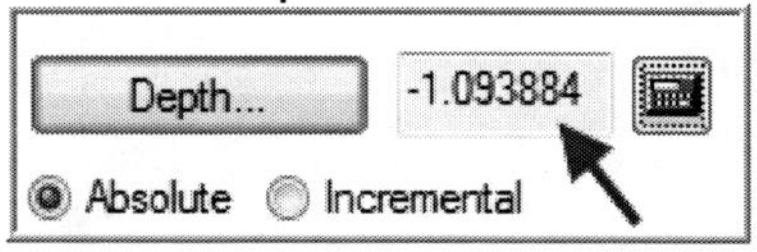

12. Select the OK button to exit **Peck drill – full retract.**

TASK 14:
TAP 3/8" – 16 UNC
➲ In this task you will tap the 3/8"-16 hole 1" deep.

1. From the menu bar select **Toolpaths>Drill...**

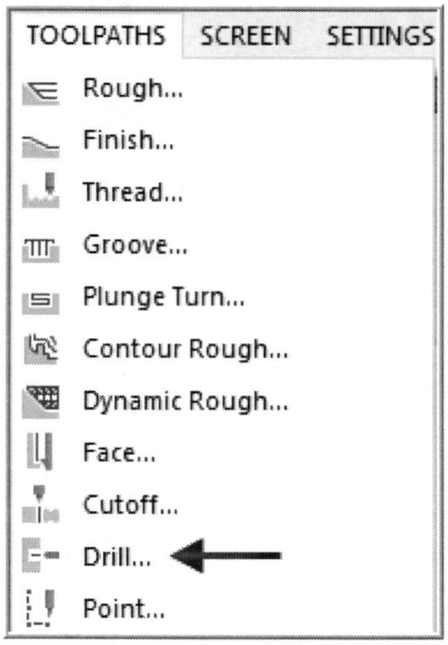

2. Click on the **Select library tool...** button in the lower left corner of the Toolpath parameters page as shown below:

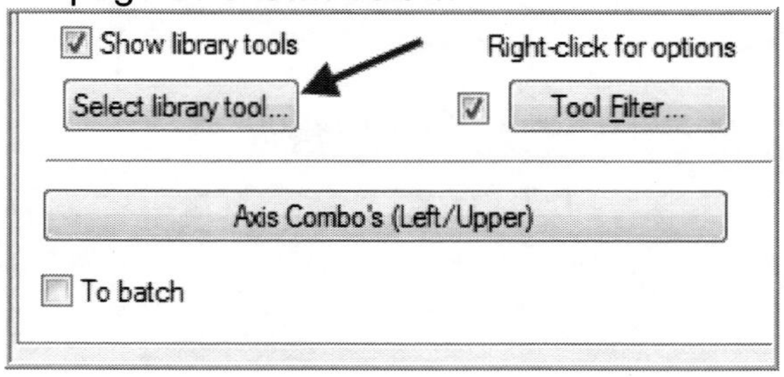

3. Select the **select new folder** icon at the top of the dialog box and then the **LTAPS** from the list as shown below. Now click on the **Open button** to select **LTAPS**.

LREAMERM.tooldb	27/03/2014 10:01 AM	TOOLDB File	
LREAMERS.tooldb	27/03/2014 10:01 AM	TOOLDB File	
LTAPS.tooldb	27/03/2014 10:01 AM	TOOLDB File	
LTAPSM.tooldb	27/03/2014 10:01 AM	TOOLDB File	

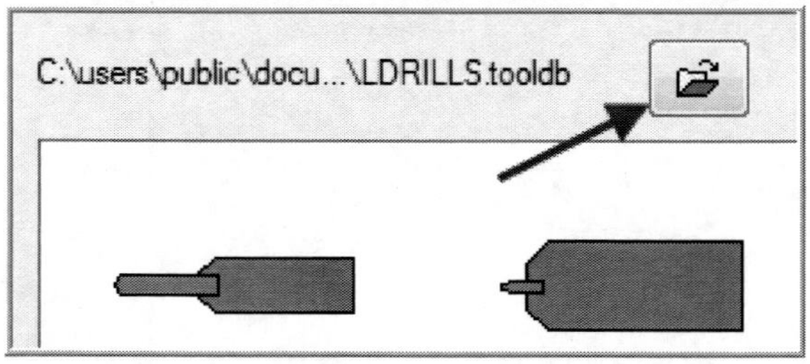

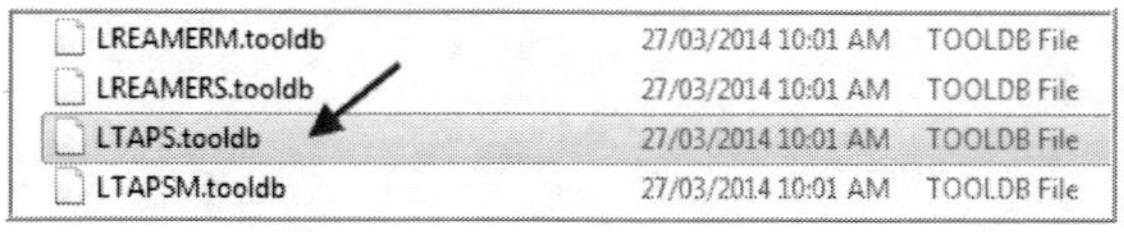

4. Select the OK button ✔ after selecting **LTAPS**.
5. Scroll down and select **the 0.375 Dia. 3/8"-16 RH TAP** from the list.
6. Select the OK button ✔.

7. Ensure necessary settings are as shown below:

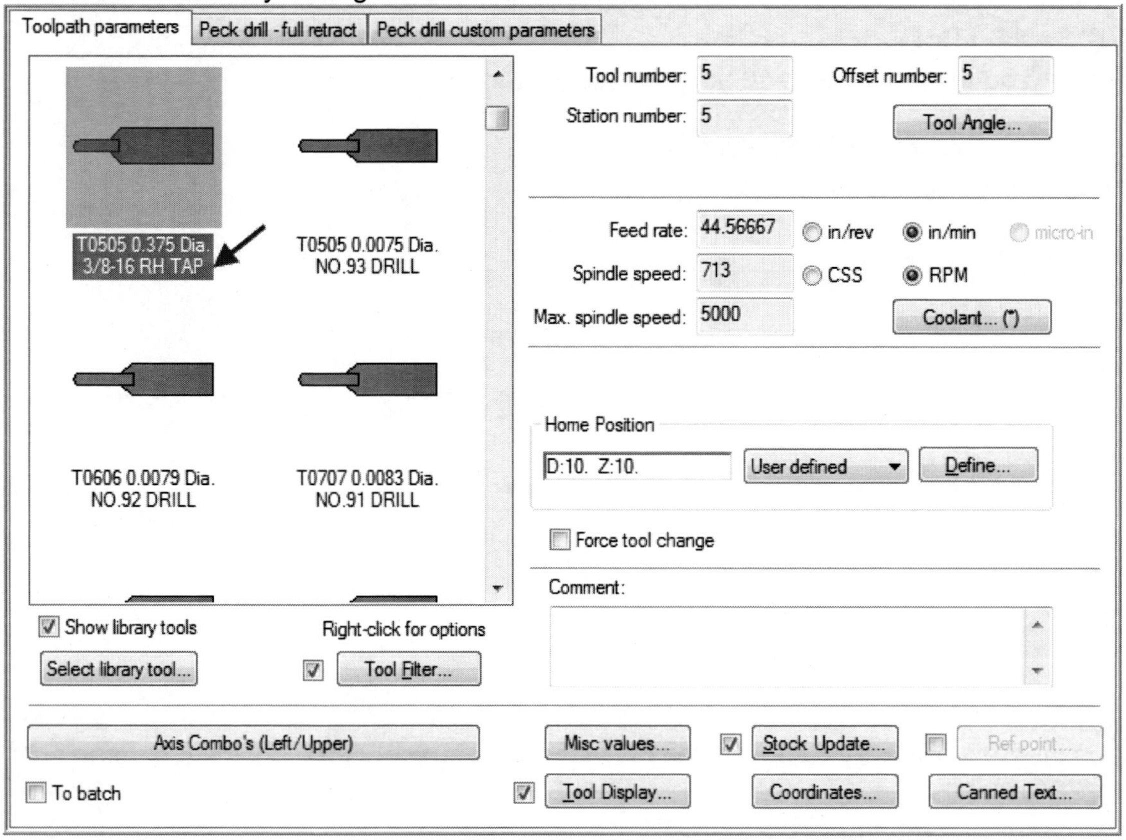

8. Select the **Peck drill – full retract** page and make changes to tap as shown below:

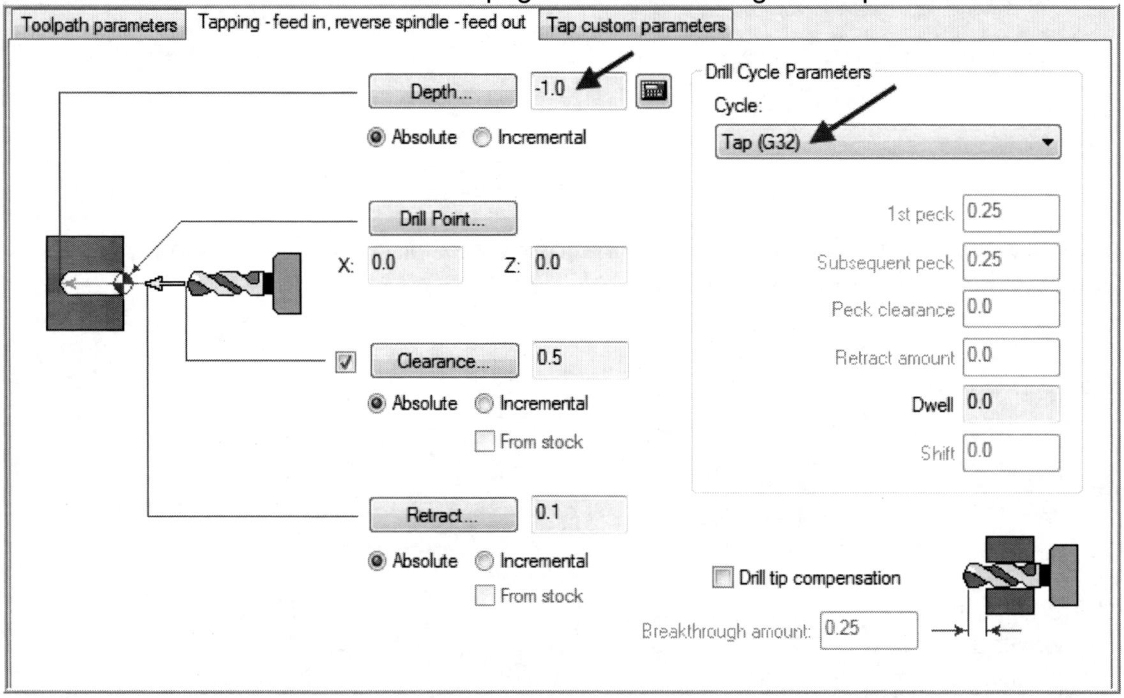

9. Select the OK button to exit **Tapping – feed in, reverse spindle – feed out.**

TASK 15:
CUT OFF THE PART

➲ In this task you will finish the outside diameters in one cut using **Tool #6 Cutoff Right Width .125.**

1. From the menu bar select **Toolpaths> Cutoff…**

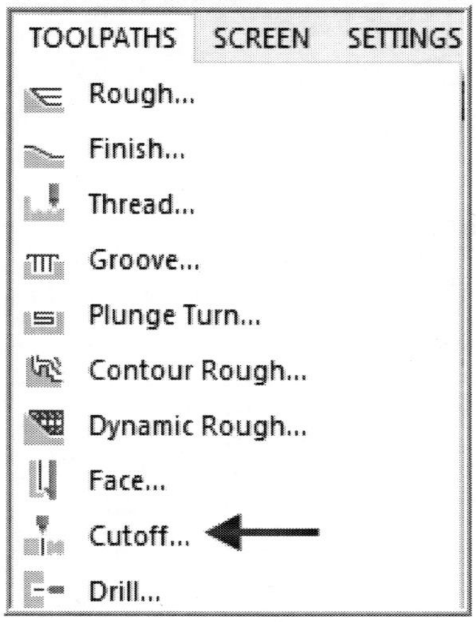

2. Select the **Alt key** and the **T** key on the keyboard to hide the toolpath lines.

Toolpath Lines visible:

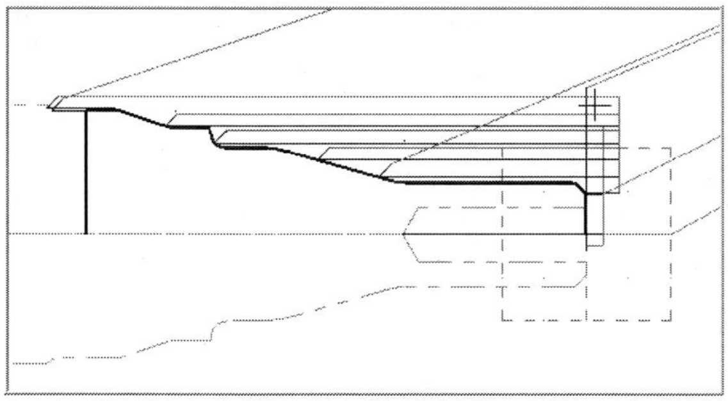

Press Alt T to hide toolpath Lines:

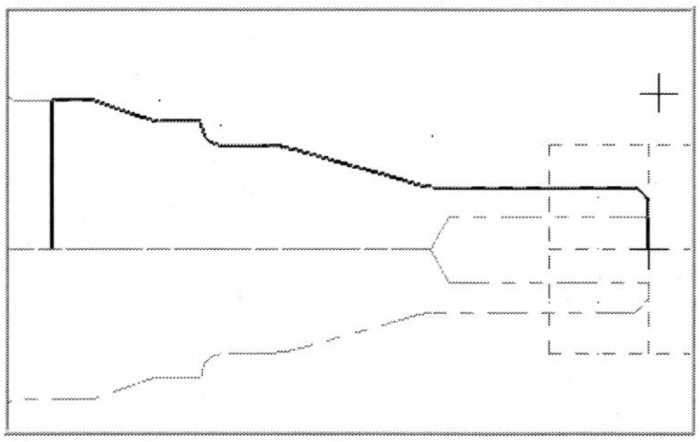

3. Pick where **Line 8 and Line 9** meet as shown below: (Move the cursor over the corner until the visual cue  for End point displays and then click on this point.)

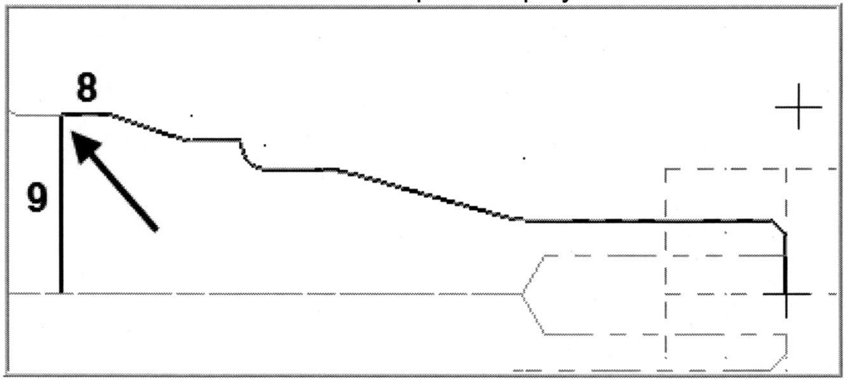

4. Click on the **Select library tool…** button.

5. Select the **select new folder** icon  at the top of the dialog box and then the **Lathe_Inch** from the list as shown below:

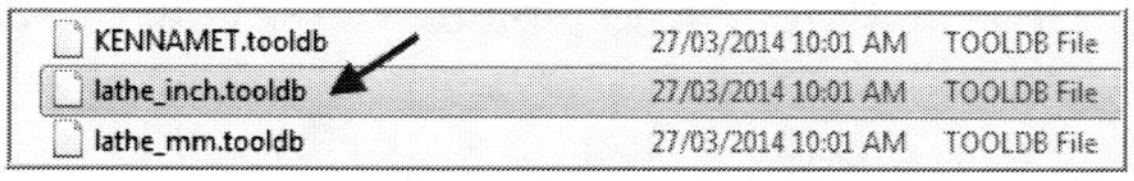

6. Select the OK button  after selecting **Lathe_Inch**.
7. Scroll down and select **OD Cutoff Right Width .125** from the list.
8. Select the OK button .
9. Make changes as shown below in the **Toolpath parameters** page.

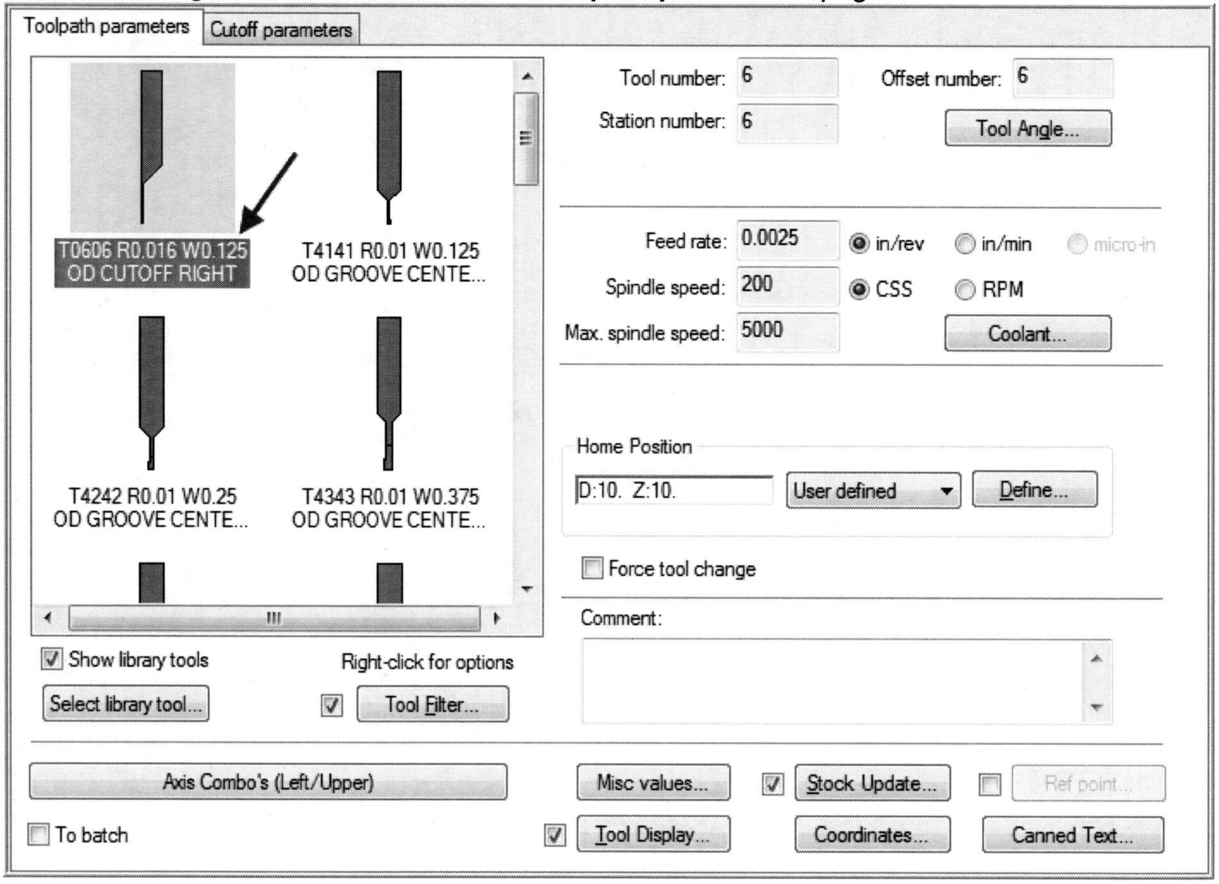

10. Select the **Cutoff parameters** page and make sure the settings are as shown below:

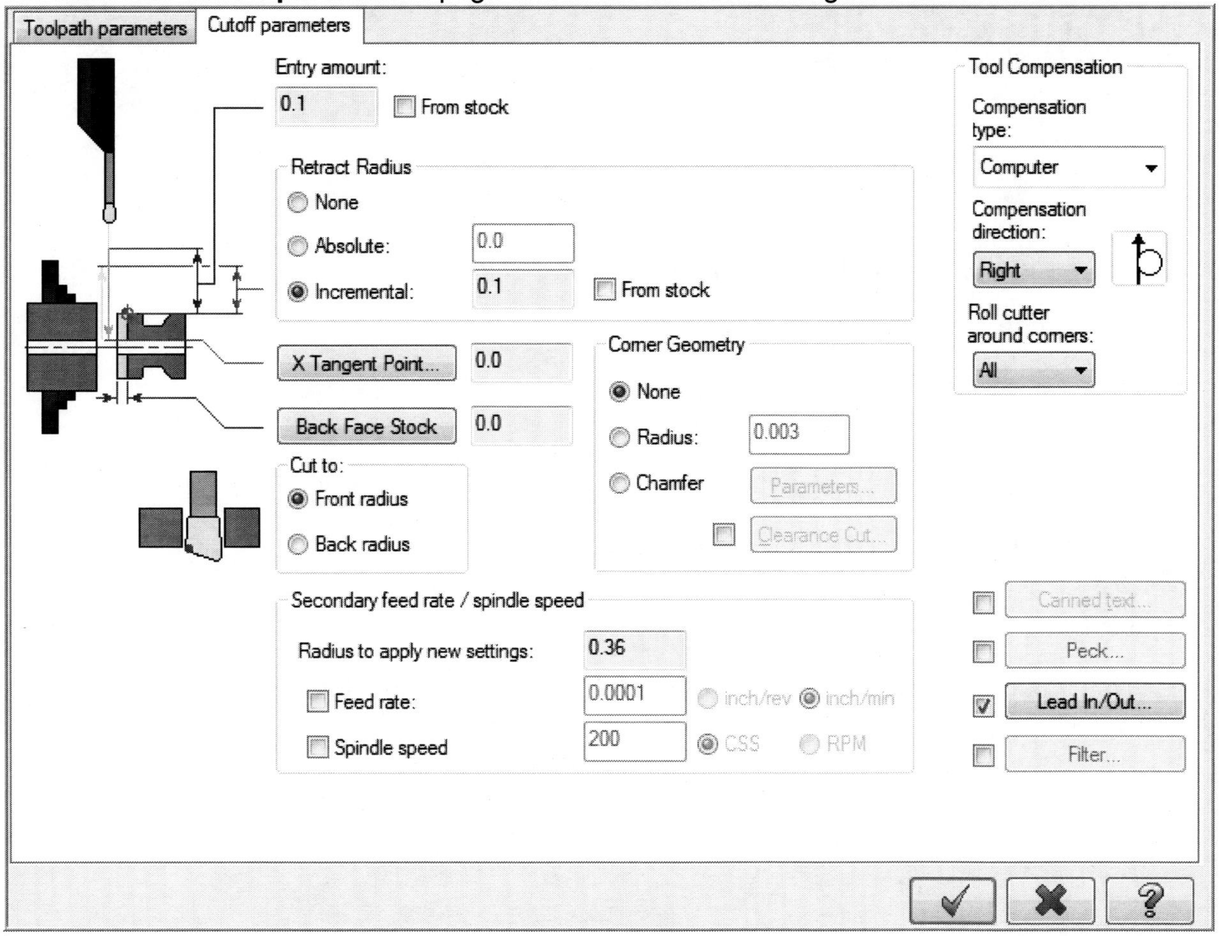

11. Select the OK button  to exit **Cutoff parameters.**

TASK 16:
VERIFY THE TOOLPATH

➲ Mastercam's Verify utility allows you to use solid models to simulate the machining of a part. The model created by the verification represents the surface finish, and shows collisions, if any exist.

1. In the Toolpaths Manager pick all the operations to Verify by picking the **Select All** icon .
2. Select the **Verify selected operations** icon shown below:

3. **Maximize** the Backplot/Verify window if required.
4. Now select the **Home** Tab if required.

5. Activate the options shown below in the **Visibility** section of the Home tab. **Initial Stock** not activated.

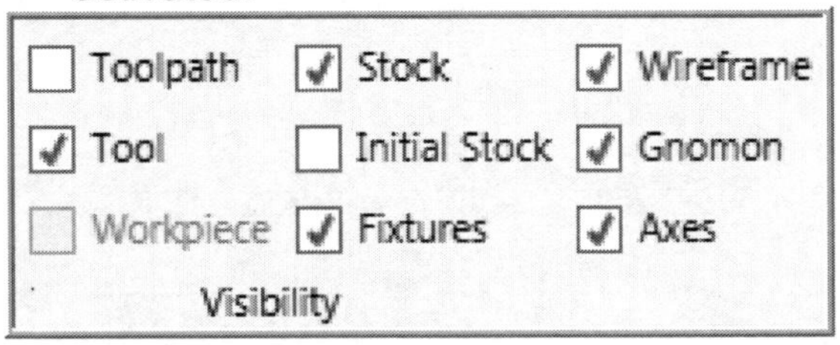

6. Activate the **Color Loop** to change the color of the tools for the verified part.

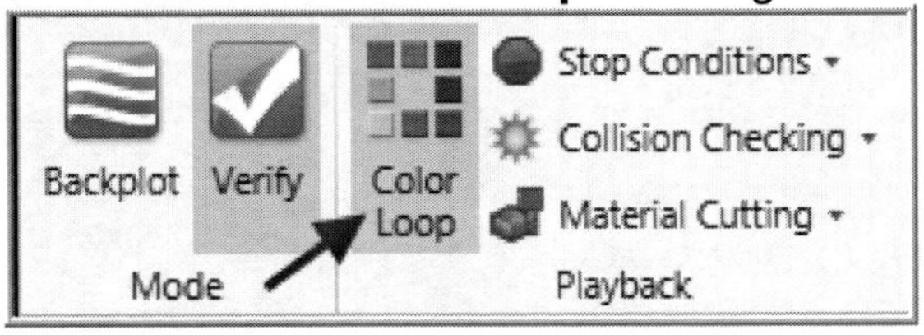

Color Loop
Changes the color of the toolpath or cut stock by operation or by tool change.

Choose **File Options** to set the colors.

7. At the top of the screen select the **View** tab, the **Isometric** icon and then select **Fit**.

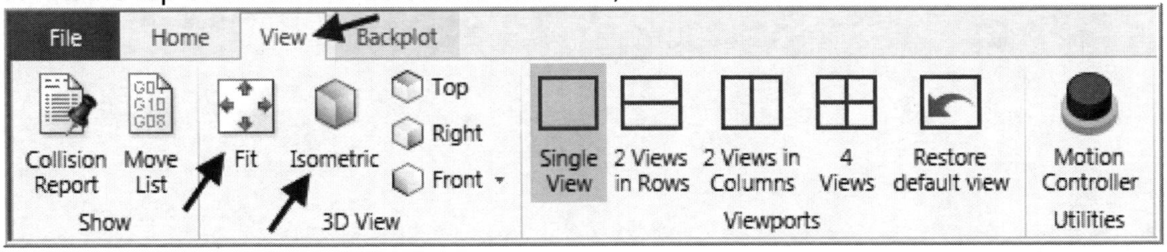

8. In the lower right corner of the screen now set the run **Speed** to slow by moving the slider bar pointer over to the left as shown below.

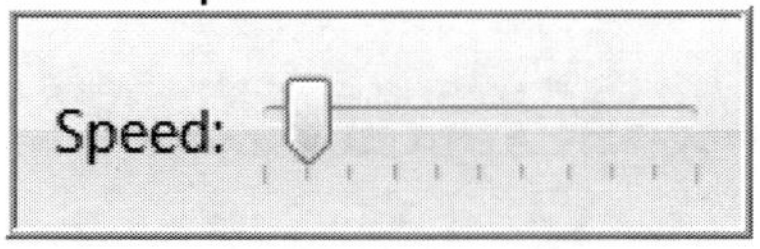

9. Now select the **Play Simulation** button to review the toolpaths.

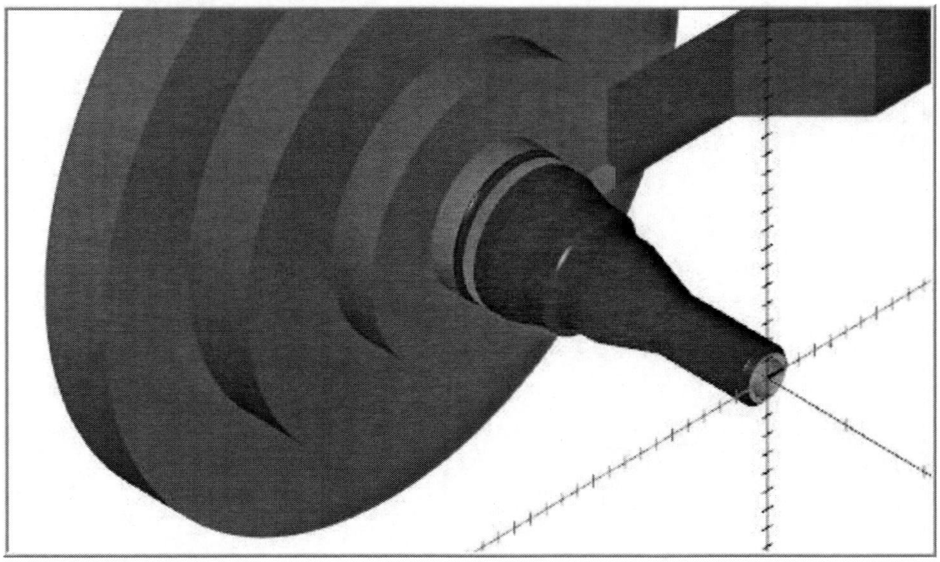

10. Select the **Close** button  in the top right hand corner to exit Verify.

TASK 17:
SAVE THE UPDATED MASTERCAM FILE

1. Select the save icon from the toolbar 

.

TASK 18:
POST AND CREATE THE CNC CODE FILE

1. Ensure all the operations are selected by picking the **Select All** icon  from the Toolpaths manager.

2. Select the **Post selected operations** button from the Toolpaths manager.

➲ **Please Note:** If you cannot see **G1** click on the right pane of the Toolpaths manager window and expand the window to the right.

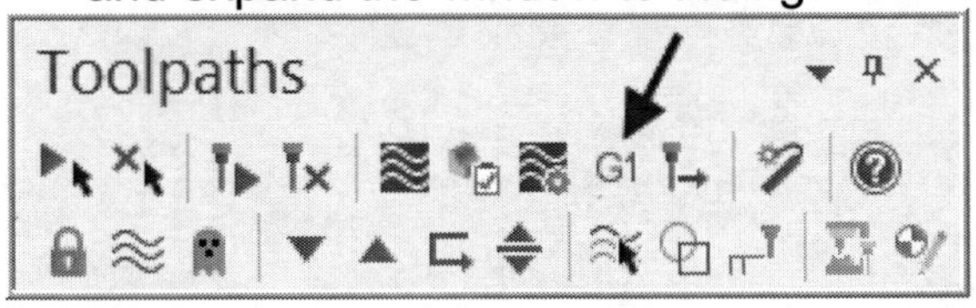

3. In the Post processing window, make the necessary changes as shown below:

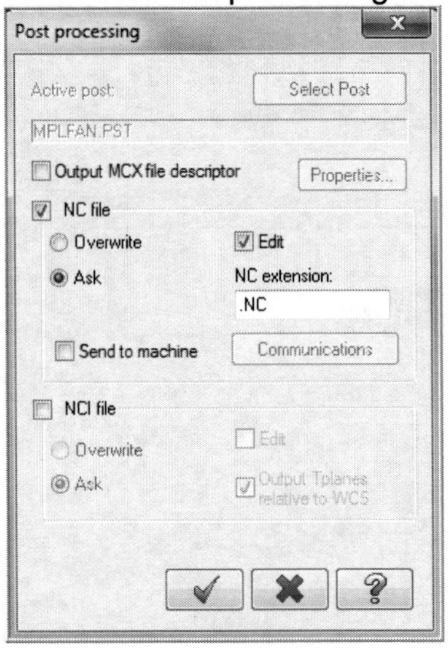

About Post Processing

NC file:
Select this option to save the NC file. The file name and extension are stored in the machine group properties for the selected operation. If you are posting operations from different machine groups or Mastercam files, or batch processing, Mastercam will create several files according to the settings for each machine group.

Edit:
When checked, automatically launches the default text editor with the file displayed so that you can review or modify it.

4. Select the OK button  to continue.

5. Ensure the same name as your Mastercam part file name is displayed in the **NC File name** field as shown below:

File name: LATHE-LESSON-3
Save as type: NC Files (*.NC)

6. Select the **Save** button.
7. The CNC code file opens up in the default editor.

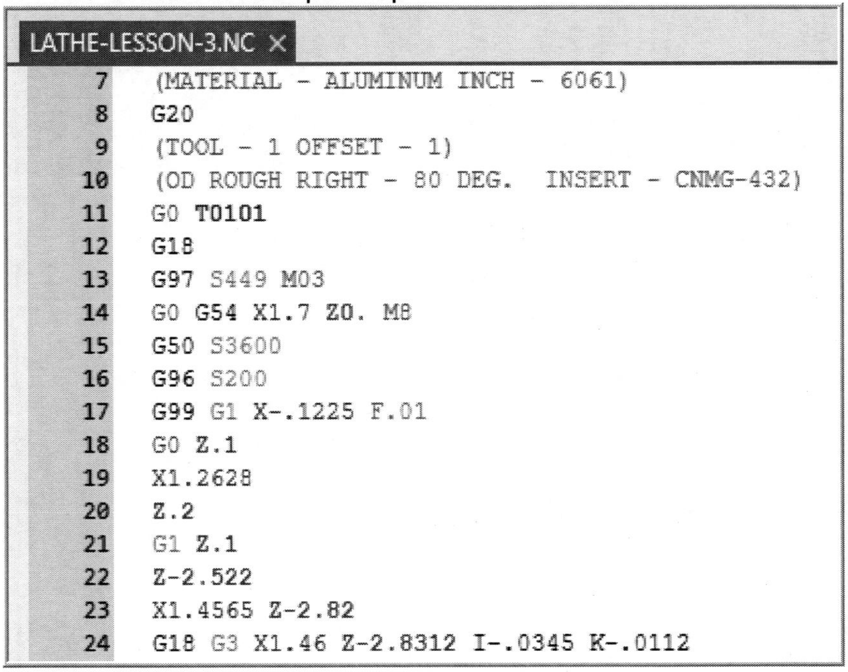
LATHE-LESSON-3.NC
(MATERIAL - ALUMINUM INCH - 6061)
G20
(TOOL - 1 OFFSET - 1)
(OD ROUGH RIGHT - 80 DEG. INSERT - CNMG-432)
G0 T0101
G18
G97 S449 M03
G0 G54 X1.7 Z0. M8
G50 S3600
G96 S200
G99 G1 X-.1225 F.01
G0 Z.1
X1.2628
Z.2
G1 Z.1
Z-2.522
X1.4565 Z-2.82
G18 G3 X1.46 Z-2.8312 I-.0345 K-.0112

8. Select the 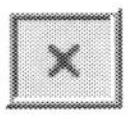 in the top right corner to exit the CNC editor.

9. This completes LATHE-LESSON-3.

LATHE-LESSON-3 EXERCISE

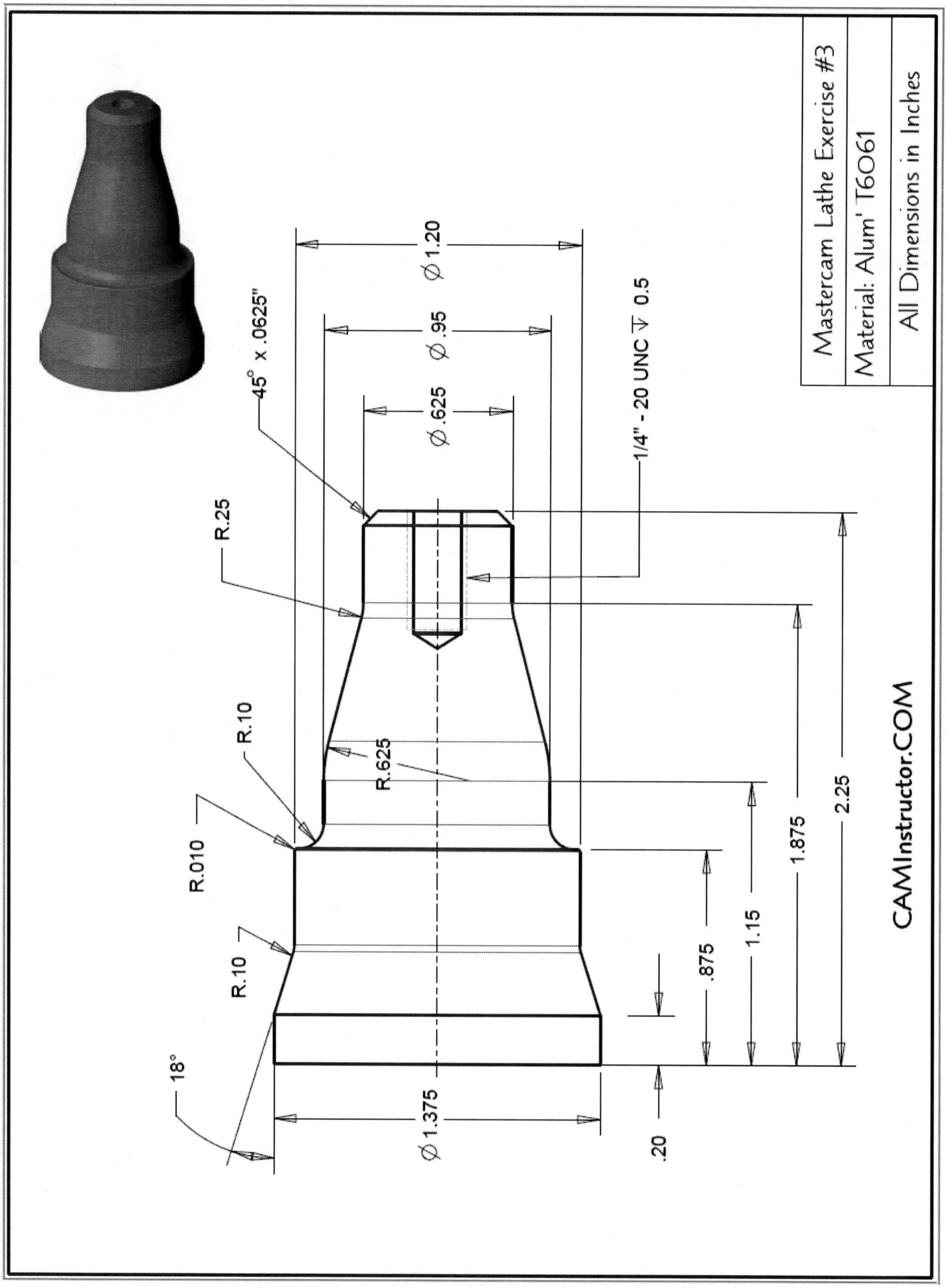

Mastercam® X9

TRAINING GUIDE

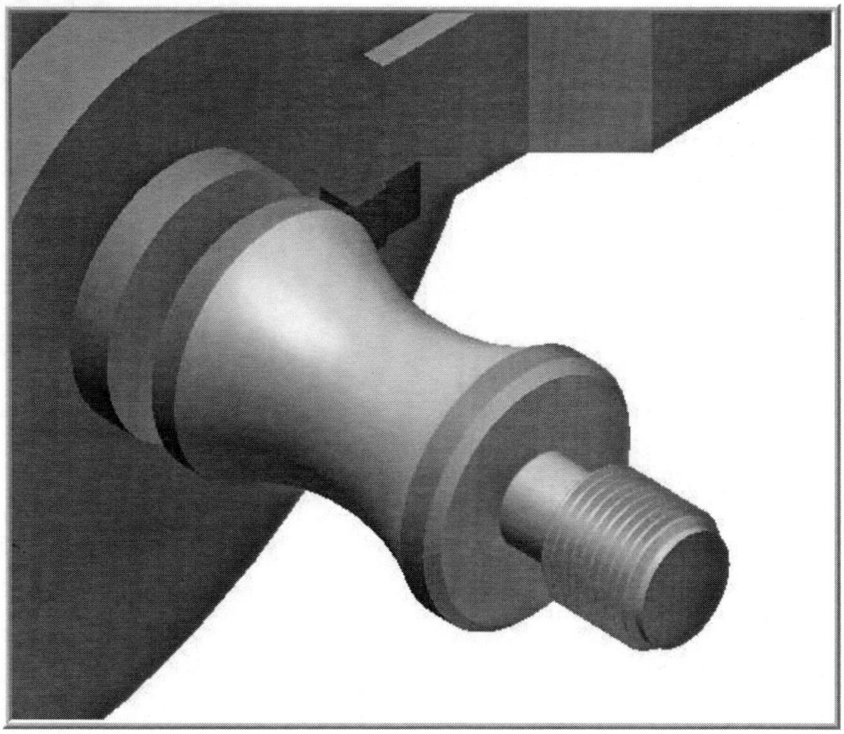

LATHE-LESSON-4

FACE, ROUGH, FINISH, GROOVE, THREAD AND CUTOFF

camInstructor

Objectives

You will create the geometry for Lathe Lesson 2, and then generate a toolpath to machine the part on a CNC lathe. This lesson covers the following topics:

➲ **Create a 2-dimensional drawing by:**
Creating lines.
Creating fillets.
Creating chamfers.

➲ **Establish Stock and Chuck Setup settings:**
Stock size.
Chuck Configuration.
Material for the part.
Feed calculation.

➲ **Generate a 2-dimensional lathe toolpath consisting of:**
Lathe Face.
Lathe Rough.
Lathe Finish.
Lathe Groove.
Lathe Thread.
Lathe Cutoff.

➲ **Inspect the toolpath using Mastercam's Verify and Backplot by:**
Launching the Verify function to machine the part on the screen.
Generating the NC- code.

LATHE - LESSON - 4 DRAWING

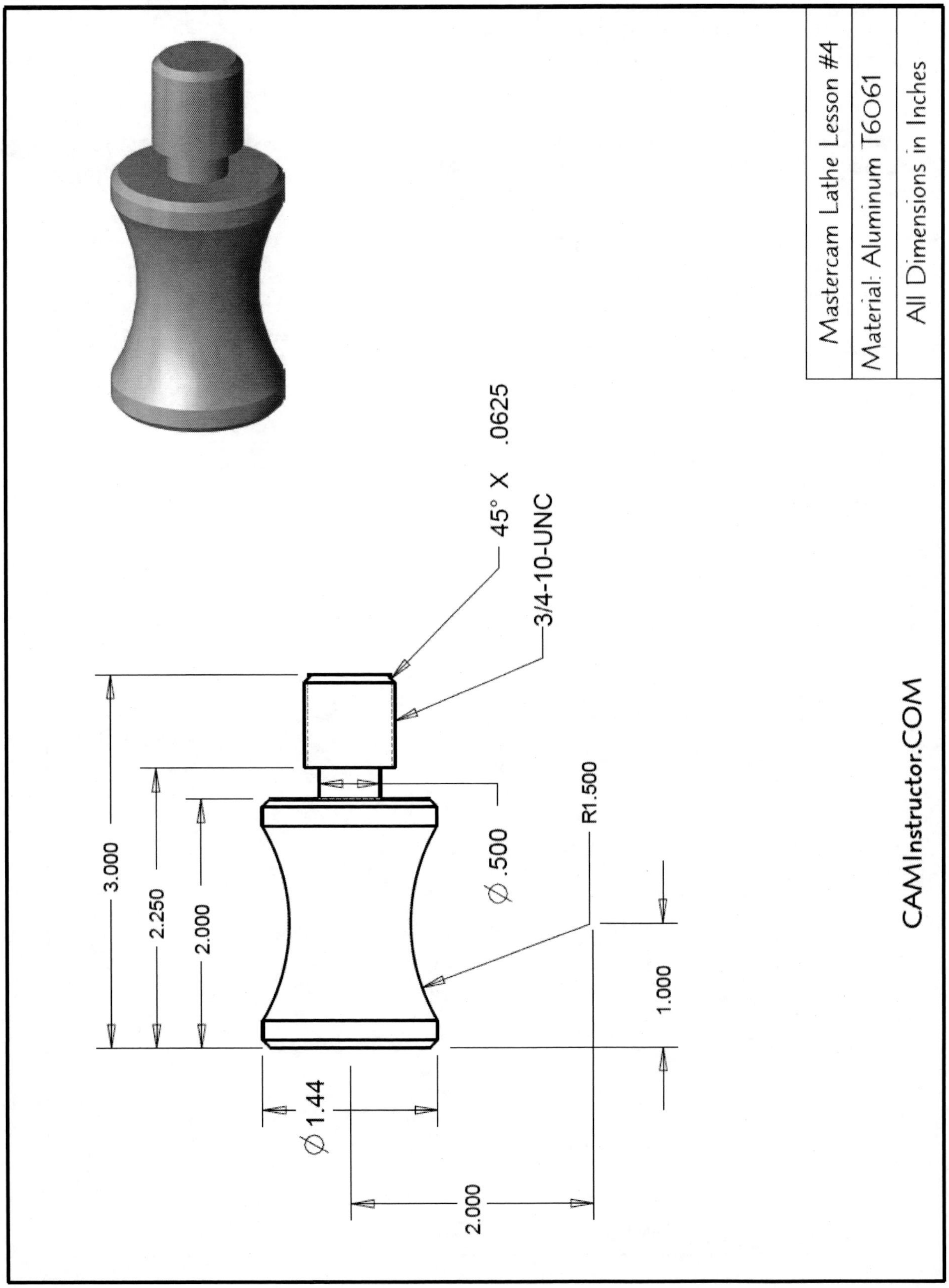

TOOL LIST

Five tools will be used to create this part.

- **Tool #1 Face and Rough the outside diameters**
  Holder: Outside Diameter Rough Right Hand - DCGNR-164D.
  Insert: 80 Degree Diamond Insert – CNMG-432

- **Tool #2 Finish the outside diameters**
  Holder: Outside Diameter Finish Right Hand - MVJNR-164D.
  Insert: 35 Degree Diamond Insert – VNMG-431.

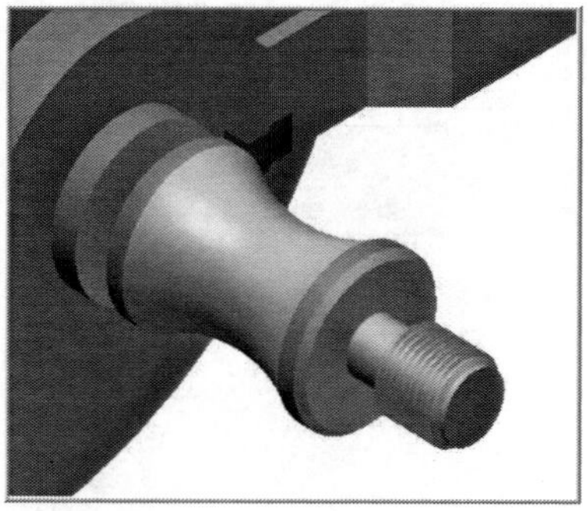

- **Tool #3 Machine the Groove and Cut-Off the part**
  Holder: Outside Diameter Groove Right Hand - Narrow.
  Insert: 0.125" Wide - GC-4125

- **Tool #4 Machine the Thread**
  Holder: Outside Diameter Thread Right Hand.
  Insert: UN/NPT 60 Degree

- **Tool #5 Finish the 1.5" radius**
  Holder: Outside Diameter - Cutting direction: Neutral
  Insert: 35 Degree Diamond Insert – VNMG-431

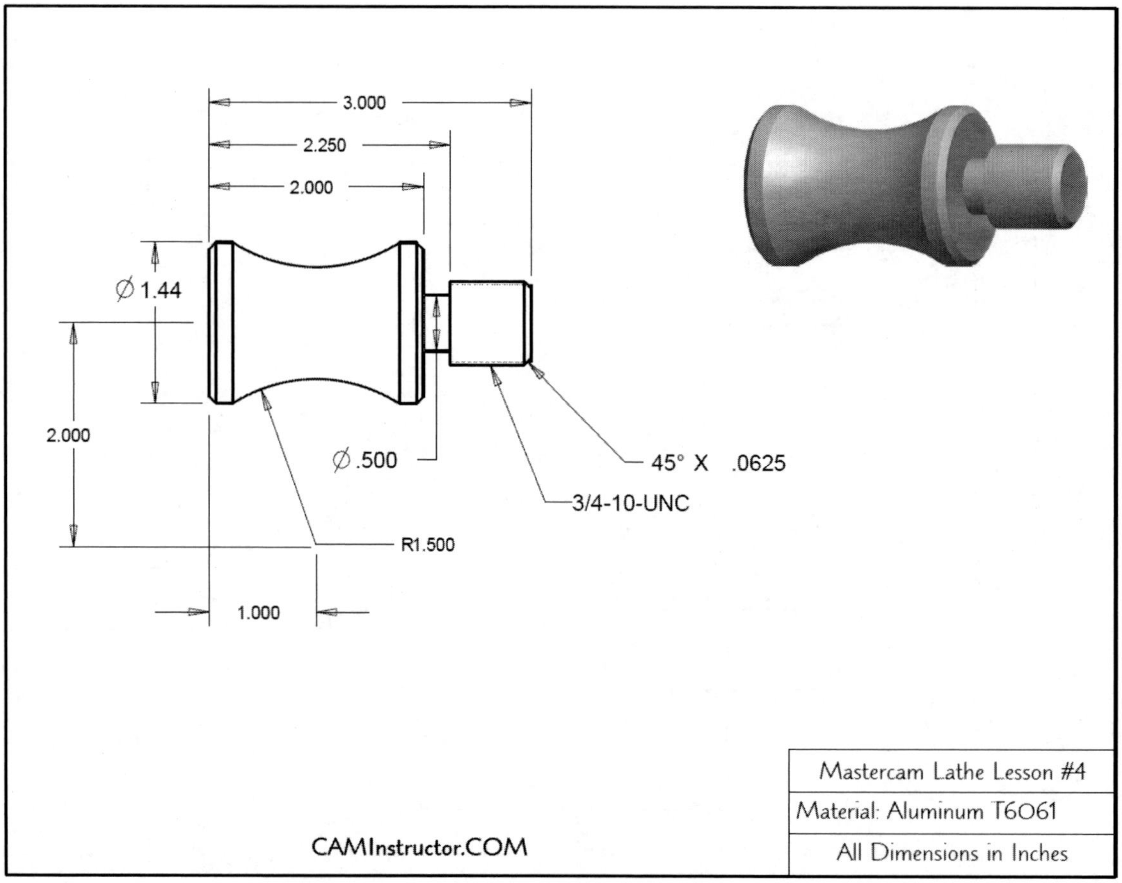

LESSON - 4 - THE PROCESS

Geometry Creation

TASK 1: Setting the Environment
TASK 2: Setting the Construction Planes
TASK 3: Create the Geometry
TASK 4: Create the 1.5" Radius
TASK 5: Create the Chamfers
TASK 6: Save the Drawing

Toolpath Creation

TASK 7: Define the Stock and Chuck Parameters
TASK 8: Face the Front of the Part
TASK 9: Rough the Outside Diameters
TASK 10: Finish the Outside Diameters
TASK 11: Cut the Groove
TASK 12: Cut the Thread
TASK 13: Finish the Radius
TASK 14: Cut off the Part
TASK 15: Verify the toolpath
TASK 16: Save the updated Mastercam file
TASK 17: Post and create the CNC code file

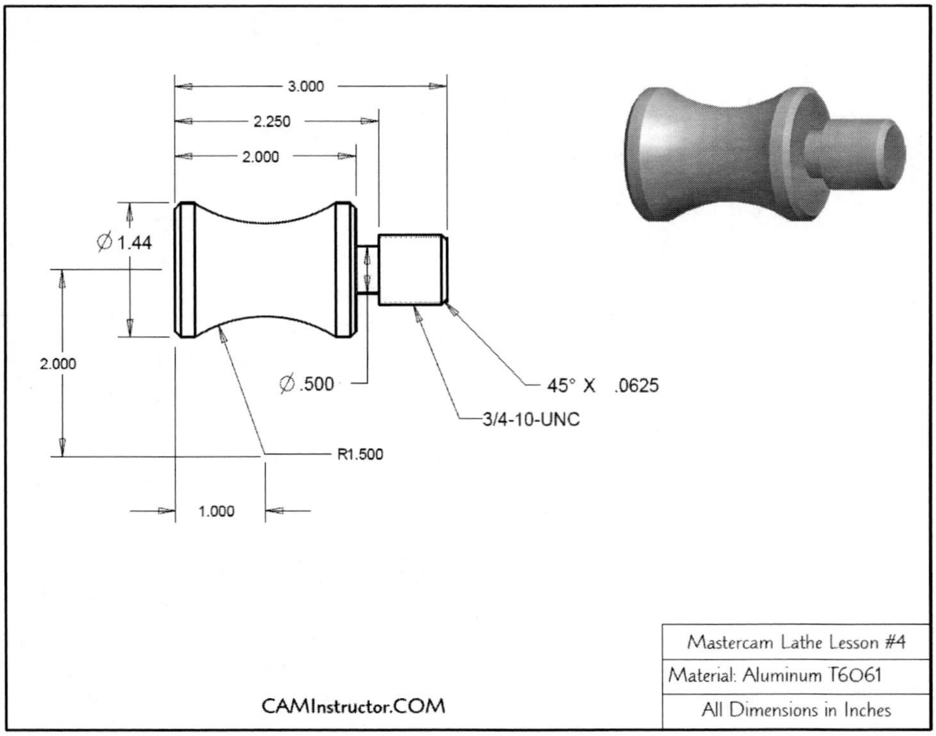

Geometry Creation

TASK 1:
SETTING THE ENVIRONMENT

Before starting the geometry creation you should set up the grid and toolbars as outlined in the **Setting the Environment** section at the beginning of this text:

1. Set up the Grid. This will help identify the location of the origin.
2. Load the Workspace – **SETTINGS>Load Workspace>Lathe** to machine a part on the Lathe.
3. Set the machine type to the default Lathe.

TASK 2:
SETTING THE CONSTRUCTION PLANES:

➲ **Set the Construction Plane to Lathe diameter +D +Z (WCS)**

1. Click on Planes at the bottom of the screen as shown below:

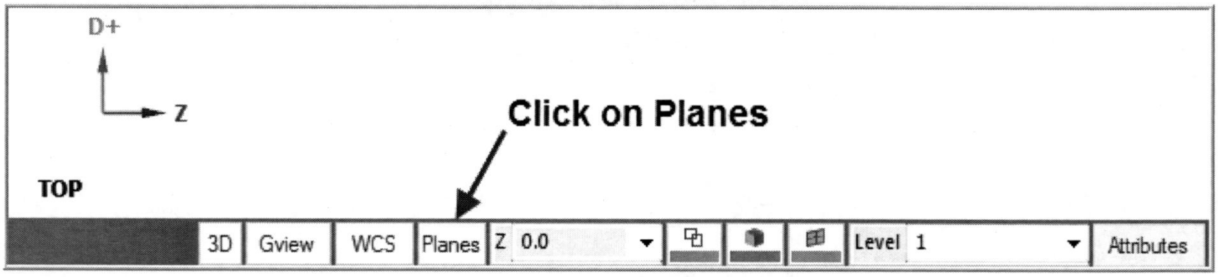

2. Click on Lathe diameter>+D +Z (WCS) as shown below:

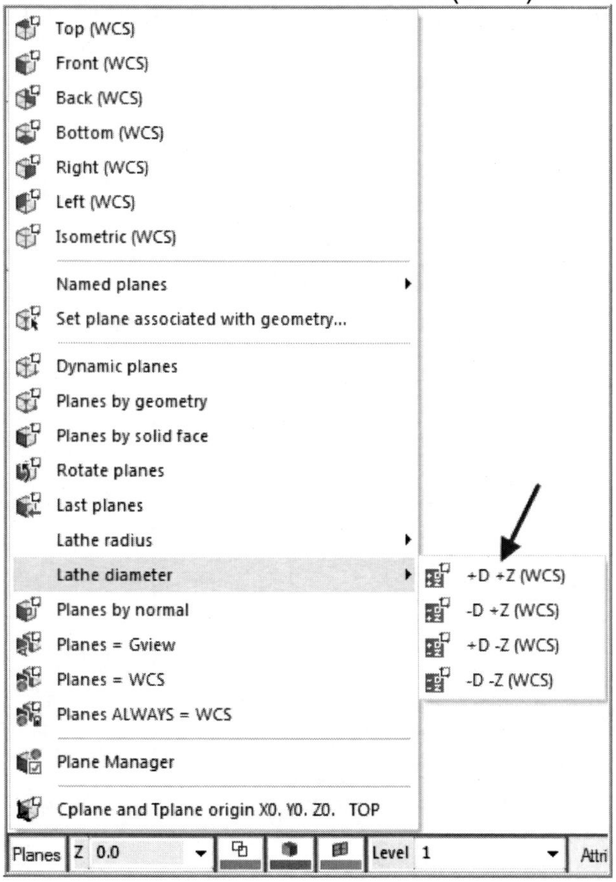

Work coordinate system (WCS)
The Work Coordinate System (WCS) is the active coordinate system in use by Mastercam at any given time.

The WCS contains the orientation of the X-Y-Z axes plus the location of the zero point (the origin).

The plane which you set as the WCS typically equals the Top, or XY, plane of the part. Another way to look at it is that it tells the software how your part is positioned or oriented in the machine tool. Think of the WCS plane as defining the 'shop floor' relative to your part.

Gviews, Cplanes, and Tplanes are all oriented relative to the WCS. To change the WCS, use the Plane Manager to select a different plane that the WCS will be aligned with, or create a custom plane.

TASK 3:
CREATE THE GEOMETRY

➲ This task explains how to create the geometry of this part. In this lathe part you only need to create **half of the geometry**, the geometry above the center line.

➲ Lines 1 through 7 will be created first and then the radius and chamfer will be created.

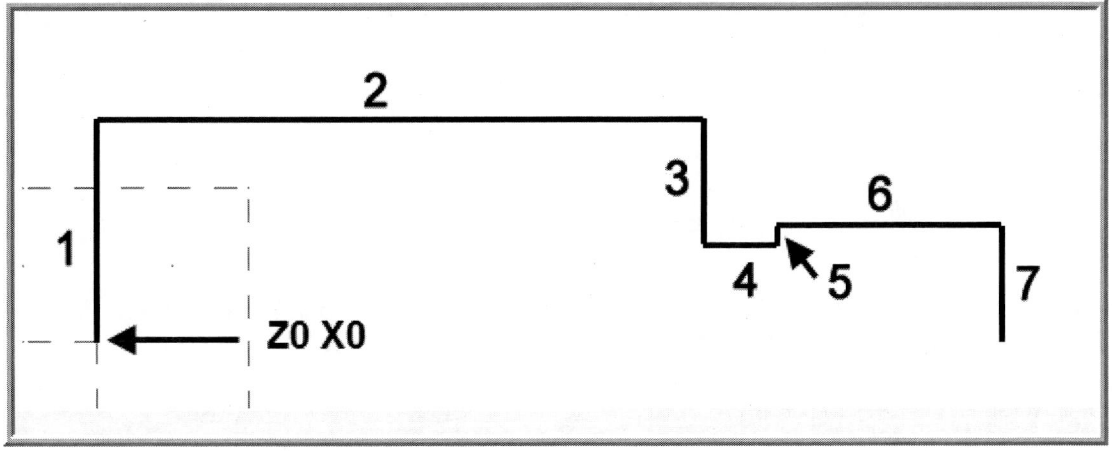

➲ **Create Line #1**

1. Select from the pull down menu **CREATE>Line>Endpoint…**

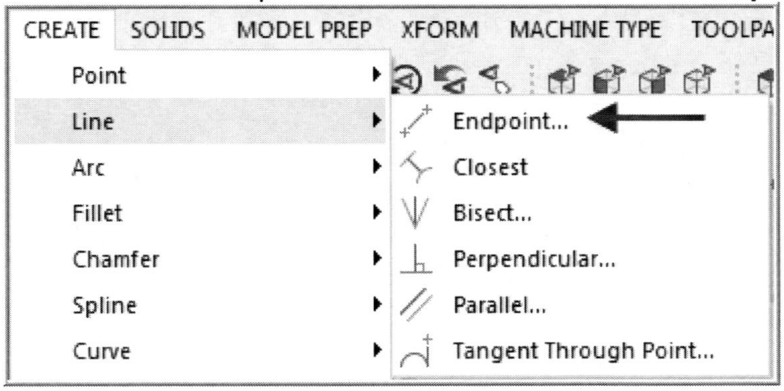

2. The Line ribbon bar appears:

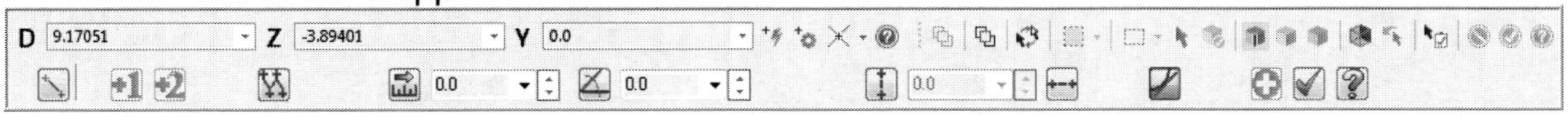

3. Move the cursor over the **center of the grid** and as you get close to the origin a visual cue appears. 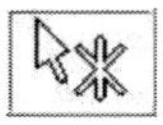 This is the cue that will allow you to snap to the **origin**. With this visual cue highlighted pick the **origin.**

AutoCursor: Visual Cues detects and highlights endpoints and midpoints of curves, lines, arc center points, and point entities.

In addition, AutoCursor can snap to angle, nearest, tangent, perpendicular, horizontal, and vertical conditions.

➲ The following are Mastercam Visual Cues:

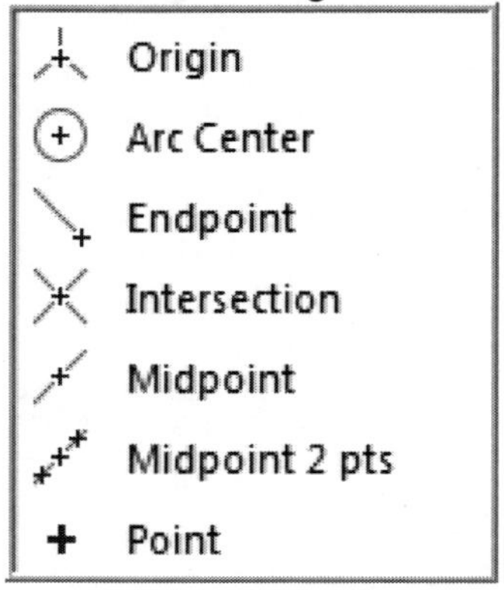

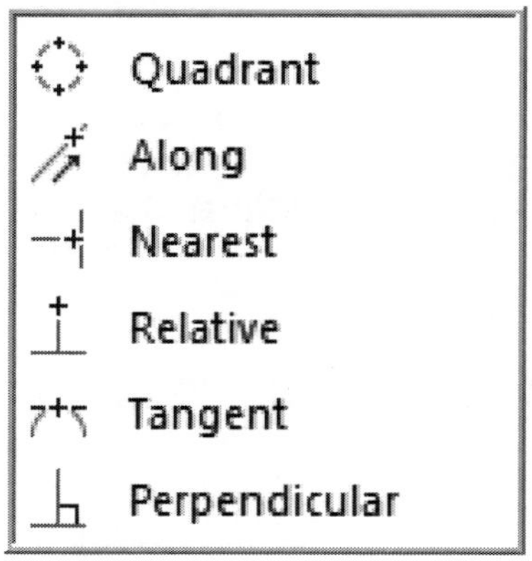

4. You are next prompted to **"Specify the second endpoint".** On the left hand side of the Line ribbon bar click on the **Multi-Line** button to activate it as shown below by the arrow:

5. Click in the **D** value space (Diameter) (as shown by the arrow below) and enter a value of **1.44**. Hit the Enter key and enter a value of **0 for the Z**, hit the Enter key again. **Note** the value of Y is set to **Zero**, this does not need to be input.

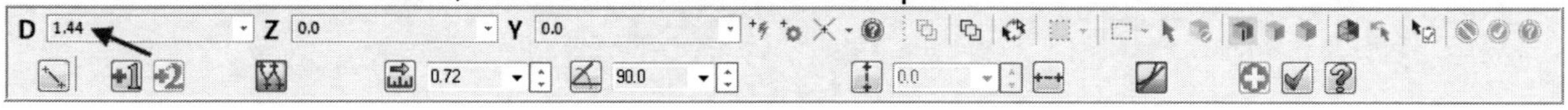

6. A vertical line should be visible as shown below:

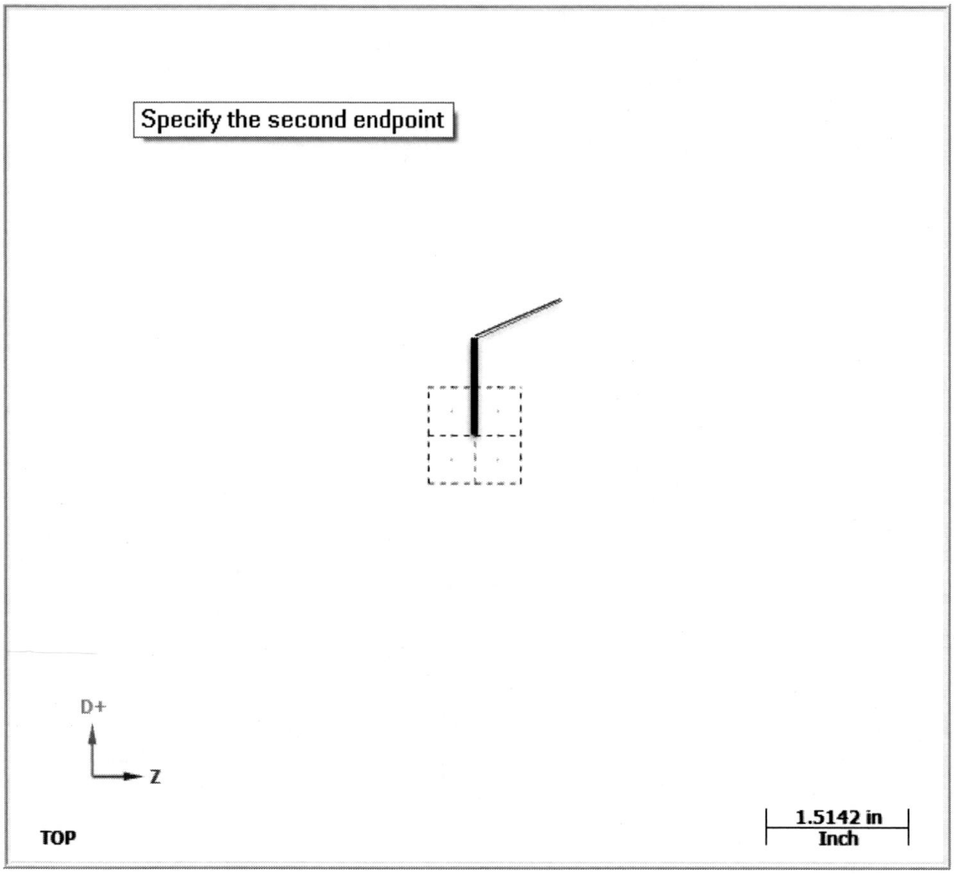

➲ **Create Line #2**

7. **"Specify the second endpoint";** Type in **1.44 in D** hit Enter, type in **2.0 in Z. Note** the value of Y is set to **Zero**, this does not need to be input. Hit the Enter key once again to complete this line.

➲ **Create Line #3**

8. **"Specify the second endpoint";** Type in **.625 in D** hit Enter, type in **2.0 in Z.** Hit the Enter key once again to complete this line.

➲ **Create Line #4**

9. **"Specify the second endpoint";** Type in **.625 in D** hit Enter, type in **2.250 in Z.** Hit the Enter key once again to complete this line.

10. Fit the image to the screen by clicking on the **Fit** icon as shown below:

11. Then unzoom by clicking on the **Un-Zoom Previous / .5** icon as shown below:

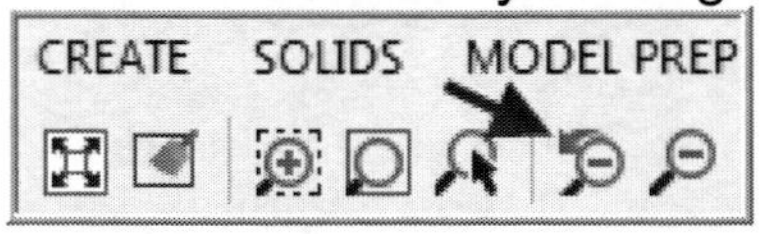

➲ **Create Line #5**

12. **"Specify the second endpoint";** Type in **.75 in D** hit Enter, type in **2.250 in Z.** Hit the Enter key once again to complete this line.

➲ **Create Line #6**

13. **"Specify the second endpoint";** Type in **0.75 in D** hit Enter, type in **3.0 in Z.** Hit the Enter key once again to complete this line.

➲ **Create Line #7**

14. **"Specify the second endpoint";** Type in **0.0 in D** hit Enter, type in **3.0 in Z.** Hit the Enter key once again to complete this line.

15. Click on the **OK** icon to complete this feature.

16. Select the **Screen Fit** icon to fit the part to the screen.

17. Your geometry should look like the figure below.

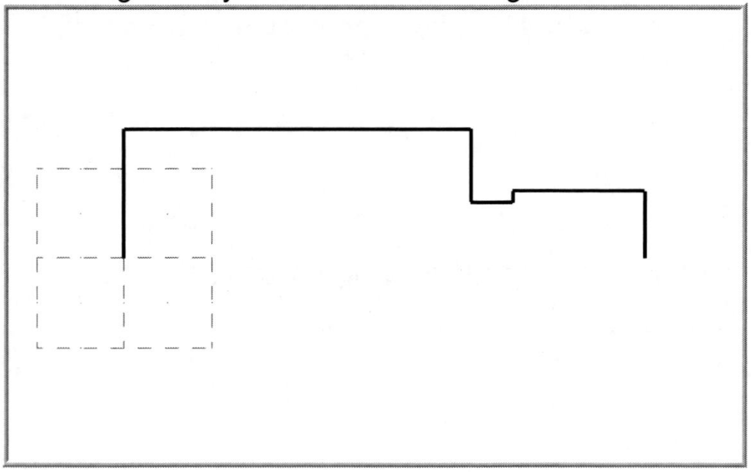

TASK 4:
CREATE THE 1.5" RADIUS

➲ **Create the Arc Center Point.**

1. Select **CREATE>Point>Dynamic…**

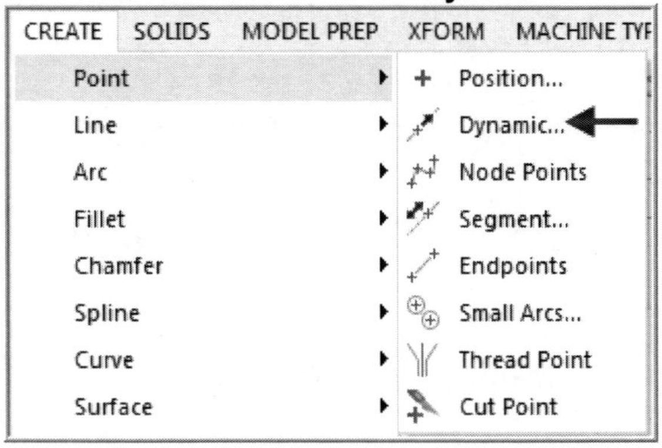

Point dynamic ribbon bar
Use this ribbon bar to create a point and/or a line anywhere along an existing entity. When you select an entity in the graphics window, a **green dynamic arrow appears.** Normal information is also displayed on the ribbon bar in vector format. You can then **move your cursor along the entity and click to create one** or more points or lines. Click Apply, or press [Enter] when finished.

2. The **Create Point Dynamic** ribbon bar appears and you are prompted to;

Select line, arc, spline, surface, or solid face

3. Select **line 1** below the half way point as shown below:

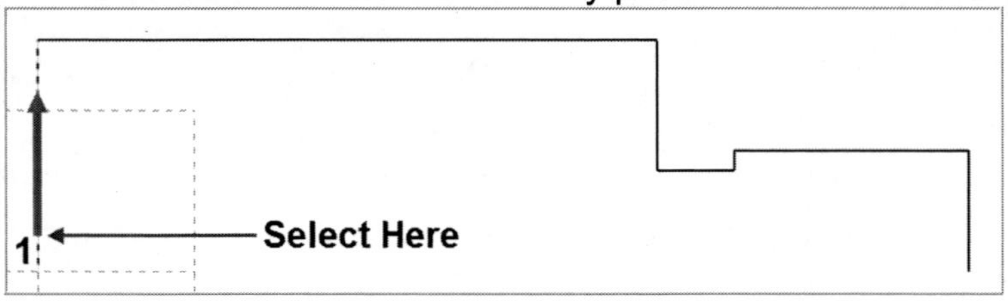

Green Dynamic Arrow Note:
We will not be using the green arrow to position the point but the **Distance** and **Offset** options.

4. Click in the space of the distance window and enter **2.0** and hit the tab key.
5. Enter **1.0** in the **offset** window and hit the tab key.

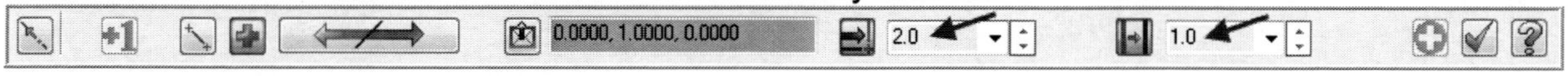

6. Click on OK .
7. Click on OK .
8. **Fit** the image to the screen .
9. A point will be created as shown in the image below:

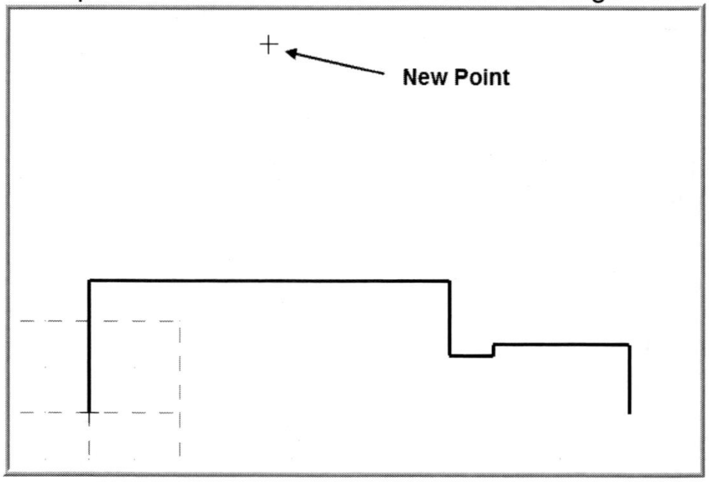

➲ **Create the 1.5" Arc**

10. Select **CREATE>Arc>Circle Center Point…**

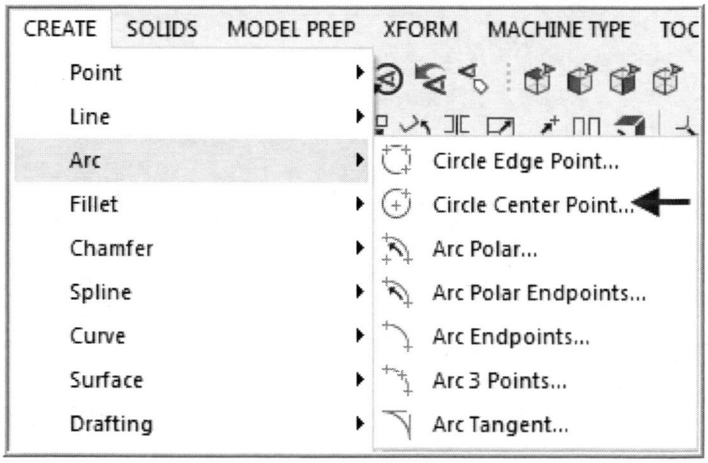

11. The **Create Circle** ribbon bar appears and you are prompted to Enter the center point.
12. Click on the **newly created point**.
13. Click in the **Radius** window and type **1.5** as shown below and hit the **enter** key:

14. Click on OK .

15. An Arc is created as shown below:

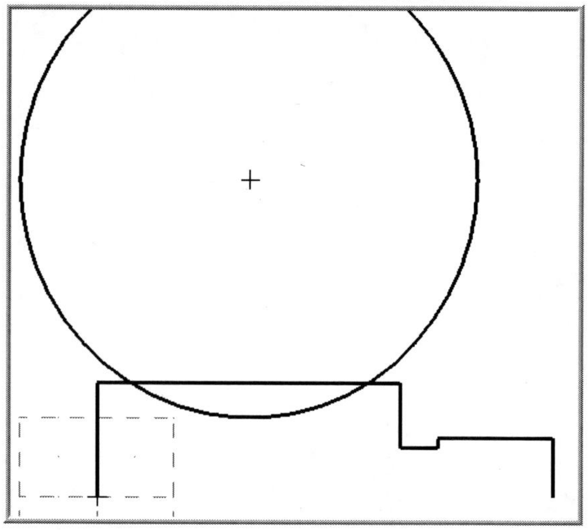

➲ **Trim the Arc**

16. Select **EDIT>Trim/Break>Trim/Break/Extend…**

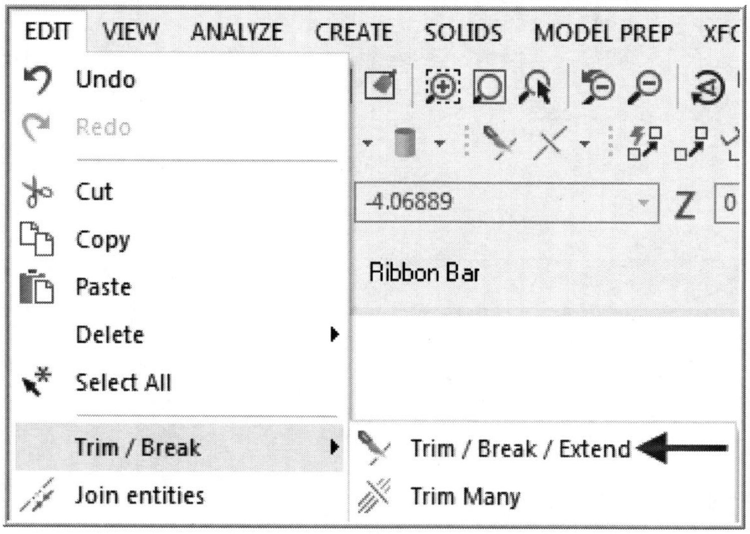

17. **The Trim/Break** ribbon bar appears and you are prompted to Select the entity to trim/extend.
18. Click on the **Divide** Button as shown below:

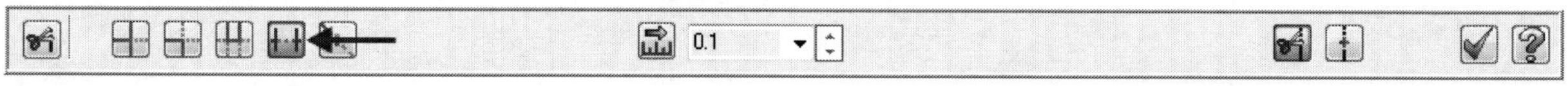

Divide/Delete Entities
Trims a line, arc, or spline into two disjointed segments by removing the segment that lies between two dividing intersections.

When you choose the **Divide/Delete** function and select an entity in the graphics window, Mastercam uses the **nearest two intersections** on each end to divide the entity.

19. **Fit** the image to the screen.

20. You are prompted to Select the curve to divide.

21. Click on the entities you **DO NOT want to keep**; **Entity 1, Entity 2 and Entity 3** as shown below:

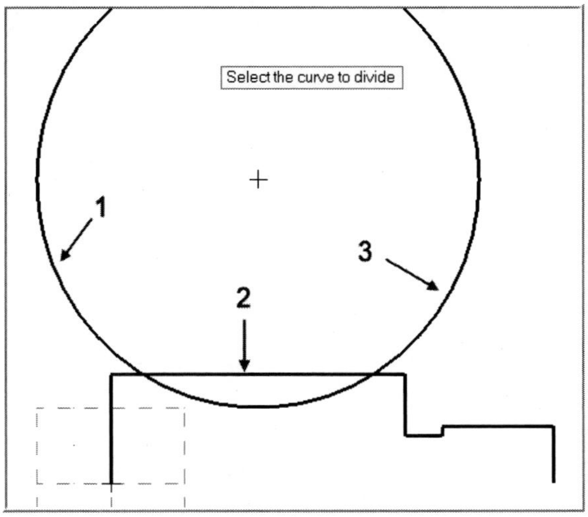

22. Click on OK.
23. The geometry should look like the image below:

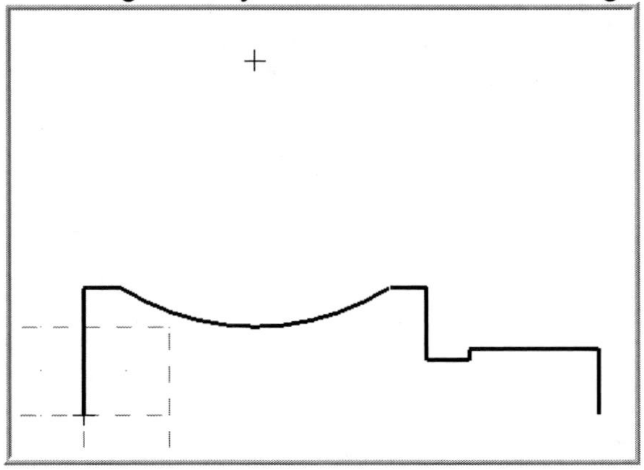

➲ Delete the Point

24. Select the point shown above. It should change color.
25. Hit the **Delete** key.
26. **Fit** to Screen.

TASK 5:
CREATE THE CHAMFERS

➲ **Create 3 Chamfers 45 degrees x .0625.**

1. Select **CREATE>Chamfer>Entities…**

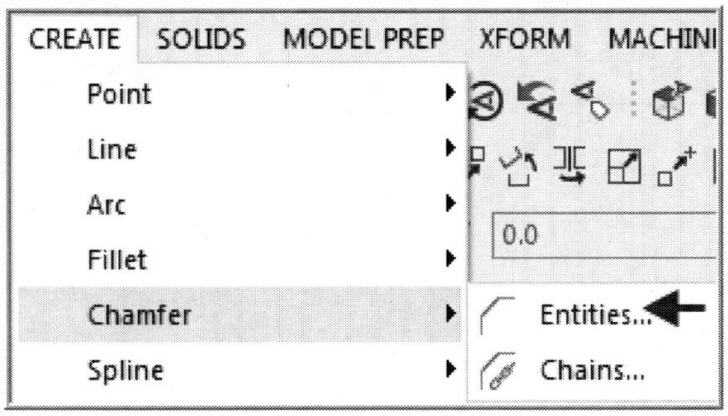

2. You are prompted to Select line or arc.
3. Click in the Distance window as shown below and type in **.0625** and hit enter:

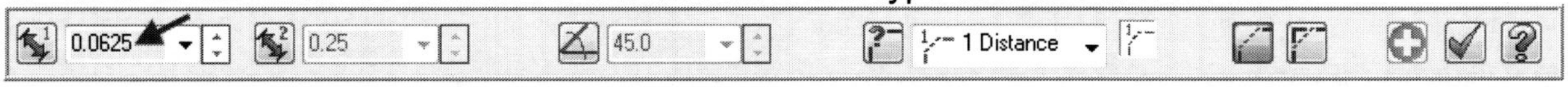

4. Ensure the **1 Distance** option is selected as shown below:

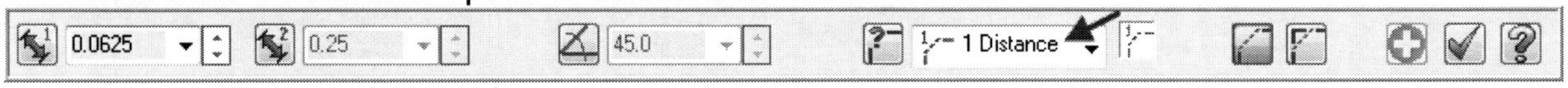

5. Click on **line 1** and then **line 2** as shown below:

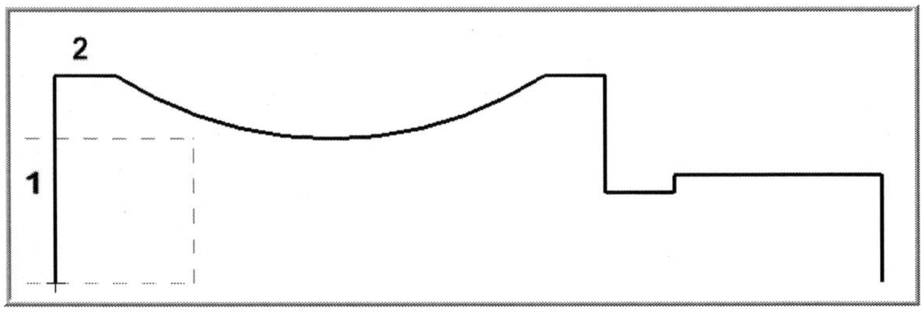

6. Click on **Apply** 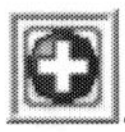.
7. Click on **line 3** and then **line 4** as shown below:

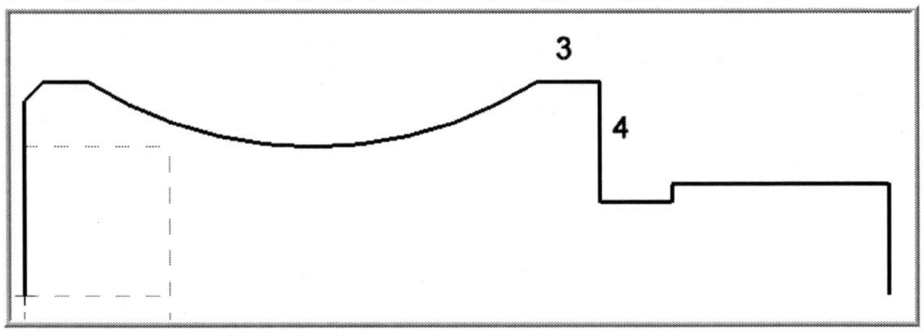

8. Click on **Apply** 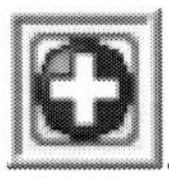.

9. Click on **line 5** and then **line 6** as shown below:

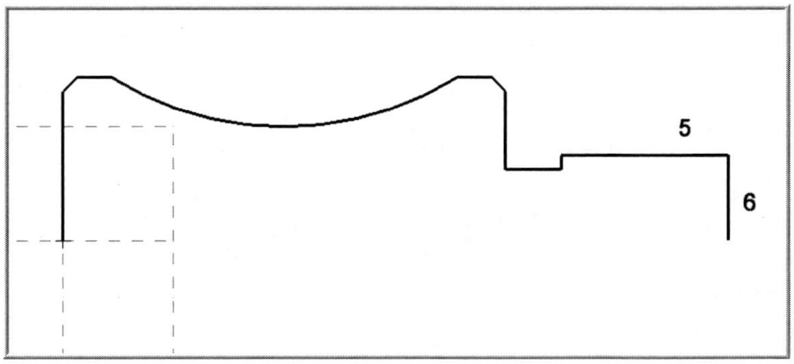

10. Click on OK .
11. The completed geometry should look like the image below:

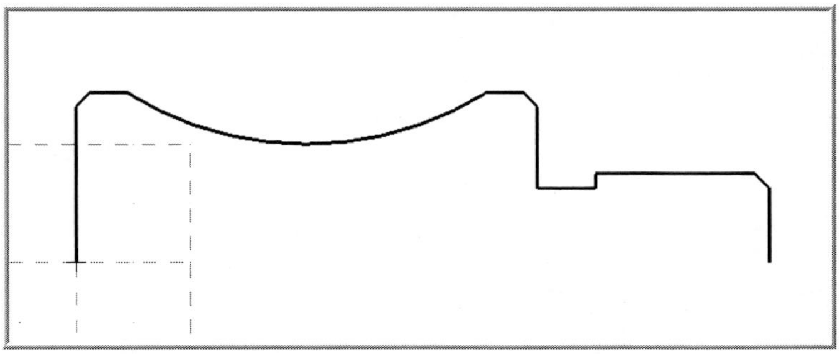

TASK 6:
SAVE THE DRAWING

1. Select **File.**
2. Select **Save as.**
3. In the **"File name"** box, type **"Lathe-Lesson-4".**
4. Save to an appropriate location.
5. Select the Save button to save the file and complete this function.

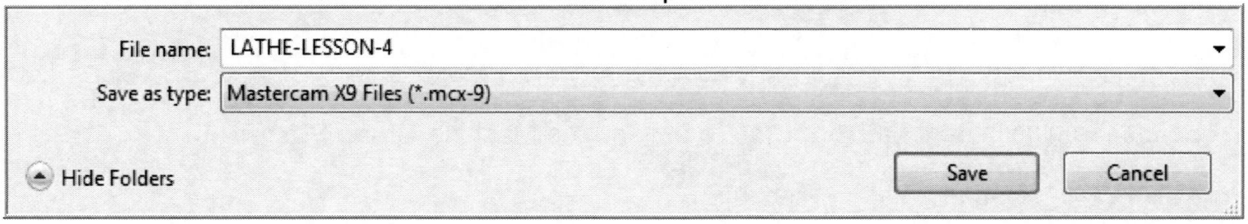
File name: LATHE-LESSON-4
Save as type: Mastercam X9 Files (*.mcx-9)
Hide Folders
Save
Cancel

Toolpath Creation

TASK 7:
DEFINING THE STOCK AND CHUCK PARAMETERS

1. Ensure your screen looks like the image below:
   a. The Toolpaths Manager is open, if it is not Select Alt and O on your keyboard to open it.
   b. The properties icon displays **Lathe Default**. If it is not refer to **Setting the Environment** chapter at the beginning of the book.
   c. The **Lathe Lesson-4** Geometry is showing.
2. Select the screen fit icon  to display the geometry.

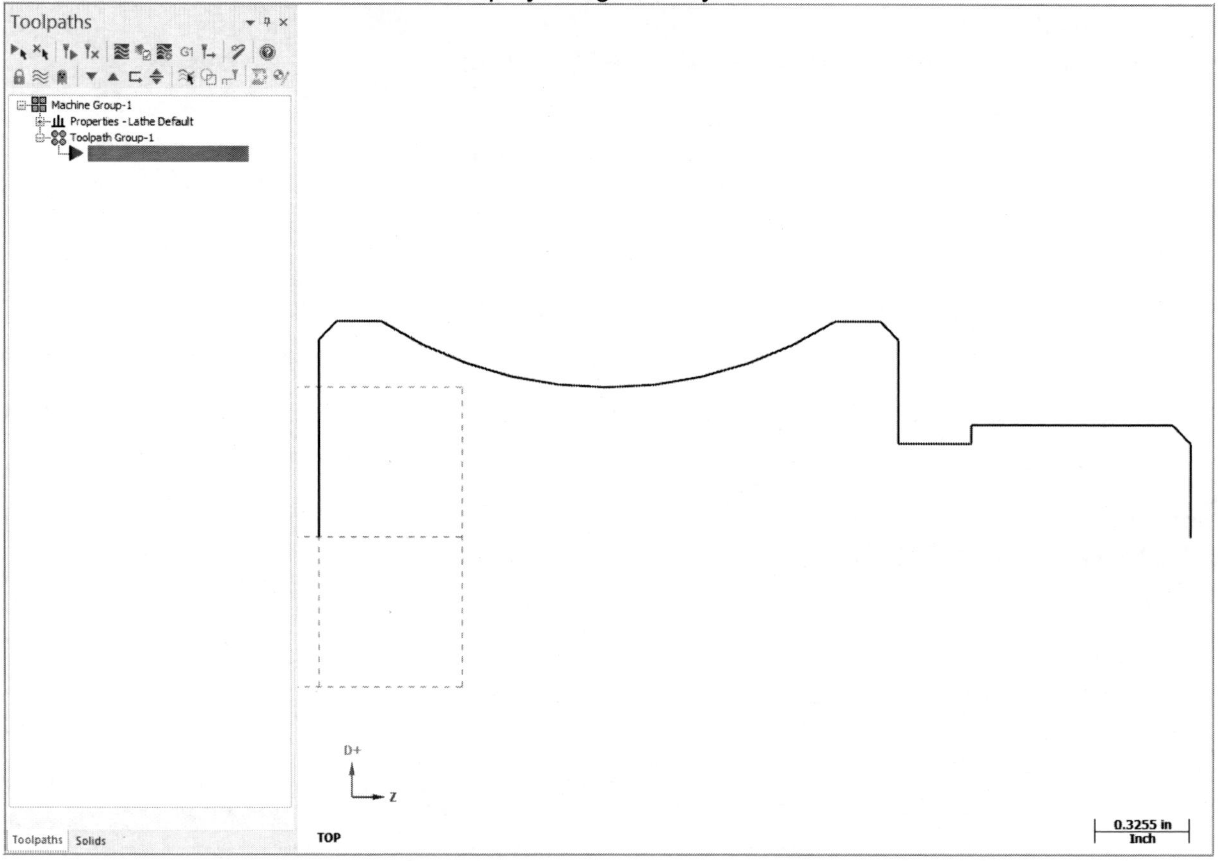

3. Select the plus in front of **Properties** to expand the Machine Group Properties.

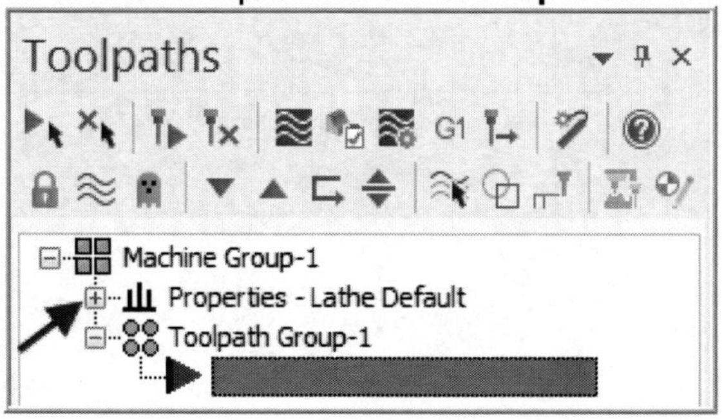

4. Select **Stock setup** in the Toolpaths Manager window.

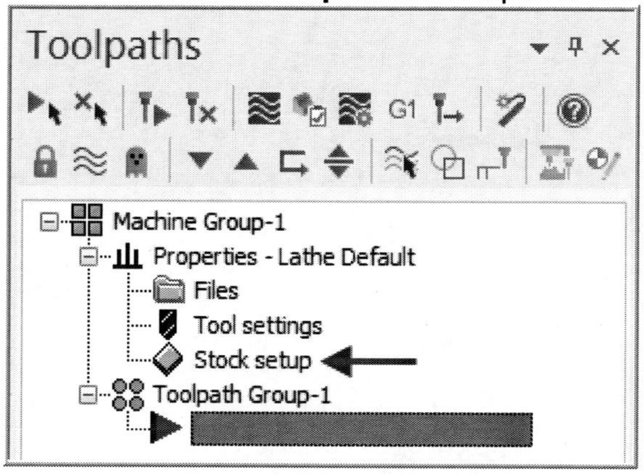

5. Select the **Stock Properties** button in the **Stock Setup** page as shown in the screenshot below:

Note: To learn more about Stock Setup refer to the Tips and Techniques section on the Mastercam Training Guide – Lathe DVD that accompanies this book.

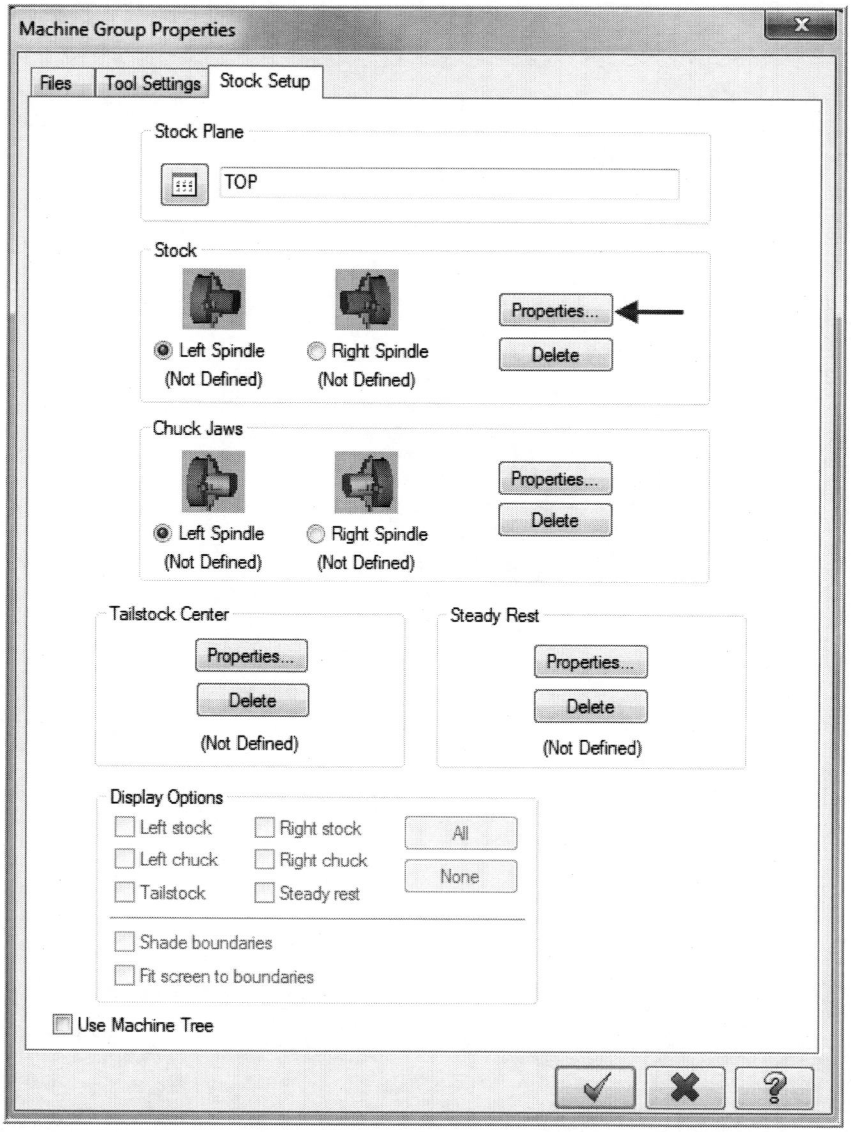

6. In the **Machine Component Manager-Stock** window click on the **Geometry** button and select **Cylinder** as shown below:

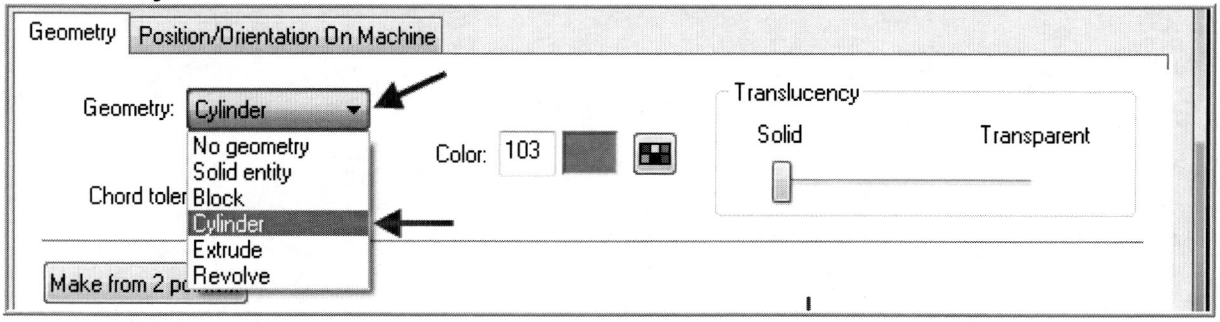

7. In the **Stock setup** set the values as shown below. **Axis is set to +Z**.

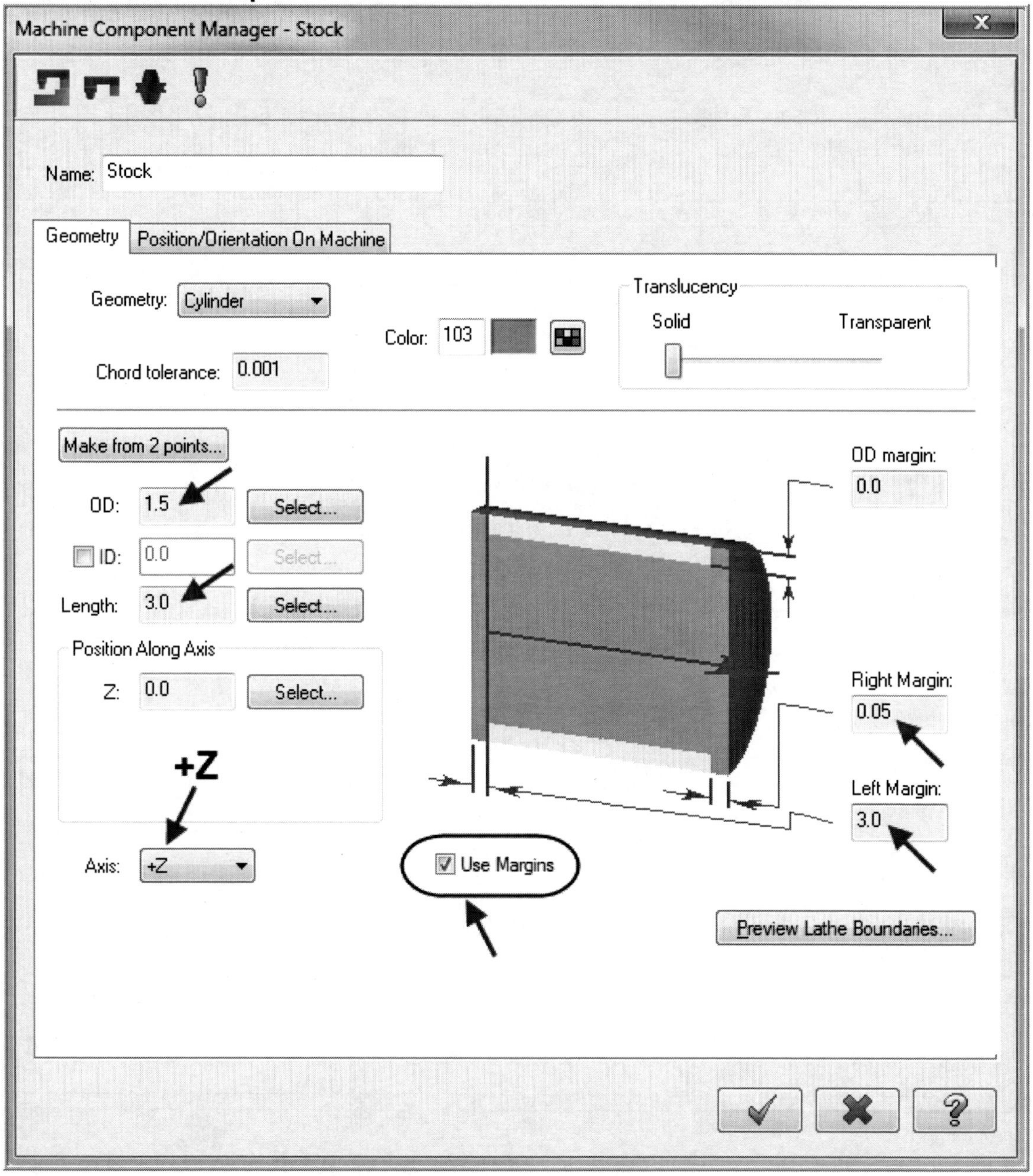

8. Click on the OK icon ✓ to complete this feature.

9. Still on the Stock Setup page activate **Fit screen to boundaries**.

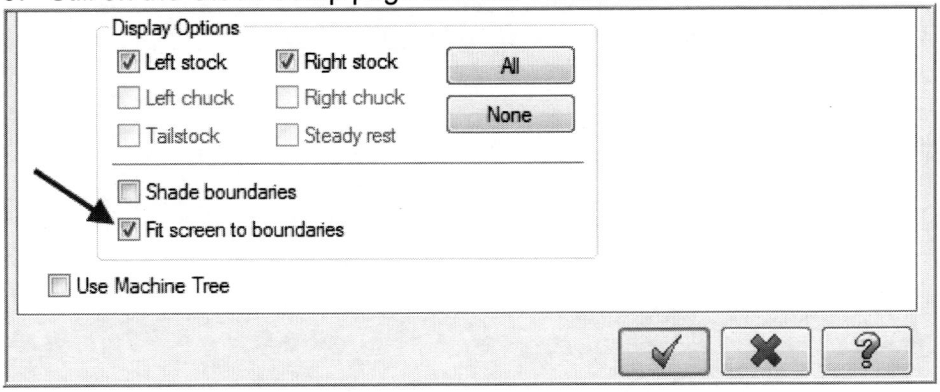

10. Select the **Chuck Properties** button in the **Stock Setup** page as shown in the screenshot below:

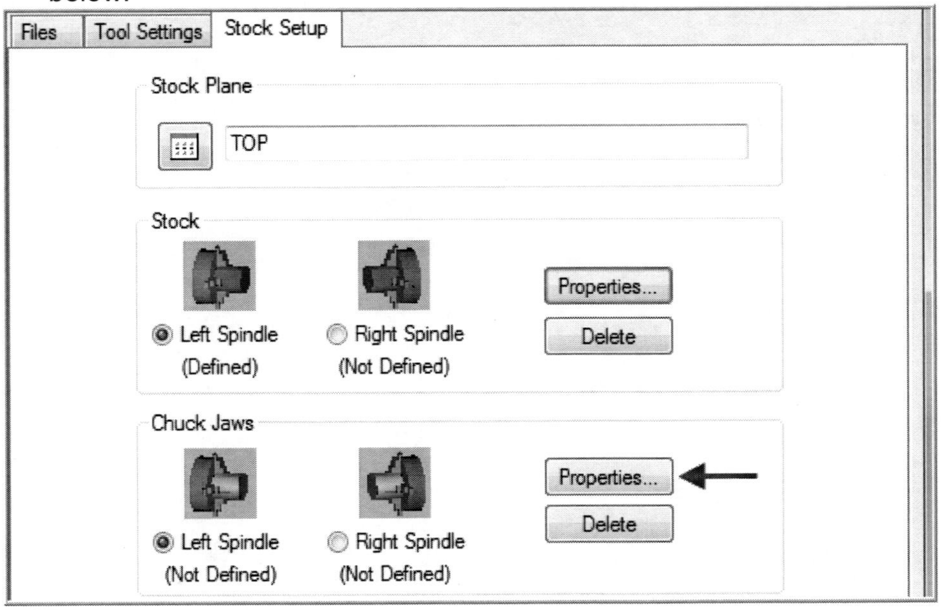

11. In the **Chuck Jaws** setup set the values as shown below:

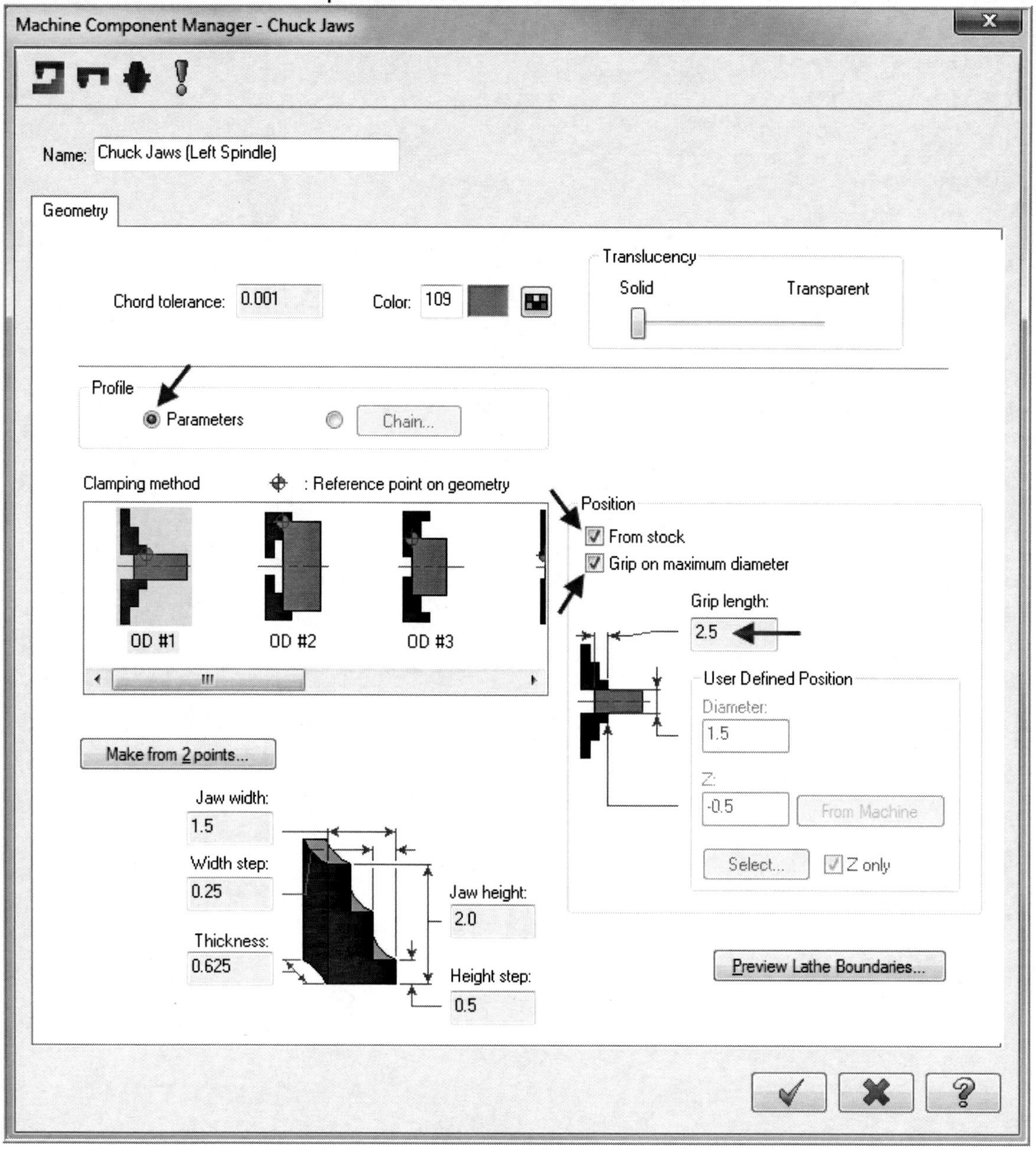

12. Click on the OK icon  to complete this feature.

13. Click on the **Tool Settings** page and make changes as shown below:

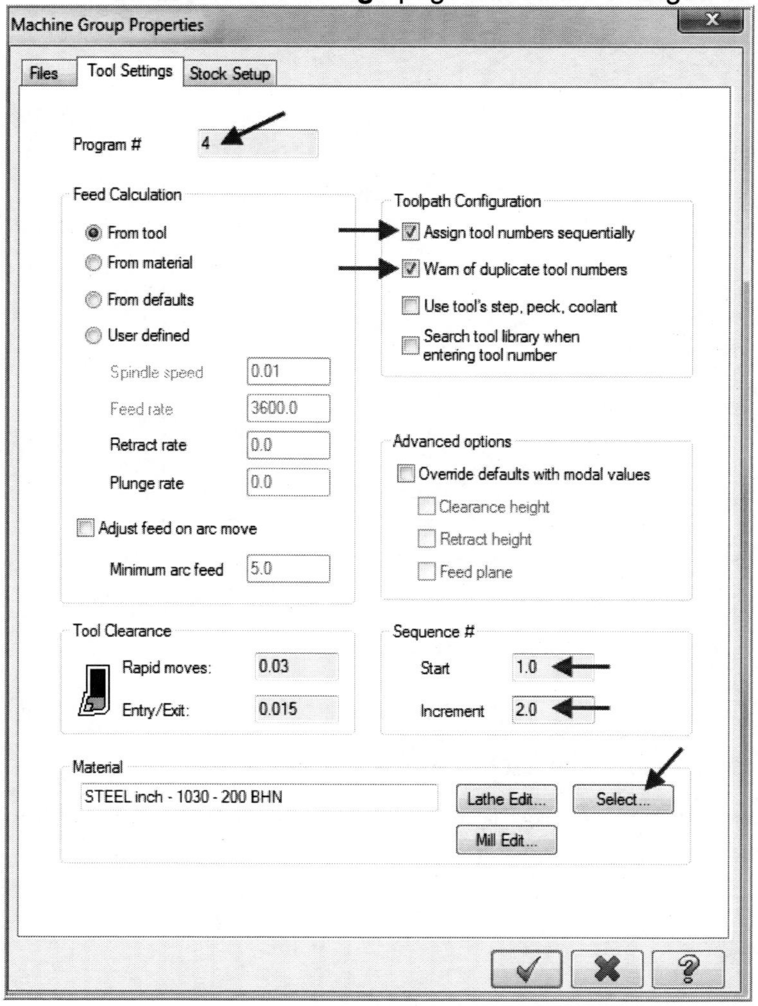

14. To change the **Material** type to Aluminum 6061 pick the **Select** button at the bottom of the Tool Settings page.
15. At the **Material List** dialog box open the Source drop down list and select **Lathe – library.**

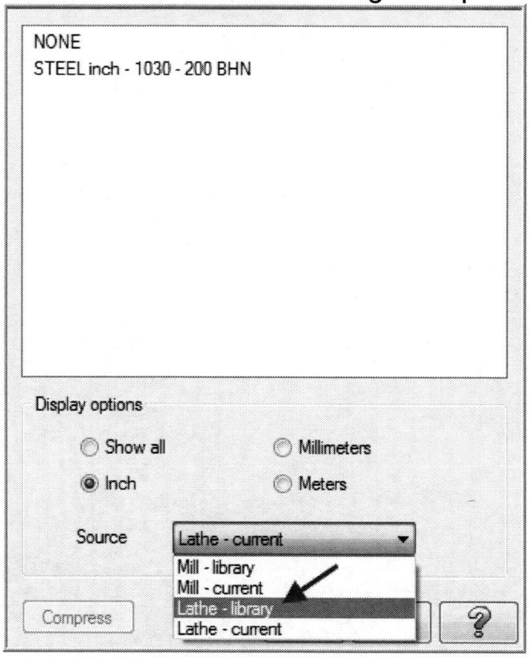

16. From the **Default Materials** list select **ALUMINUM inch - 6061** and then select ✔.

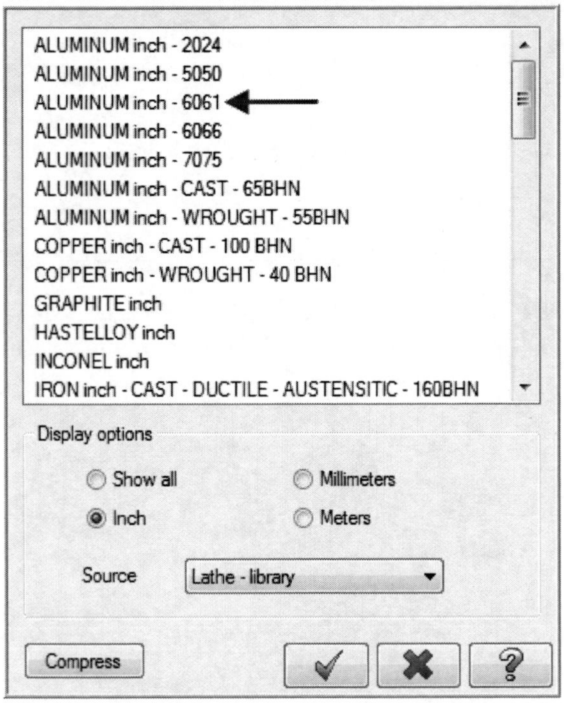

17. Select the OK button ✔ again to complete this **Stock Setup** function.

18. Select the **Screen Fit** icon to fit the part to the screen.
Notice the stock setup outline as indicated by broken lines as shown below:

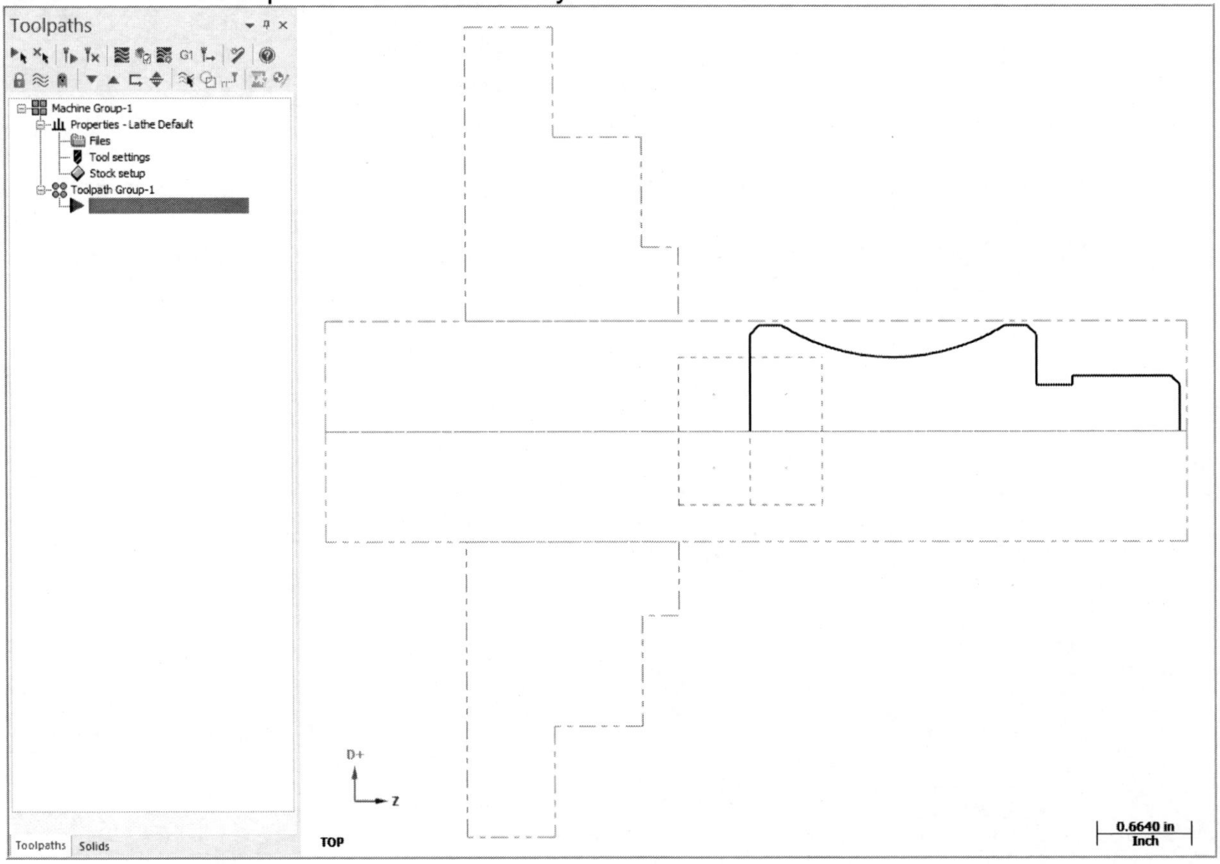

TASK 8:
FACE THE FRONT OF THE PART:

➲ In this task you will use a facing tool to face the front of the part in one cut.

1. Select the **Screen Fit** icon to fit the part to the screen if required.
2. From the menu bar select **TOOLPATHS>Face...**

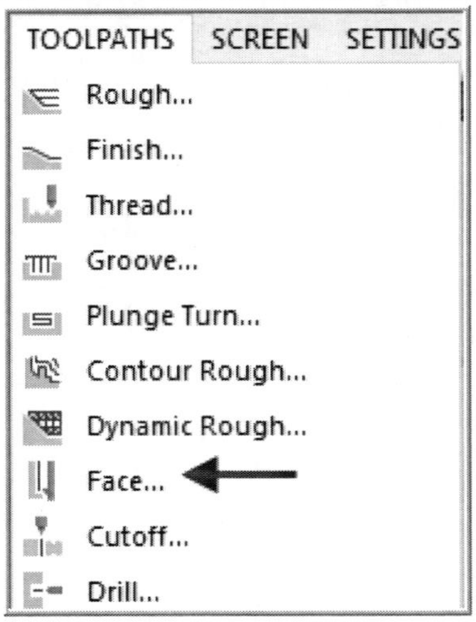

3. When prompted to **"Enter new NC name"** Ensure **LATHE-LESSON-4** is entered and then select the OK button.

➲ After selecting the OK button you are confronted with **Toolpath parameters** page. The first task here will be to select **Tool #1 a Roughing – 80 deg.**

4. Click on **Tool 0101 Roughing – 80 degree** and ensure the settings are the same as in the Toolpath parameters page as shown below:

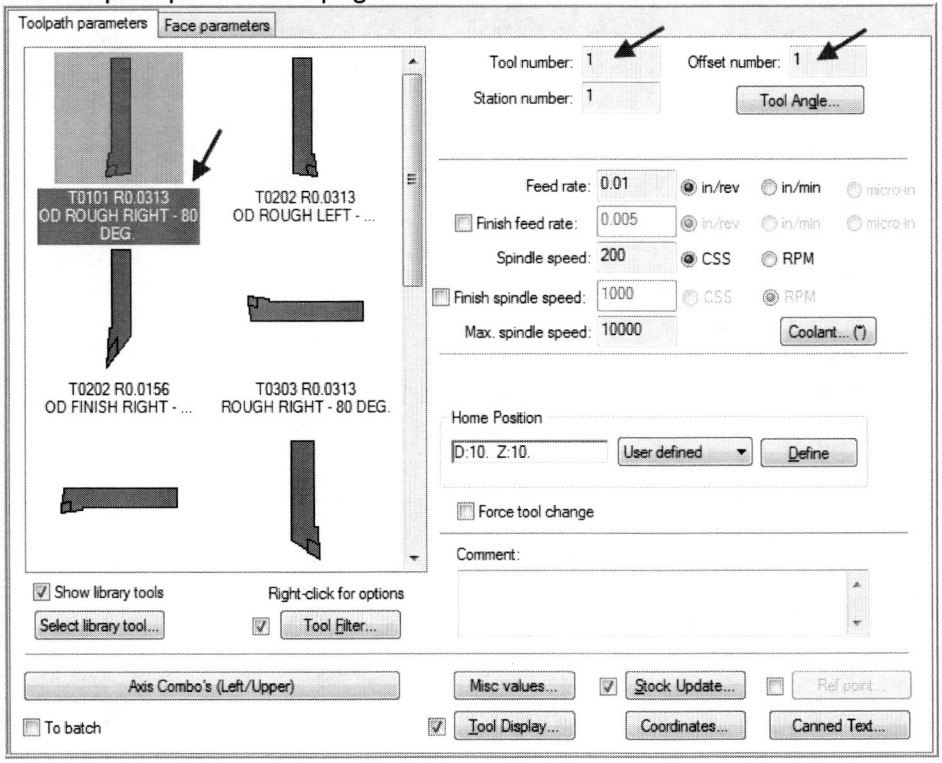

Use the Toolpath parameters tab to: Select a tool, set feeds and speeds, and set other general toolpath parameters.

This tab is very similar for most Lathe toolpaths.

5. Select the **Face parameters** page and make changes as shown below:

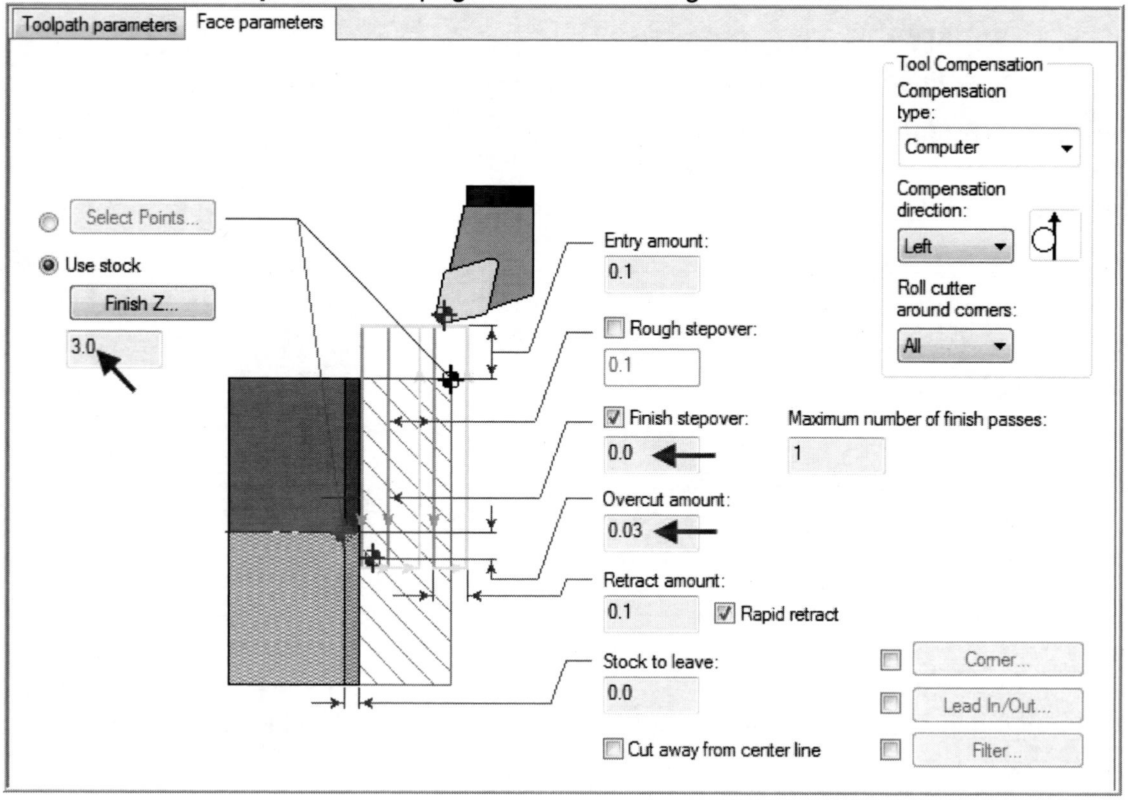

6. Select the OK button ✓ to complete this **Lathe Face** operation.

TASK 9:
ROUGH THE OUTSIDE DIAMETERS

➲ In this task you will use a Lathe toolpath called Lathe Quick Toolpaths.
➲ In this task you will use the same tool as used for the previous facing operation **Tool #1 an OD Rough- Right – 80 deg.**

1. From the menu bar select **TOOLPATHS>Quick>Rough …**

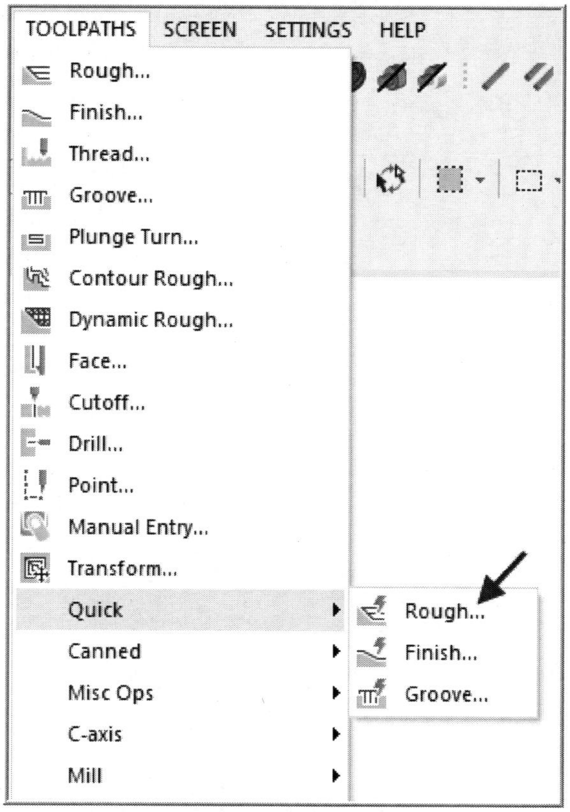

2. In the **Chaining** window Chaining mode is set to **Partial** by default.

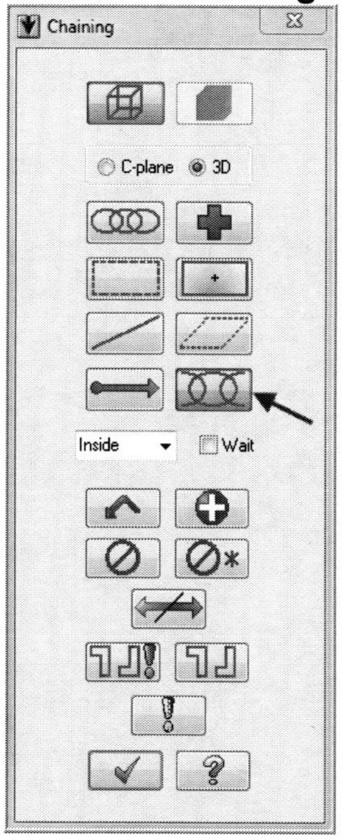

3. Select the chamfer, Line 1 as the start of the **Partial chain**.

After you have selected the chamfer **ensure** that the arrows are pointing up and to the left of the part**.** If it is not select the reverse button in the Chaining dialog box.

4. Then select the chamfer, Line 2 as the end entity in this chain.

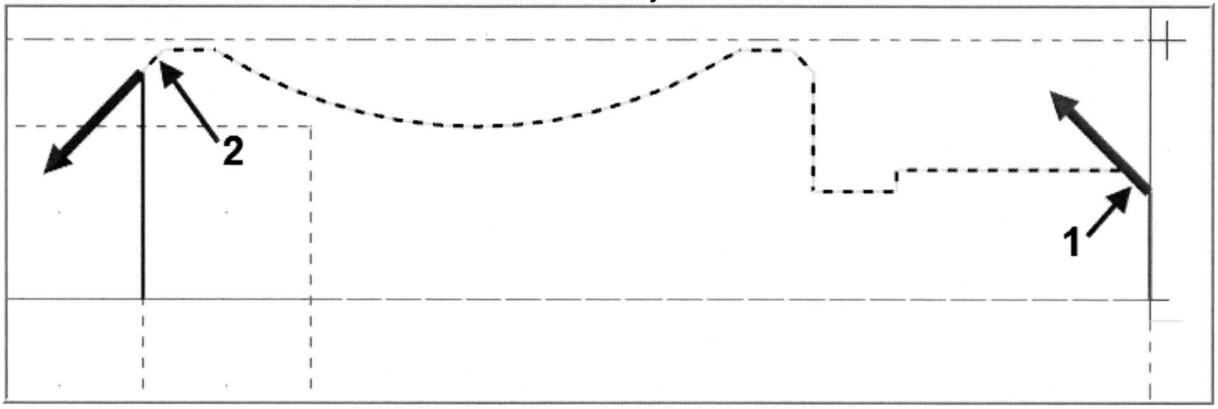

5. Select the OK button  to exit the Chaining dialog window.
6. In the **Quick tool parameters** page select the **Tool #1 an Roughing – 80 deg** and make any necessary changes as shown below:

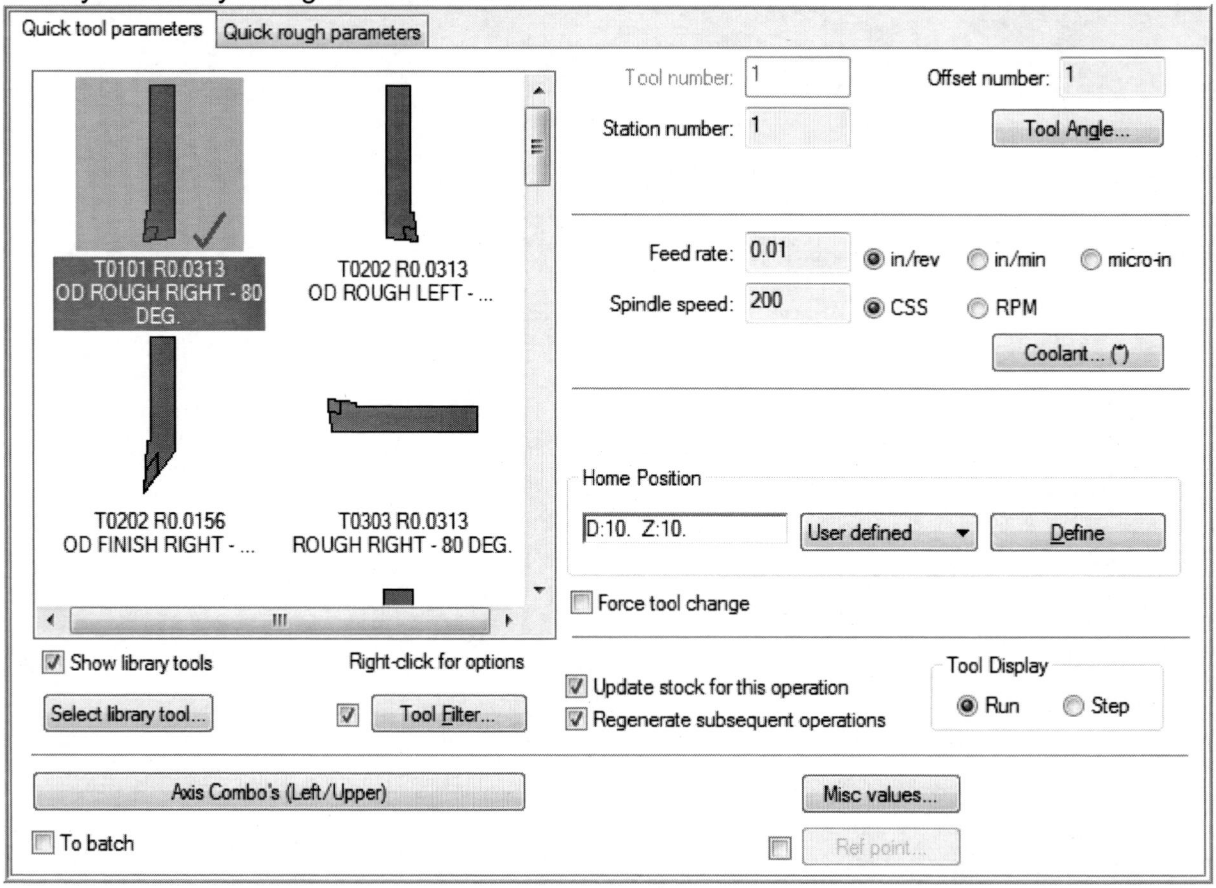

7. Select the **Quick Rough parameters** page and make any necessary changes as shown below:

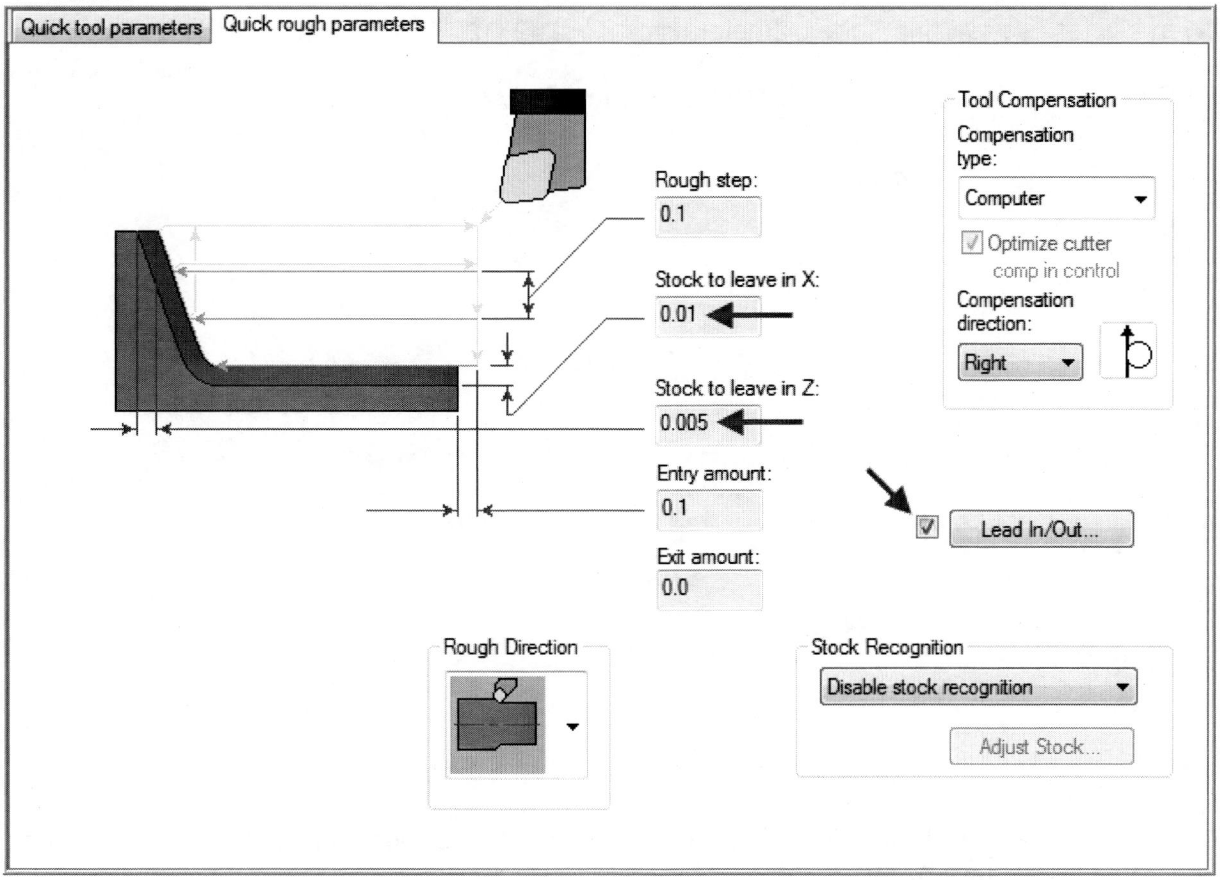

8. Select the OK button  to exit Rough Parameters.

TASK 10:
FINISH THE DIAMETER

➲ In this task you will finish the diameter using **Tool #2 OD Finish Right – 35 DEG.**

1. From the menu bar select **TOOLPATHS>Quick>Finish…**

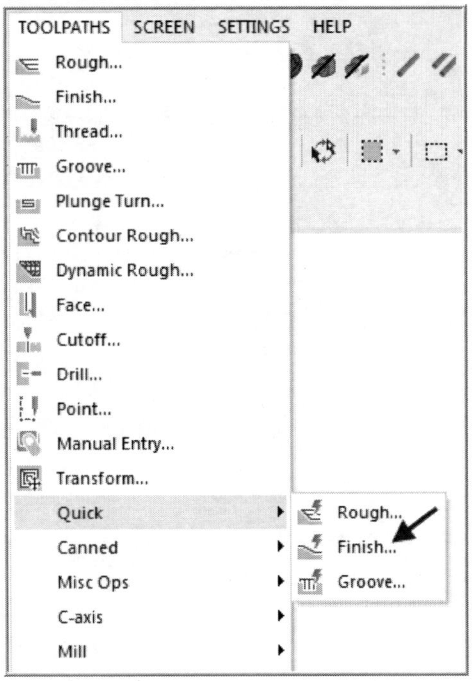

2. Select **Tool #2 OD Finish Right – 35 DEG** tool from the tool list and make any necessary changes as shown below:

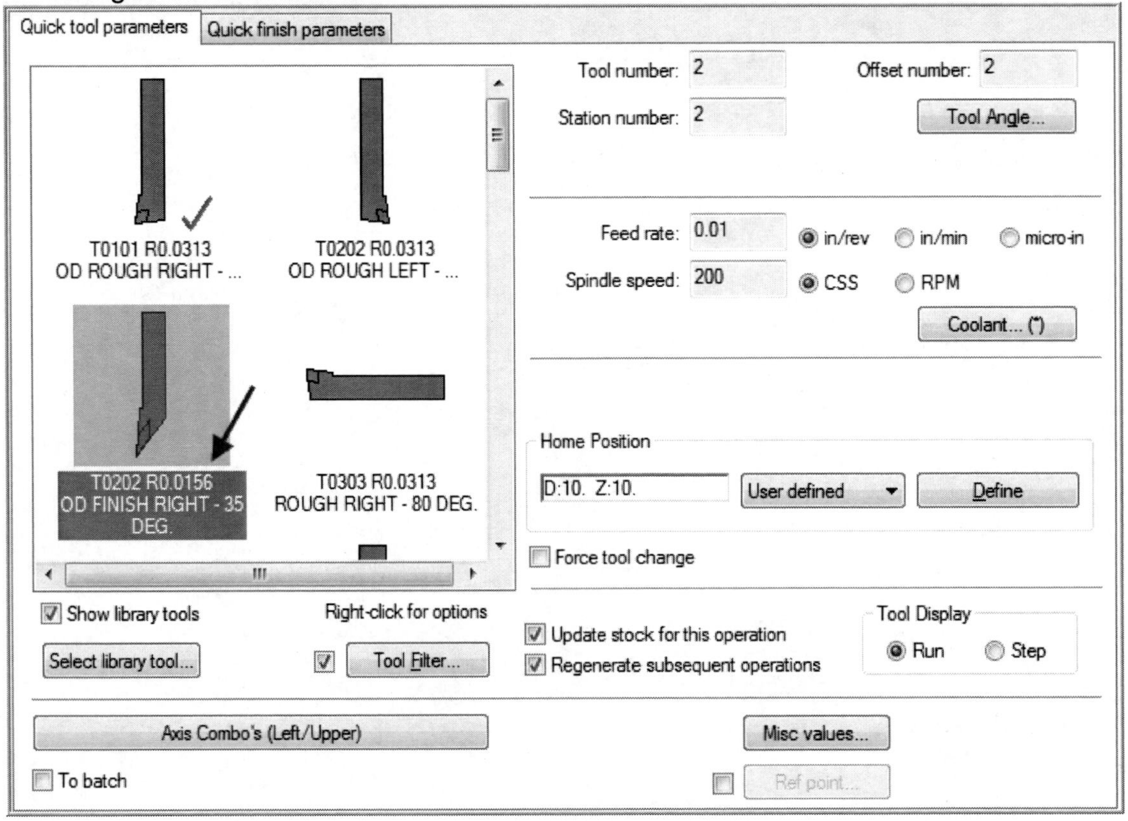

3. Click on the **Quick finish parameters** page and make changes as shown below:

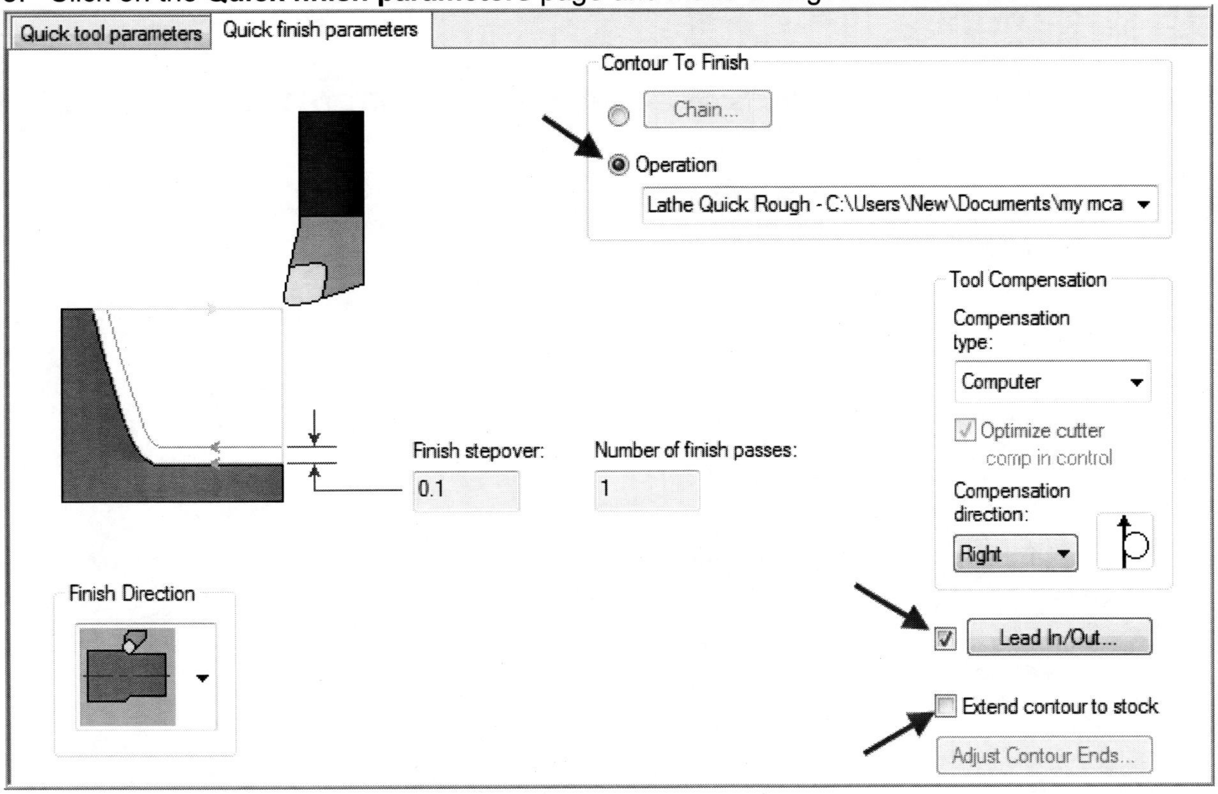

4. Click on the **Lead In/Out** button.
5. Make the necessary changes as shown below on the **Lead in** page. In order to adjust the **dial (#1),** click on the desired location of the arrow:

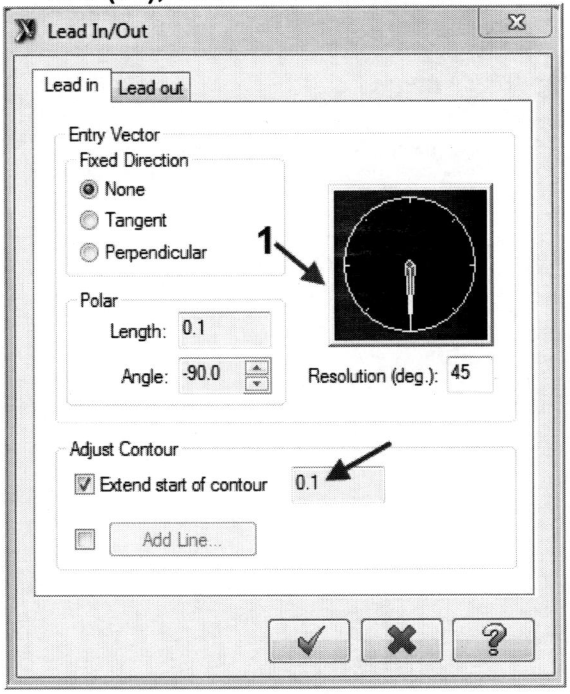

6. Select the OK button ✓ to exit the **Lead In/Out** window.
7. Select the OK button ✓ to exit the **Lathe Quick Finish** parameters.

TASK 11:
CUT THE GROOVE

➲ In this task you will use the Lathe Groove toolpath using **Tool #3 OD Groove Right Width .125.**

1. From the menu bar select **TOOLPATHS>Groove…**

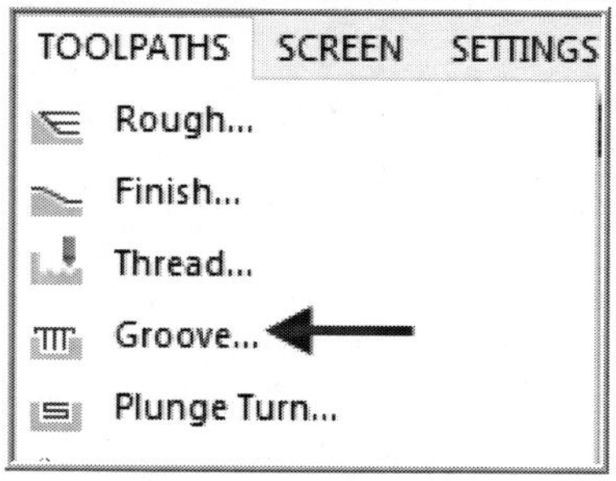

2. The **Grooving Options** window appears. Click on the 2 Points option as shown below:

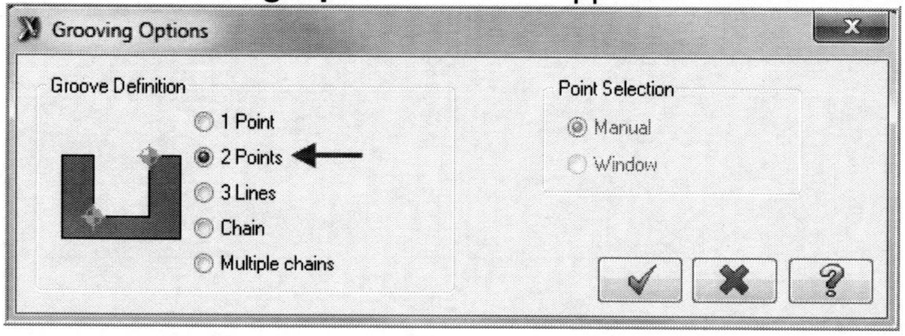

Grooving Options
Use this dialog box to tell Mastercam how you will identify the grooves for a groove toolpath. You can identify grooves by one or both corner points, by three rectangular lines, or, for standard groove toolpaths, you can select a non-rectangular chain of curves.

The **2 Points Groove Definition** will enable you to pick 2 points of the groove to define the groove.

3. Click on OK .
4. **Alt and T** on the keyboard to hide the toolpath.
5. Click on the **2 points** as shown below:

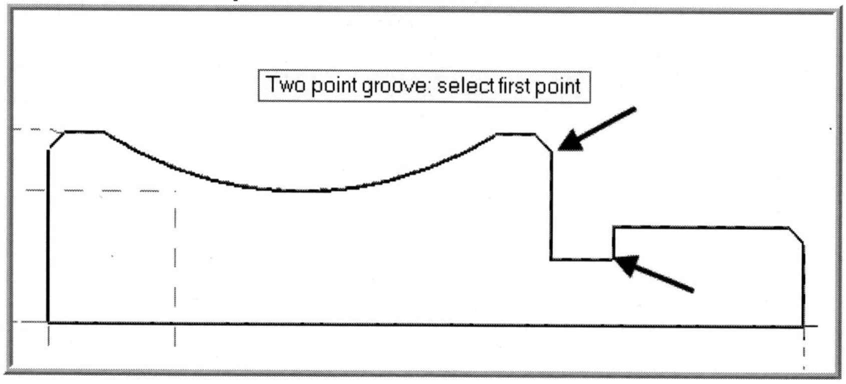

6. Hit **Enter**.

7. Select **Tool #3 OD Groove Right Width .125** tool from the tool list and make any necessary changes as shown below:

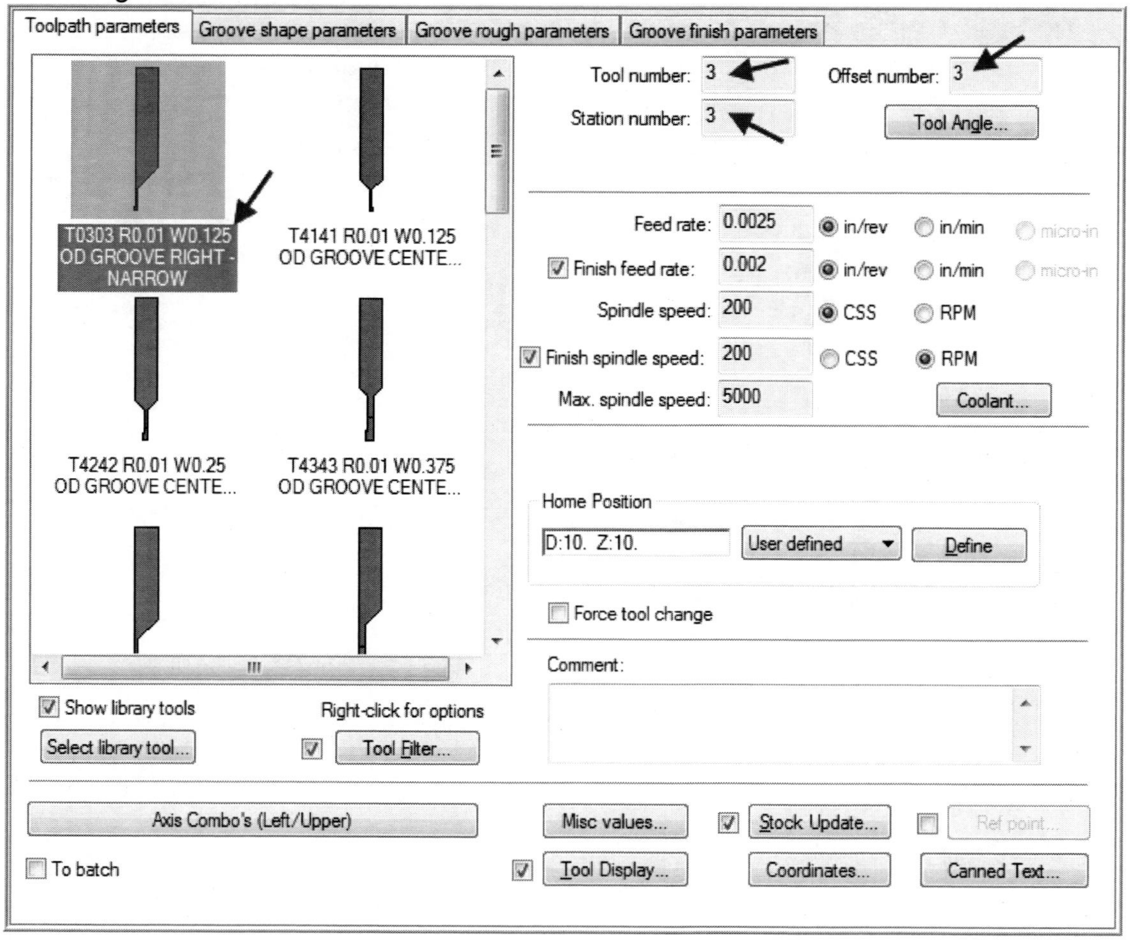

8. Click on the **Groove shape parameters** and take note of the settings. No changes will need to be made:

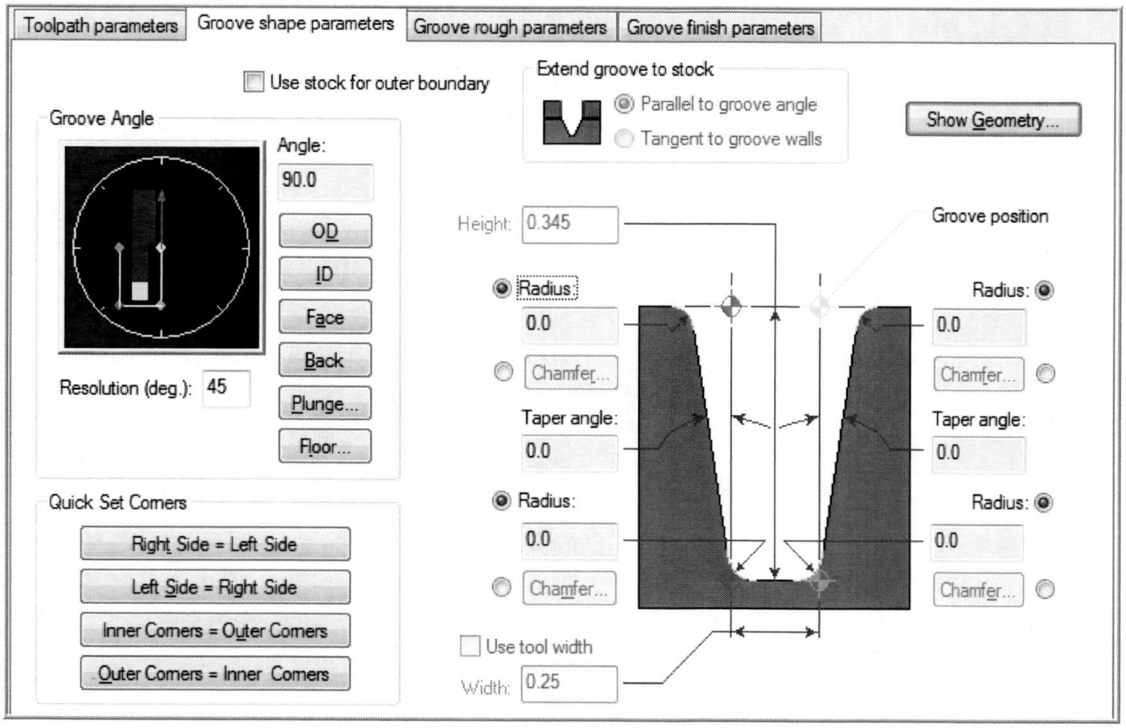

9. Click on the **Groove rough parameters** and take note of the settings. No changes will need to be made:

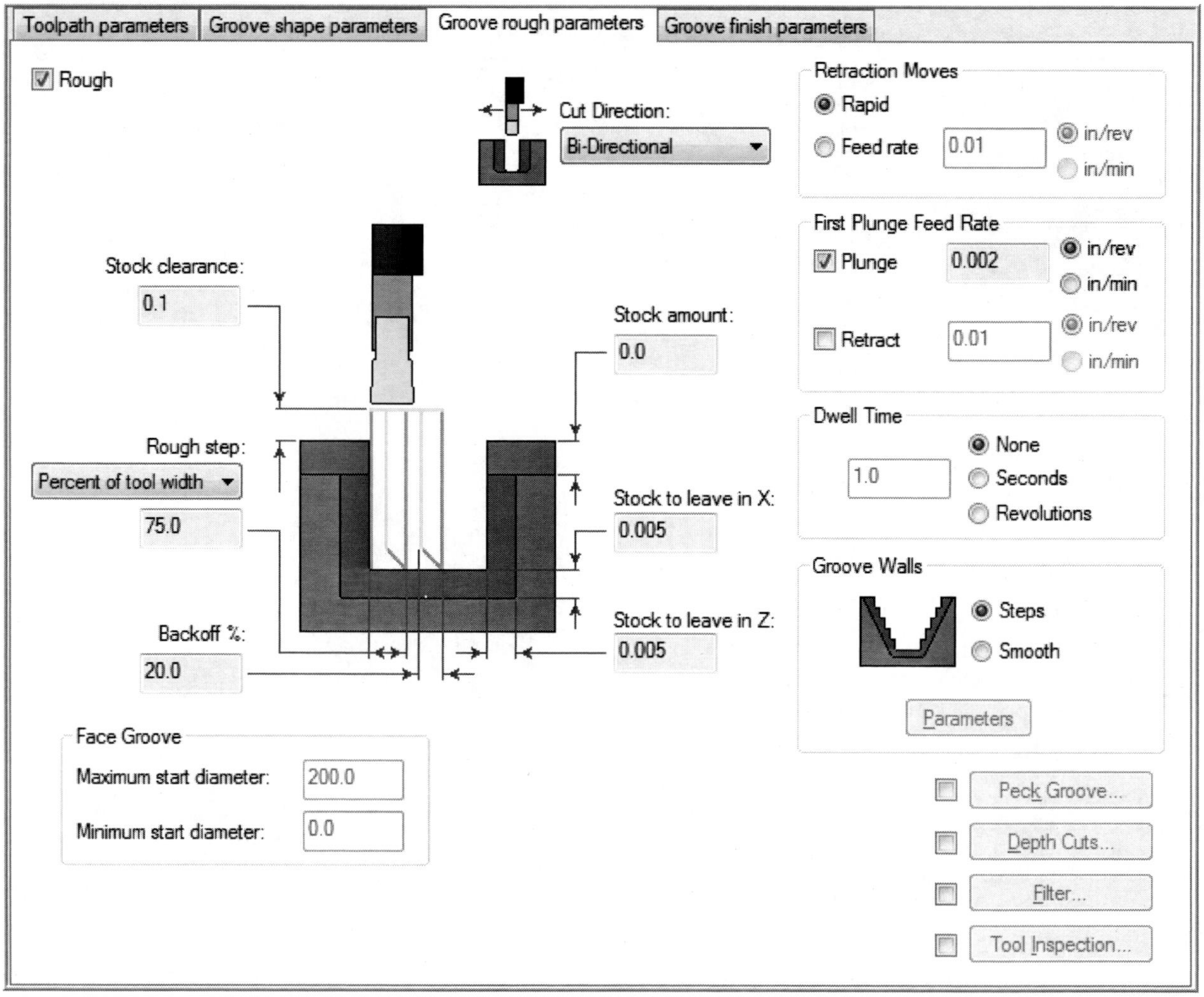

10. Click on the **Groove finish parameters** and take note of the settings. No changes will need to be made:

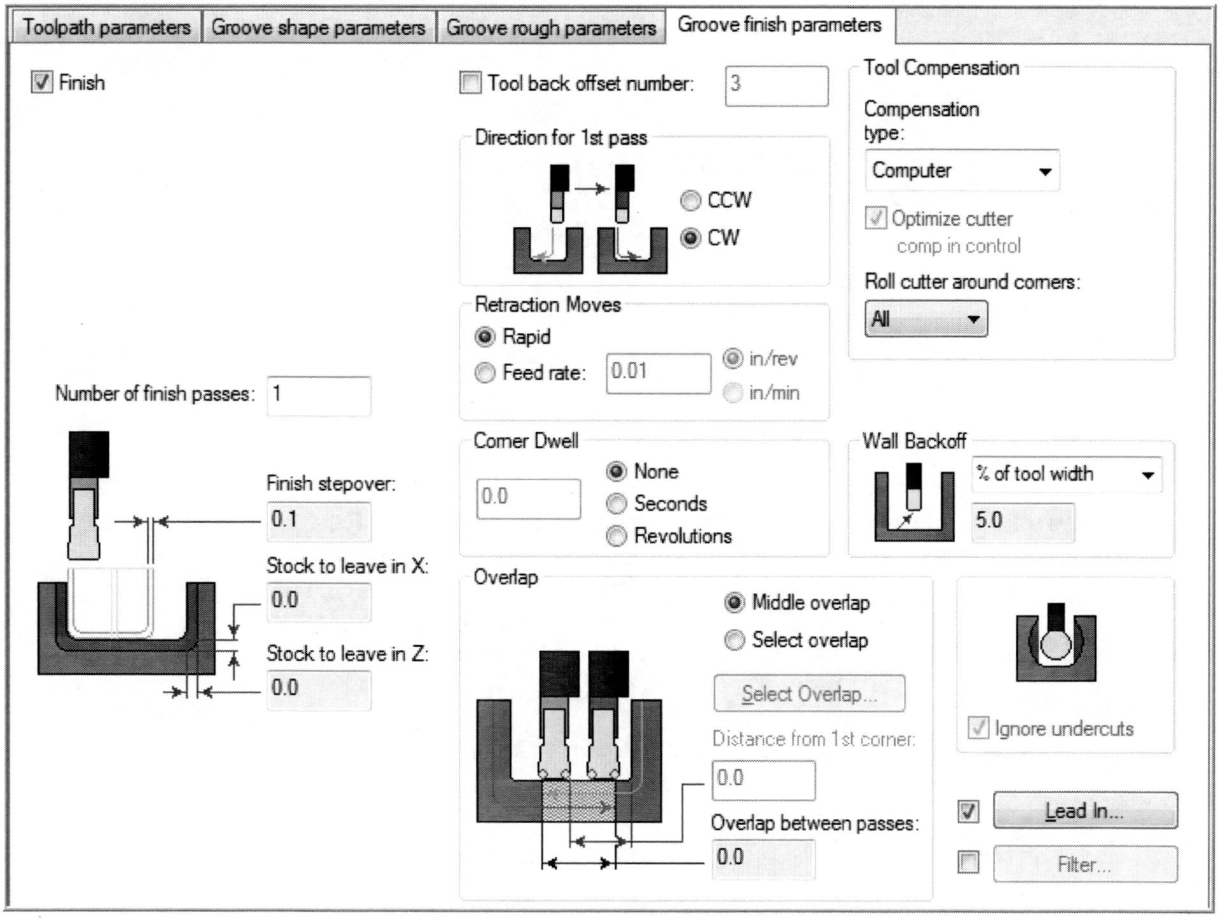

11. Click on OK .

TASK 12:
THREAD THE PART

➲ In this task you will thread the outside diameter using **Tool #4 R0.0144 OD THREAD RIGHT.**

1. From the menu bar select **TOOLPATHS>Thread…**

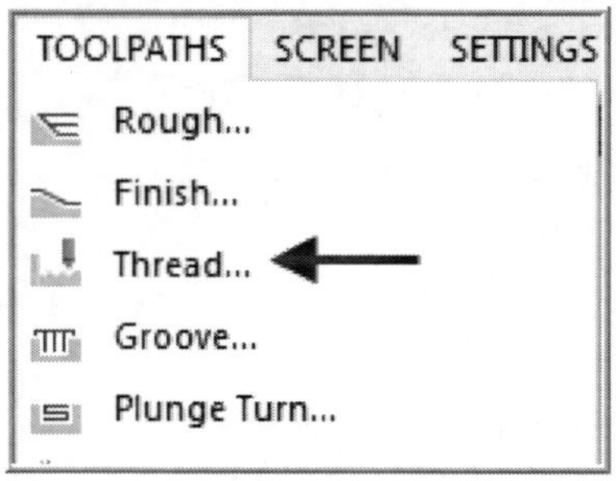

2. Scroll down the tool window if necessary and select the **Tool #4 R0.0144 OD THREAD RIGHT** tool and make changes as shown below in the **Toolpath parameters** page.

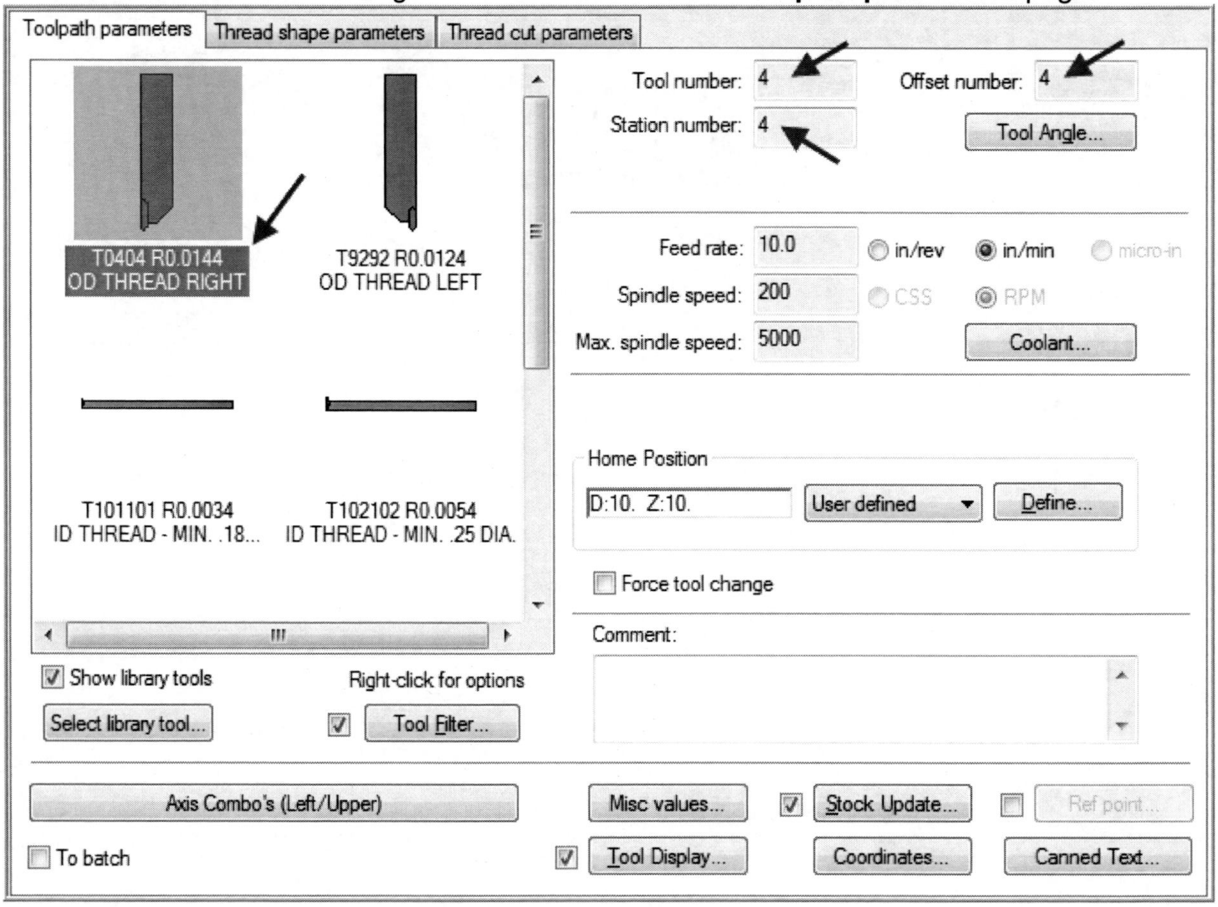

3. Click on the **Thread shape parameters** tab.

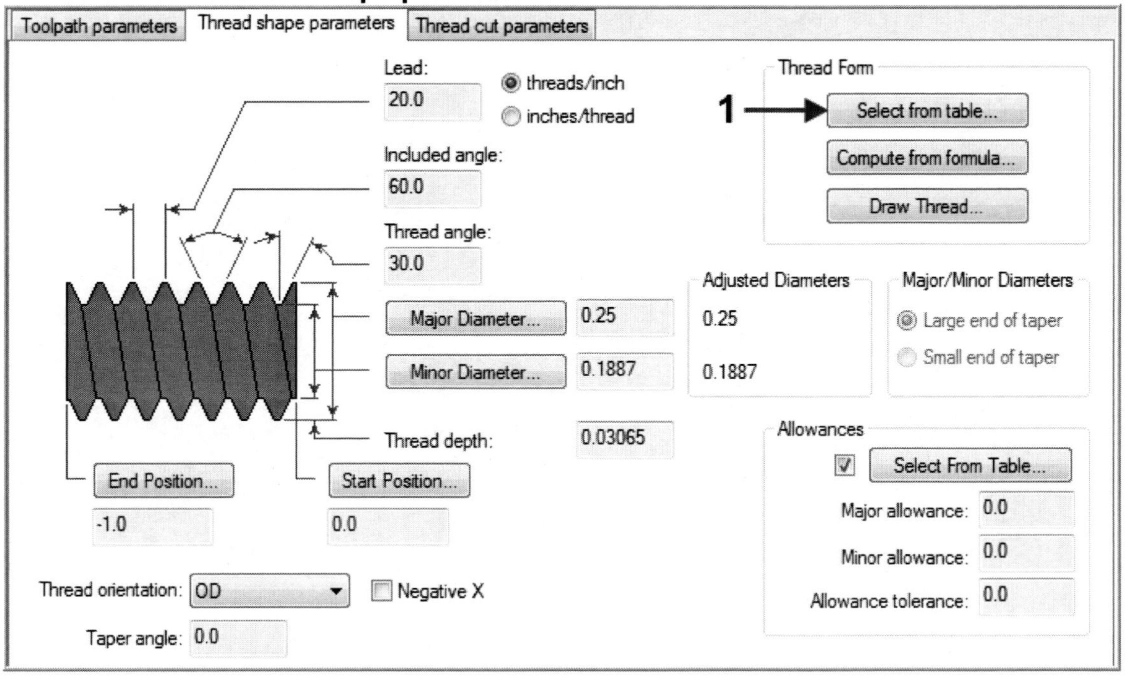

4. Click on **Select from table** (1) as shown above:
5. Click on the **Thread forms** button (1) and select **Unified – UNC, UNF** (2) as shown below:

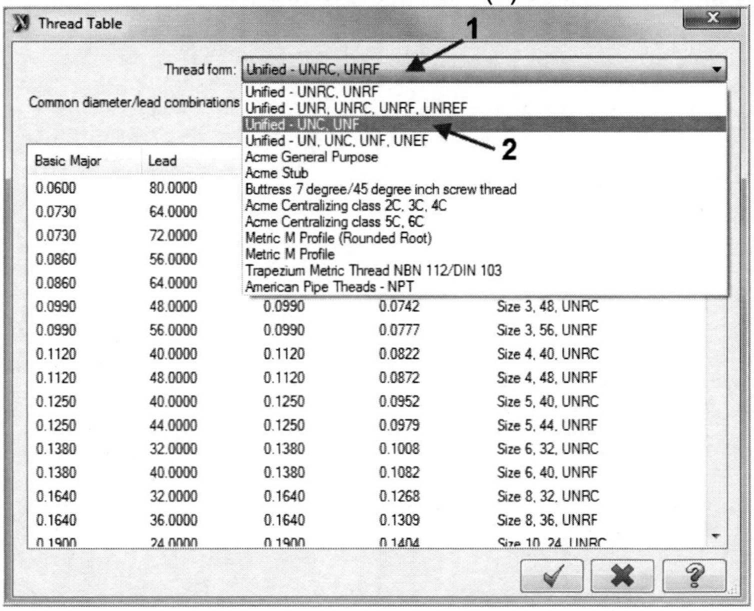

6. Scroll down and click on the **0.7500 10.000 (3/4, 10. UNC)** thread as shown below:

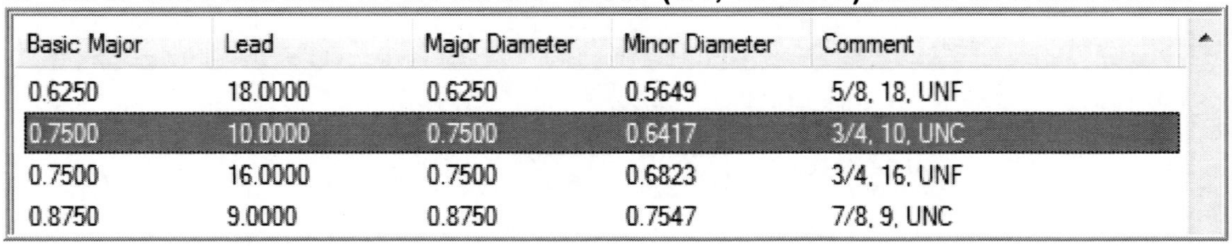

Basic Major	Lead	Major Diameter	Minor Diameter	Comment
0.6250	18.0000	0.6250	0.5649	5/8, 18, UNF
0.7500	10.0000	0.7500	0.6417	3/4, 10, UNC
0.7500	16.0000	0.7500	0.6823	3/4, 16, UNF
0.8750	9.0000	0.8750	0.7547	7/8, 9, UNC

7. Click on OK .

8. Click on the **Start Position** button (1) as shown below:

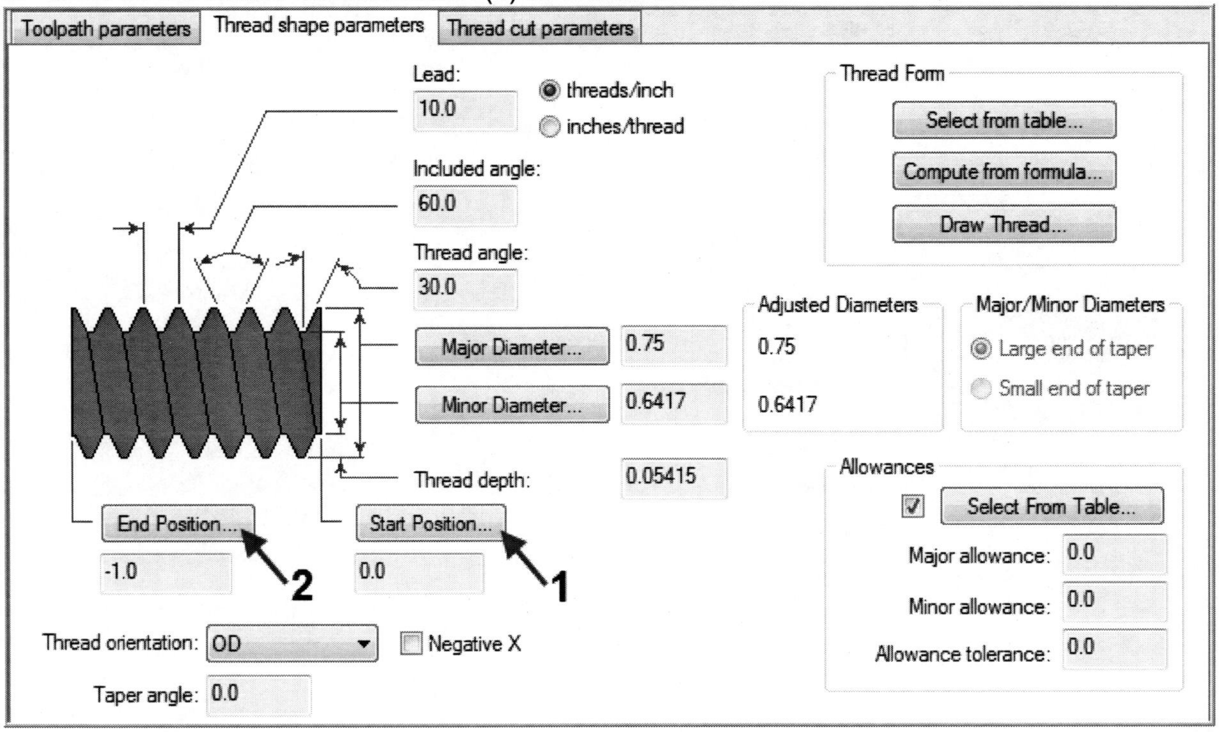

9. Click on the point as shown below:

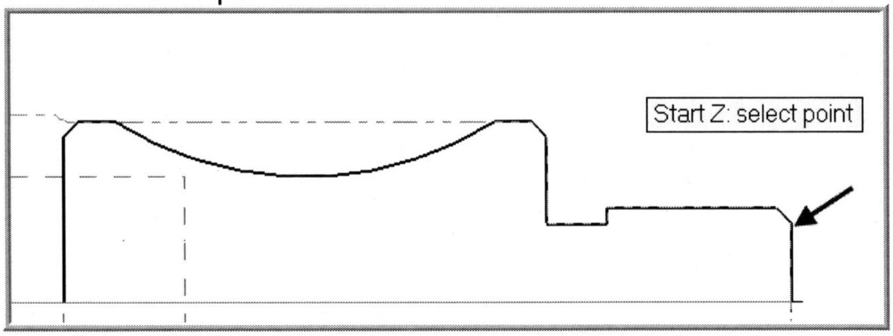

10. Click on the **End Position** button (2) as shown in step 8.
11. Click on the point as shown below:

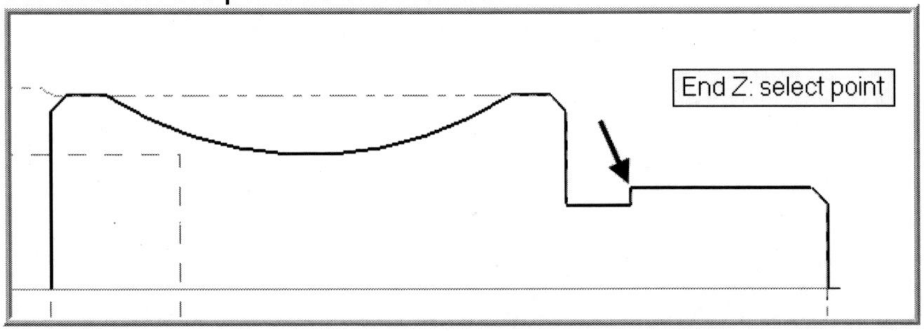

12. Your Start and End Positions should be as below:

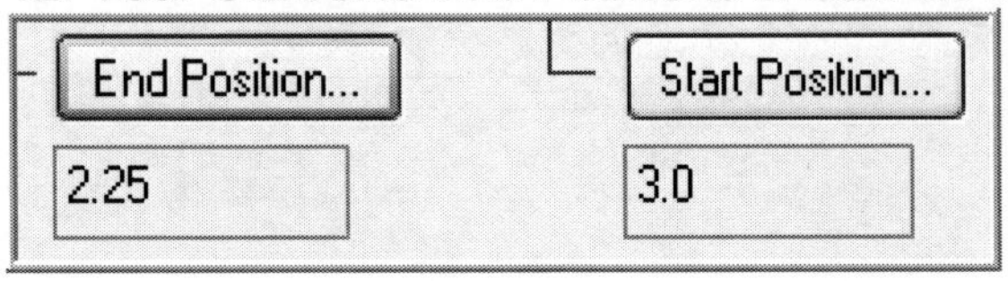

13. Click on the **Thread cut parameters** tab and makes changes as shown below:

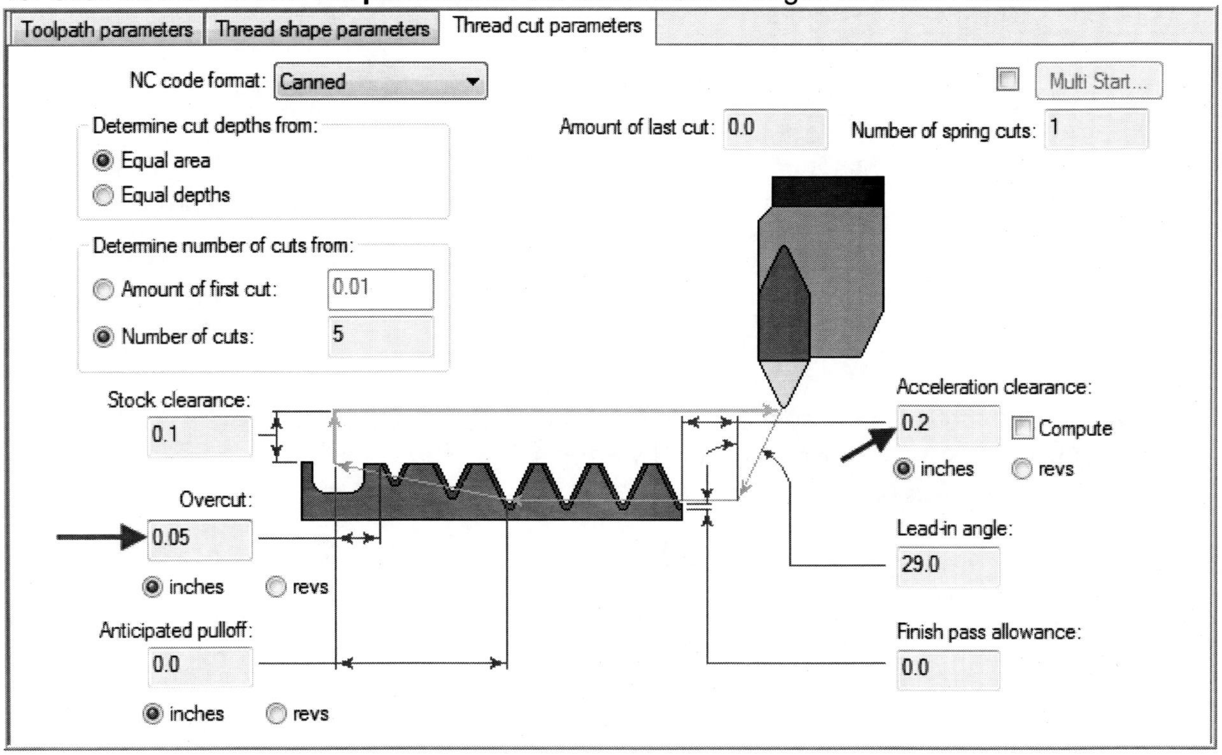

14. Click on the OK icon .

TASK 13:
FINISH THE RADIUS

➲ In this task you will create a new Tool to machine and finish the 1.5" Radius.

1. From the menu bar select **TOOLPATHS>Finish…**

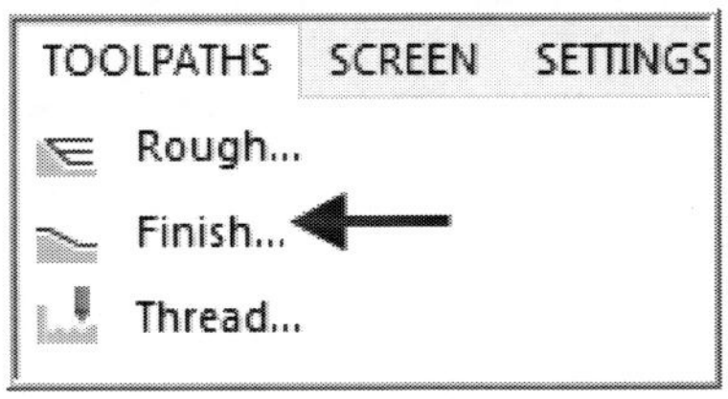

2. With the Chaining dialog box set to Partial, click on the radius as shown below:

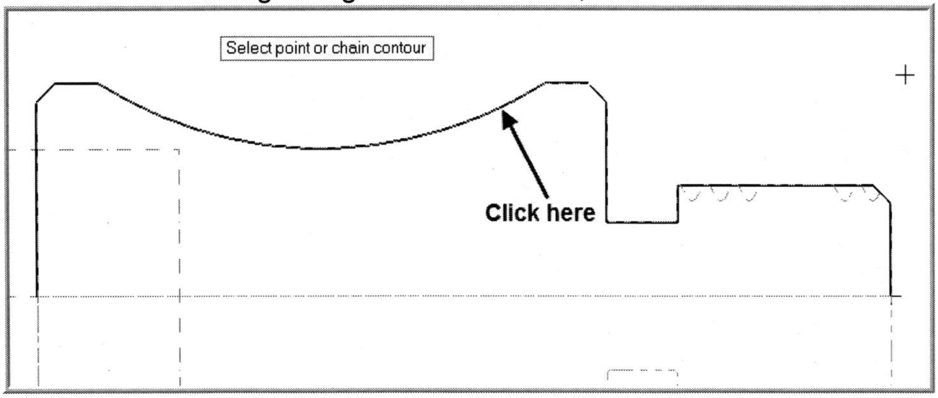

3. Click on the chamfer as shown below left: Arrows should be in the direction as shown below right after clicking on the chamfer.

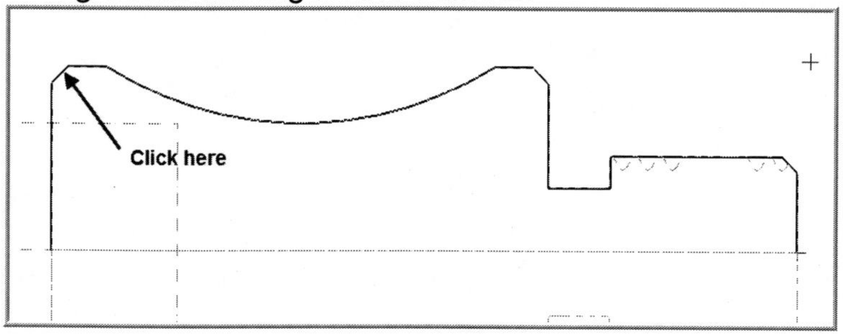

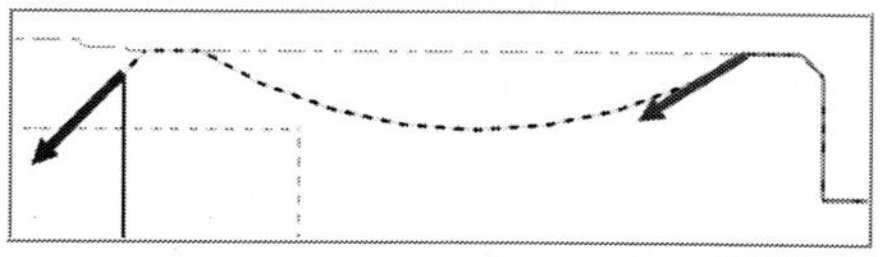

4. Click on OK  in the Chaining box.
5. Right Click the mouse in the space as indicated by arrow # 1 shown below:
6. Click on **Create new tool...** as indicated by arrow # 2 as shown below:

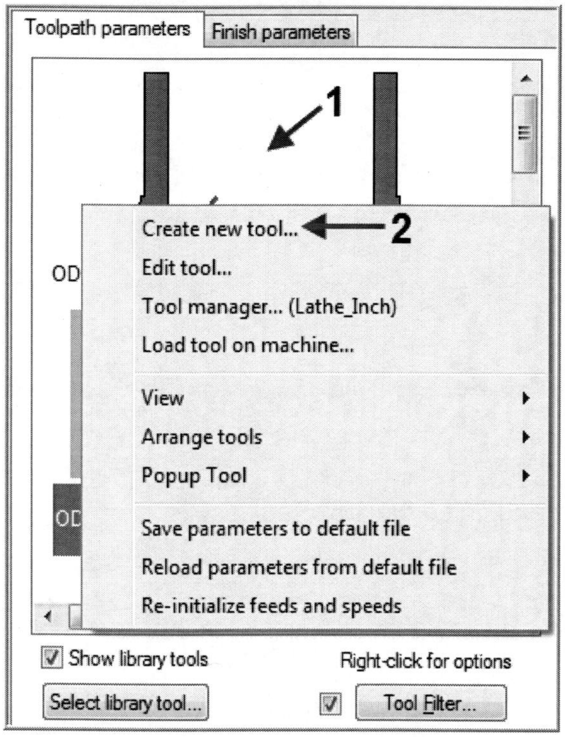

7. Click on the **General Turning** Button as shown below:

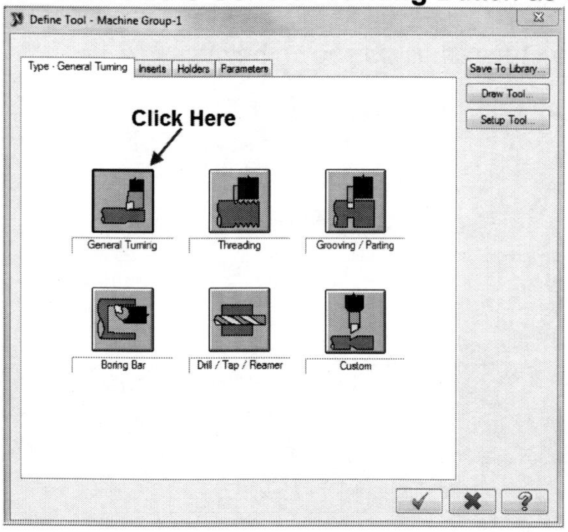

8. Click on the **V (35 deg. Diamond)** insert as shown below:

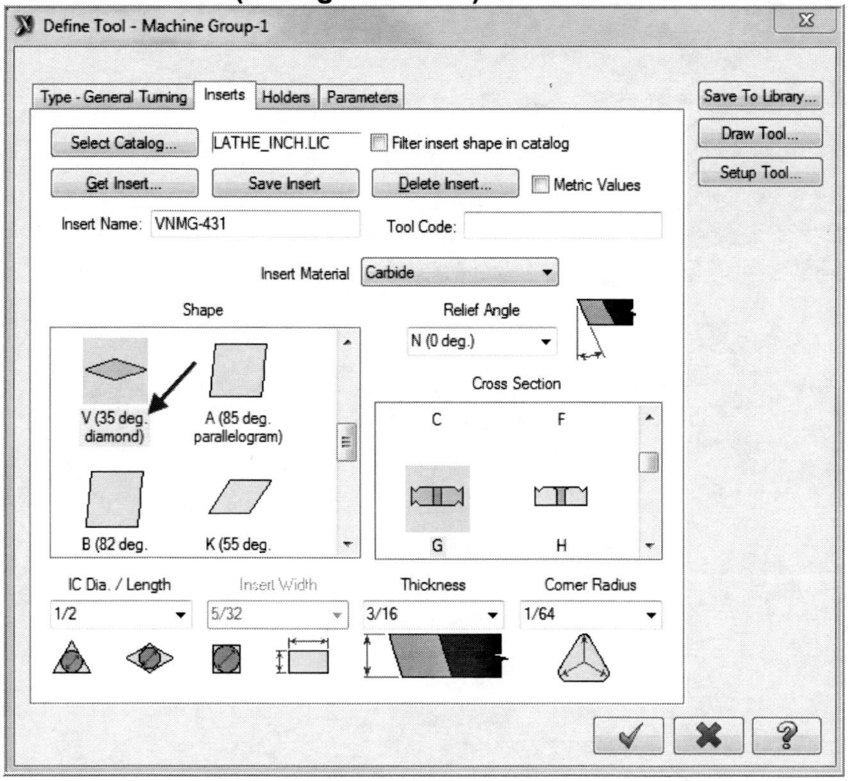

9. Click on the **Holders** Tab.
10. Scroll down and click on the **V (17.5 deg. Side clr.)** as shown below:

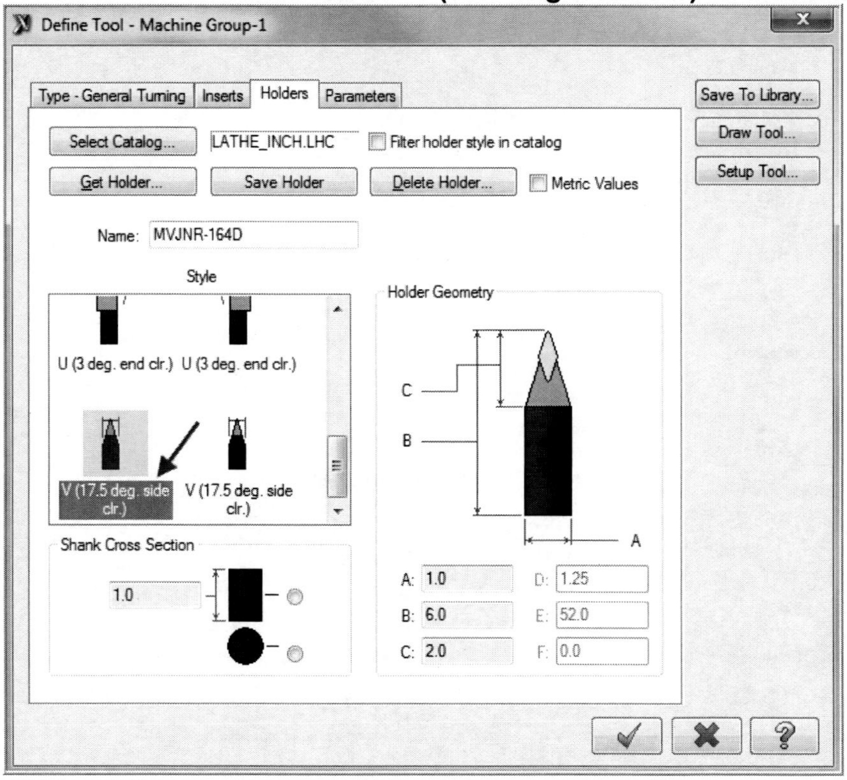

11. Click on the OK icon ✔.

12. Make any necessary changes as shown below:

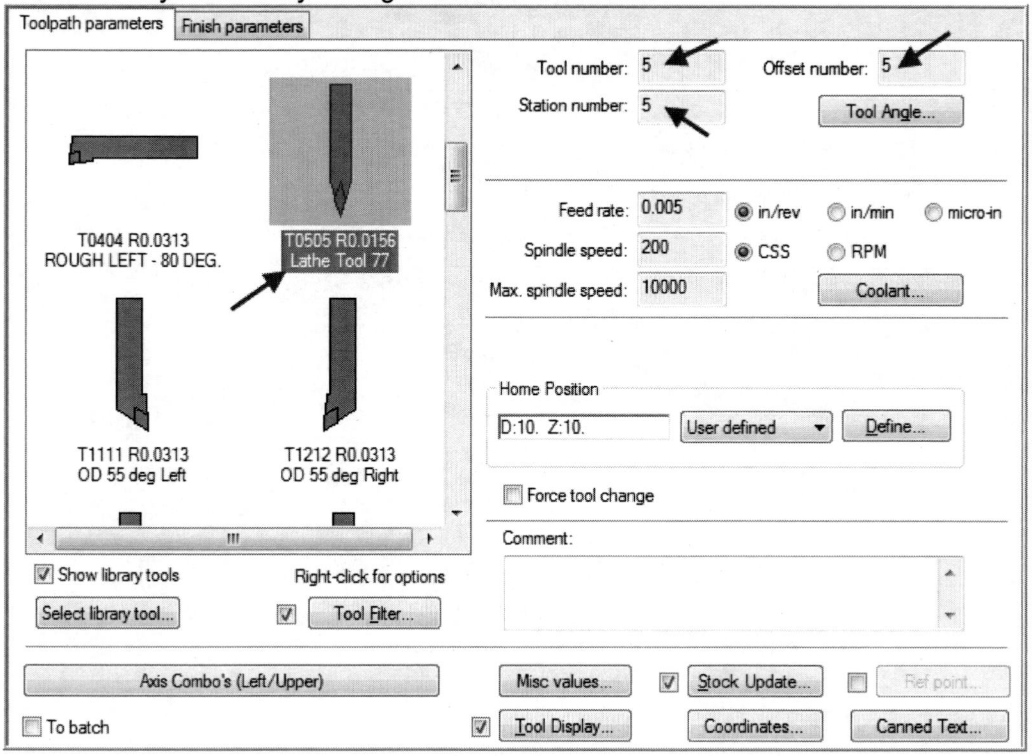

13. Click on the **Finish parameters** tab and make any necessary changes as shown below:

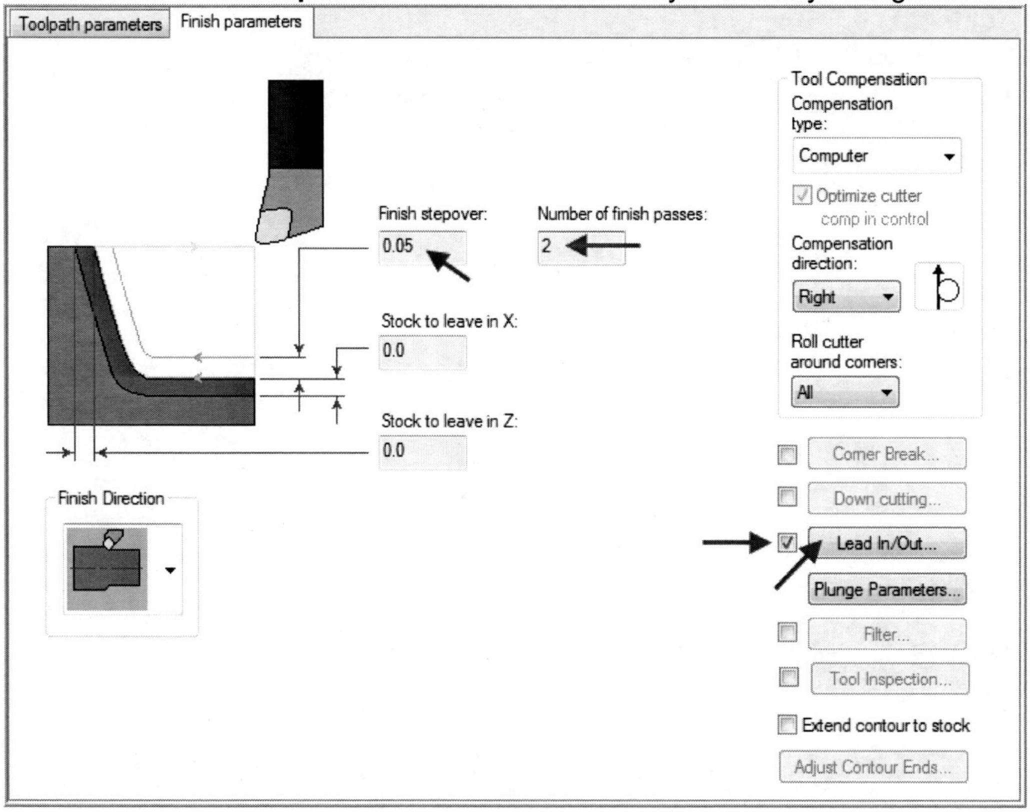

14. Click on the **Lead in/Out Button** as shown above:

15. Make the necessary changes as shown below. In order to adjust the dial (#1), click on the desired location of the arrow:

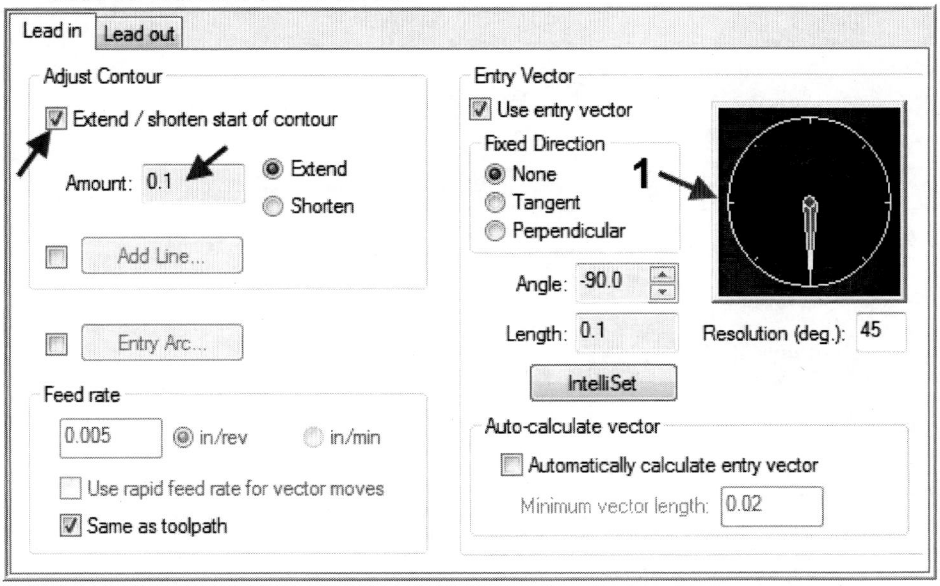

16. Click on the **Lead out Tab** and make the necessary changes as shown below:

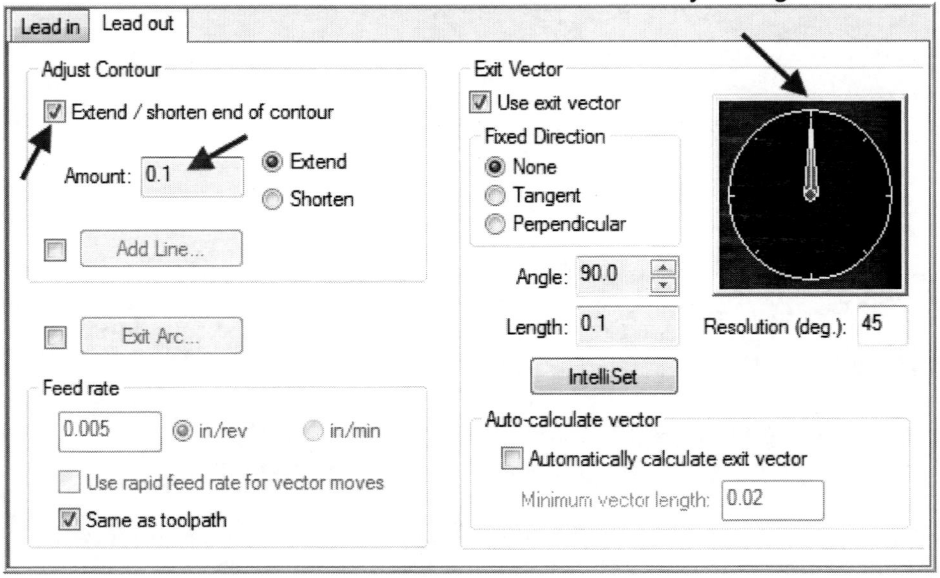

17. Click on OK  to exit the Lead In/out window.

18. Click on the **Plunge Parameters** button as shown below:

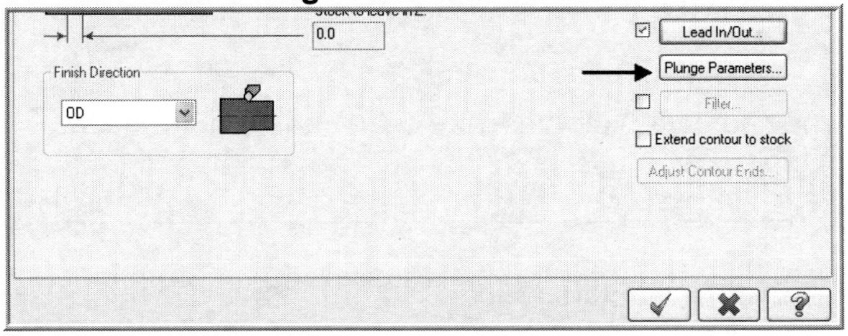

19. Make the necessary changes as shown below:

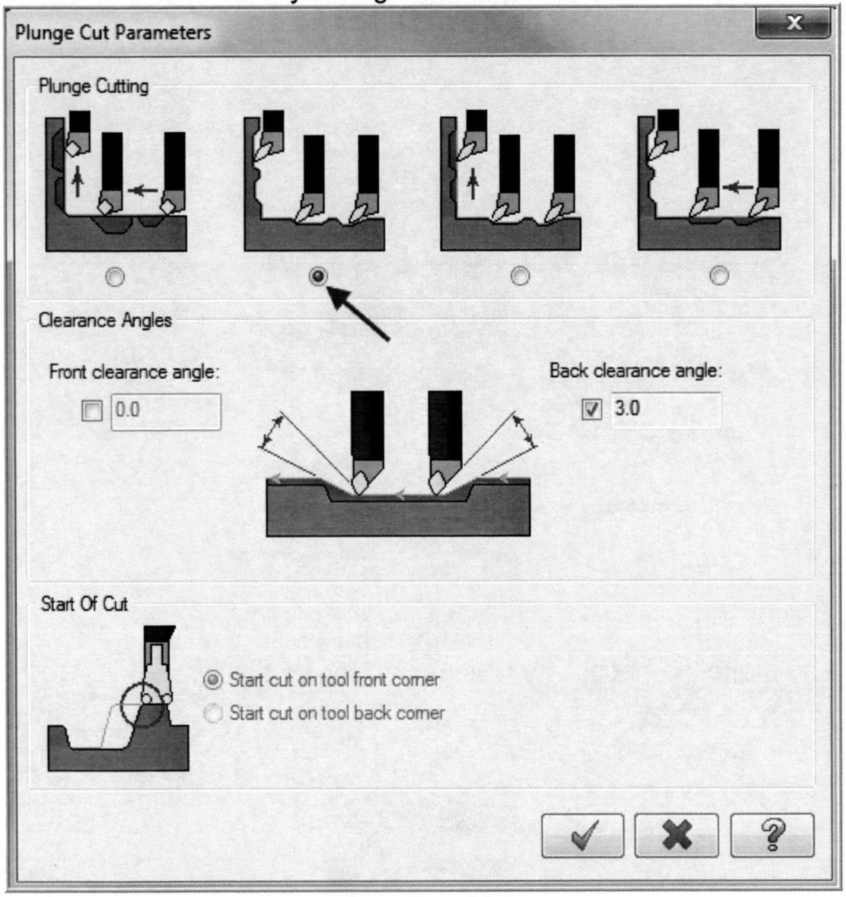

Plunge Cut Parameters dialog box
Use this dialog box to determine how you want the tool to handle undercuts along the toolpath. You can choose to plunge into undercuts in either X, Z, or both axes.

If you activate any of the plunge methods, use the other options to tell Mastercam how to begin the plunge move. Choose the options that fit best with your tool and part geometry.

You can choose whether or not to plunge at an angle for additional clearance at the undercut wall, and whether to start the plunge at the front or back of the tool.

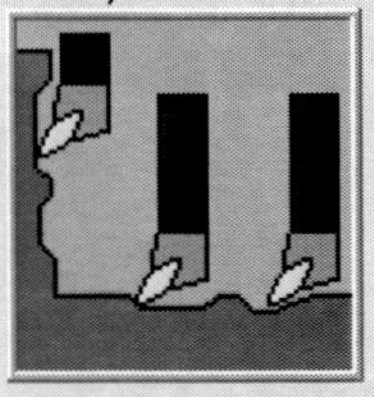

Allow plunging in both directions
The tool cuts into all undercuts on the chained path. Activates the Tool Width Compensation options. Not available for canned rough toolpaths.

20. Click on Ok to exit the **Plunge Cut Parameters** window.

21. Click on Ok to exit the **Lathe Finish parameters** window.

TASK 14:
CUT OFF THE PART

➲ In this task you will cut off the part using **Tool #3 0.125 OD GROOVE RIGHT HAND TOOL**

1. From the menu bar select **TOOLPATHS>Cutoff…**

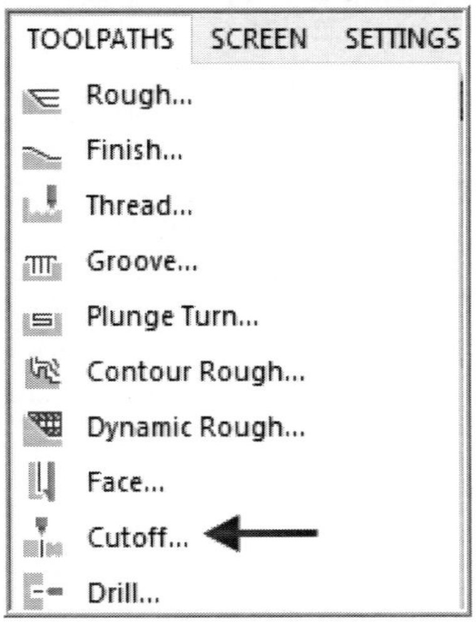

2. Pick the end point of the line shown below. Move the cursor over the corner until the visual cue for End point displays and then click on this point.

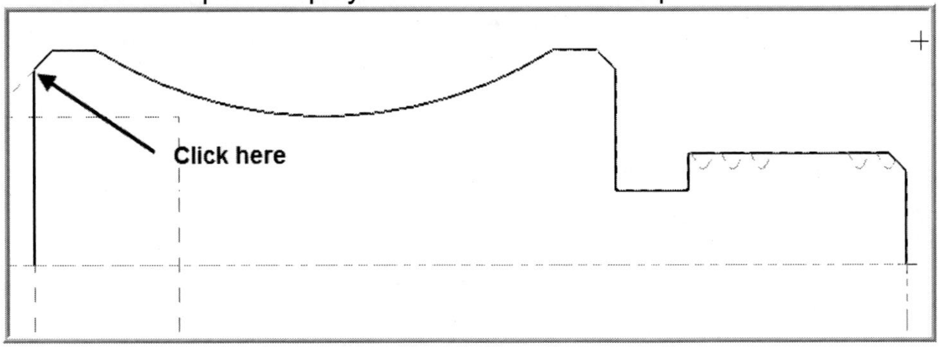

3. Select **Tool #3 OD GROOVE RIGHT WIDTH .125** tool from the tool list and make any necessary changes as shown below:

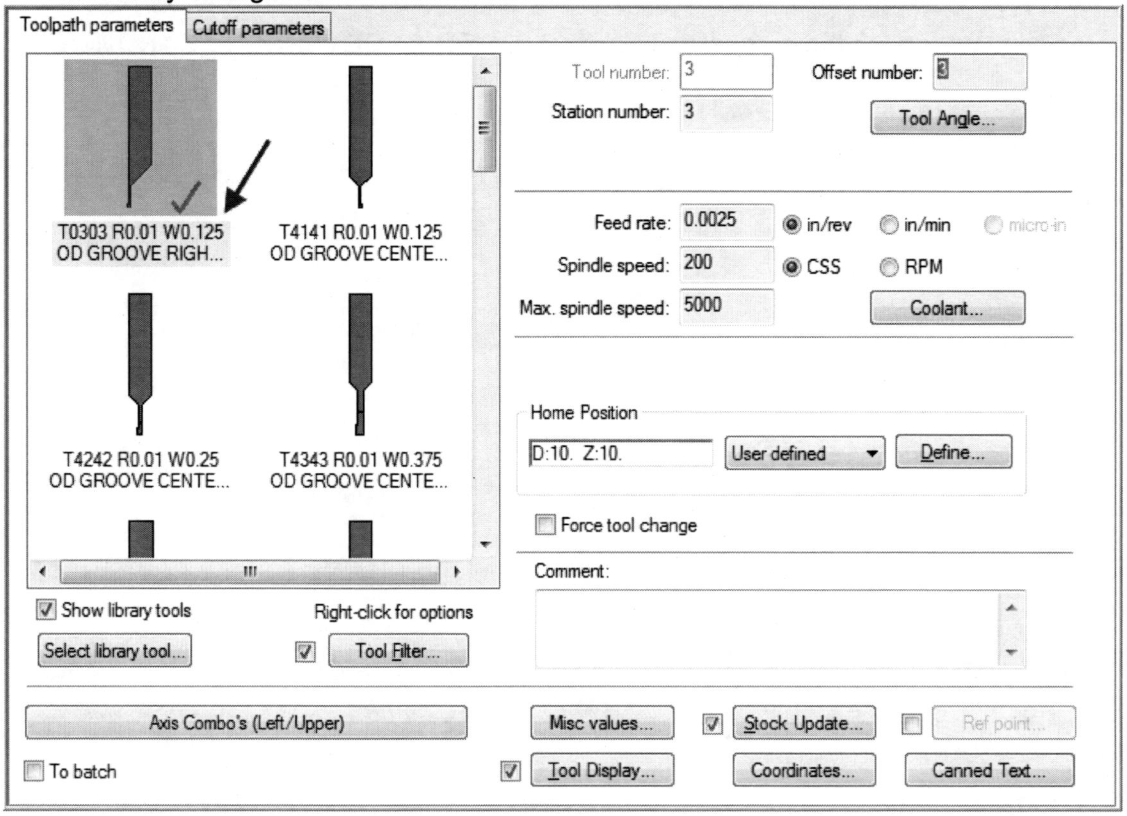

4. Still on the **Toolpath parameters** page click on the Stock Update button .

5. Ensure **Keep separated piece** is activated.

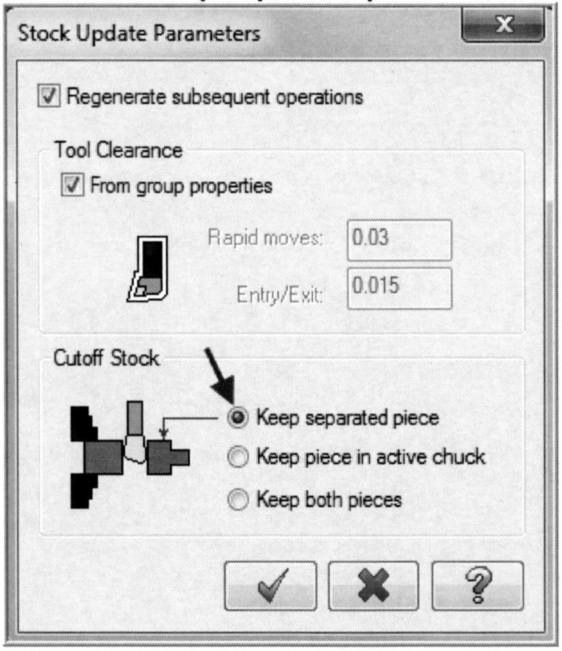

Stock Update Parameters
Use this dialog box to tell Mastercam to regenerate operations which follow the current operation when you finish editing it.
This lets you update those operations to take into account changes in the stock model caused by the current operation.
You can leave this option unselected if the only changes you are making to the operation don't affect the stock model—for example, changing the feed rate.
You can also use this dialog box to override the stock clearance values from the machine group properties, and, for cutoff operations, select whether the stock model will be based on the finished part or leftover stock.
Keep separated piece
Check to display the part boundary after the part is cut off. This option is available only with cutoff operations.

6. Select the **Cutoff parameters** page and make sure the settings are as shown below:

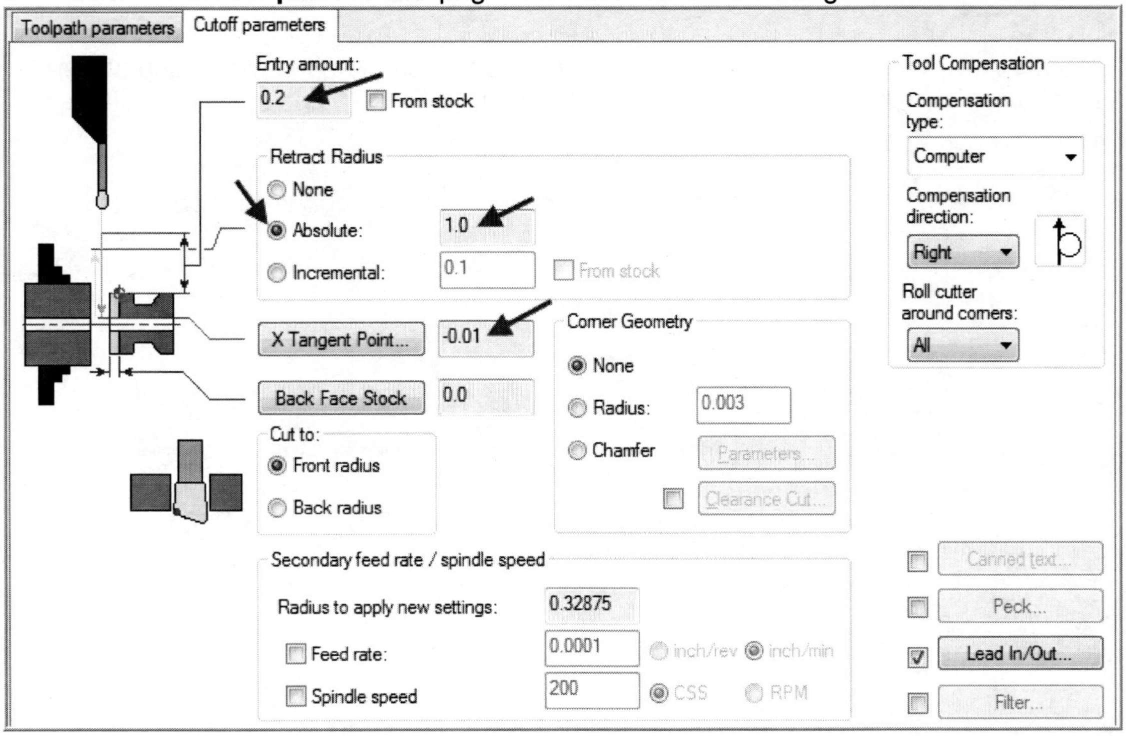

7. Select the OK button to exit **Lathe Cutoff parameters.**

TASK 15:
VERIFY THE TOOLPATH

➲ Mastercam's Verify utility allows you to use solid models to simulate the machining of a part. The model created by the verification represents the surface finish, and shows collisions, if any exist.

1. In the Toolpaths Manager pick all the operations to Verify by picking the **Select All** icon  .
2. Select the **Verify selected operations** icon shown below:

3. **Maximize** the Backplot/Verify window if required.
4. Now select the **Home** Tab if required.

5. Activate the options shown below in the **Visibility** section of the Home tab. **Initial Stock** not activated.

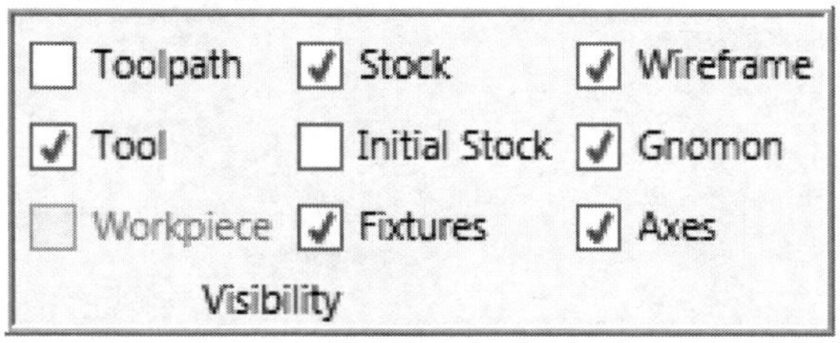

6. Activate the **Color Loop** to change the color of the tools for the verified part.

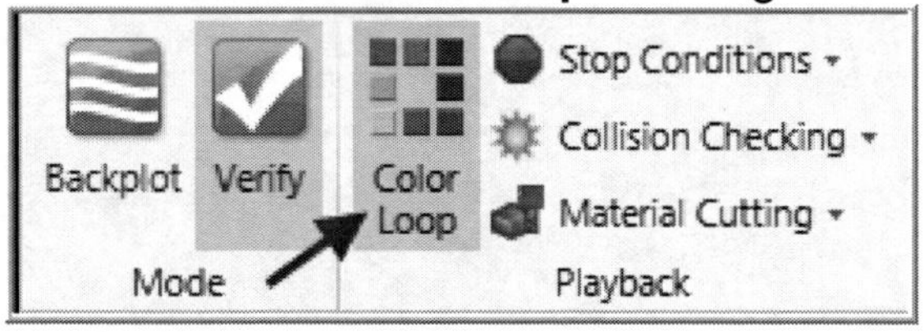

Color Loop
Changes the color of the toolpath or cut stock by operation or by tool change.

Choose **File Options** to set the colors.

7. At the top of the screen select the **View** tab, the **Isometric** icon and then select **Fit**.

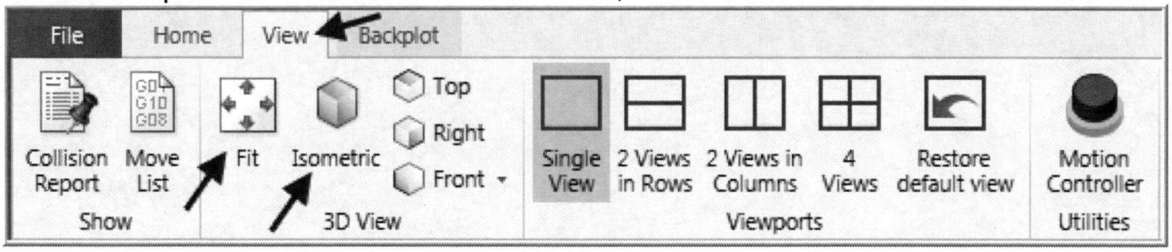

8. In the lower right corner of the screen now set the run **Speed** to slow by moving the slider bar pointer over to the left as shown below.

9. Now select the **Play Simulation** button to review the toolpaths.

10. Select the Close button  in the top right hand corner to exit Verify.

TASK 16:
SAVE THE UPDATED MASTERCAM FILE

1. Select the save icon from the toolbar 

.

TASK 17:
POST AND CREATE THE CNC CODE FILE

1. Ensure all the operations are selected by picking the **Select All** icon  from the **Toolpaths manager.**

2. Select the **Post selected operations** button from the Toolpaths manager.

➲ **Please Note:** If you cannot see **G1** click on the right pane of the Toolpaths manager window and expand the window to the right.

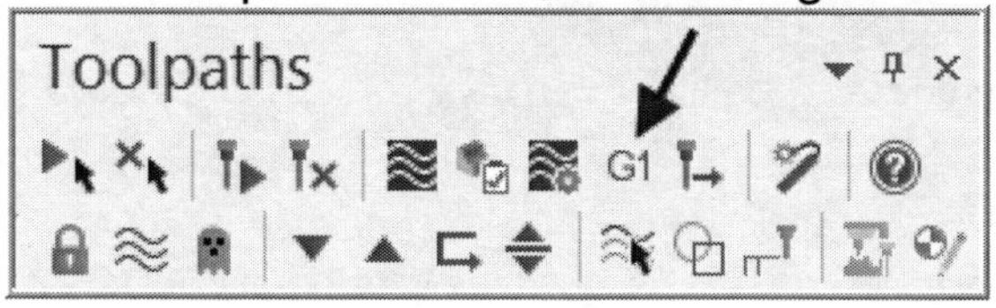

3. In the Post processing window, make the necessary changes as shown below:

About Post Processing

NC file:
Select this option to save the NC file. The file name and extension are stored in the machine group properties for the selected operation. If you are posting operations from different machine groups or Mastercam files, or batch processing, Mastercam will create several files according to the settings for each machine group.

Edit:
When checked, automatically launches the default text editor with the file displayed so that you can review or modify it.

4. Select the OK button  to continue.

5. Ensure the same name as your Mastercam part file name is displayed in the **NC File name** field.
6. Select the **Save** button.
7. The CNC code file opens up in the default editor.

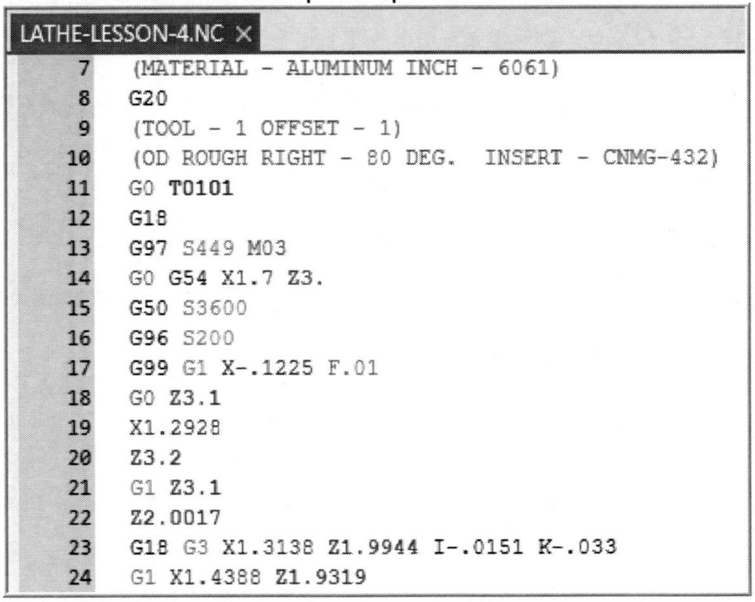

8. Select the 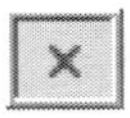 in the top right corner to exit the CNC editor.
9. This completes LATHE-LESSON-4.

LATHE-LESSON-4 EXERCISE

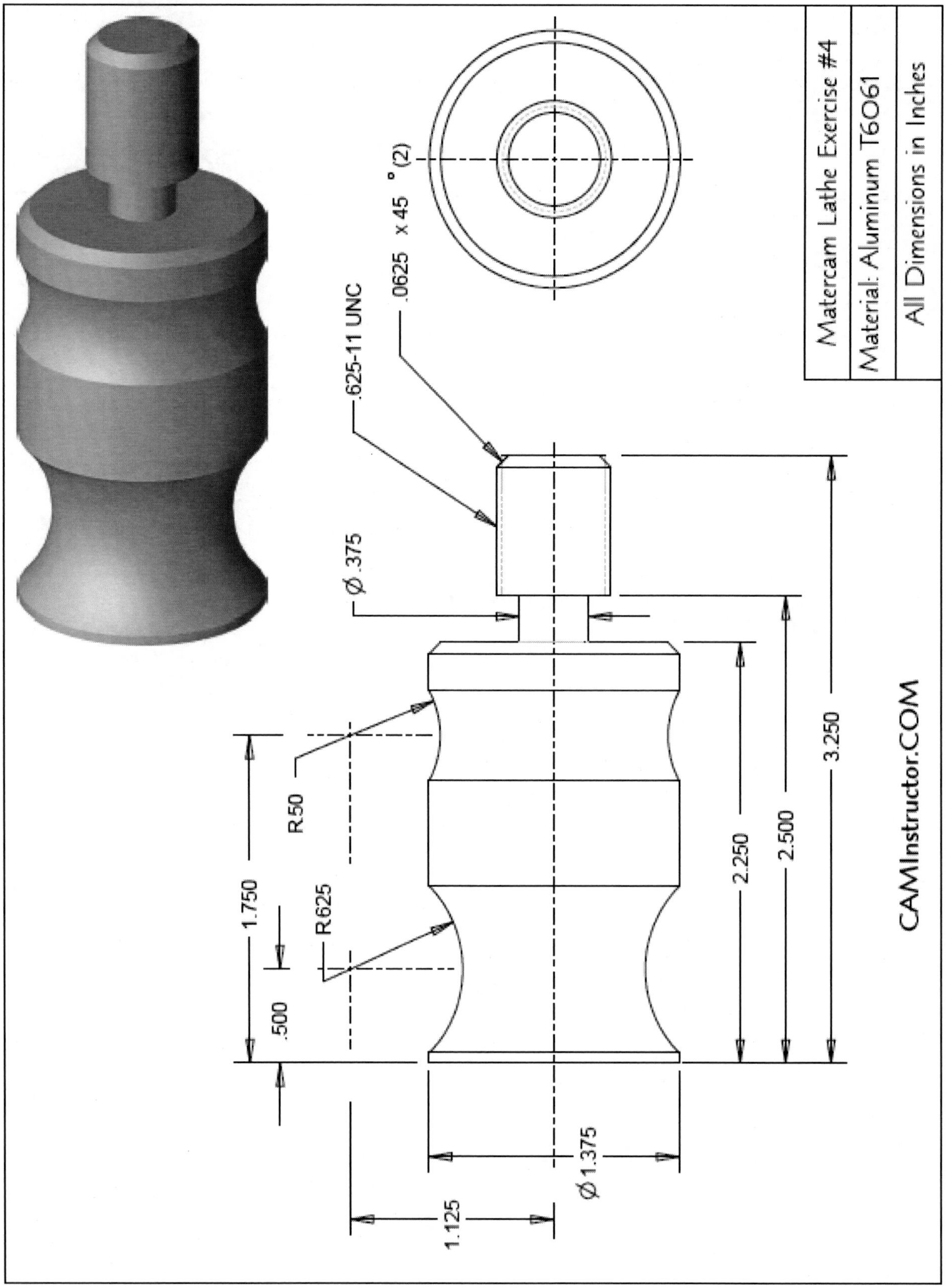

Mastercam® X9

TRAINING GUIDE

LATHE-LESSON-5

FACE, ROUGH, FINISH, DRILL, BORE AND CUTOFF

camInstructor

Objectives

You will create the geometry for Lathe Lesson 5, and then generate a toolpath to machine the part on a CNC lathe. This lesson covers the following topics:

➲ **Create a 2-dimensional drawing by:**
Creating lines.
Creating fillets.
Creating chamfers.
Trimming geometry.

➲ **Establish Stock and Chuck Setup settings:**
Stock size.
Chuck Configuration.
Material for the part.
Feed calculation.

➲ **Generate a 2-dimensional lathe toolpath consisting of:**
Lathe Face.
Lathe Rough.
Lathe Finish.
Lathe Drill.
Lathe Cutoff.

➲ **Inspect the toolpath using Mastercam's Verify and Backplot by:**
Launching the Verify function to machine the part on the screen.
Generating the NC- code.

LATHE - LESSON - 5 DRAWING

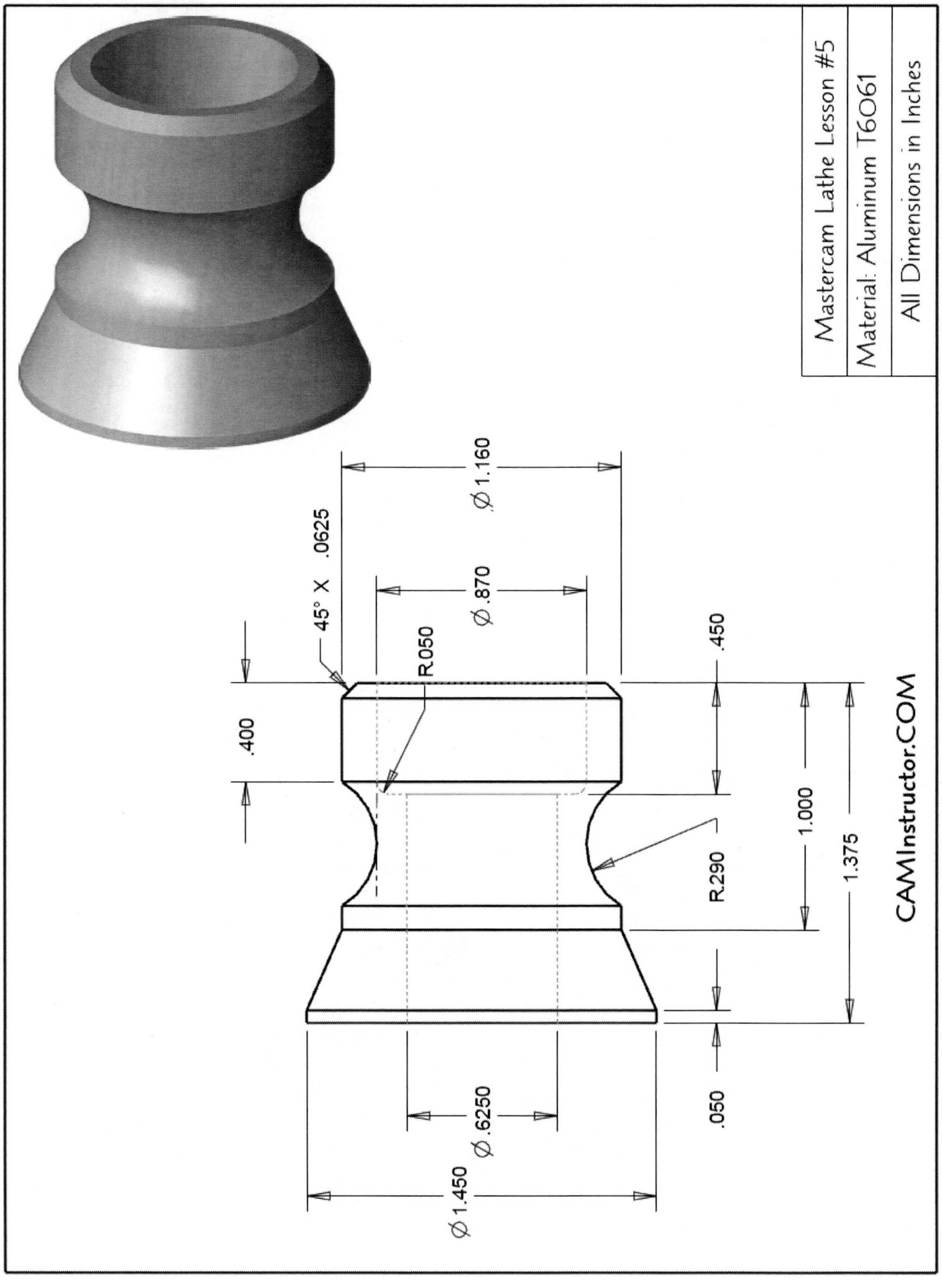

TOOL LIST

Seven tools will be used to create this part.

- **Tool #1 Face and Rough the outside diameters**
  Holder: Outside Diameter Rough Right Hand - DCGNR-164D.
  Insert: 80 Degree Diamond Insert – CNMG-432

- **Tool #2 Finish the outside diameters**
  Holder: Outside Diameter Finish Right Hand - MVJNR-164D.
  Insert: 35 Degree Diamond Insert – VNMG-431.

- **Tool #3 Center drill**
  Centre Drill – body diameter 0.250”

- **Tool #4 0.375 diameter drill**
  Drill 0.375” diameter

- **Tool #5 0.500 diameter drill**
  Drill 0.375” diameter

- **Tool #6 Boring tool**
  Holder: Boring Bar – minimum diameter 0.375”.
  Insert: 75 Degree Diamond Insert

- **Tool #7 Cutoff tool**
  Holder: Outside Diameter Groove Right Hand - Narrow.
  Insert: 0.125” Wide - GC-4125

LESSON - 5 - THE PROCESS

Geometry Creation

TASK 1: Setting the environment
TASK 2: Setting the construction planes
TASK 3: Create the geometry
TASK 4: Create the 0.290" radius
TASK 5: Create the geometry for the bore
TASK 6: Create the chamfers
TASK 7: Save the drawing

Toolpath Creation

TASK 8: Define the stock and chuck parameters
TASK 9: Face the front of the part
TASK 10: Rough the outside diameters
TASK 11: Finish the outside diameters
TASK 12: Center drill hole
TASK 13: Pre drill the 0.625" hole 0.375 diameter
TASK 14: Pre drill the 0.625" hole 0.5 diameter
TASK 15: Rough the bore
TASK 16: Finish the bore
TASK 17: Cut off the part
TASK 18: Verify the toolpath
TASK 19: Save the updated Mastercam file
TASK 20: Post and create the cnc code file

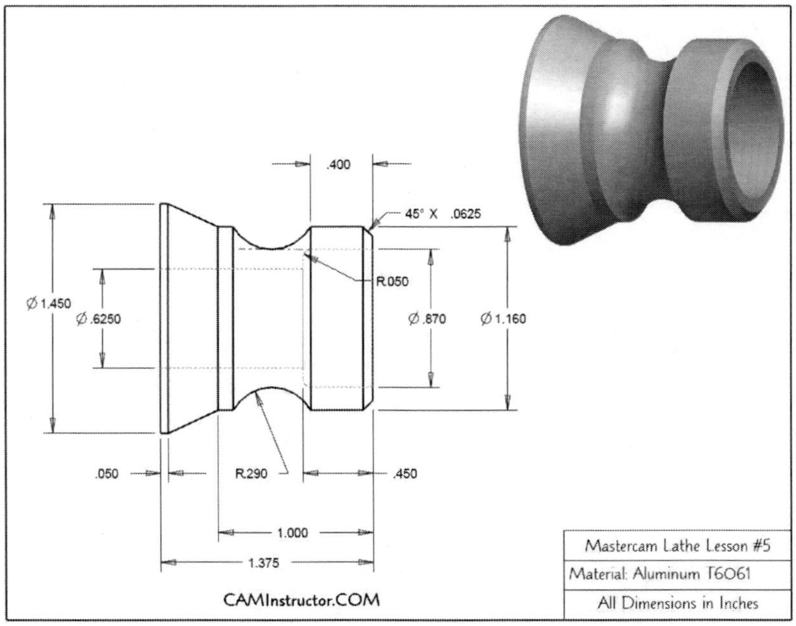

Geometry Creation

TASK 1:
SETTING THE ENVIRONMENT

Before starting the geometry creation you should set up the grid and toolbars as outlined in the **Setting the Environment** section at the beginning of this text:

1. Set up the Grid. This will help identify the location of the origin.
2. Load the Workspace – **SETTINGS>Load Workspace>Lathe** to machine a part on the Lathe.
3. Set the machine type to the default Lathe.

TASK 2:
SETTING THE CONSTRUCTION PLANES:

➲ **Set the Construction Plane to Lathe diameter +D +Z (WCS)**

1. Click on Planes at the bottom of the screen as shown below:

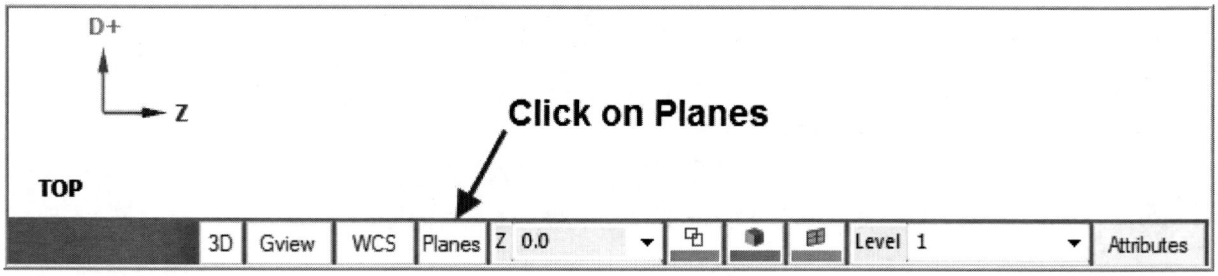

2. Click on **Lathe diameter>+D +Z (WCS)** as shown below:

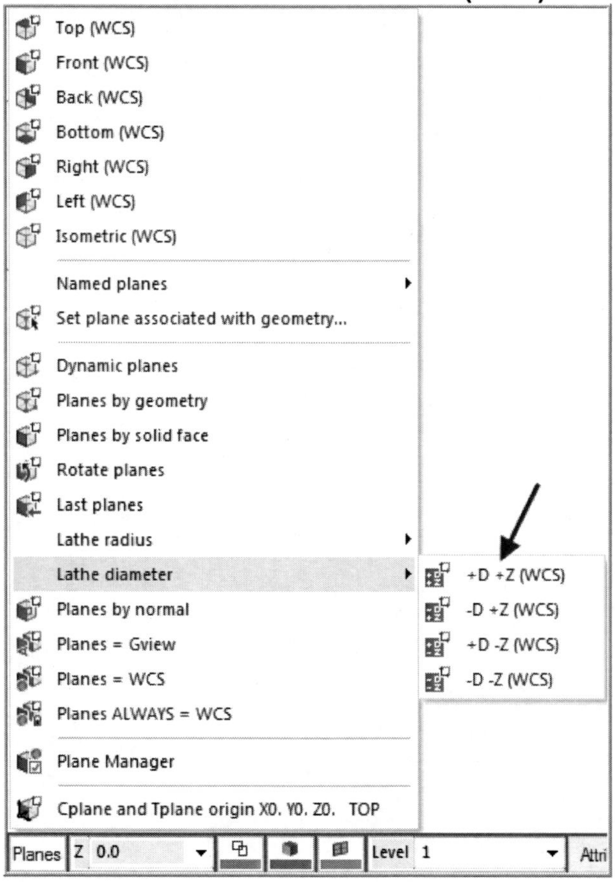

TASK 3:
CREATE THE GEOMETRY

➲ This task explains how to create the geometry of this part. In this lathe part you only need to create **half of the geometry**, the geometry above the center line.

➲ Lines 1 through 6 will be created first and then the radius and chamfer will be created.

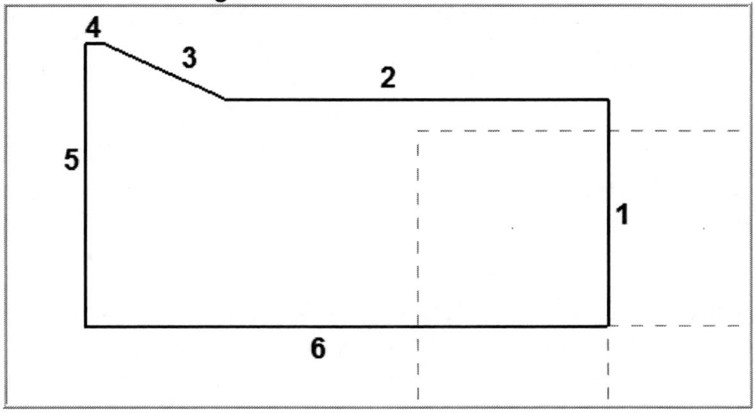

➲ **Create Line #1**

1. Select **Alt-O** on your keyboard to turn off the display of the Toolpaths Manager.
2. Select from the pull down menu **CREATE>Line>Endpoint…**

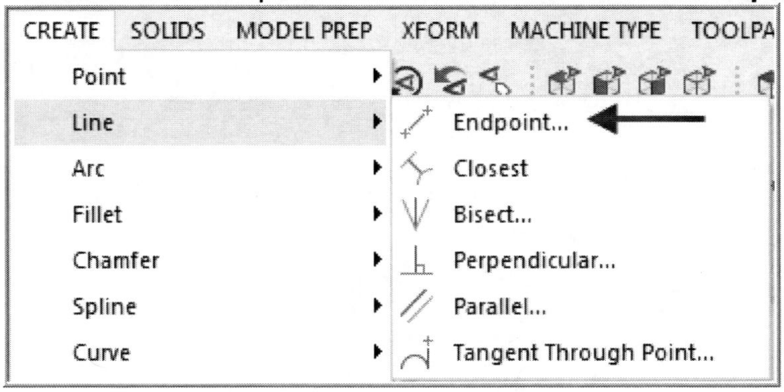

3. The Line ribbon bar appears:

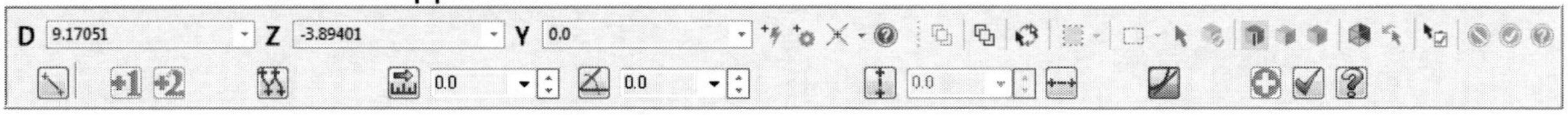

4. Move the cursor over the **center of the grid** and as you get close to the origin a visual cue appears.  This is the cue that will allow you to snap to the **origin**. With this visual cue highlighted pick the **origin.**

AutoCursor: Visual Cues detects and highlights endpoints and midpoints of curves, lines, arc center points, and point entities.

In addition, AutoCursor can snap to angle, nearest, tangent, perpendicular, horizontal, and vertical conditions.

➲ The following are Mastercam Visual Cues:

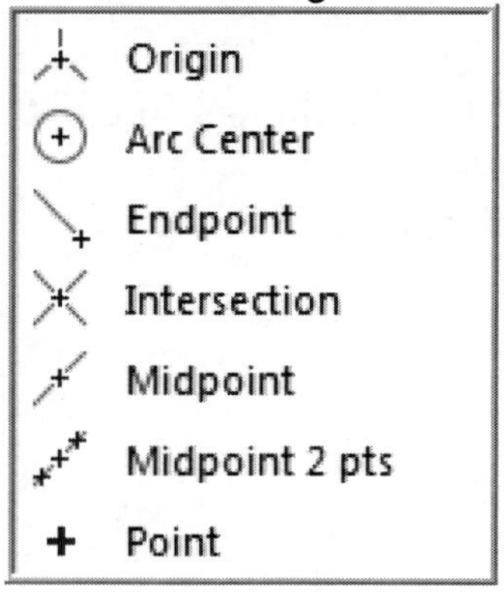

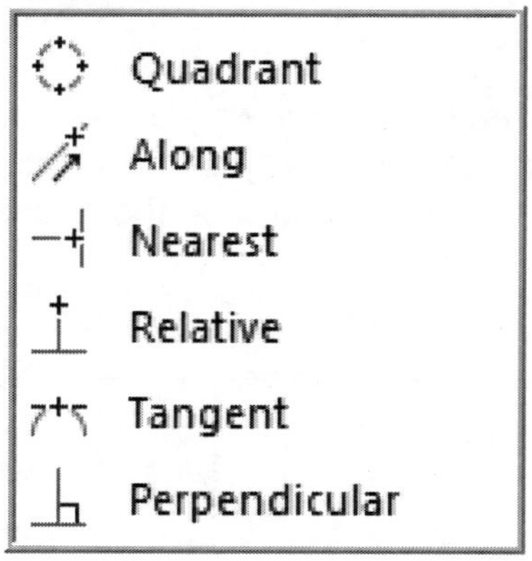

5. You are next prompted to **"Specify the second endpoint".** On the left hand side of the Line ribbon bar click on the **Multi-Line** button to activate it as shown below by the arrow:

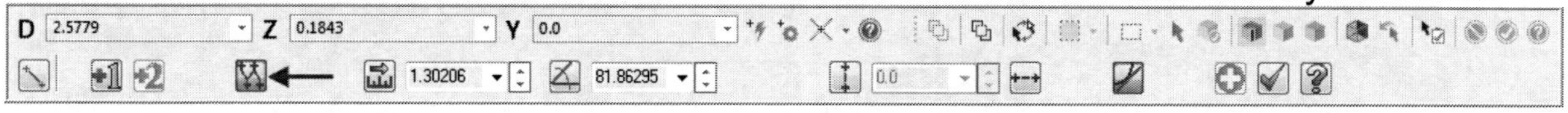

6. Click in the **D** value space (Diameter) (as shown by the arrow below) and enter a value of **1.16**. Hit the Enter key and enter a value of **0 for the Z**, hit the Enter key again and enter a value of **0 for the Y** and hit Enter.

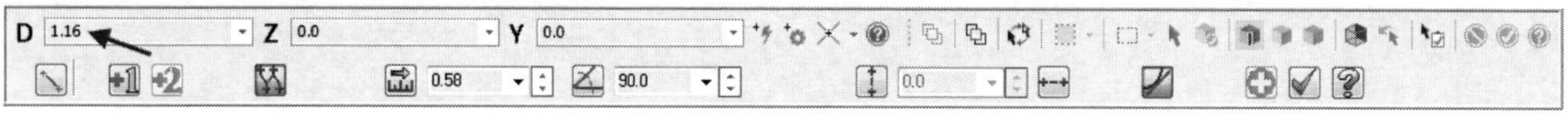

7. A vertical line should be visible as shown below:

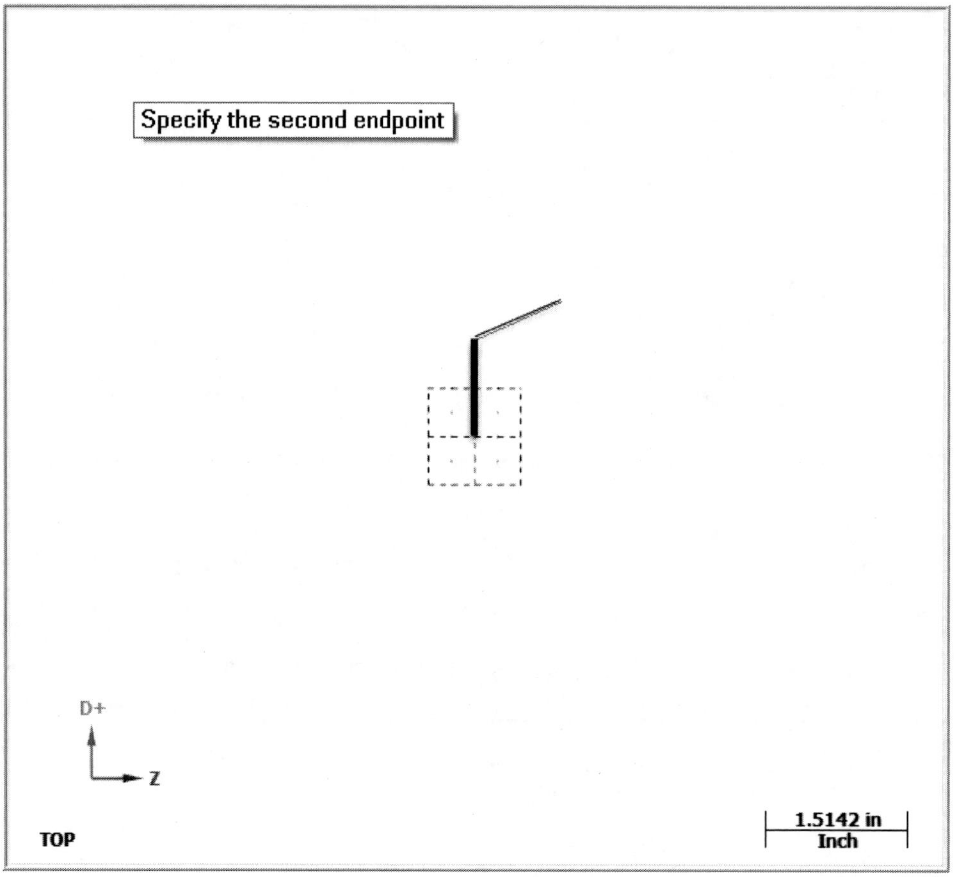

➲ **Create Line #2**

8. **"Specify the second endpoint";** Type in **1.16 in D** hit Enter, type in **-1.0 in Z. Note** the value of Y is set to **Zero**, this does not need to be input. Hit the Enter key once again to complete this line.

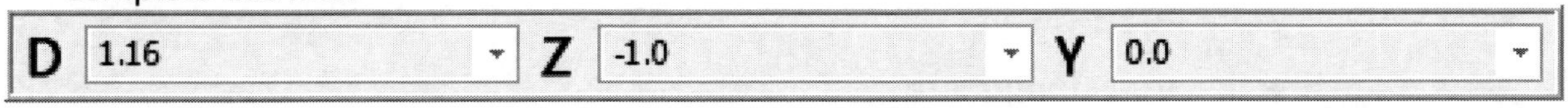

➲ **Create Line #3**

9. **"Specify the second endpoint";** Type in **1.45 in D** hit Enter, type in **-1.375-0.05 in Z.** Hit the Enter key once again to complete this line.

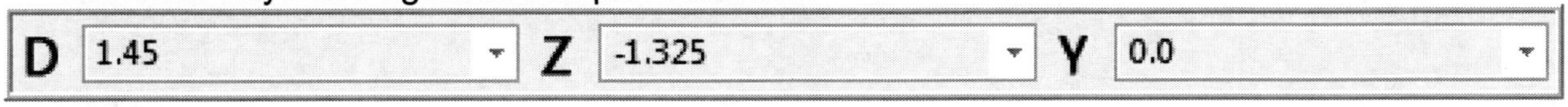

➲ **Create Line #4**

10. **"Specify the second endpoint";** Type in **1.45 in D** hit Enter, type in **-1.375 in Z.** Hit the Enter key once again to complete this line.

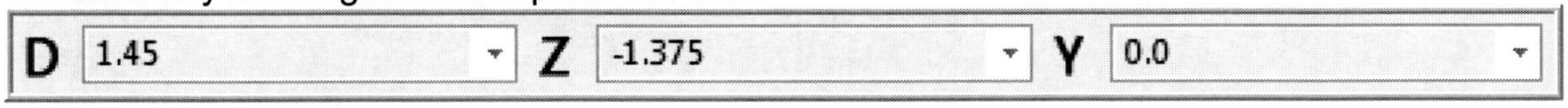

➲ **Create Line #5**

11. **"Specify the second endpoint";** Type in **0.0 in D** hit Enter, type in **-1.375 in Z.** Hit the Enter key once again to complete this line.

➲ **Create Line #6**

12. **"Specify the second endpoint";** Move the cursor over the **center of the grid** and as you get close to the origin a visual cue appears.  Click on this point.
13. Click on the **OK** icon  to complete this feature.
14. Fit the image to the screen by clicking on the **Fit** icon as shown below:

15. Then unzoom by clicking on the **Un-zoom Previous / .5** icon as shown below:

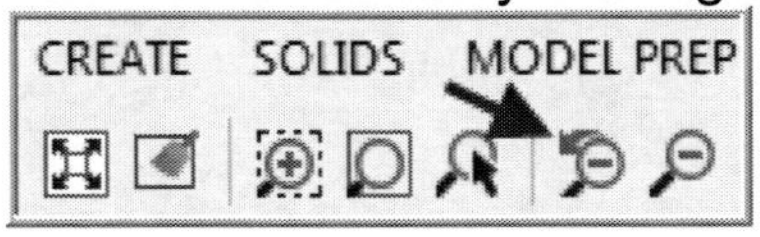

16. Your geometry should look like the figure below.

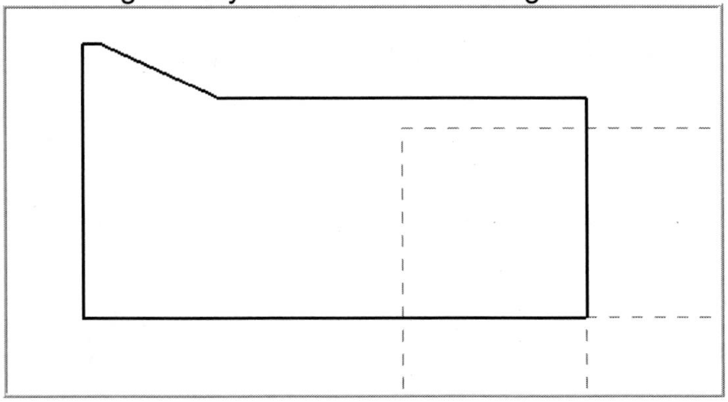

TASK 4:
CREATE THE 0.290" RADIUS

➲ In this task you will create the 0.290 arc. It is an arc tangent to a line and passes through a point.

➲ **Create the line the arc is tangent to.**

1. Select from the pull down menu: **CREATE>Line>Parallel….**
2. On the graphics screen you are prompted: Select a line and the Line Parallel ribbon bar appears.
3. To satisfy the prompt **Select a line**, select the line shown below.

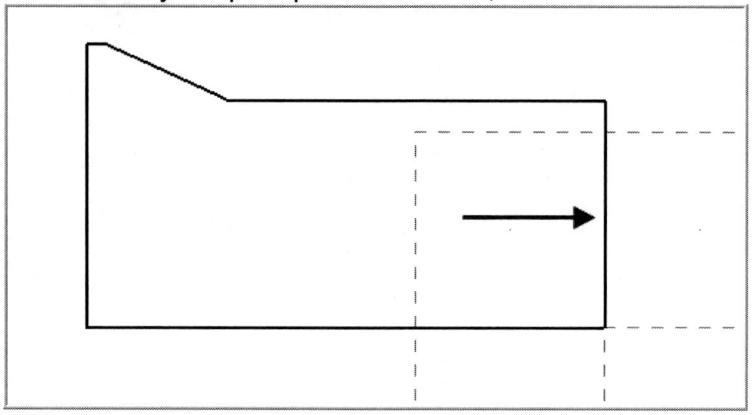

4. To satisfy the next prompt **Select the point to place a parallel line through** move the cursor to the left of the line and pick a point.
5. For the **Distance** input **0.4** then hit **enter**.
6. On the ribbon bar click on **Apply**  to fix the entity,
7. To satisfy the prompt **Select a line**, select the line shown below.

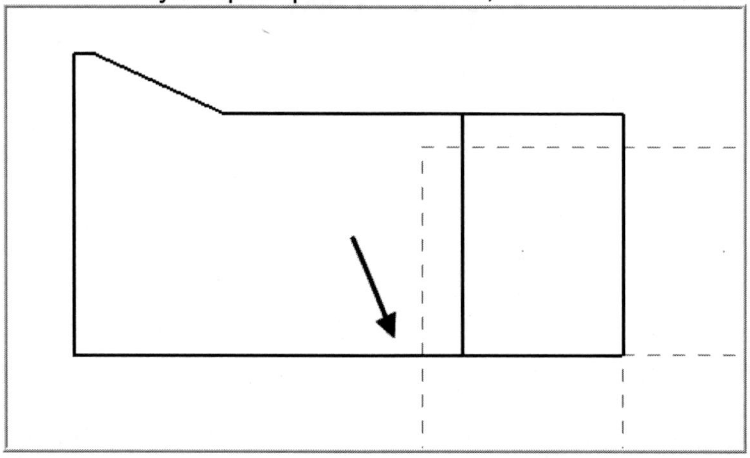

8. To satisfy the next prompt **Select the point to place a parallel line through** move the cursor above the line and pick a point.
9. For the **Distance** input **0.870/2** then hit **enter**
10. Click on the OK icon  to complete this feature.

11. The completed geometry is shown below:

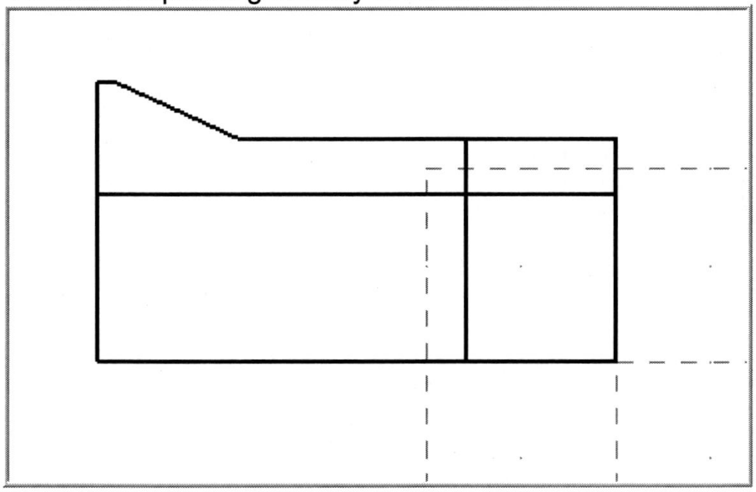

➲ **Create the 0.290" Arc**

12. Select **CREATE>Arc> Arc Tangent…**

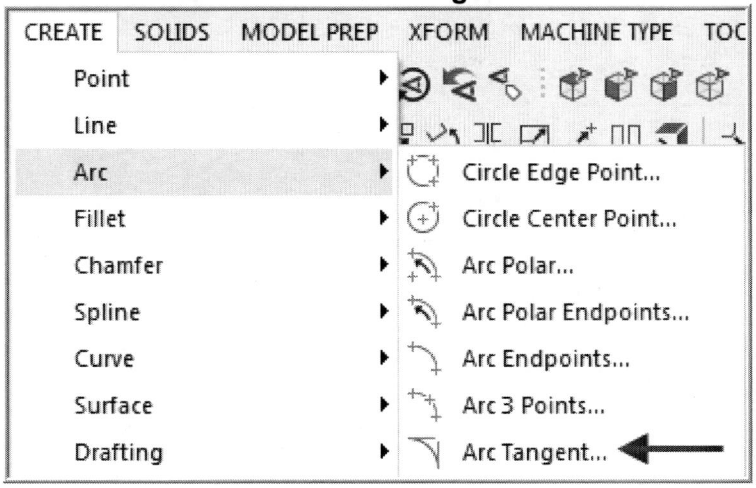

13. The **Arc Tangent** ribbon bar appears and you are prompted to **Select the entity that the arc is to be tangent to**.

14. Click on the **Tangent point**  icon to activate it as shown above. Ensure the icon is pressed down to signal that it is activated.
15. Click in the space for **Radius** (shown above) and enter a value of **0.290** and then hit the **enter** key.

16. To satisfy the prompt **Select the entity that the arc is to be tangent to** move the cursor over the line shown below and select it:

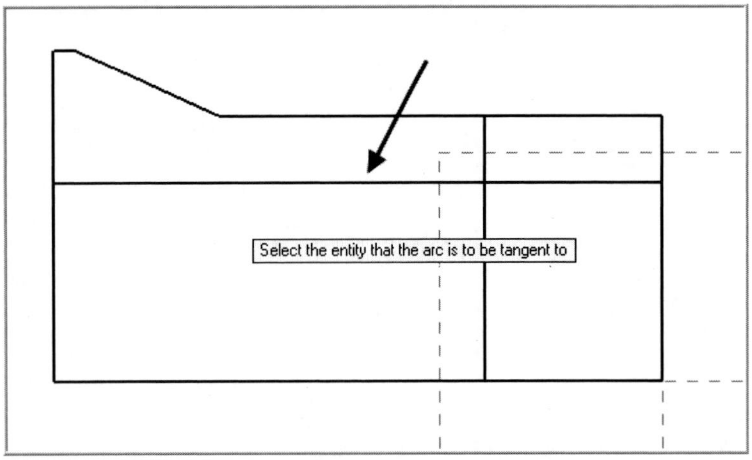
Select the entity that the arc is to be tangent to

17. To satisfy the prompt **Specify the thru point** move the cursor over the endpoint of the line shown below. When the visual cue for endpoint appears click on this point.

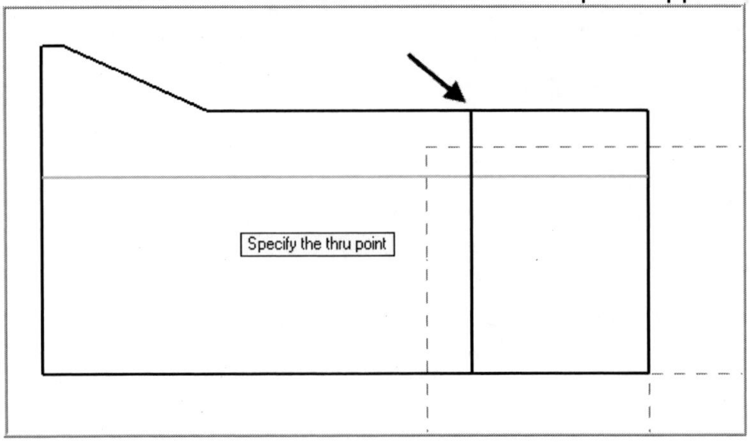
Specify the thru point

18. After selecting this endpoint you a confronted with a selection of arcs. The prompt changes to **Select an arc**. Select the arc in the position shown below:

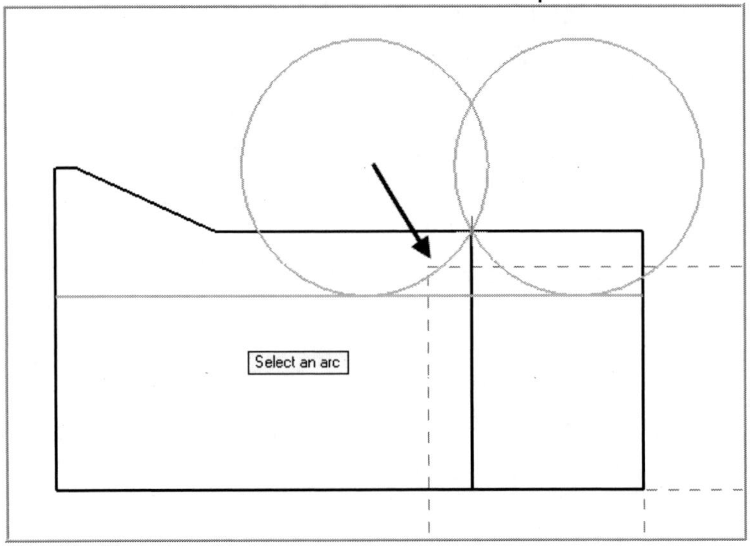
Select an arc

19. Click on the OK icon to complete this feature.

20. The completed arc is shown below.

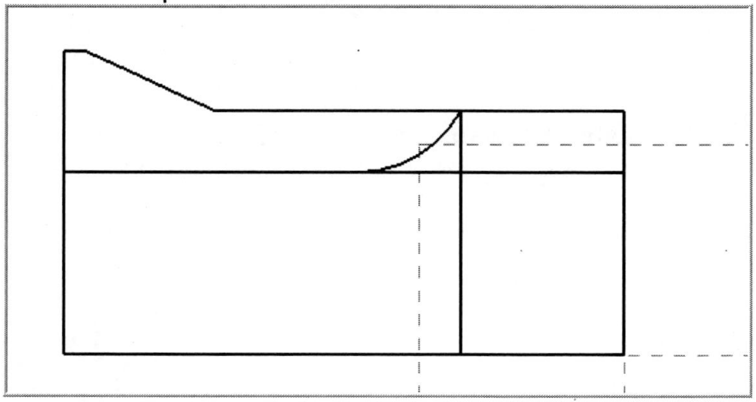

➲ **Trim the Arc**

21. Select **EDIT>Trim/Break>Trim/Break/Extend**
22. The Trim / Extend / Break ribbon bar appears and you are prompted to **Select the entity to trim/extend**.
23. Click on the **Trim 1 entity** button as shown below:

24. Now at the prompt **Select the entity to trim/extend** select the arc at **position 1,**
25. The prompt changes to **Select the entity to trim/extend to**, select the line at **position 2**

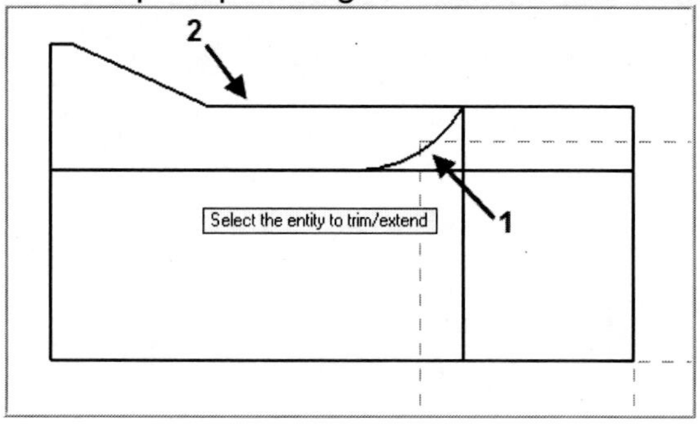

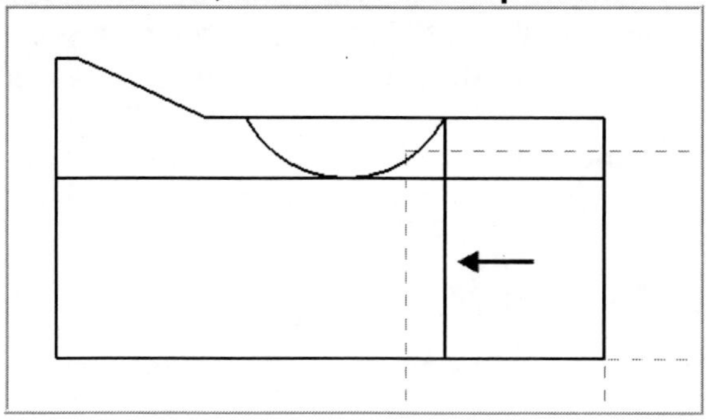

26. Click on the OK icon  to complete this feature.
27. The geometry should look like the image above right.
28. **Delete** the construction line shown above right. Select the line and hit the Delete key on your keyboard.

TASK 5:
CREATE THE GEOMETRY FOR THE BORE

➲ In this task you will create the geometry that make up the bore of this part

1. Select from the pull down menu: **CREATE>Line>Parallel….**
2. **On the graphics screen you are prompted**: **Select a line** and the Line Parallel ribbon bar appears.
3. To satisfy the prompt **Select a line**, select the line shown below.

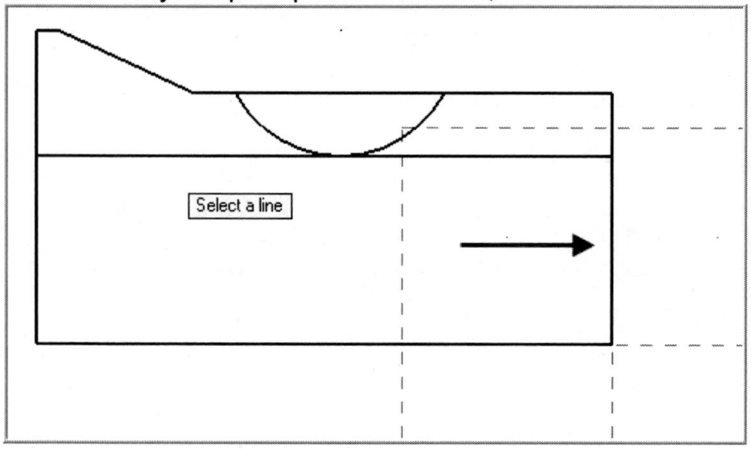

4. To satisfy the next prompt **Select the point to place a parallel line through** move the cursor to the left of the line and pick a point.
5. For the **Distance** input **0.450** then hit **enter**.
6. On the ribbon bar click on **Apply**  to fix the entity.
7. To satisfy the prompt **Select a line**, select the line shown below.

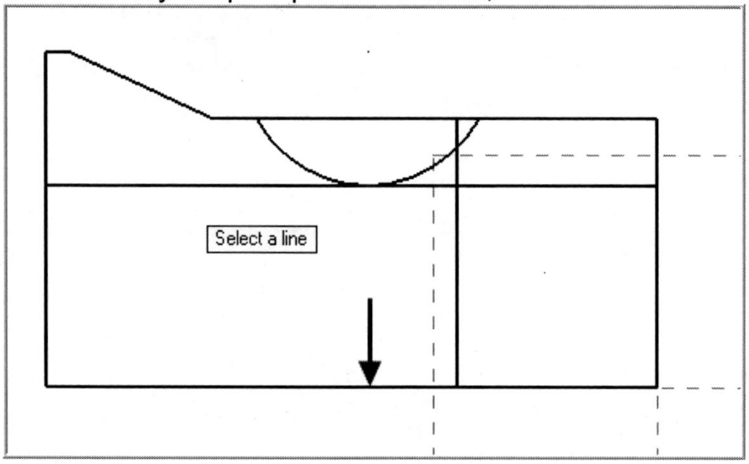

8. To satisfy the next prompt **Select the point to place a parallel line through** move the cursor above the line and pick a point.
9. For the **Distance** input **0.625/2** then hit **enter.**
10. Click on the OK icon  to complete this feature.

➲ **Create 0.050 fillet**

11. Select **CREATE>Fillet>Entities…**

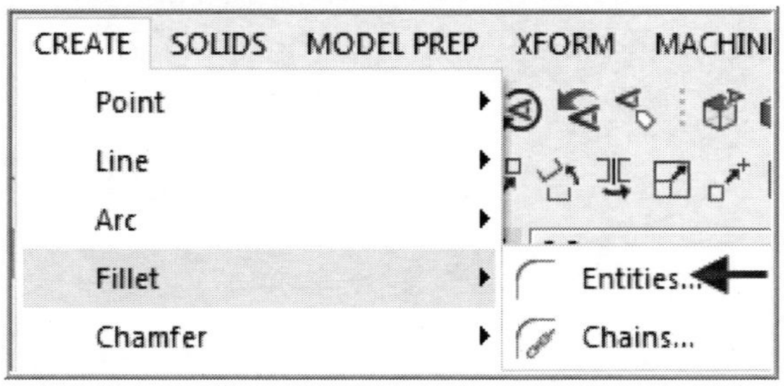

12. On the Fillet ribbon bar enter **0.05 for the radius**. Ensure the **Style** of radius is set to **Normal** and the trim button is depressed to turn the **trim on**.

13. When prompted to **Fillet: Select an entity,** select Line 1 and 2 as shown below. The fillet radius appears at the corner of line 1 and 2.

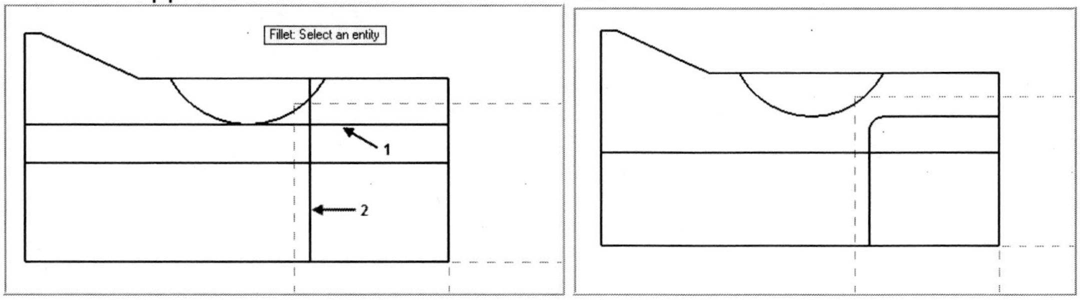

14. Click on the OK icon  to complete this feature.

➲ **Trim the bore**

15. Select **EDIT>Trim/Break>Trim/Break/Extend.**
16. The Trim / Extend / Break ribbon bar appears and you are prompted to **Select the entity to trim/extend**.
17. Click on the **Trim 2 entity** button as shown below:

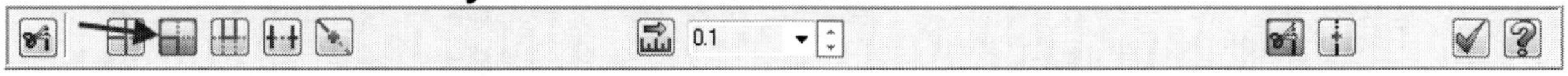

18. Now at the prompt **Select the entity to trim/extend** select the line at **position 1,**
19. The prompt changes to **Select the entity to trim/extend to**, select the line at **position 2**

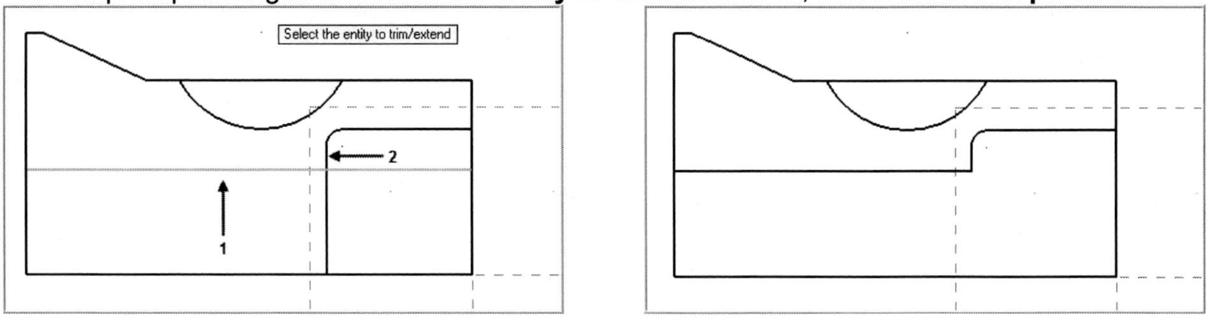

20. The trimmed geometry should look like the image above right.

➲ Trim the .290 arc

21. Now click on the Divide icon.
22. The prompt changes to **Select the curve to divide.** Move the cursor over the line and select it as shown below left.

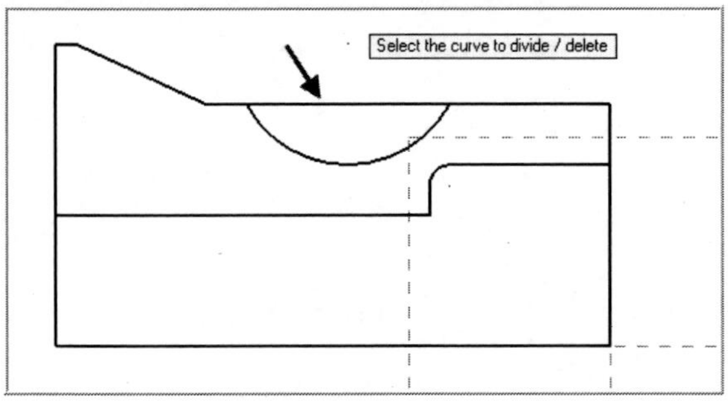
Select the curve to divide / delete

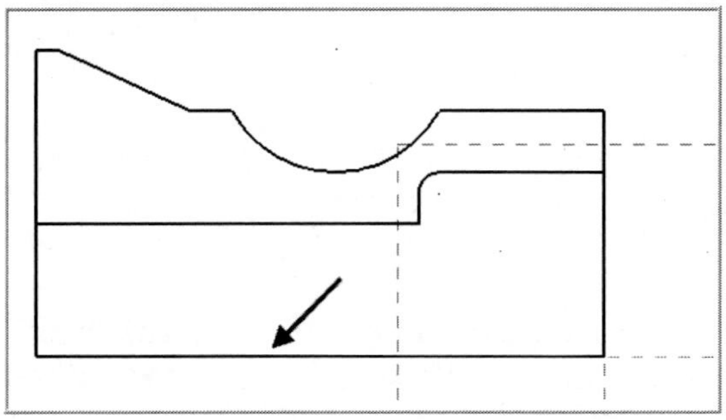

23. Click on the OK icon to complete this feature. The line is trimmed back to the two closest intersections as shown above right:
24. **Delete** the construction line shown above right. Select the line and hit the delete key on your keyboard.

TASK 6:
CREATE THE CHAMFER

➲ **Create Chamfer 45 degrees x .0625.**

1. Select **CREATE>Chamfer>Entities…**

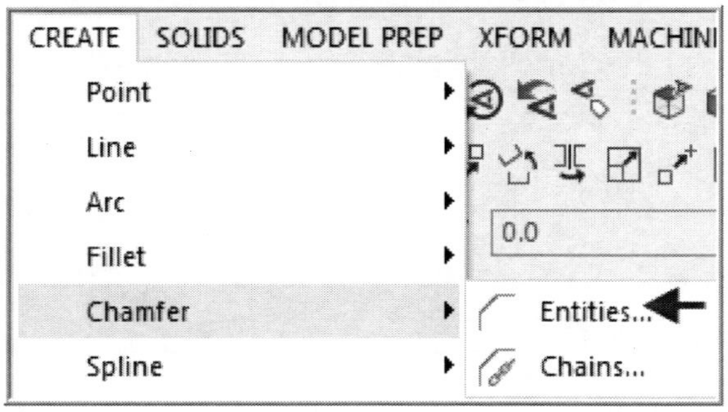

2. You are prompted to 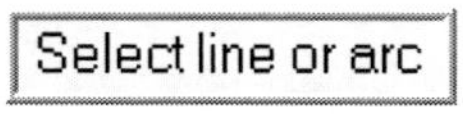.

3. Click in the Distance window as shown below and type in **.0625** and hit enter:

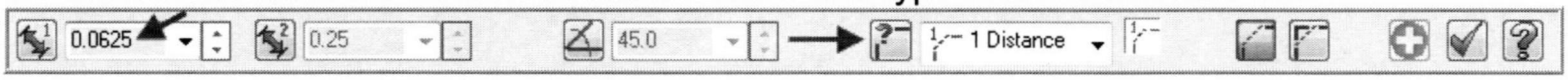

4. Ensure the 1 Distance option is selected as shown above.
5. Click on line 1 and then line 2 as shown below:

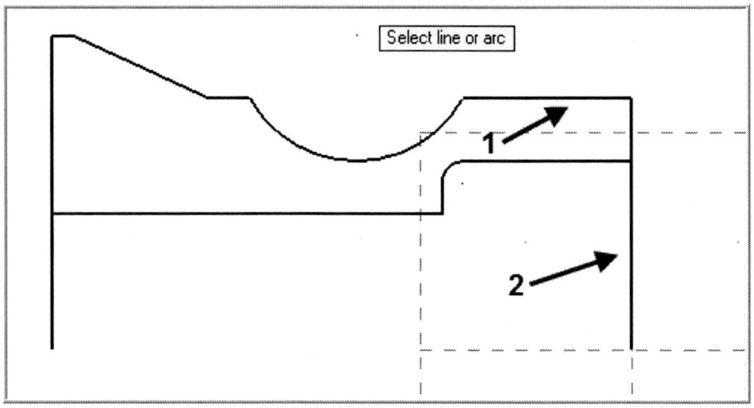

6. Click on the OK icon  to complete this feature.
7. The completed geometry should look like the image below:

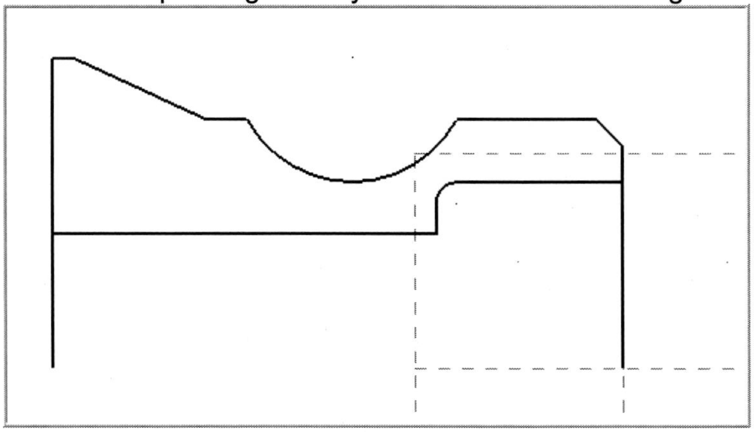

TASK 7:
SAVE THE DRAWING

1. Select **File.**
2. Select **Save as.**
3. In the **"File name"** box, type **"Lathe-Lesson-5".**
4. Save to an appropriate location.
5. Select the Save button to save the file and complete this function.

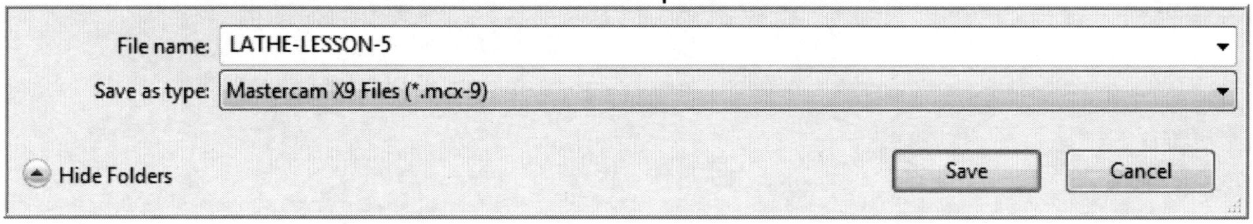

Toolpath Creation

TASK 8:
DEFINING THE STOCK AND CHUCK PARAMETERS

1. Fit the image to the screen by clicking on the Fit icon .
2. Ensure your screen looks like the image below:
   a. The Toolpaths Manager is open, if it is not Select Alt and O on your keyboard to open it.
   b. The properties icon displays Lathe Default. If it is not refer to **Setting the Environment** chapter at the beginning of the book.
   c. The Lathe Lesson-5 Geometry is displayed.

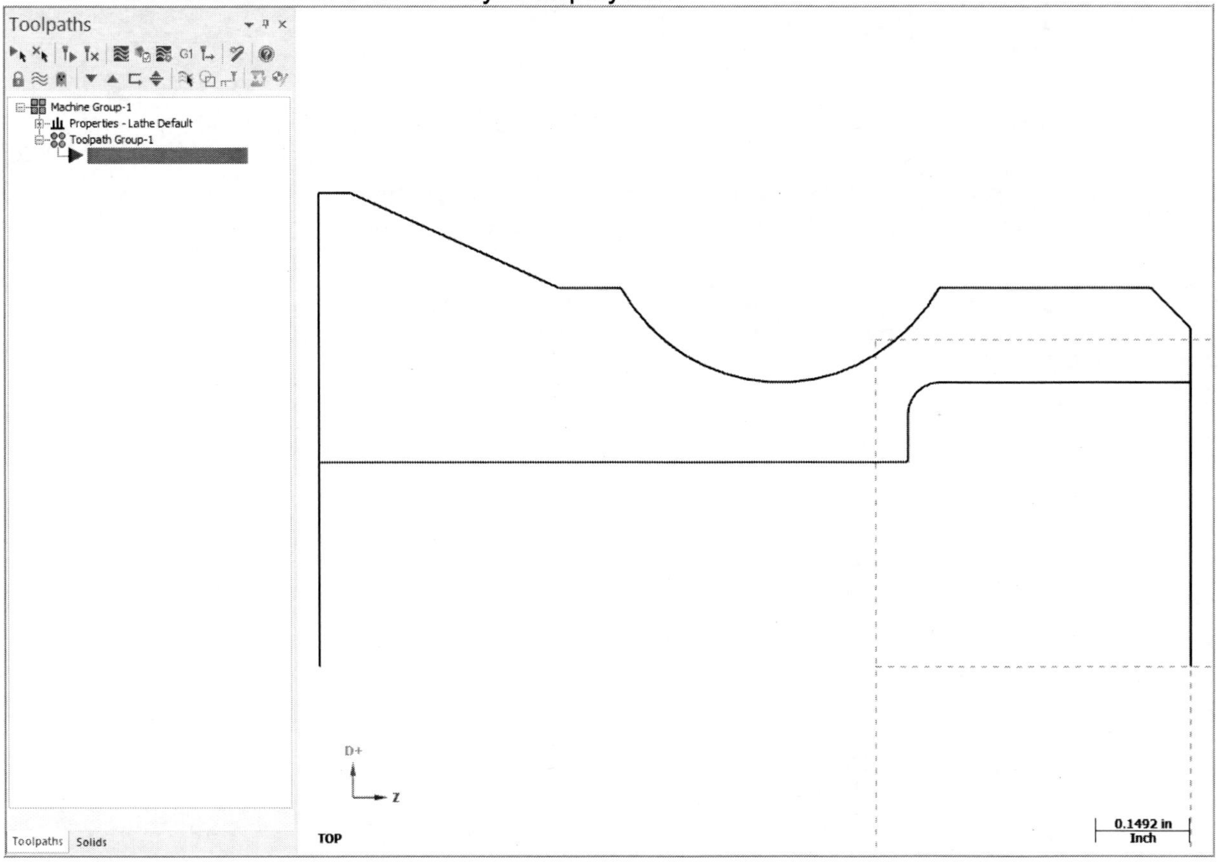

3. Select the plus in front of **Properties** to expand the Machine Group Properties.

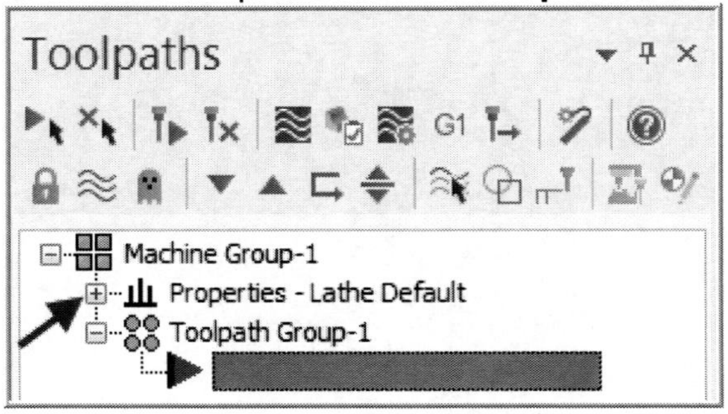

4. Select **Stock setup** in the Toolpaths Manager window.

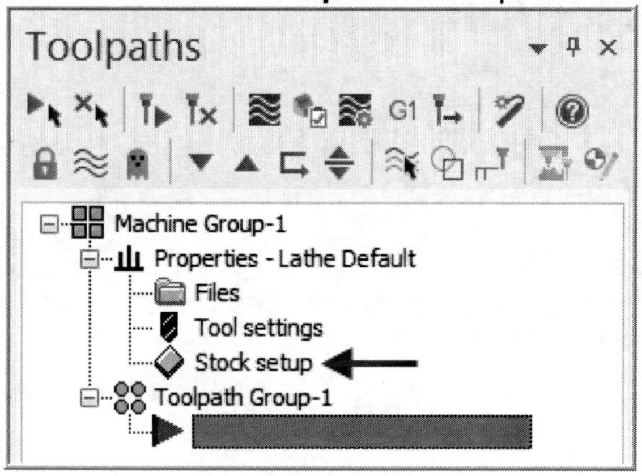

5. Select the **Stock Properties** button in the **Stock Setup** page as shown in the screenshot below:

Note: To learn more about Stock Setup refer to the Tips and Techniques section on the Mastercam Training Guide – Lathe DVD that accompanies this book.

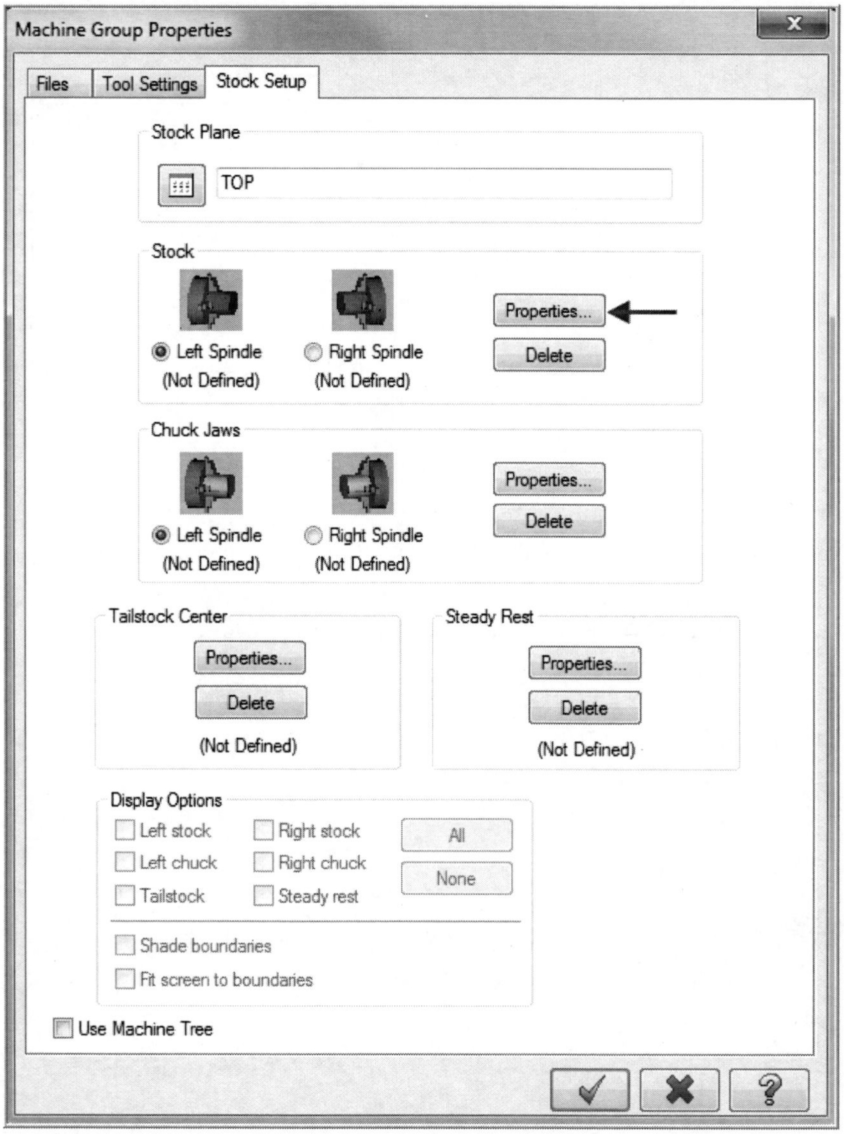

6. In the **Machine Component Manager-Stock** window click on the **Geometry** button and select **Cylinder** as shown below:

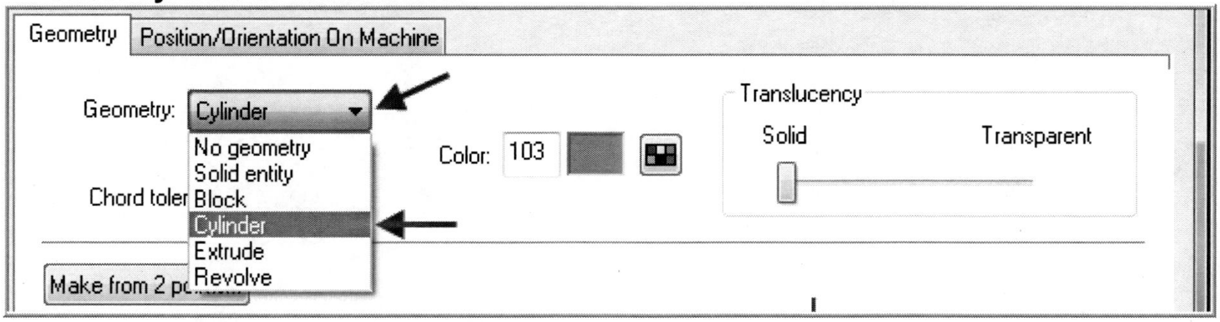

7. In the **Stock** setup set the values as shown below. **Axis is set to -Z**.

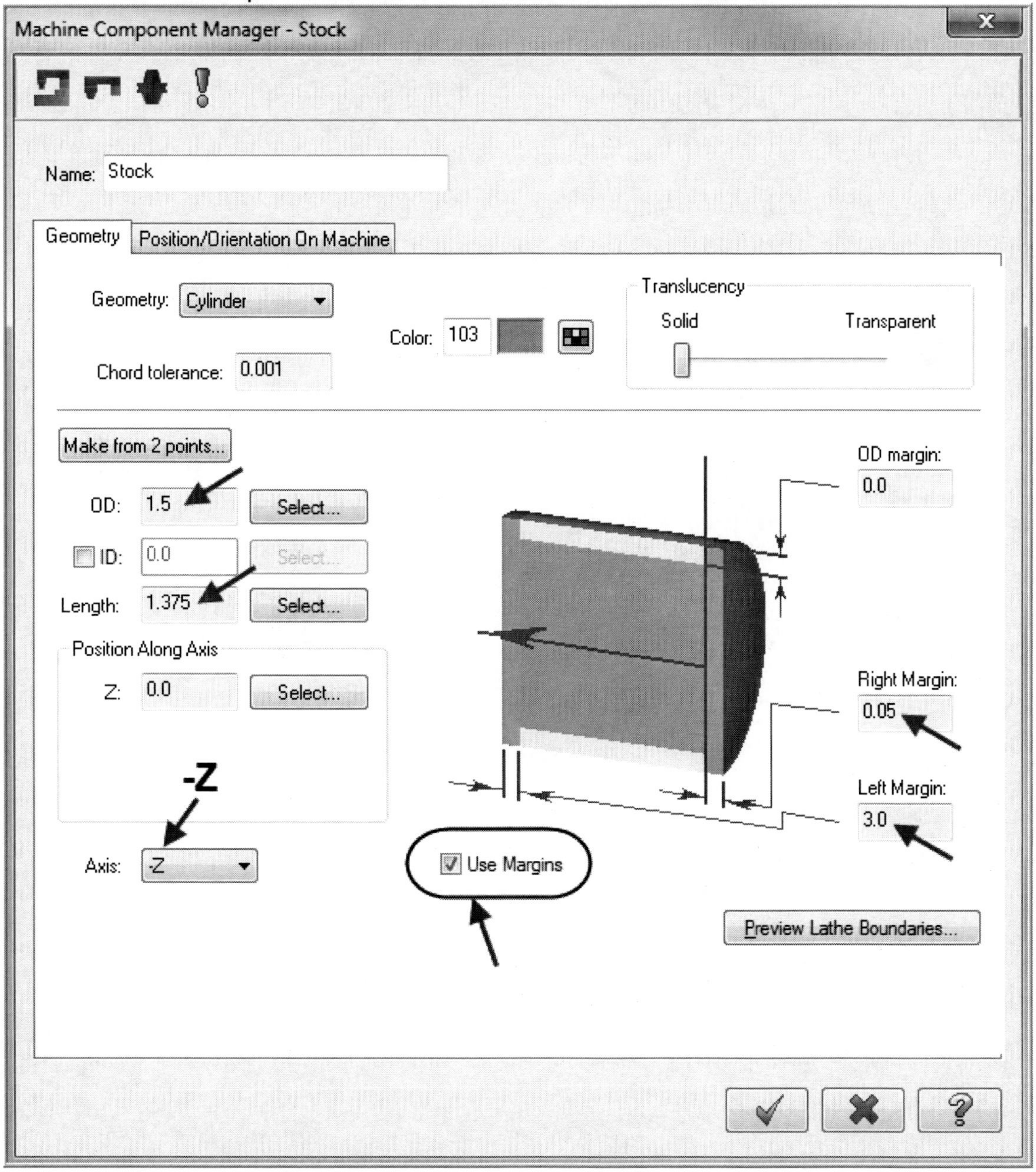

8. Click on the OK icon  to complete this feature.

9. Still on the Stock Setup page activate **Fit screen to boundaries**.

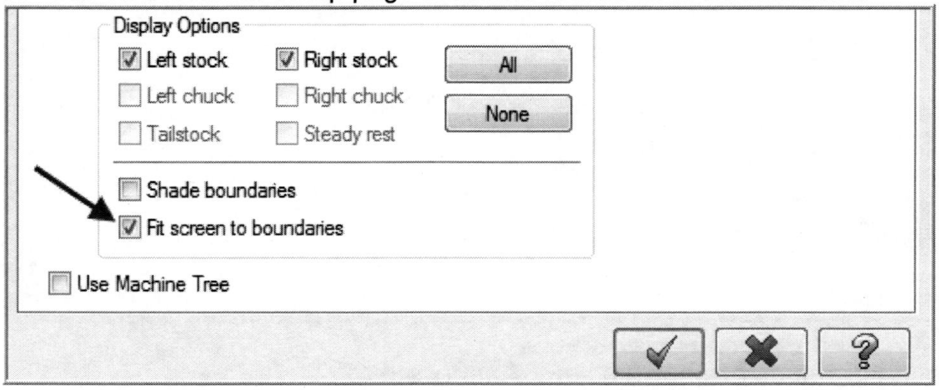

10. Select the **Chuck Properties** button in the **Stock Setup** page as shown in the screenshot below:

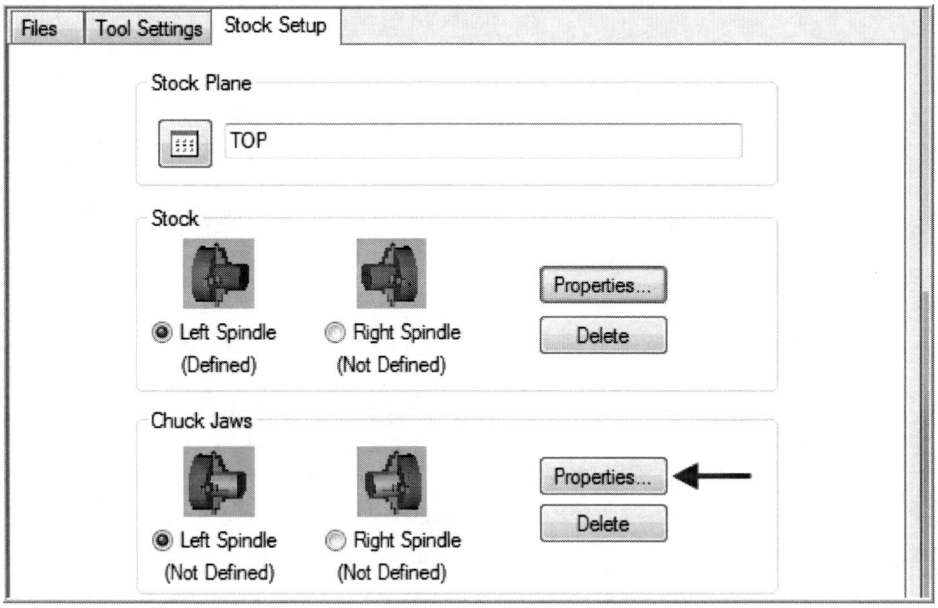

11. In the **Chuck Jaws** setup set the values as shown below:

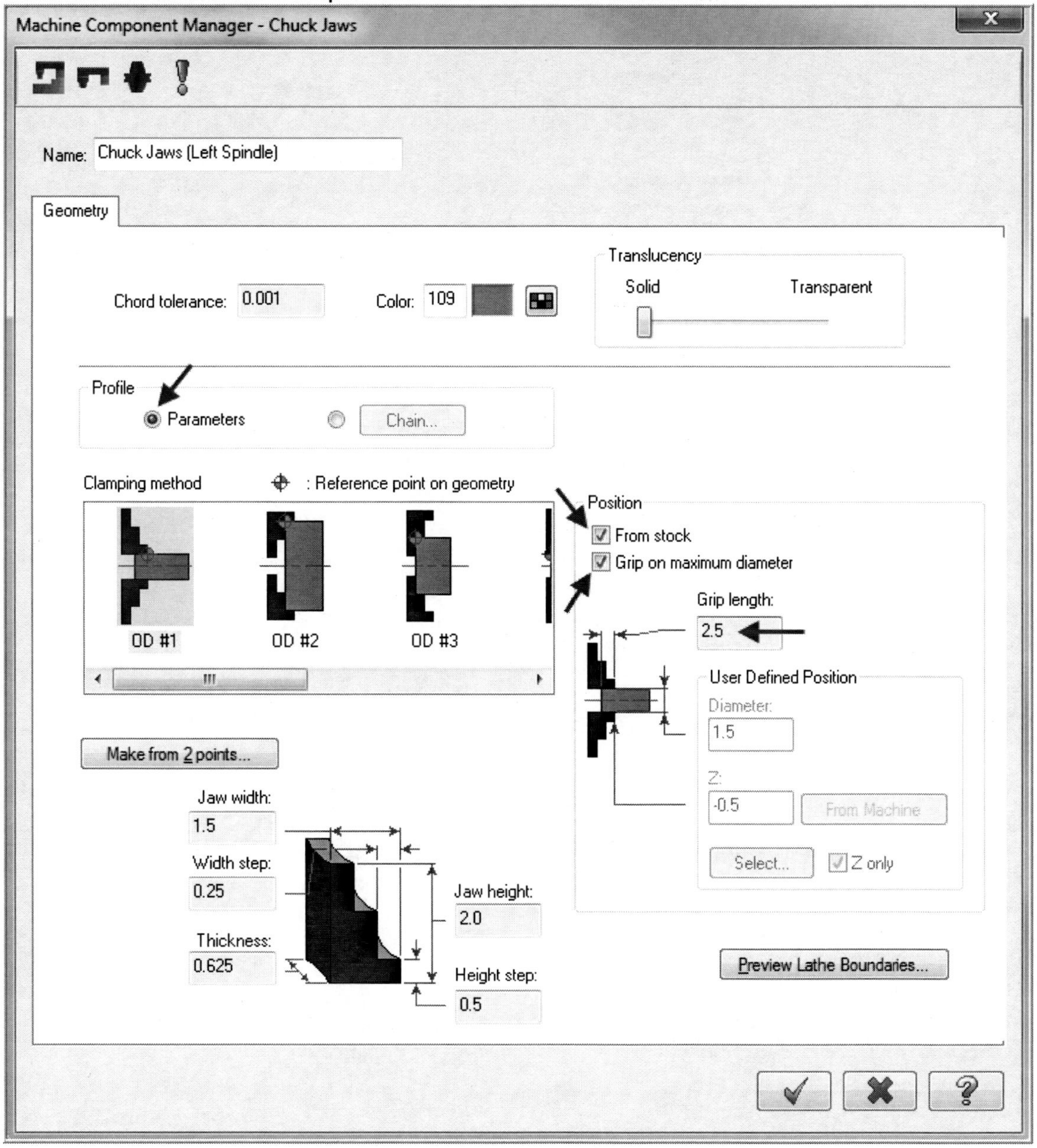

12. Click on the OK icon  to complete this feature.

13. Click on the **Tool Settings** page and make changes as shown below:

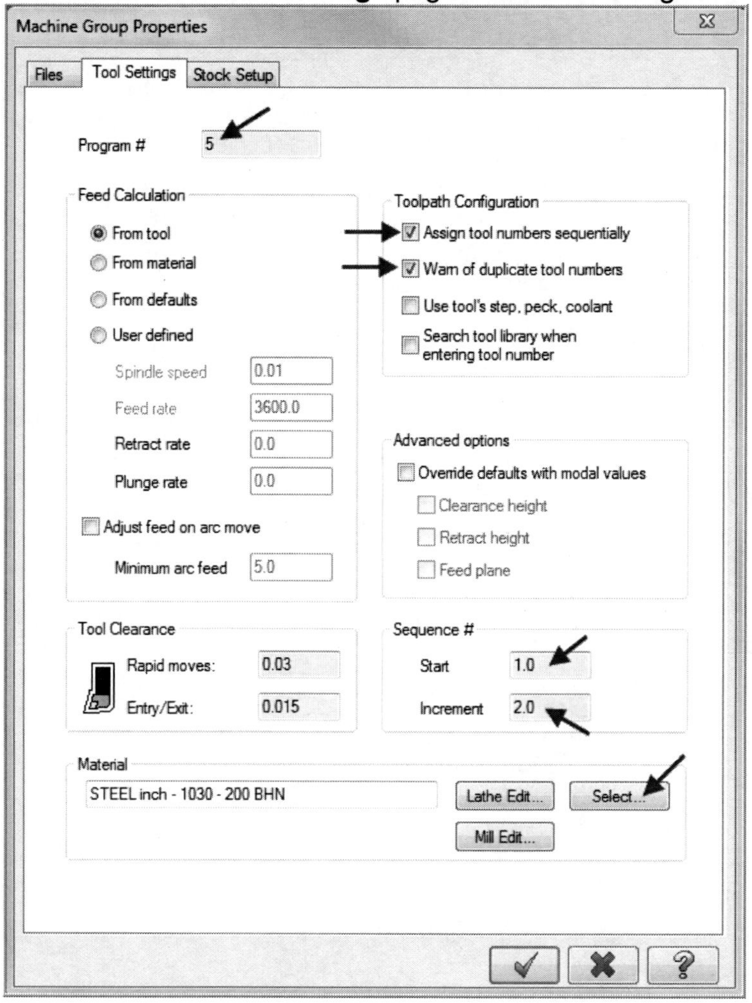

14. To change the **Material** type to Aluminum 6061 pick the **Select** button at the bottom of the Tool Settings page.
15. At the **Material List** dialog box open the Source drop down list and select **Lathe – library.**

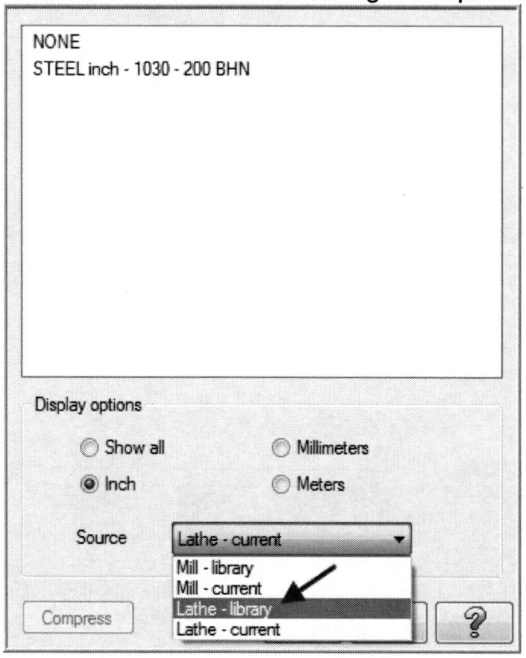

16. From the **Default Materials** list select **ALUMINUM inch - 6061** and then select .

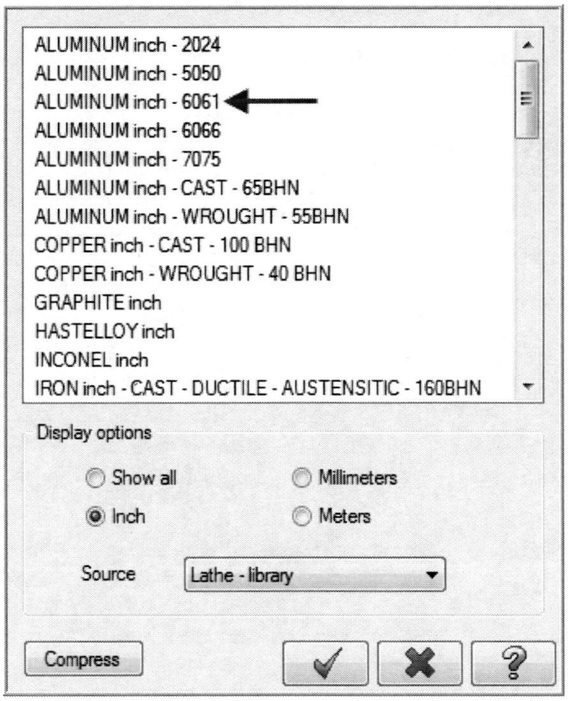

17. Select the OK button  again to complete this Stock Setup function.

18. Select the **Screen Fit** icon to fit the part to the screen .
Notice the stock setup outline as indicated by broken lines as shown below:

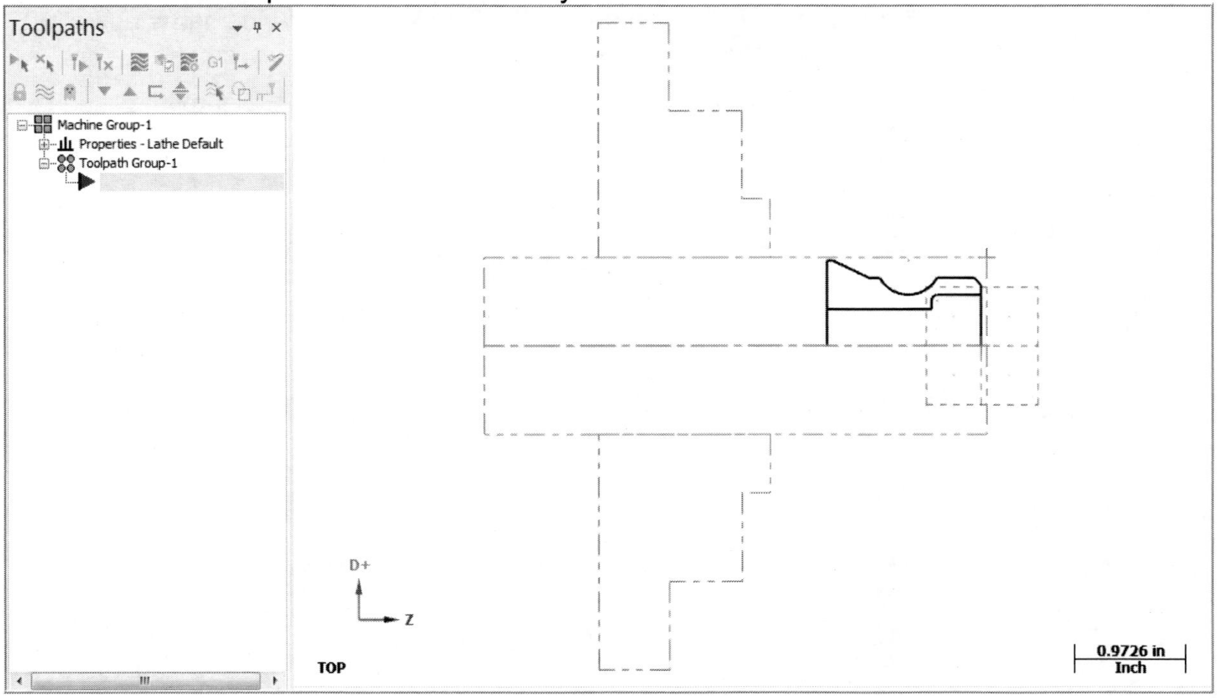

TASK 9:
FACE THE FRONT OF THE PART:

➲ In this task you will use a facing tool to face the front of the part in one cut.

1. Select the **Screen Fit** icon to fit the part to the screen if required.
2. From the menu bar select **TOOLPATHS>Face…**

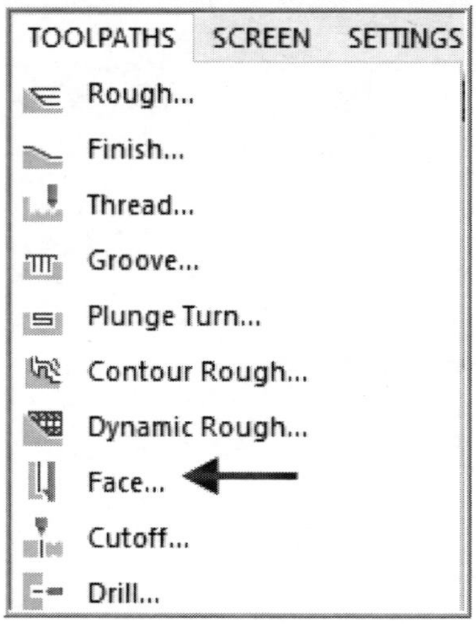

3. When prompted to **"Enter new NC name"** Ensure **LATHE-LESSON-5** is entered as shown below and then select the OK button.

➲ After selecting the OK button you are confronted with Toolpath parameters page. The first task here will be to select Tool #1 a Roughing – 80 deg.

4. Click on **Tool 0101 Roughing – 80 degree** and ensure the settings are the same as in the Toolpath parameters page as shown below:

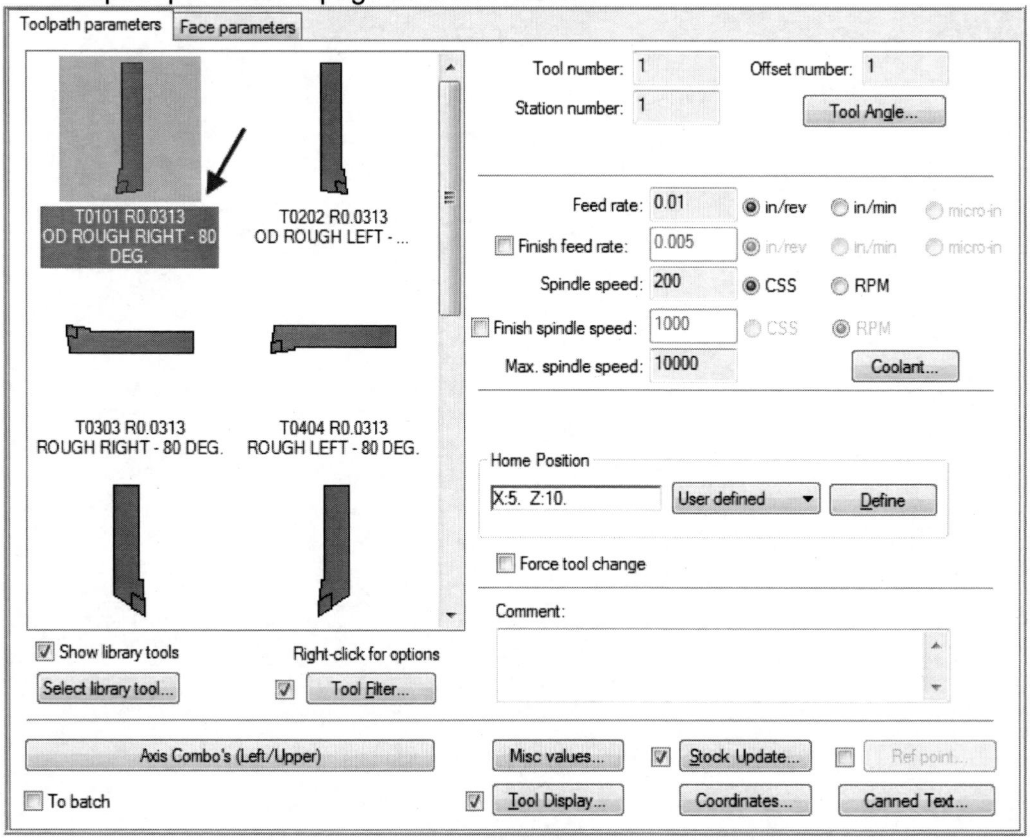

5. Select the **Face parameters** page and make changes as shown below:

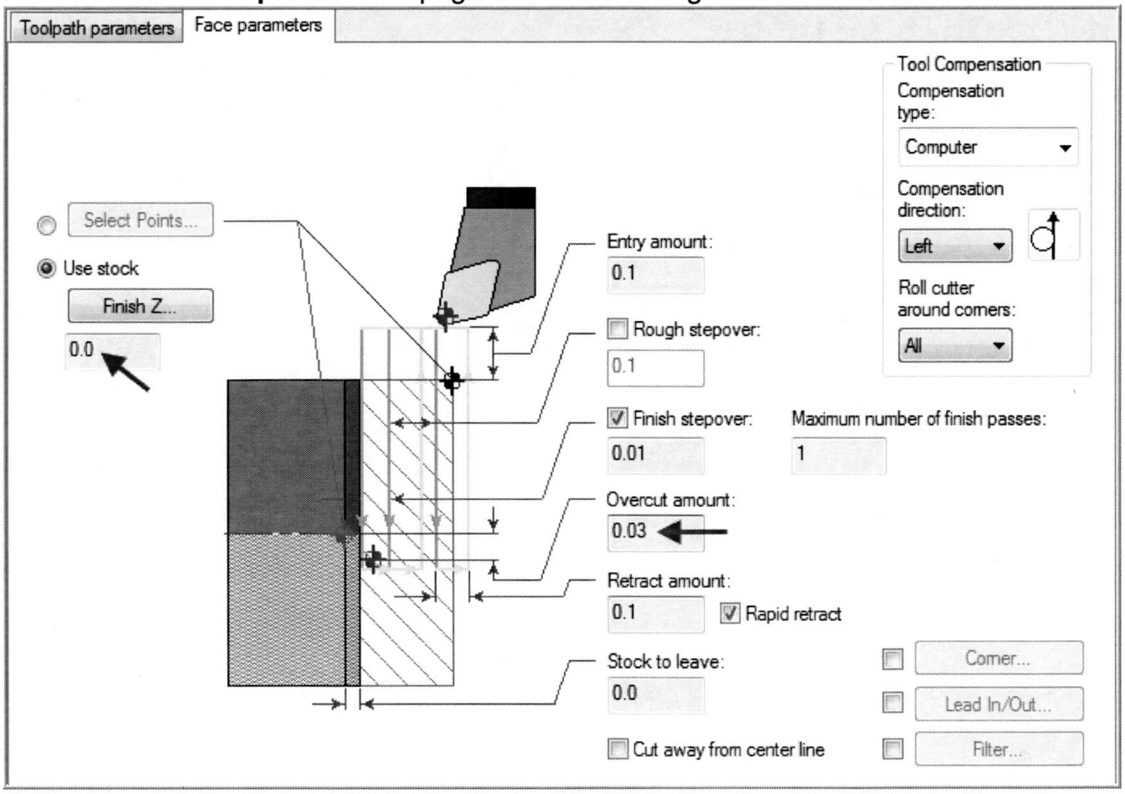

6. Select the OK button  to complete this **Lathe Face** operation.

TASK 10:
ROUGH THE OUTSIDE DIAMETERS

- In this task you will use a Lathe toolpath called Lathe Quick Toolpaths.
- You will use the same tool as used for the previous facing operation **Tool #1 an OD Rough-Right – 80 deg.**

1. From the menu bar select **TOOLPATHS>Quick>Rough…**

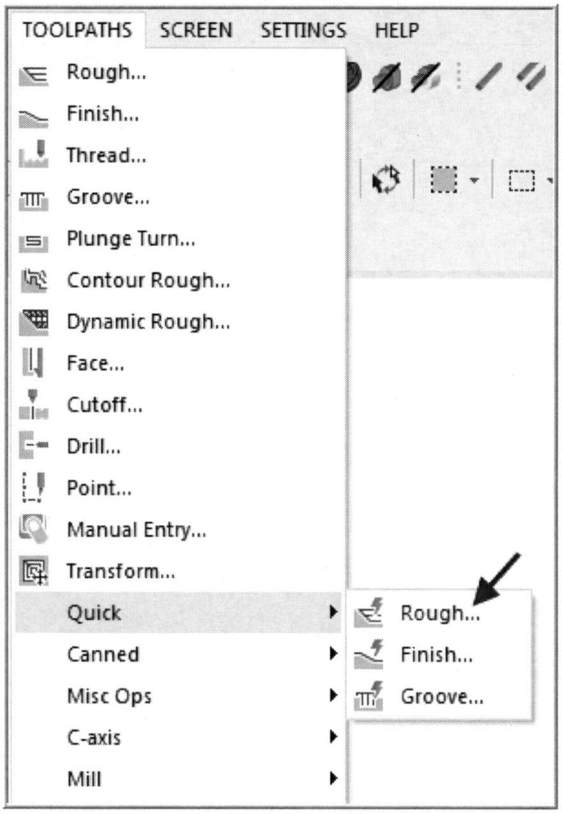

2. In the **Chaining** window Chaining mode is set to **Partial** by default.

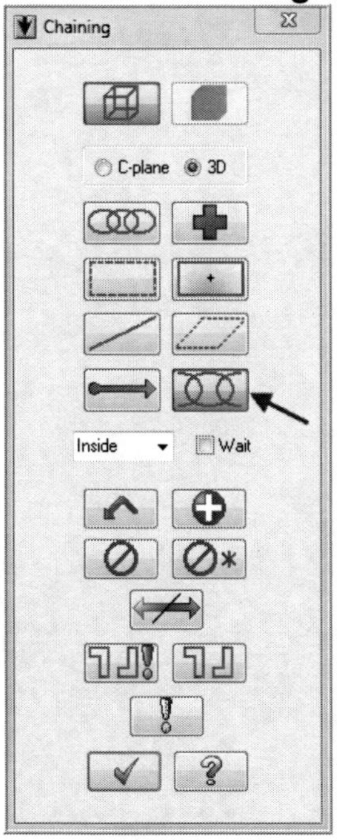

3. Select the chamfer, Line 1 as the start of the **Partial chain**.

After you have selected the chamfer **ensure** that the arrows are pointing up and to the left of the part. If it is not select the reverse button in the Chaining dialog box.

4. Then select Line 2 as the end entity in this chain.

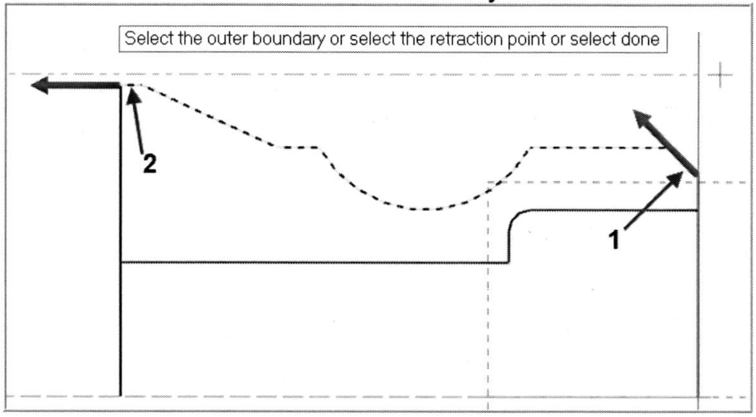

5. Select the OK button  to exit the Chaining dialog window.
6. In the **Quick Tool parameters** page select the **Tool #1 an Roughing – 80 deg** and make any necessary changes as shown below:

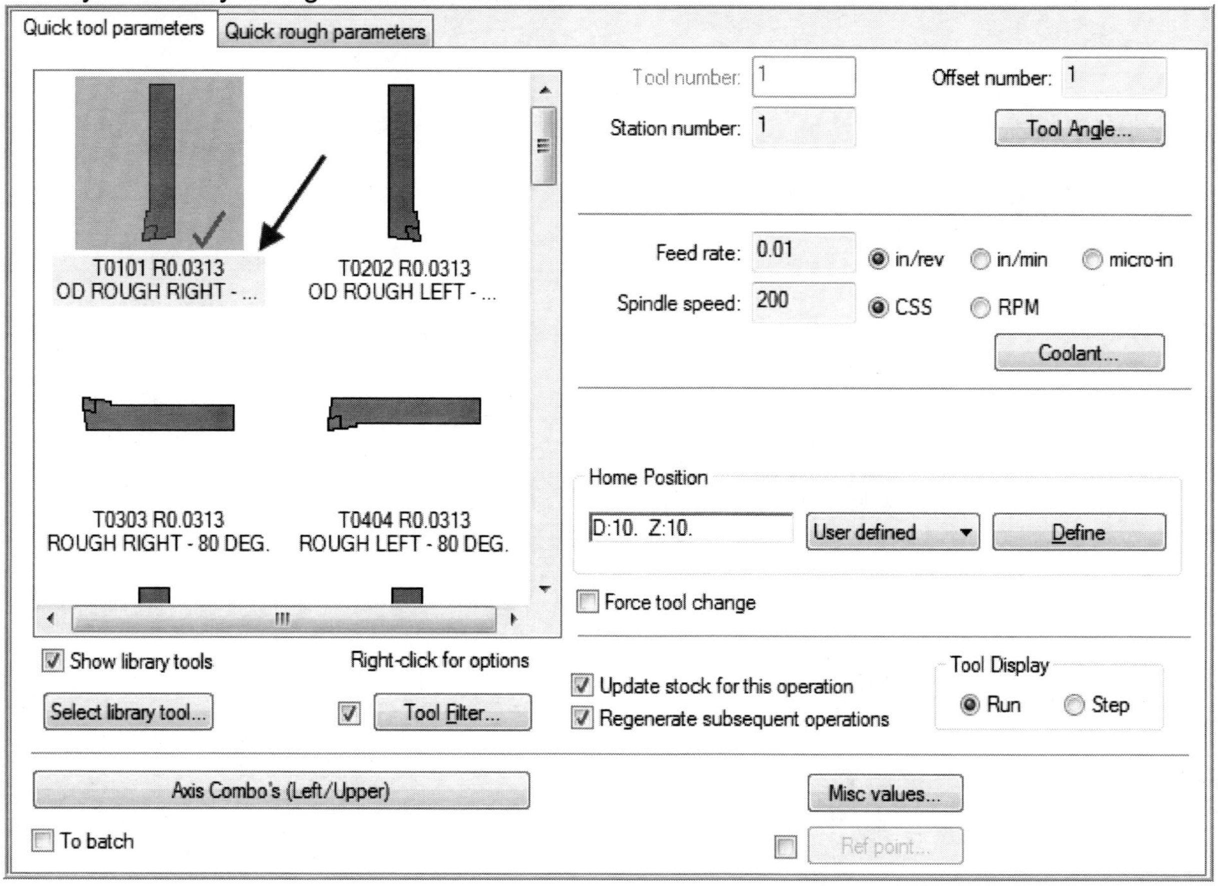

7. Select the **Quick Rough parameters** page and make any necessary changes as shown below:

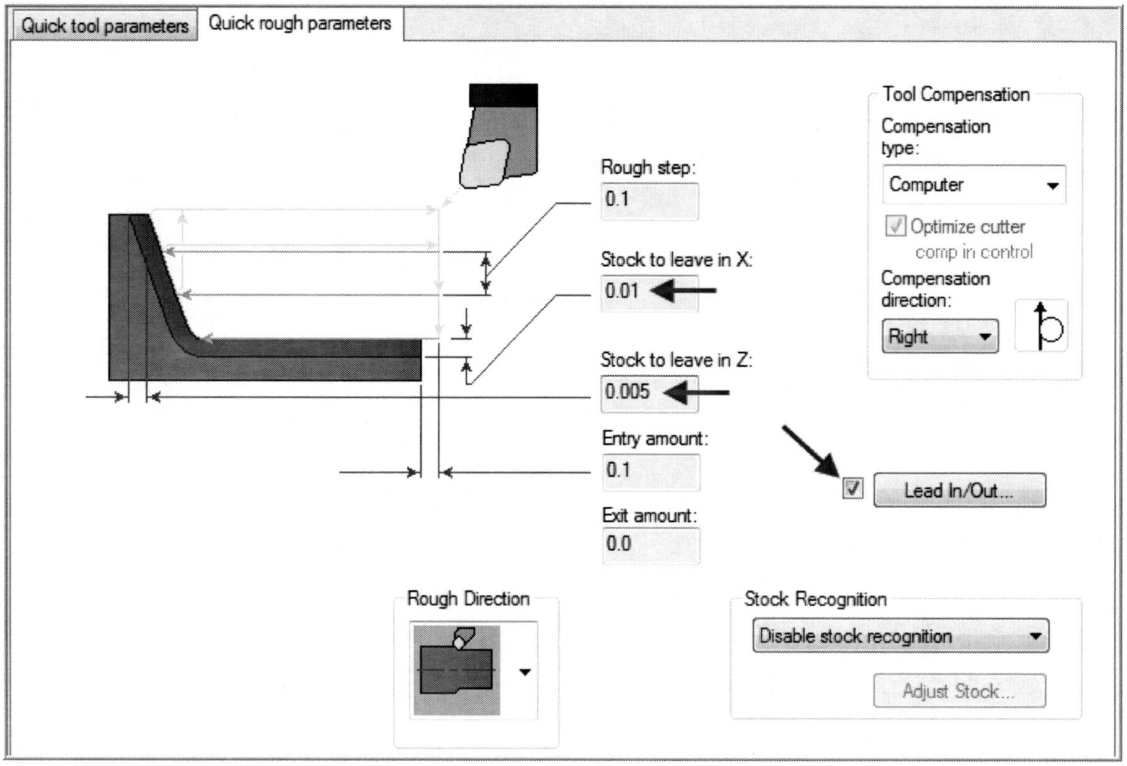

8. Select the **Lead In/Out** button, then select the **Lead out** page and extend the contour by .2 as shown below:

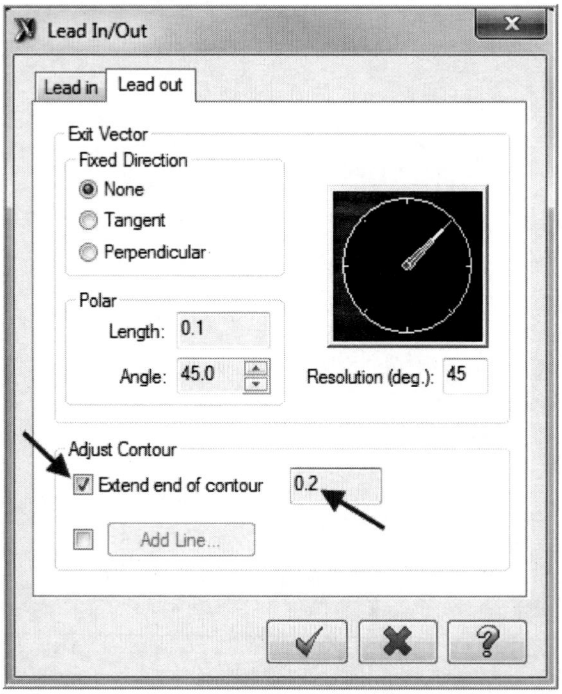

9. Select the OK button  to exit this function.
10. Select the OK button  to exit Rough Parameters.

TASK 11:
FINISH THE OUTSIDE DIAMETERS

➲ In this task you will create a new tool to finish the outside diameters.

1. From the menu bar select **TOOLPATHS>Finish…**

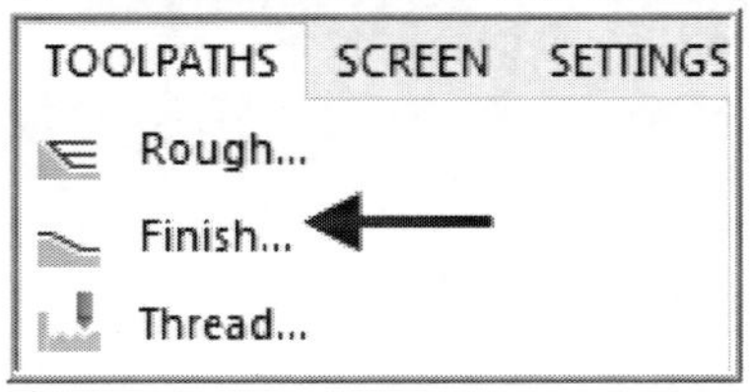

2. Click on the **Last** button  in the chaining dialog box to select the previous chain.
3. Select the OK button  to exit the Chaining dialog window.
4. Right Click the mouse in the space as indicated by arrow # 1 shown below:
5. Click on **Create new tool…** as indicated by arrow # 2 as shown below:

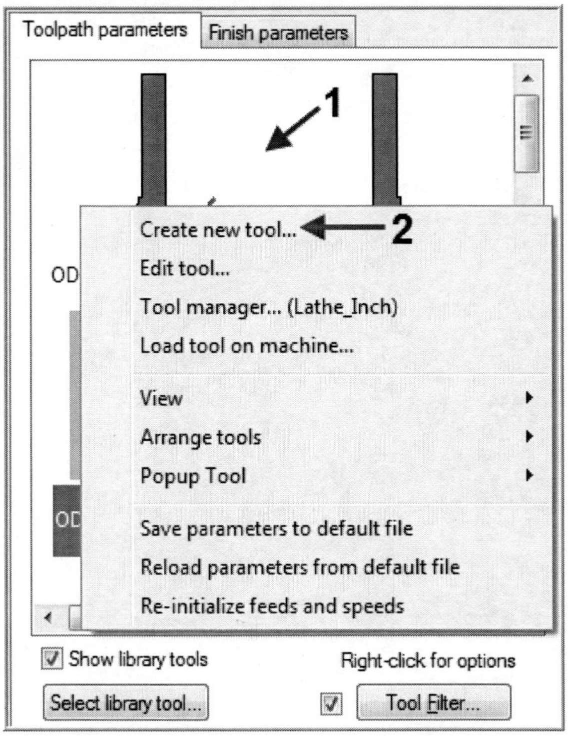

6. Click on the **General Turning** Button as shown below:

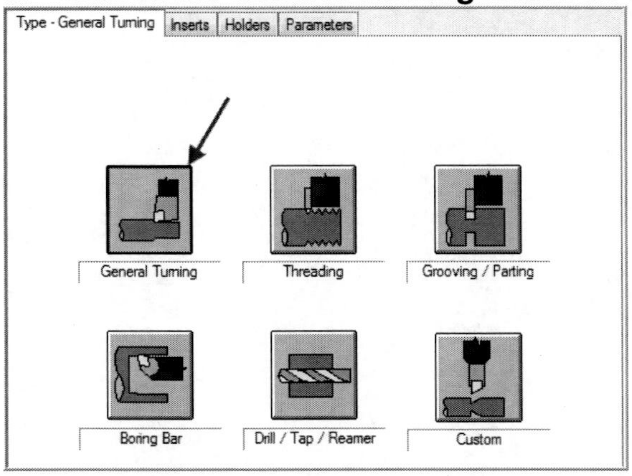

7. Scroll down and click on the **V (35 deg. Diamond)** insert as shown below:

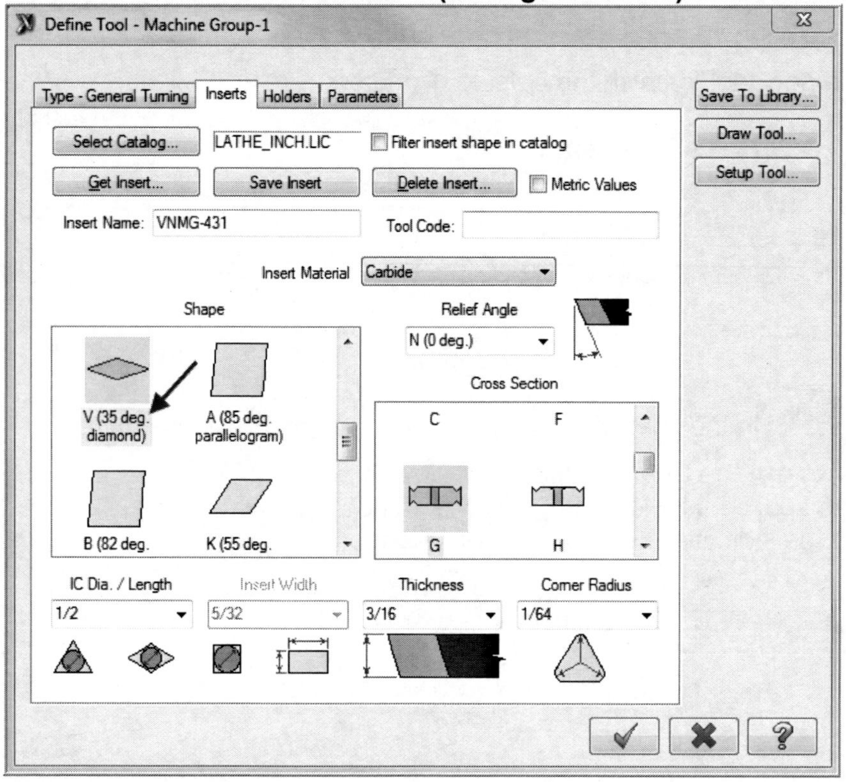

8. Click on the **Holders** Tab.
9. Scroll down and click on the **V (17.5 deg. Side clr.)** as shown below:

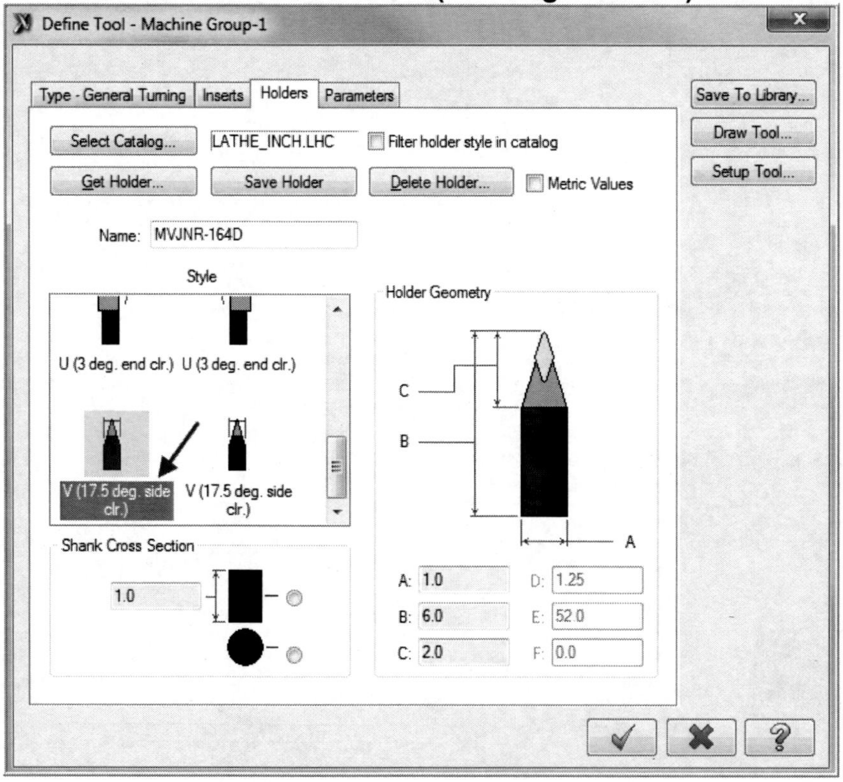

10. Click on the **Parameters** page and at the bottom of this page set the compensation for this tool as shown below:

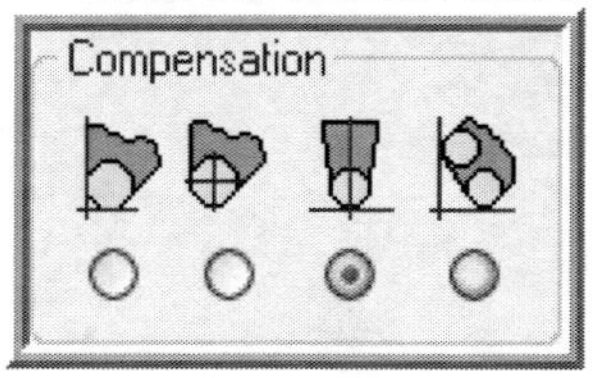

Compensation: Tip
The toolpath is programmed from the tip of the tool corner radius.

This is the only option available for threading tools, drills, taps, and reamers.

11. Click on the OK icon .
12. Make any necessary changes as shown below:

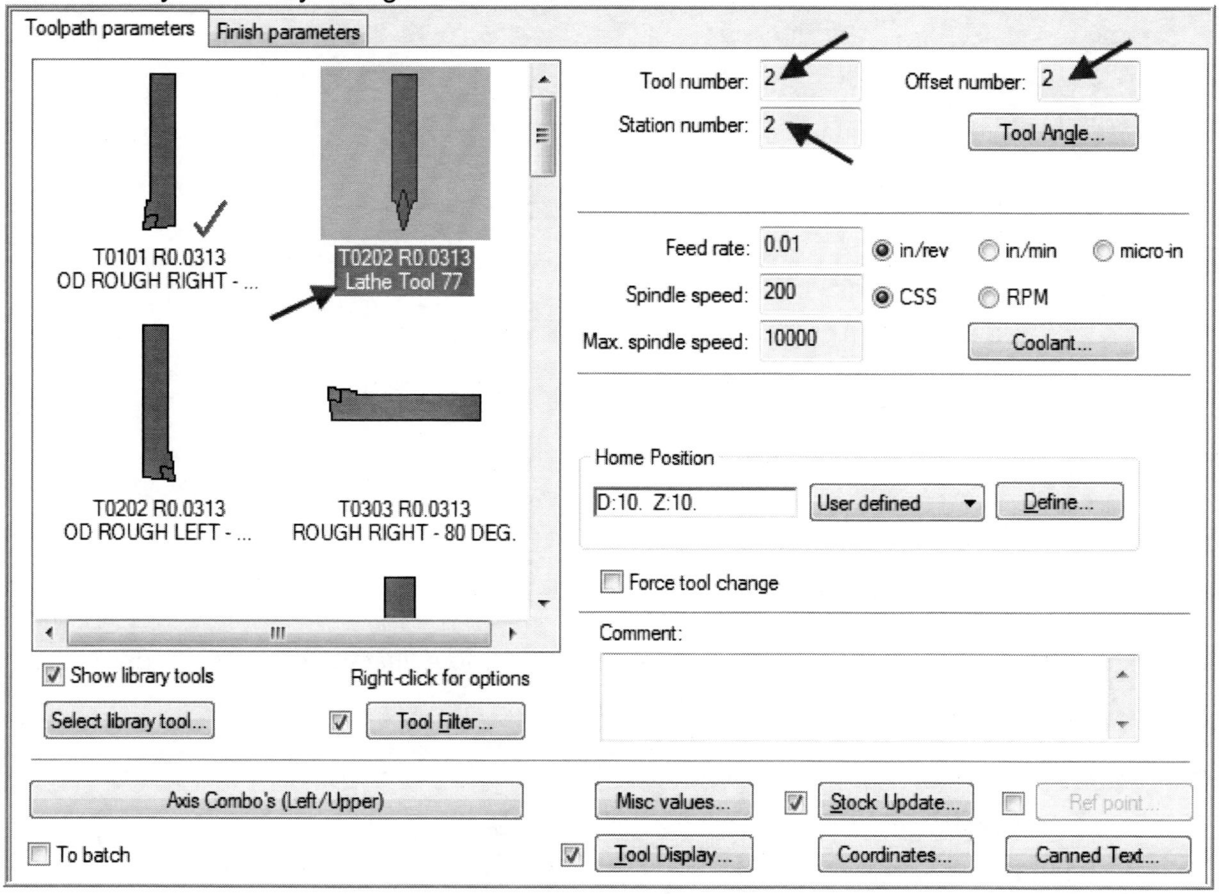

13. Click on the **Finish parameters** tab and make any necessary changes as shown below:

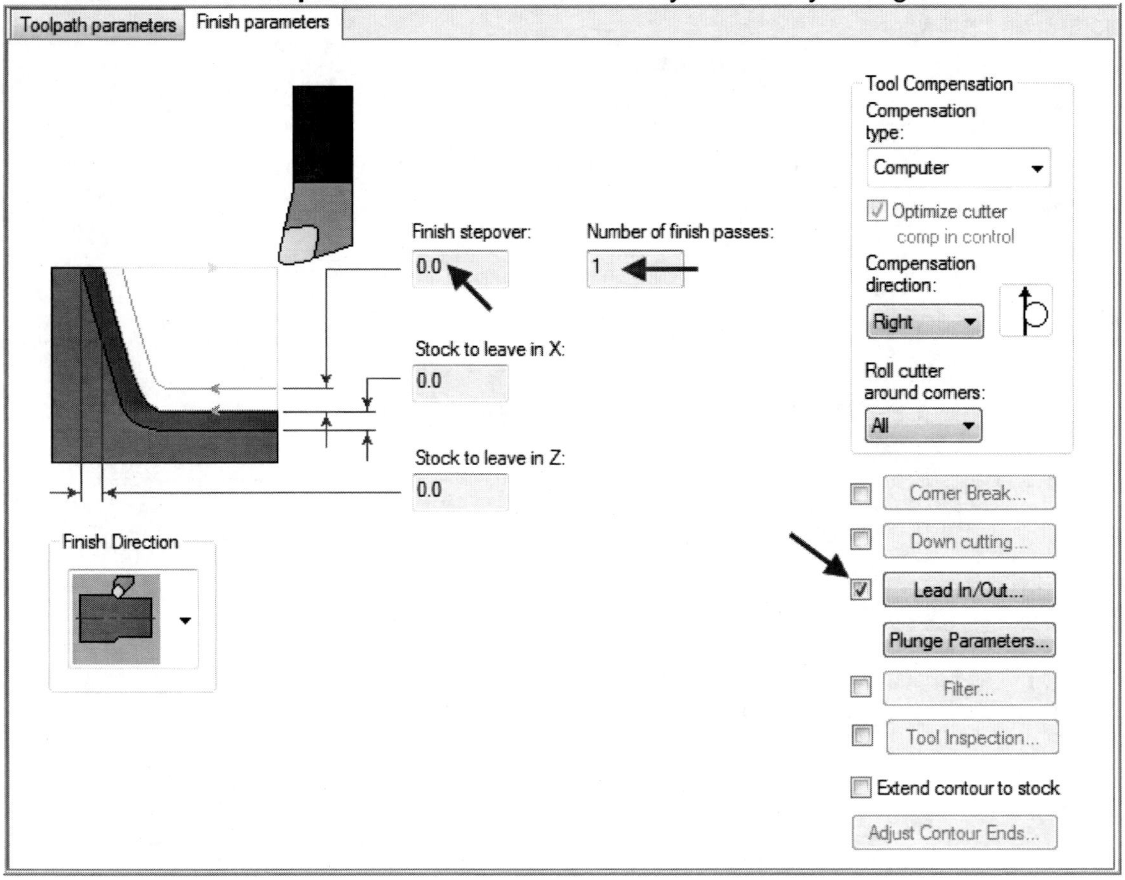

14. Click on the **Lead in/Out** button as shown above:

15. Make the necessary changes as shown below. In order to adjust the entry vector dial, click on the desired location of the arrow on the dial:

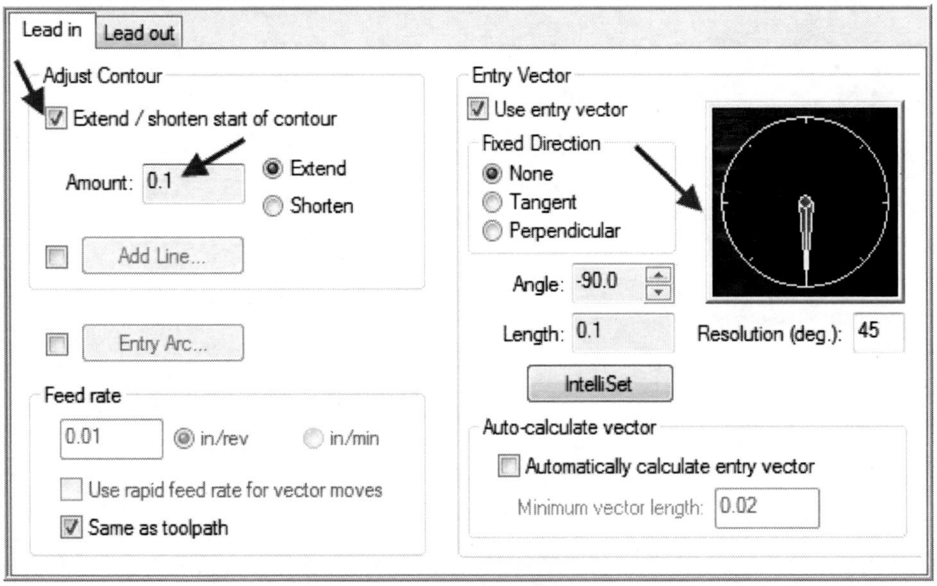

Entry vector: Select this option to create an entry vector. Use the other parameters to control the length and direction. This move will be added to the toolpath before any entry arc is defined. Use the Lead out tab to create an exit vector for the end of the toolpath.

16. Click on the **Lead out** tab and make the necessary changes as shown below:

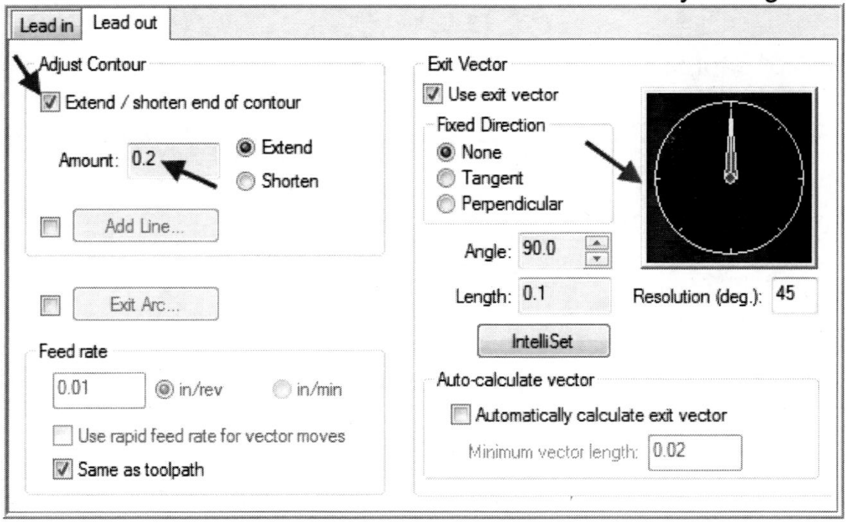

Angle dial
Set the angle of the entry or exit vector by dragging the pointer to the desired orientation.

Mastercam will automatically enter the angle in the Angle field.

17. Click on OK ✔ to exit the Lead In/out window.
18. Click on the Plunge Parameters button Plunge Parameters... .
19. Make the necessary changes as shown below:

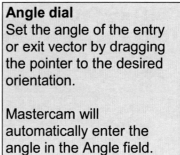

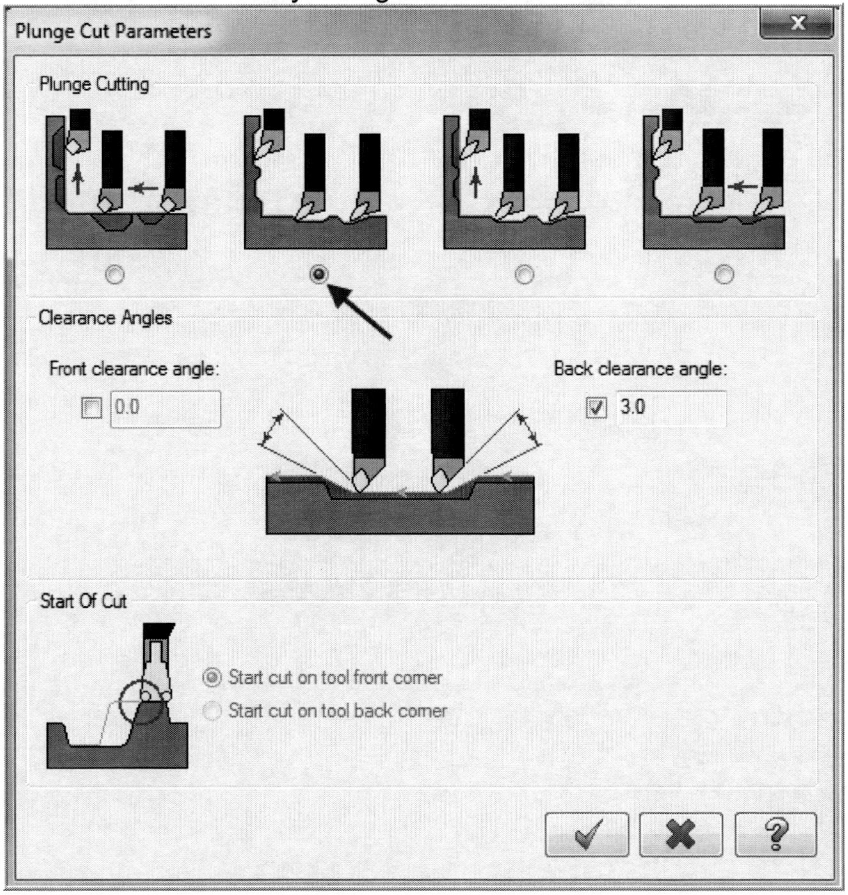

20. Click on **OK** ✔ to exit the **Plunge Cut parameters** window.
21. Click on OK ✔ to exit the Lathe Finish parameters window.

TASK 12:
CENTER DRILL HOLE

➲ In this task you will center drill .2" depth using **Tool #3 Centre Drill - .25 diameter.**

1. From the menu bar select **TOOLPATHS>Drill…**

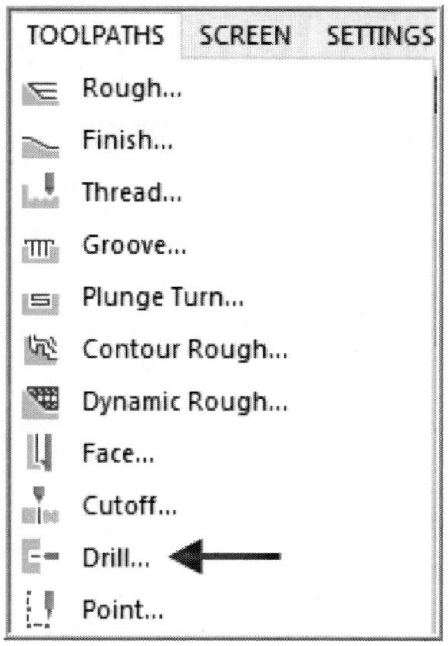

2. Select the **Centre Drill .25 diameter** tool from the tool list and make changes as shown below:

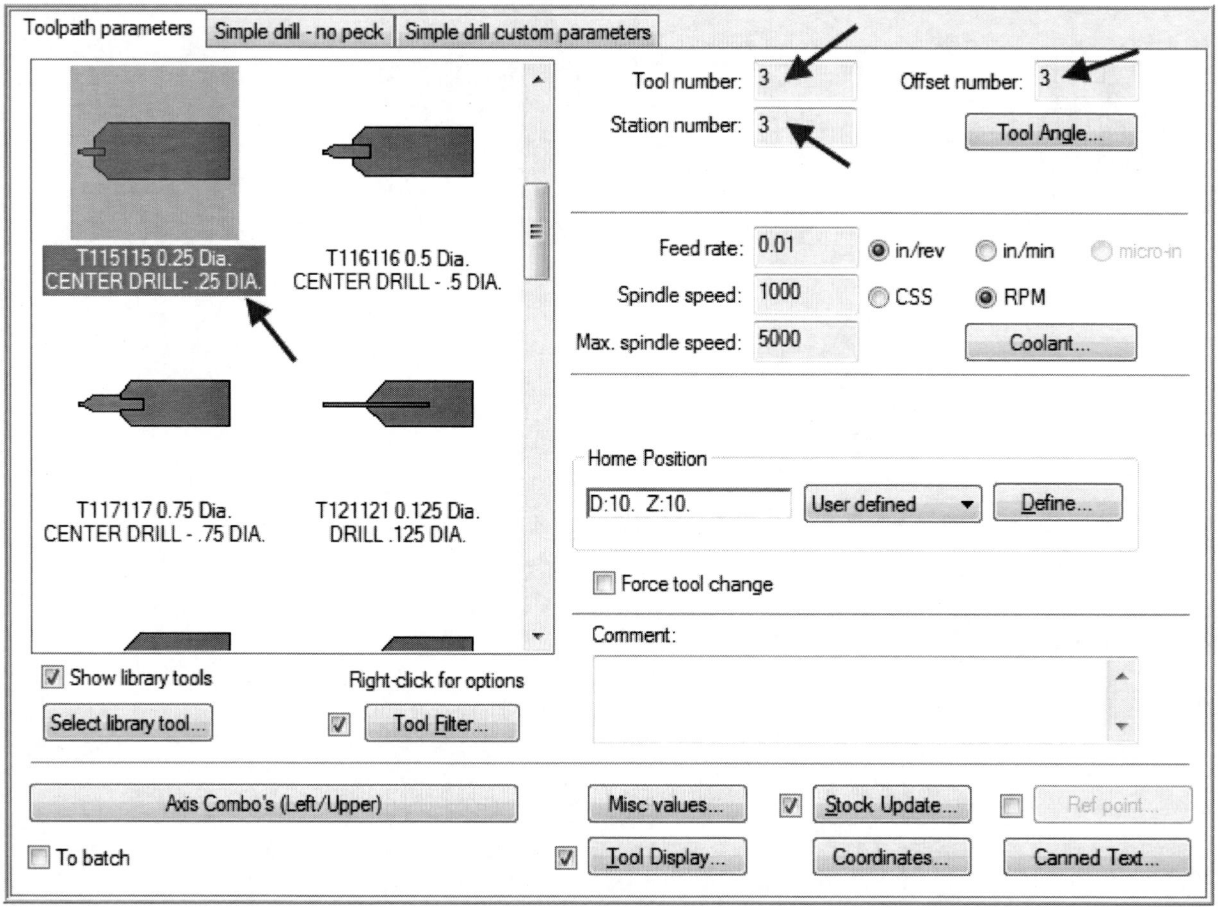

3. Select the Simple drill – no peck page and make changes as shown below:

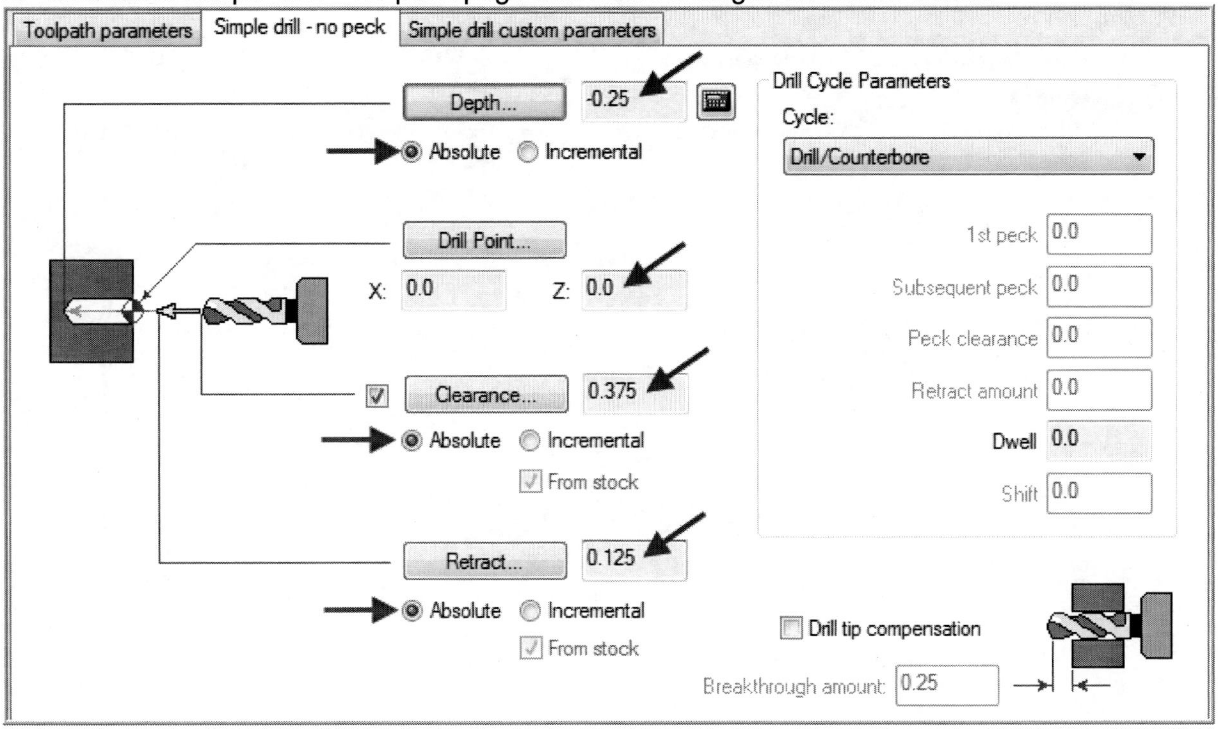

4. Select the OK button  to exit Simple drill – no peck.

TASK 13:
PRE DRILL THE 0.625" HOLE 0.375 DIAMETER

➲ In this task you will pre drill the .625" hole through the part using **Tool #4 Drill - .375 diameter.**

1. From the menu bar select **TOOLPATHS>Drill...**

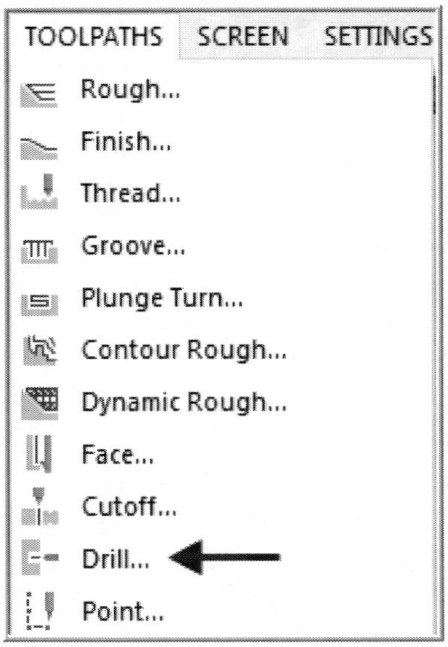

2. Scroll down and select the **Drill - .375 diameter** tool from the tool list and make changes as shown below:

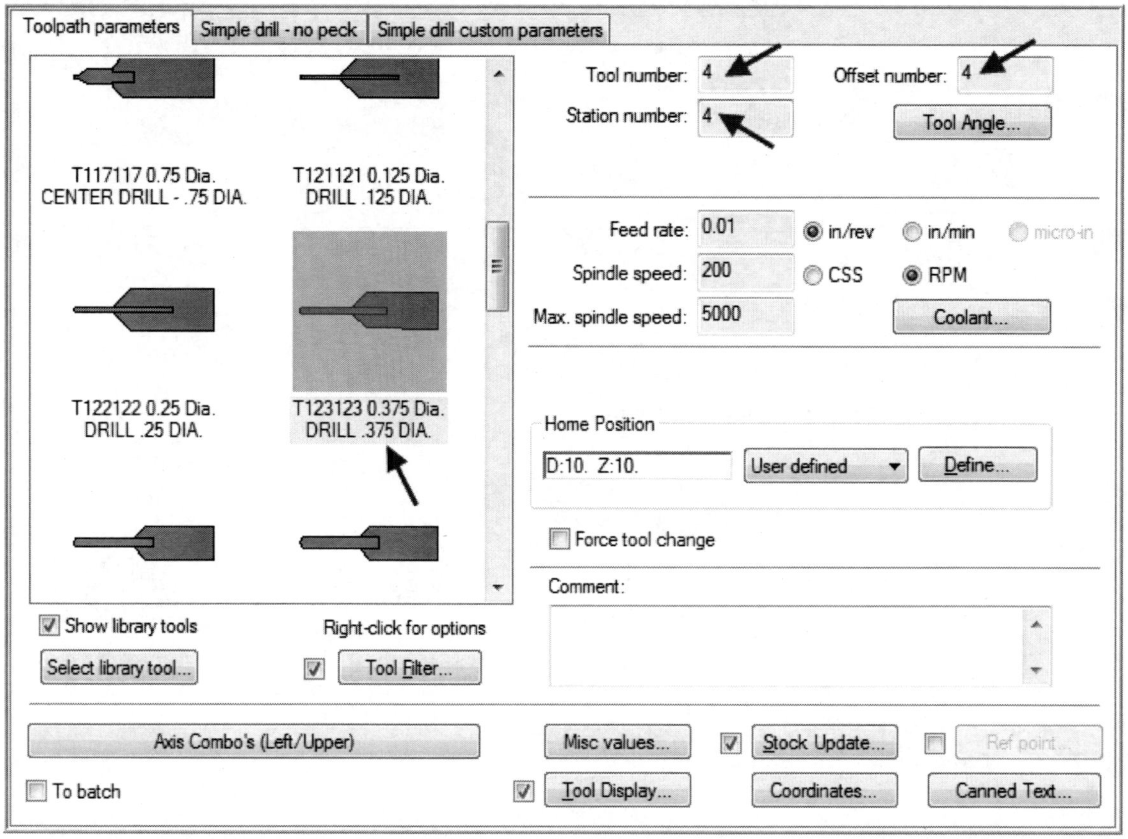

3. Select the **Simple drill – no peck** page and make changes as shown below. This hole will be **peck drilled through the part**. Make changes as shown below:

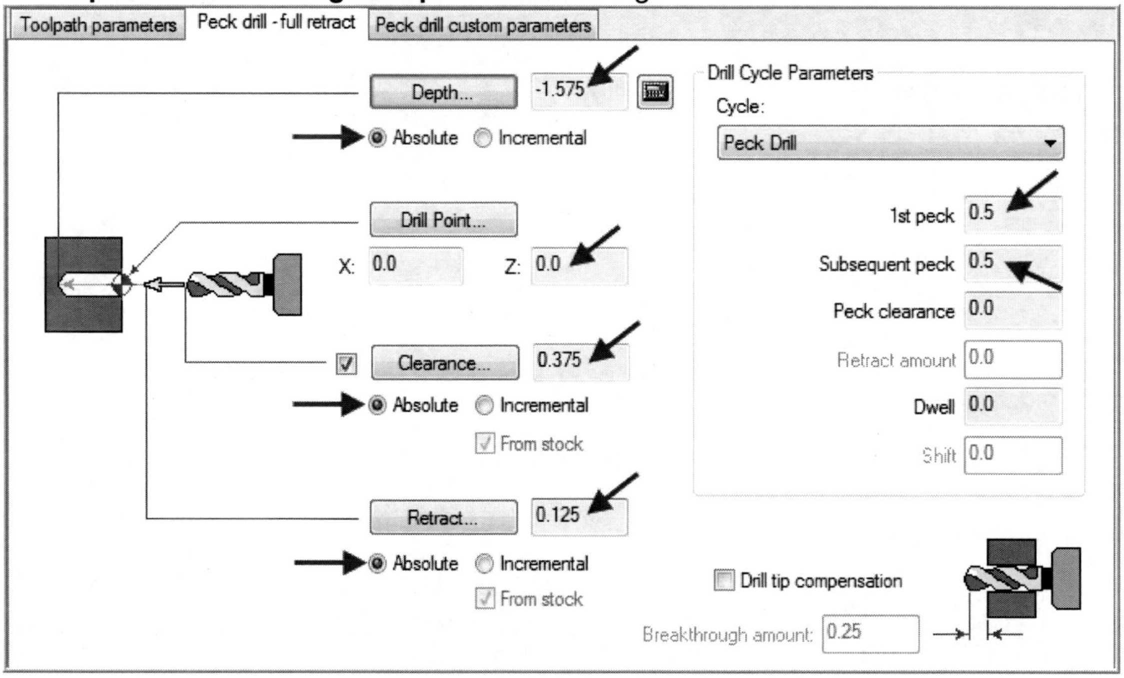

4. Select the OK button ✓ to exit Peck drill – full retract.

TASK 14:
PRE DRILL THE 0.625" HOLE 0.5 DIAMETER

➲ In this task you will peck drill through the part with a 0.5 diameter drill prior to boring.
➲ You will copy the previous peck drill operation and then modify into this peck drilling operation.

1. On the left of the screen in the Toolpaths Manager the 0.375 drill peck drilling operation is the **fifth** operation. To copy this operation hold down the **Right mouse button** over the folder for this operation. Keep holding the right mouse button down and drag below the red arrow and release.
2. Select **Copy after** from this menu.

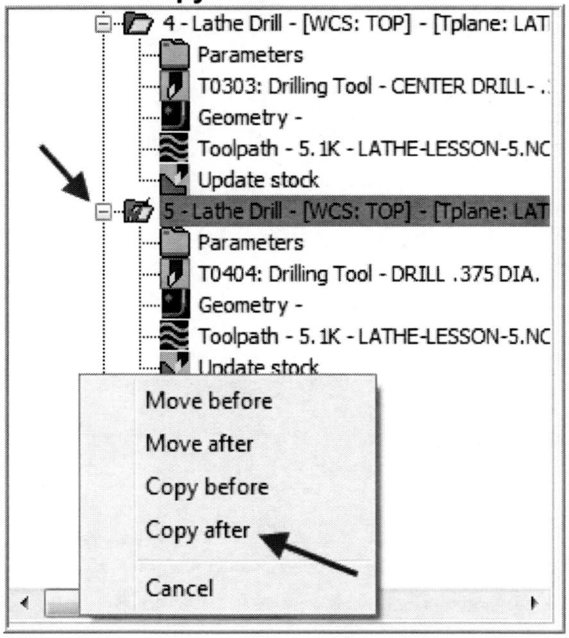

3. Move the Insert arrow 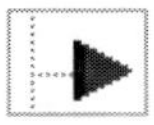 to the bottom of the list of operations by clicking the  icon on the Toolpaths Manager toolbar.
4. In the Toolpaths Manager click on the folder Parameters for the **sixth** operation as shown below:

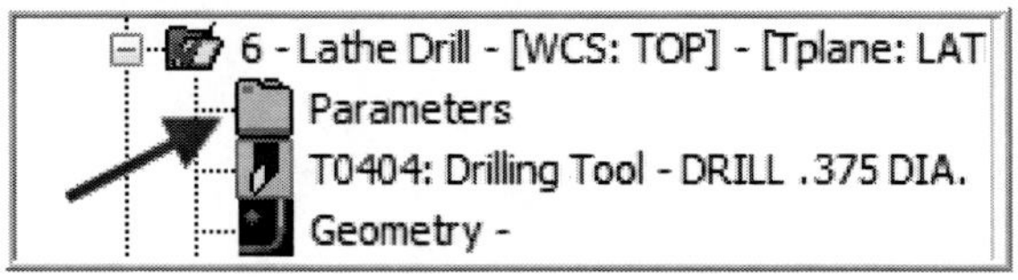

5. Select the **Toolpath parameters** page.
6. Scroll down and select the .50 diameter drill, as shown below
7. Make changes to the Toolpath parameters page as shown below.

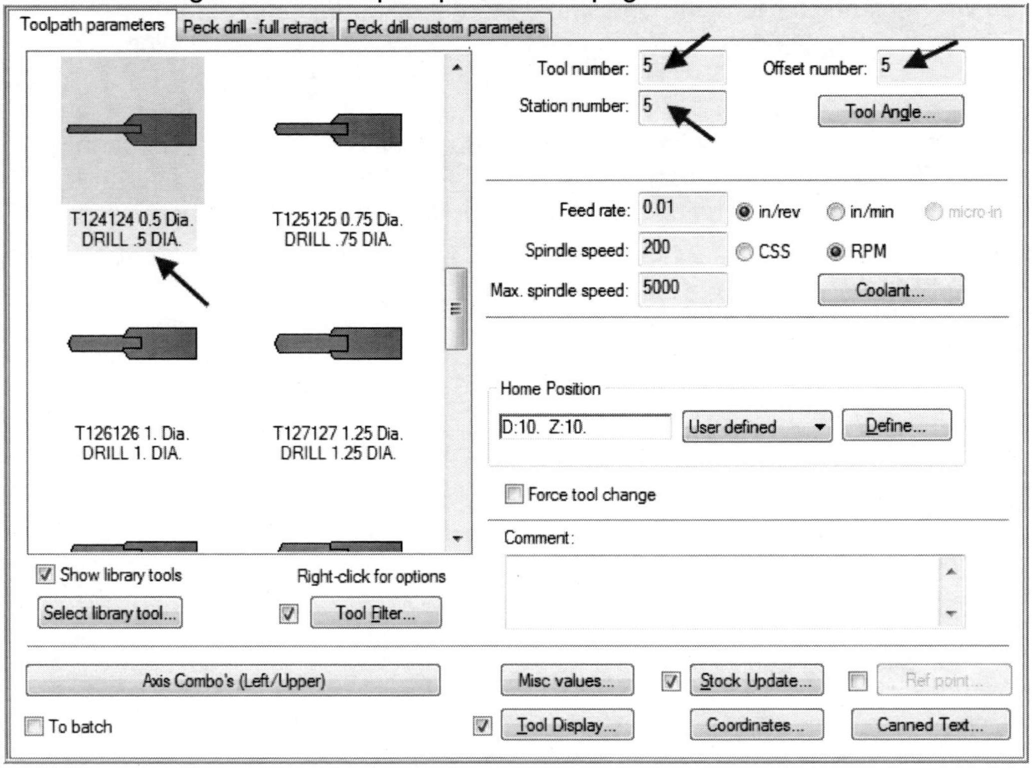

8. Select the **Peck drill – full retract** page and make changes as shown below.

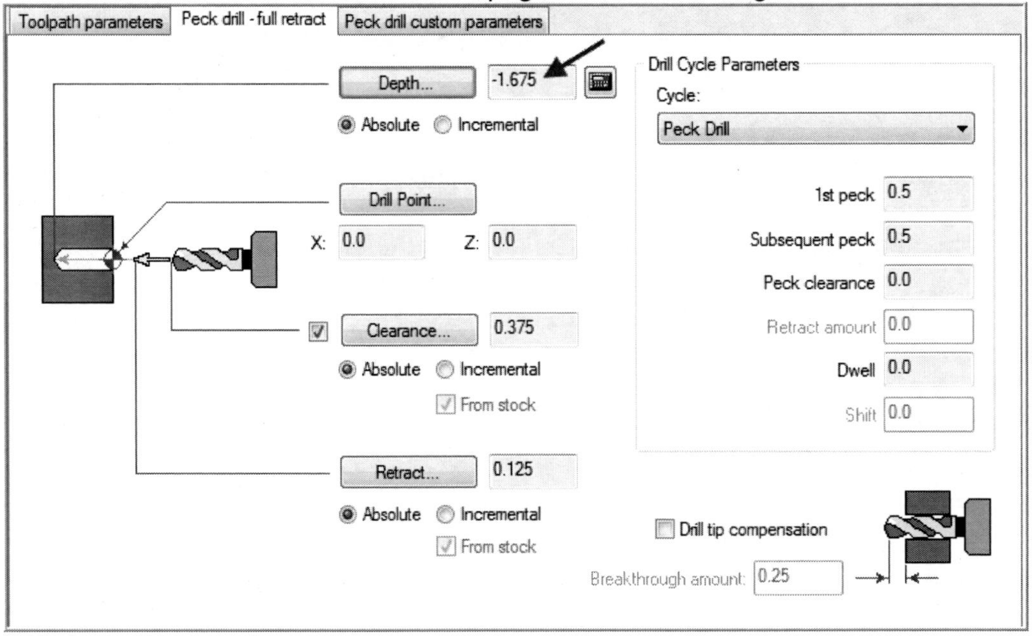

9. Select the OK button  to exit Peck drill – full retract.

10. Select the **Regenerate all dirty operations** button  to remove the red X from the drilling operation you have just edited. You need to update the toolpath with the new parameters you have just input.

TASK 15:
ROUGH THE BORE

➲ In this task you will use a boring tool to rough out the 0.870 and 0.625 diameter bores.

1. From the menu bar select **TOOLPATHS>Rough…**

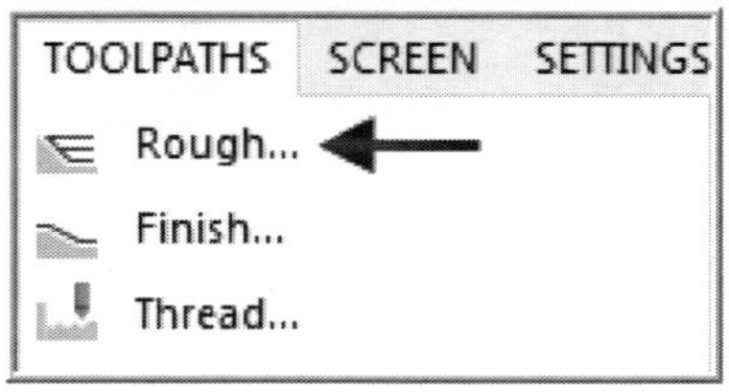

2. In the **Chaining** window Chaining mode is set to **Partial** by default.
3. Select Line 1 as the start of the **Partial chain**.

After you have selected the first line **ensure** that the arrow is pointing towards the part as shown below. If it is not select the reverse button in the Chaining dialog box

4. Then select Line 2 as the end entity in this chain.

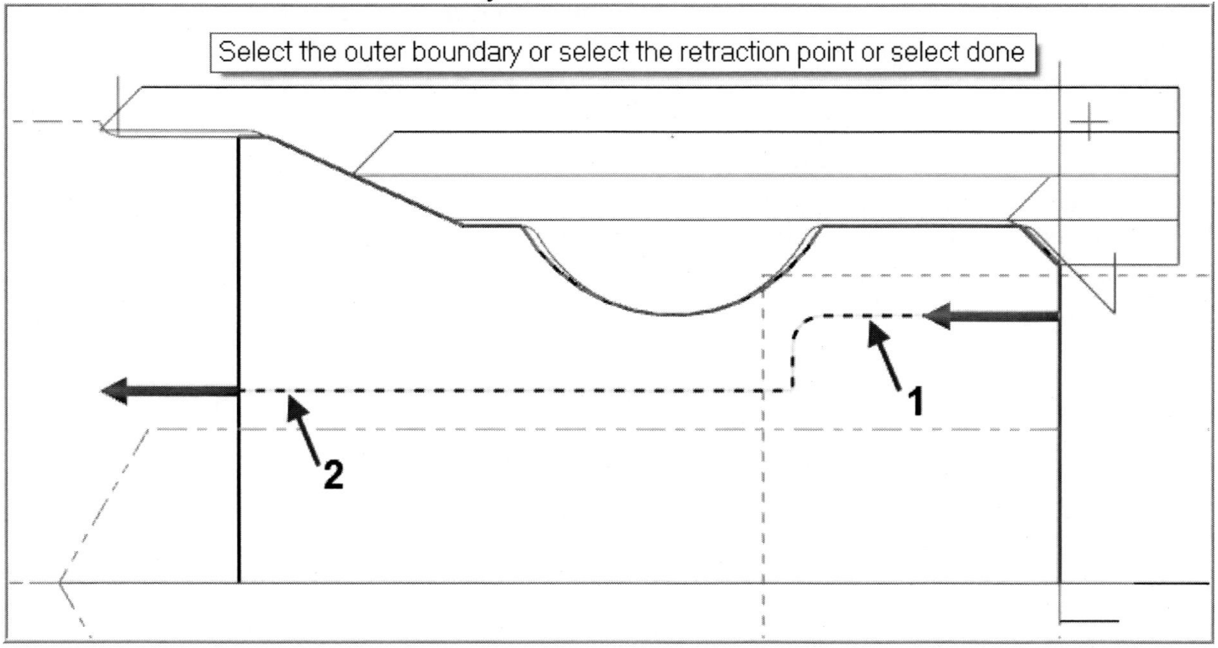

5. Select the OK button  to exit the Chaining dialog window.

6. In the **Toolpath parameters** page scroll down and select a boring tool **ID ROUGH MIN .375 DIA – 75 deg** and make any necessary changes as shown below:

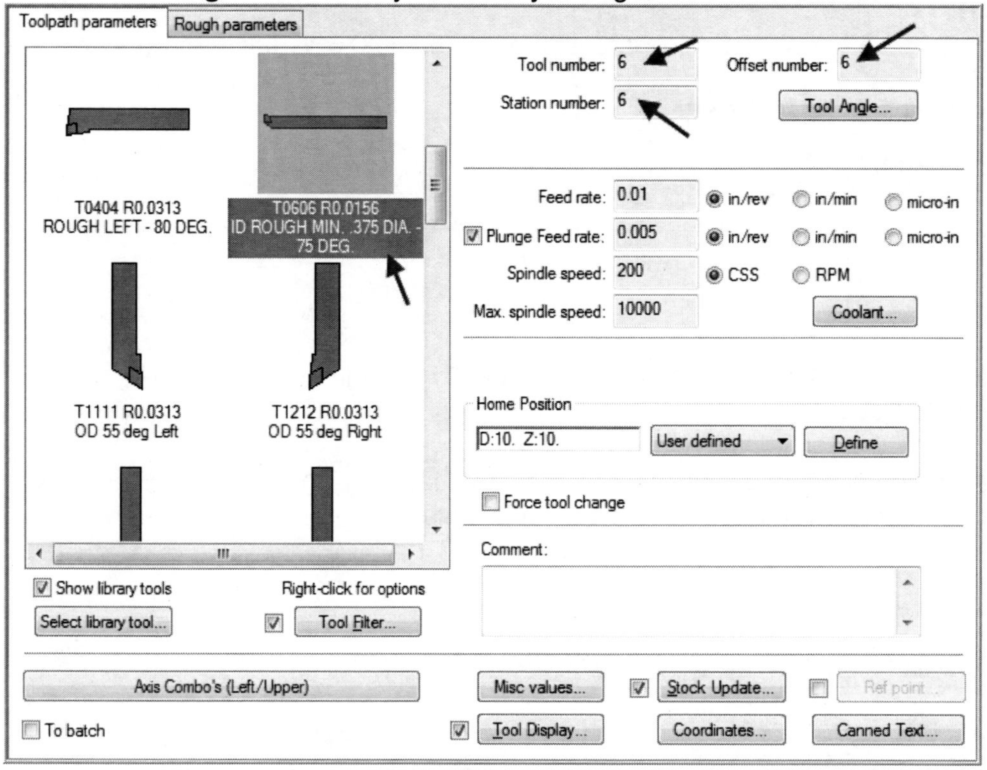

7. Double click on the picture  for this boring tool in the tool list window.
8. On the **Inserts** page change the thickness of this insert to 1/32 as shown below:

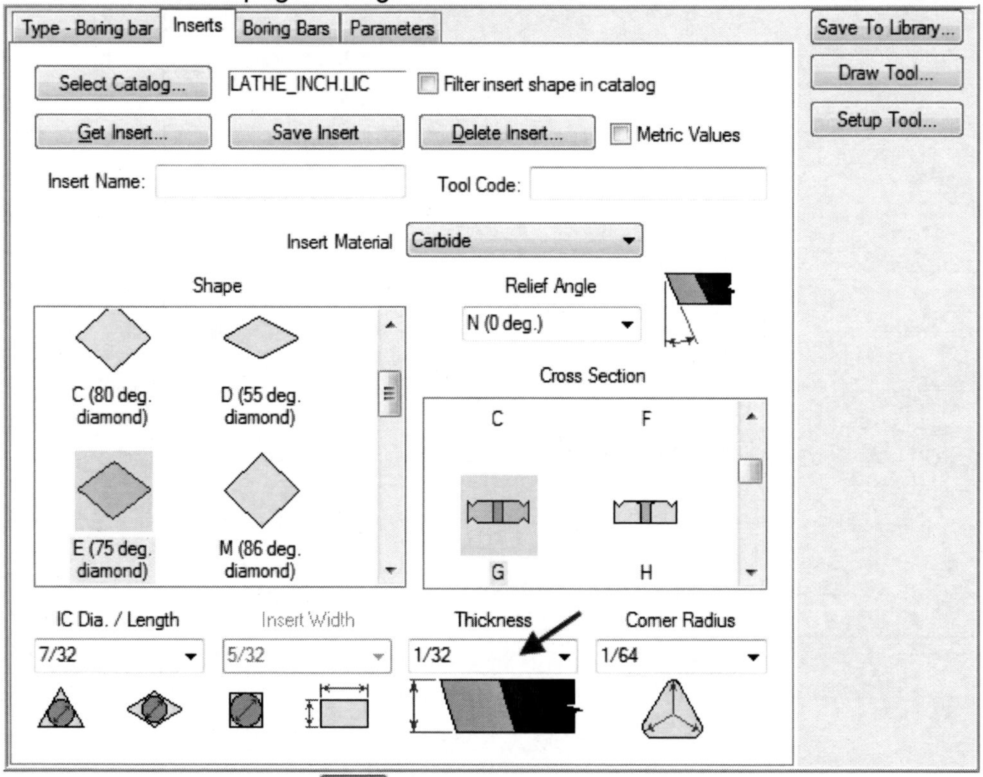

9. Select the OK button  to exit this function.

10. Select the Rough **parameters** page and make any necessary changes as shown below:

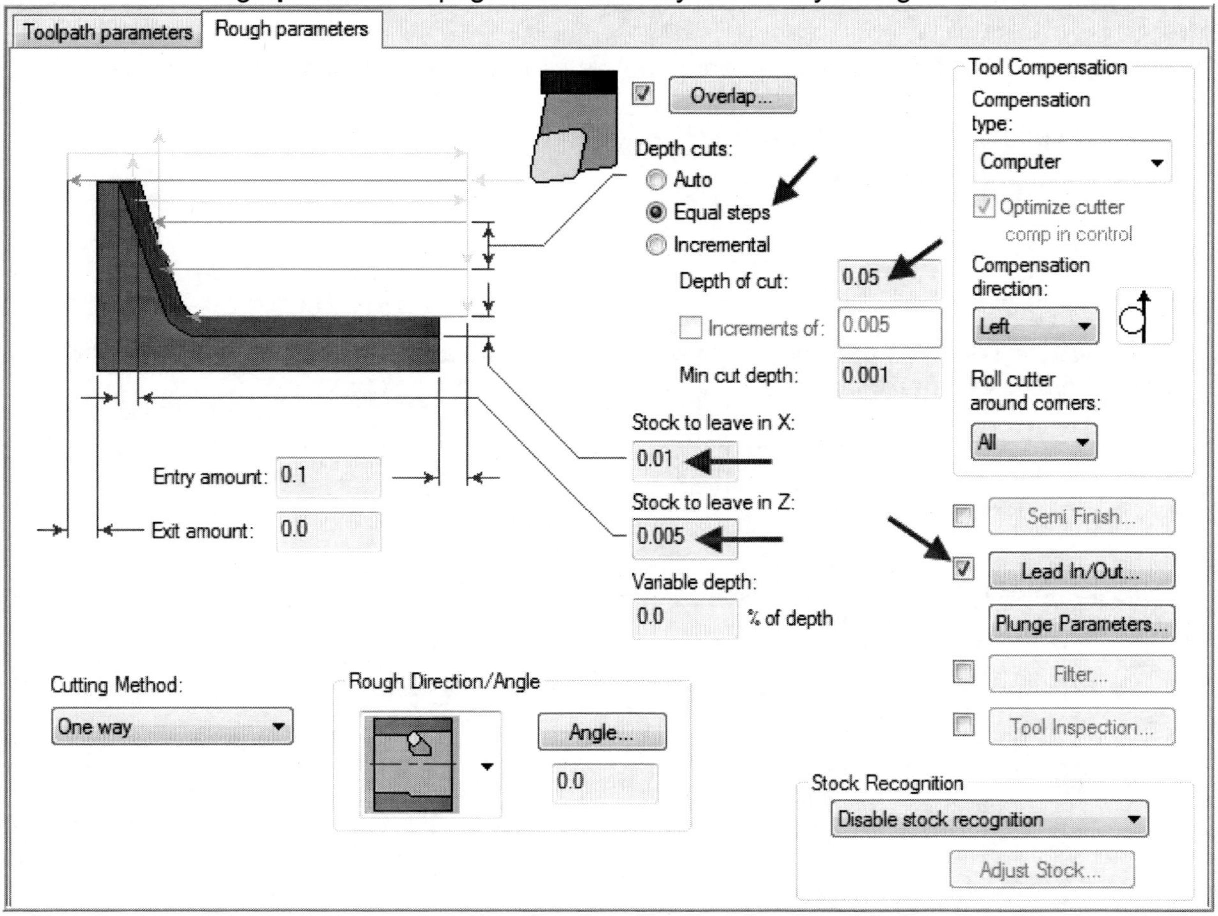

11. Select the **Lead In/Out** button select the Lead out page and extend the contour by .1 as shown below:

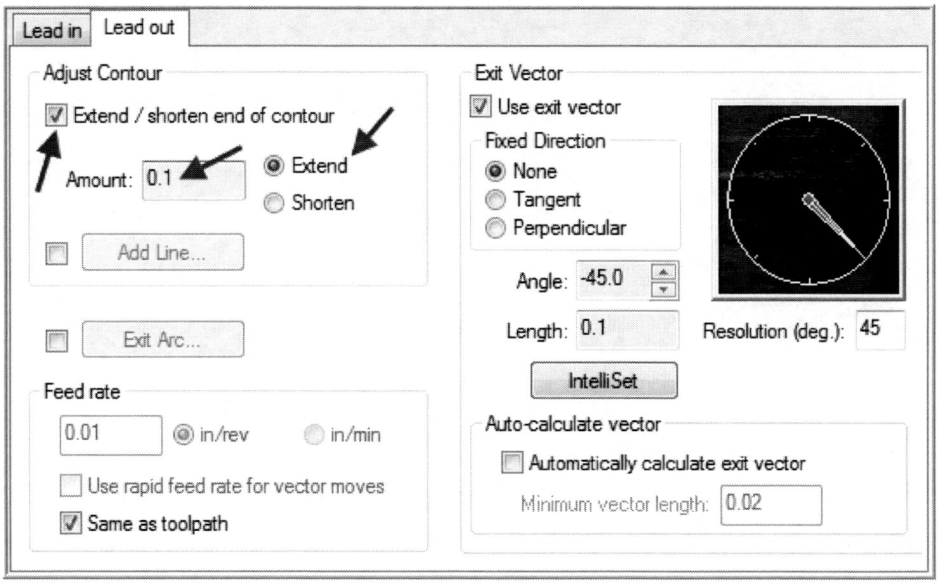

12. Select the OK button  to exit this function.

13. Select the OK button  to exit Rough Parameters.

TASK 16:
FINISH THE BORE

➲ In this task you will use the same boring tool as used for the previous rouging operation.

1. From the menu bar select **TOOLPATHS>Quick>Finish…**

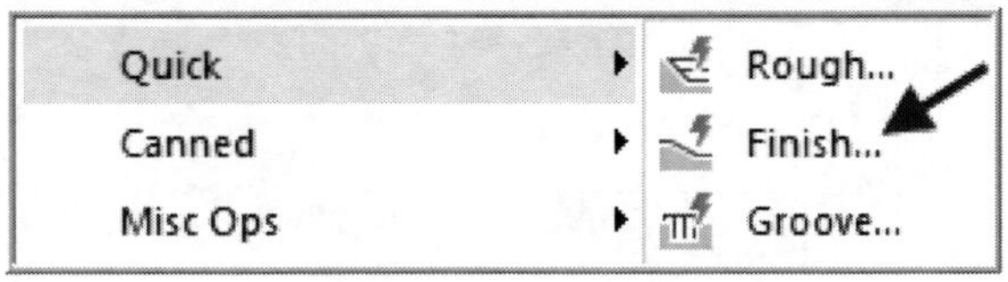

2. In the **Quick Toolpath parameters** page select **Tool #6 a boring tool ID ROUGH MIN .375 DIA – 75 deg** and make any necessary changes as shown below:

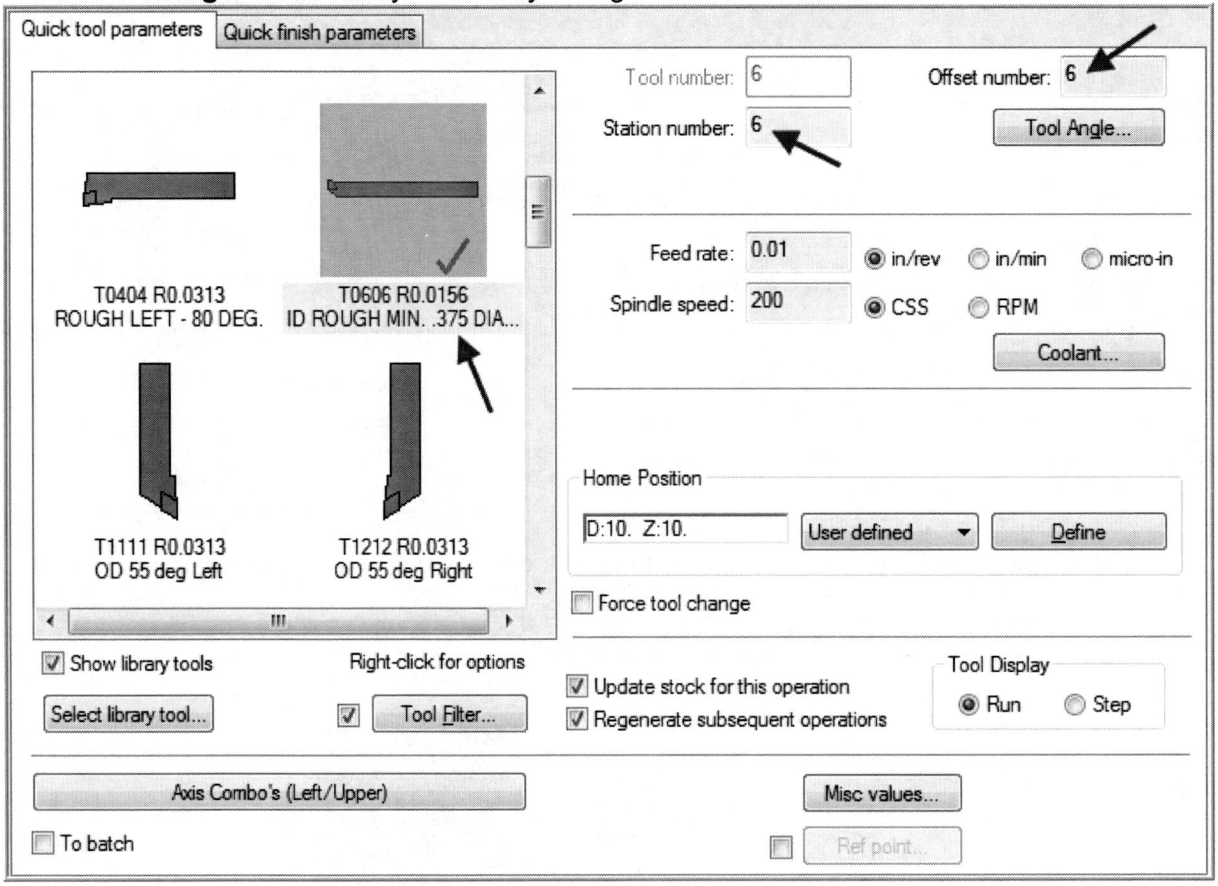

3. Select the **Quick finish parameters** page and make any necessary changes as shown below. Open up the drop down menu for operation and select the operation at the bottom of the list, this is the previous rough boring operation.

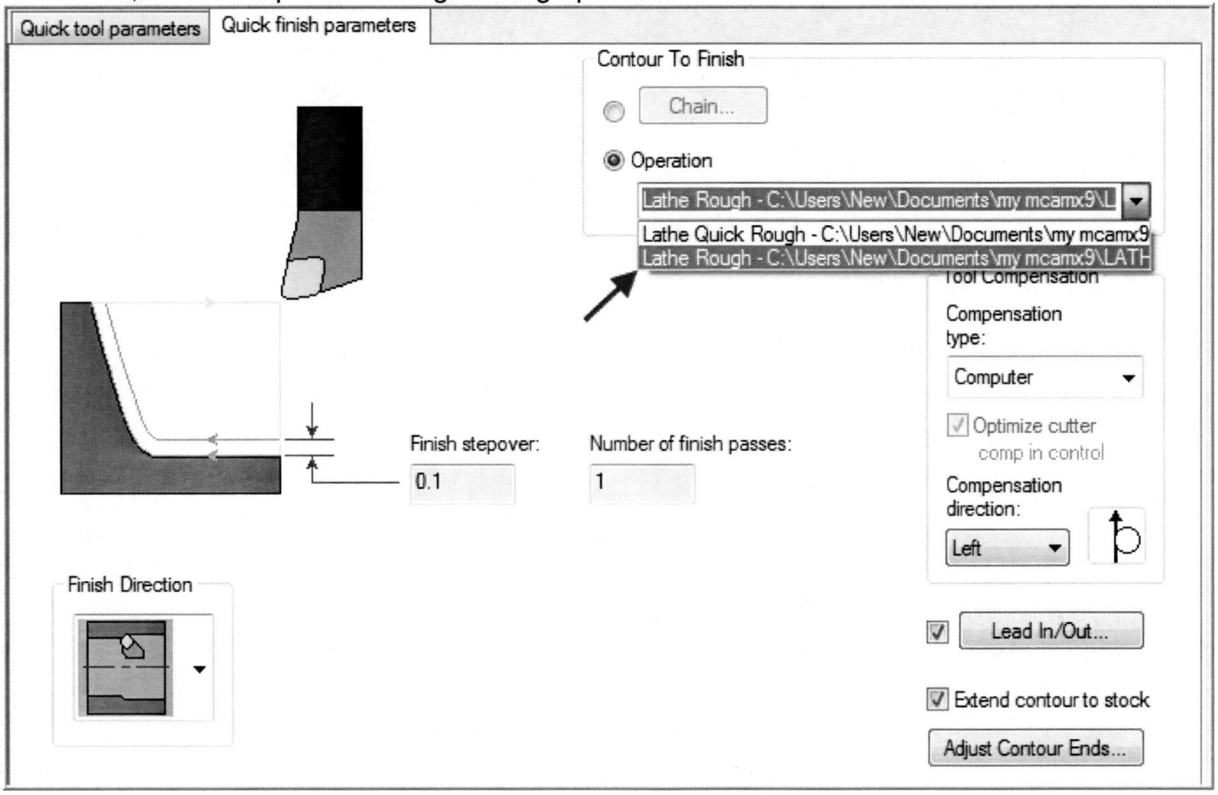

4. Select the **Lead In/Out button** select the **Lead out** page and extend the contour by .1 as shown below:

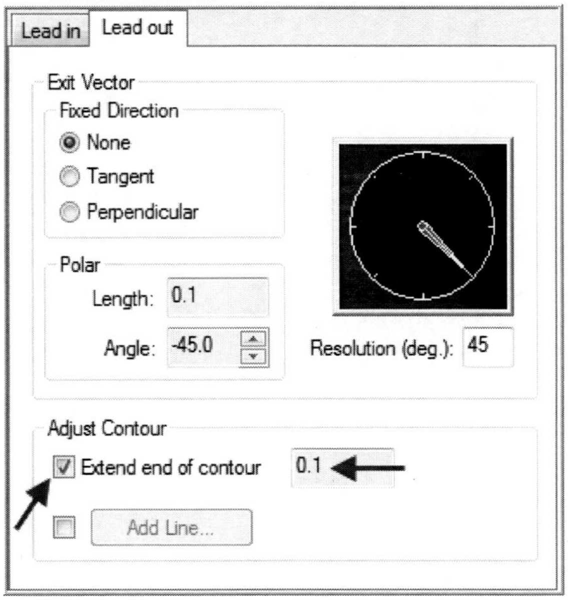

5. Select the OK button ✔ to exit this function.
6. Select the OK button ✔ to exit **Quick finish** parameters.

TASK 17:
CUT OFF THE PART

➲ In this task you will cut off the part using **Tool #7 0.125 OD GROOVE RIGHT HAND TOOL**

1. From the menu bar select **TOOLPATHS>Cutoff…**

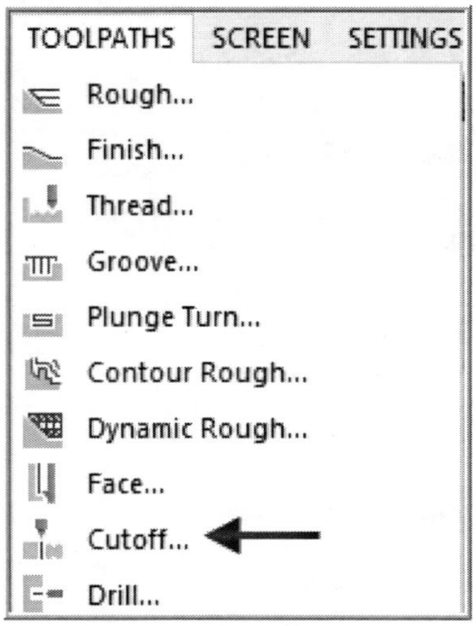

2. Select **Alt-T** on the keyboard to hide the display of toolpaths.
3. When prompted to **Select cutoff boundary point** pick the end point of the line shown below. Move the cursor over the corner until the visual cue for End point displays and then click on this point.

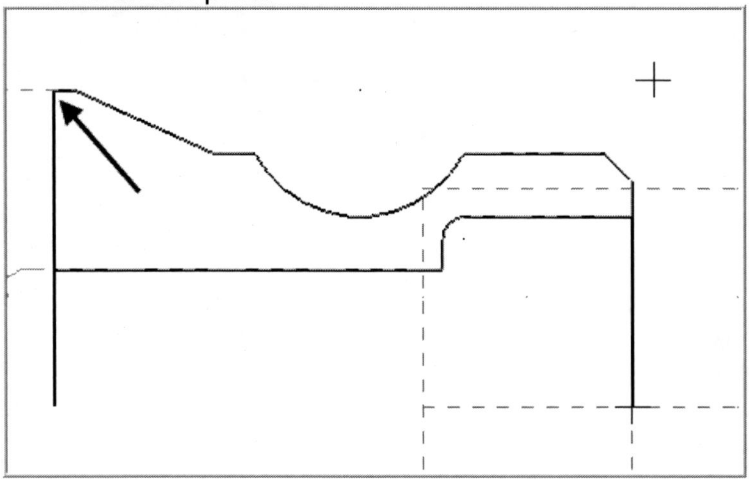

4. Select **OD GROOVE RIGHT WIDTH .125** tool from the tool list and make any necessary changes as shown below:

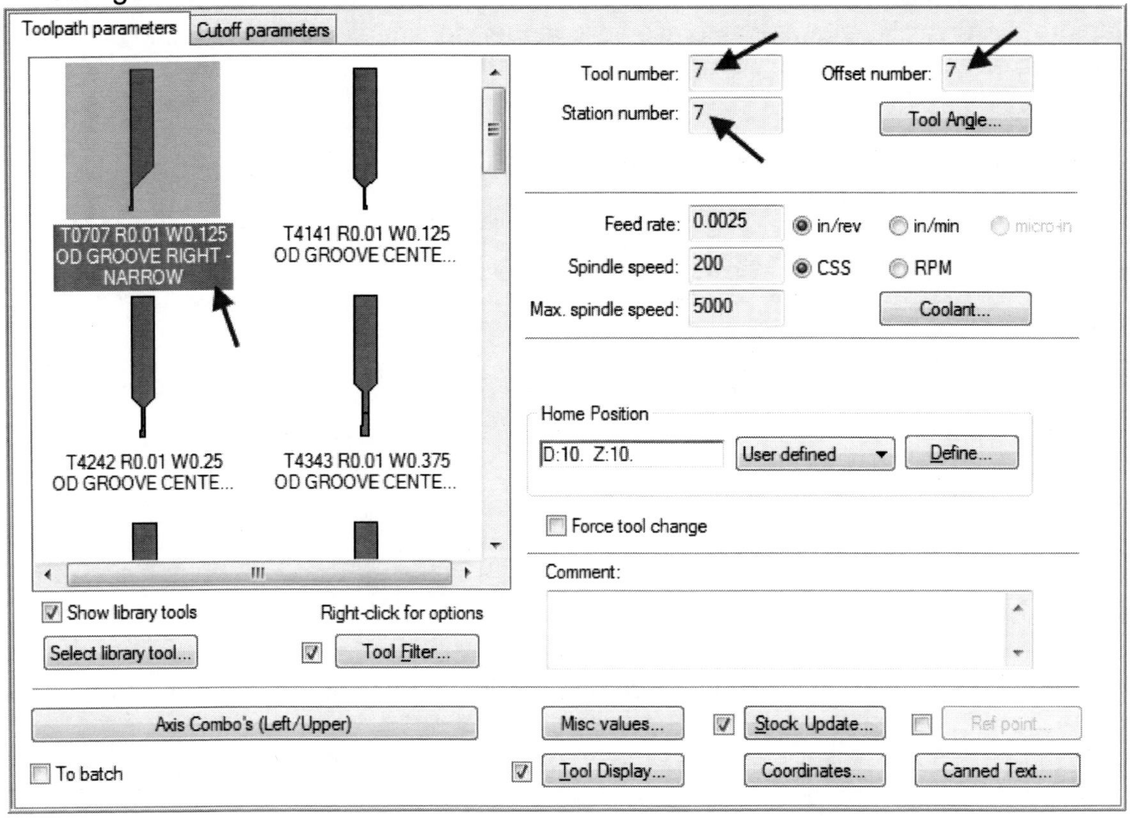

5. Select the **Cutoff parameters** page and make sure the settings are as shown below:

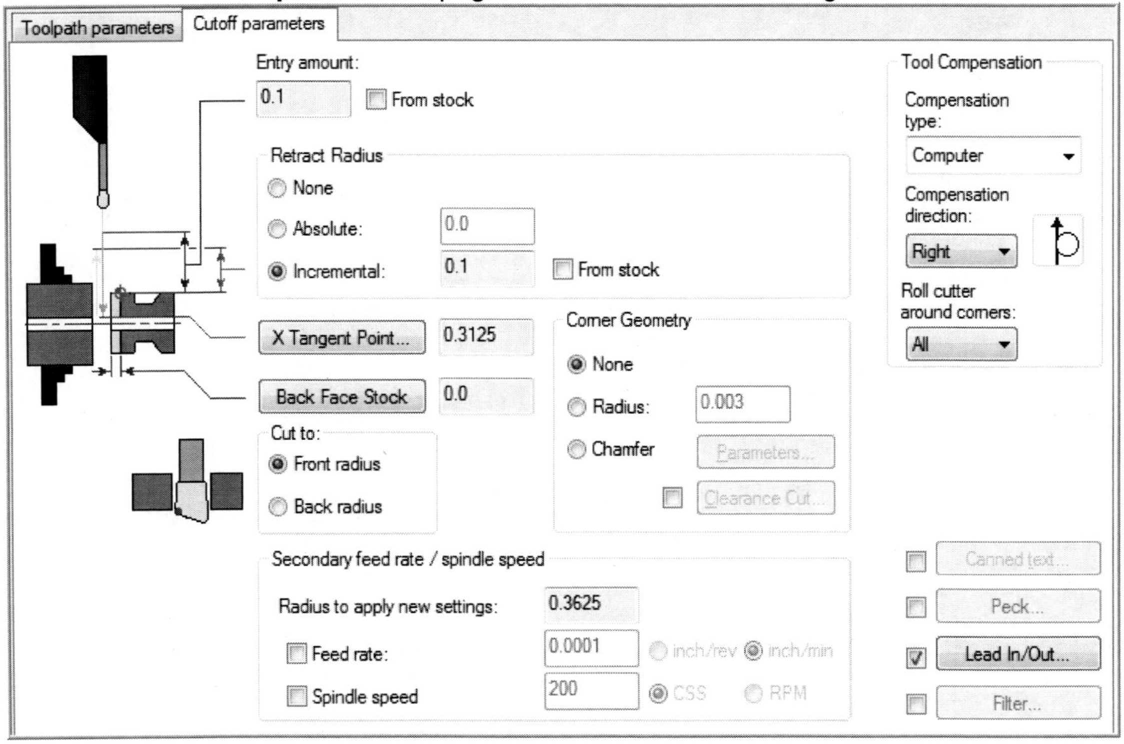

6. Select the OK button ✓ to exit **Lathe Cutoff parameters.**

TASK 18:
VERIFY THE TOOLPATH

➲ Mastercam's Verify utility allows you to use solid models to simulate the machining of a part. The model created by the verification represents the surface finish, and shows collisions, if any exist.

1. In the Toolpaths Manager pick all the operations to Verify by picking the **Select All** icon

.

2. Select the **Verify selected operations** icon shown below:

3. **Maximize** the Backplot/Verify window if required.
4. Now select the **Home** Tab if required.

5. Activate the options shown below in the **Visibility** section of the Home tab. **Initial Stock** not activated.

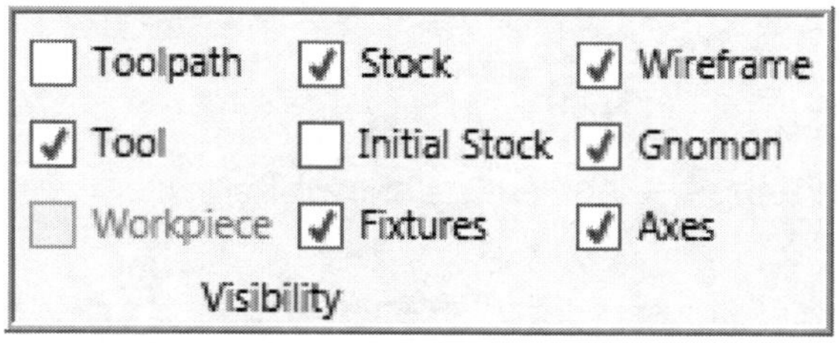

6. Activate the **Color Loop** to change the color of the tools for the verified part.

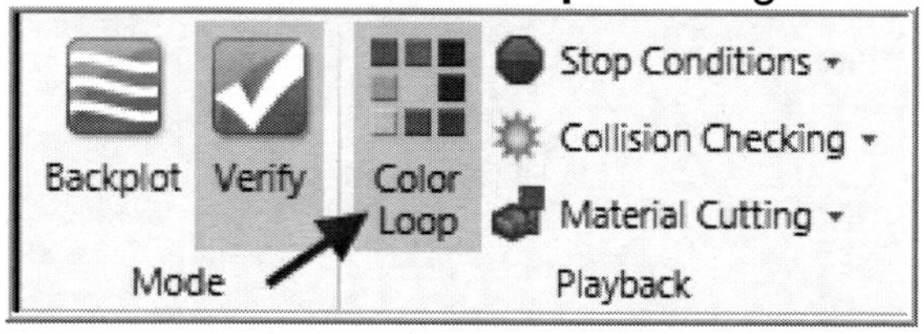

Color Loop
Changes the color of the toolpath or cut stock by operation or by tool change.

Choose **File Options** to set the colors

7. At the top of the screen select the **View** tab, the **Isometric** icon and then select **Fit**.

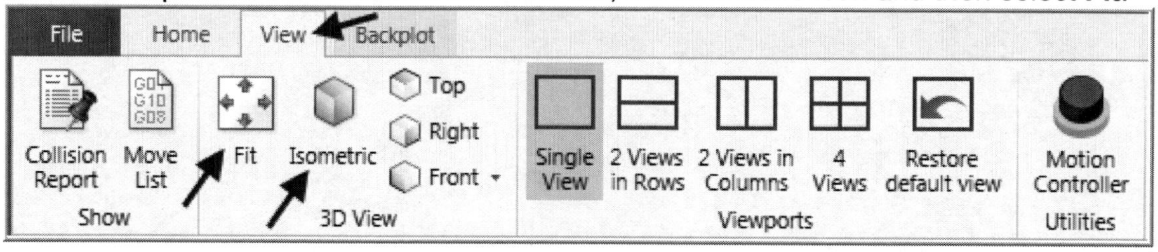

8. In the lower right corner of the screen now set the run **Speed** to slow by moving the slider bar pointer over to the left as shown below.

9. Now select the **Play Simulation** button to review the toolpaths.

10. Select the Close button 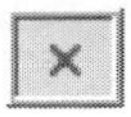 in the top right hand corner to exit Verify.

TASK 19:
SAVE THE UPDATED MASTERCAM FILE

1. Select the save icon from the toolbar 

.

TASK 20:
POST AND CREATE THE CNC CODE FILE

1. Ensure all the operations are selected **by picking the** Select All **icon** **from the** Toolpaths manager.

2. Select the **Post selected operations** button from the Toolpaths manager.

➲ **Please Note:** If you cannot see **G1** click on the right pane of the Toolpaths manager window and expand the window to the right.

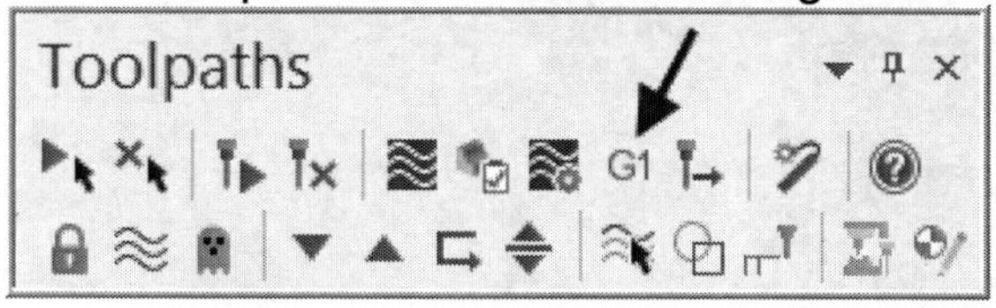

3. In the Post processing window, make the necessary changes as shown below:

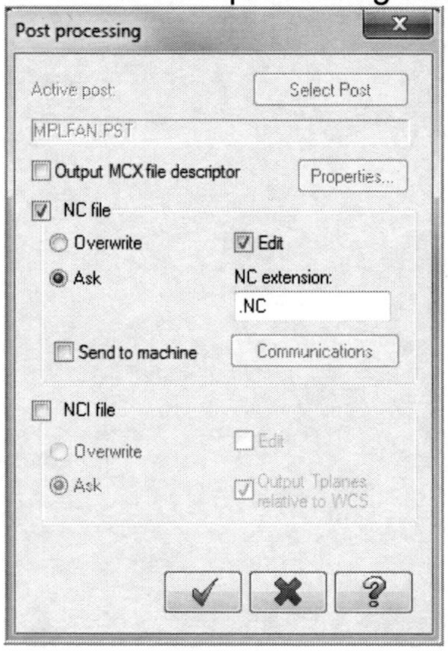

About Post Processing

NC file:
Select this option to save the NC file. The file name and extension are stored in the machine group properties for the selected operation. If you are posting operations from different machine groups or Mastercam files, or batch processing, Mastercam will create several files according to the settings for each machine group.

Edit:
When checked, automatically launches the default text editor with the file displayed so that you can review or modify it.

4. Select the OK button to continue.

5. Ensure the same name as your Mastercam part file name is displayed in the **NC File name** field.
6. Select the **Save** button.
7. The CNC code file opens up in the default editor.

LATHE-LESSON-5.NC ×

```
(MATERIAL - ALUMINUM INCH - 6061)
G20
(TOOL - 1 OFFSET - 1)
(OD ROUGH RIGHT - 80 DEG.  INSERT - CNMG-432)
G0 T0101
G18
G97 S449 M03
G0 G54 X1.7 Z0.
G50 S3600
G96 S200
G99 G1 X-.1225 F.01
G0 Z.1
X1.3246
Z.2
G1 Z.1
Z-1.1856
X1.4637 Z-1.3415
G18 G3 X1.47 Z-1.3563 I-.0331 K-.0148
G1 Z-1.6063
```

8. Select the × in the top right corner to exit the CNC editor.
9. This completes LATHE-LESSON-5.

LATHE-LESSON-5 EXERCISE

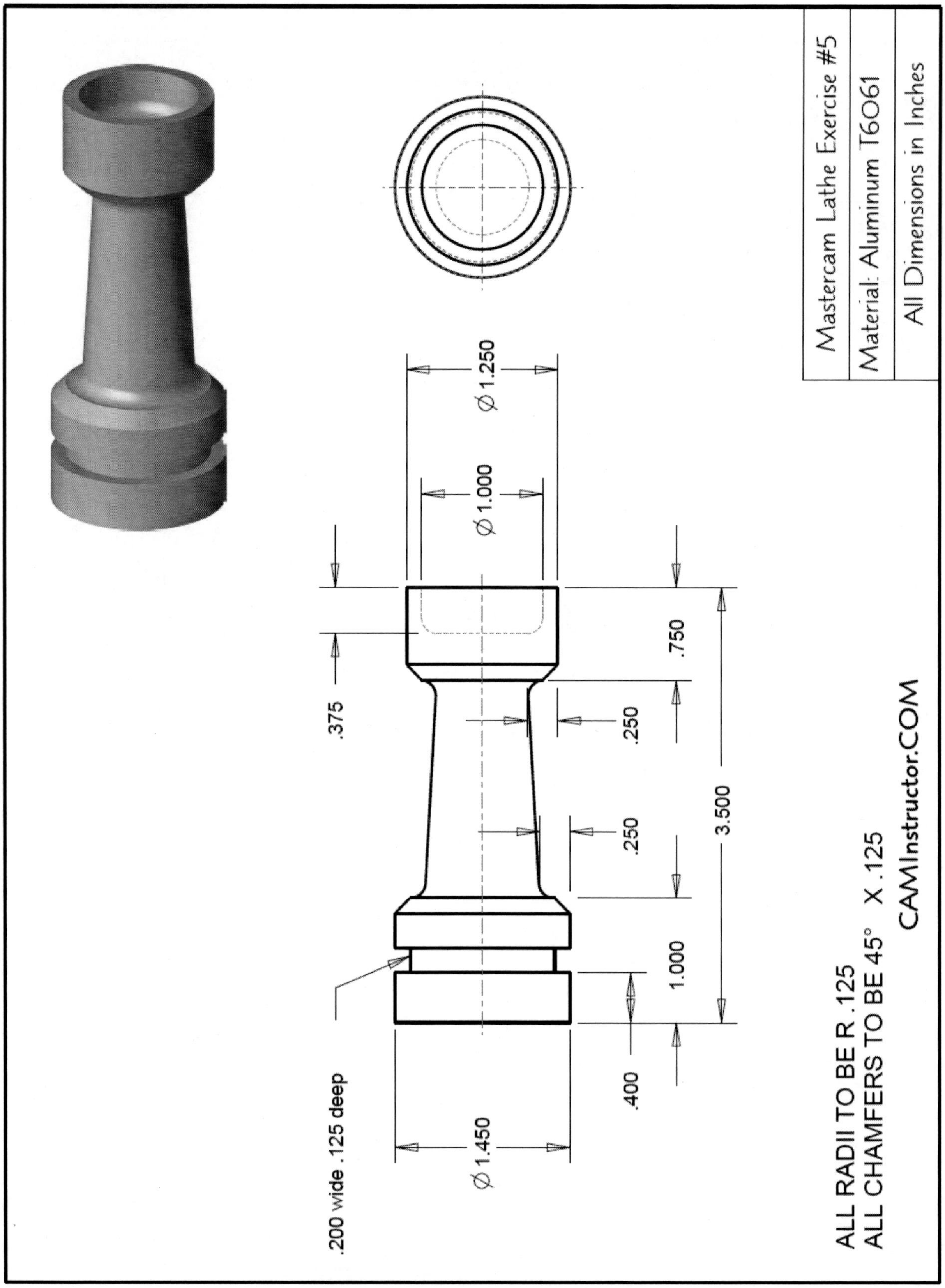

Mastercam® X9

TRAINING GUIDE

LESSON 5B

IMPORT A SOLID PART FILE

NOTE:

This Lesson is located on the accompanying DVD as a PDF file.

1. Just insert the DVD and click on **Lathe Lesson 5-Import a CAD Solid Part File** from the Menu screen.
2. The Lesson can be printed or you can follow the instructions on the computer screen.

camInstructor

Mastercam® X9

Training Guide

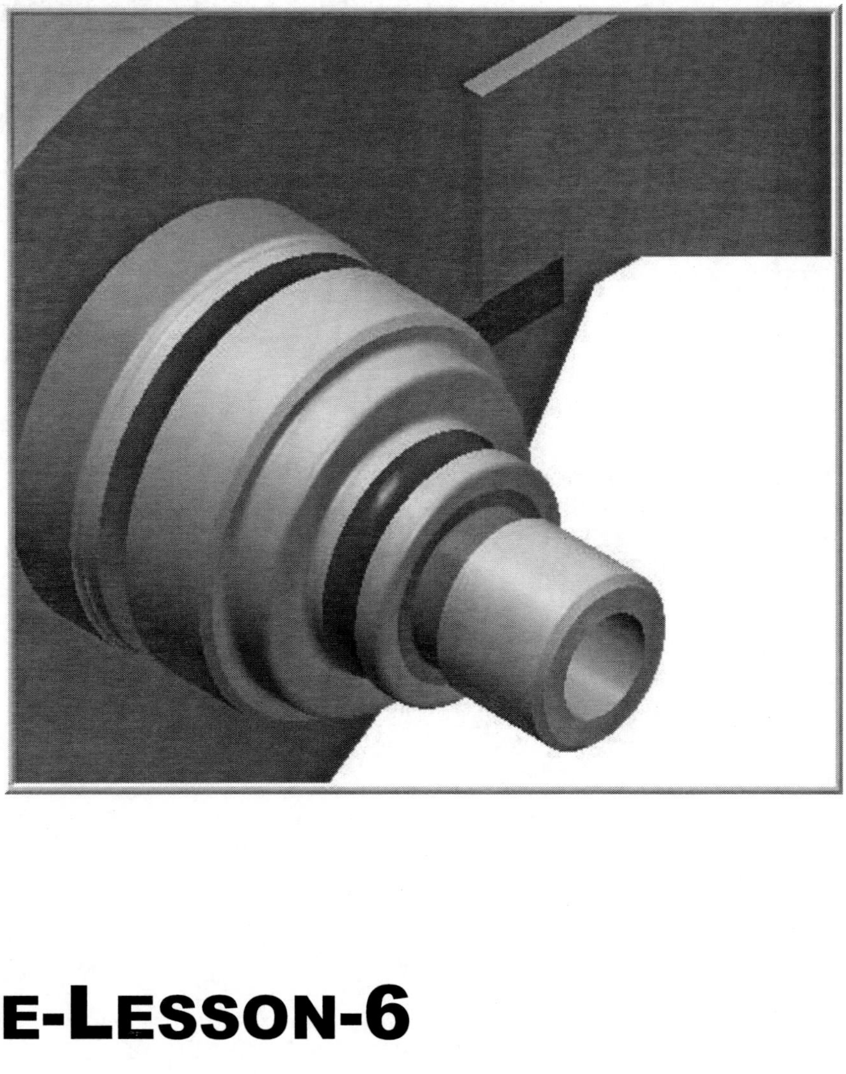

Lathe-Lesson-6

Face, Quick Rough and Finish, Drill, Groove and Cutoff

camInstructor

Objectives

You will create the geometry for Lathe Lesson 6, and then generate a toolpath to machine the part on a CNC lathe. This lesson covers the following topics:

➲ **Create a 2-dimensional drawing by:**
Creating lines.
Creating fillets.
Creating chamfers.
Trimming geometry.

➲ **Establish Stock and Chuck Setup settings:**
Stock size.
Chuck Configuration.
Material for the part.
Feed calculation.

➲ **Generate a 2-dimensional lathe toolpath consisting of:**
Lathe Face.
Lathe Quick Rough.
Lathe Quick Finish.
Lathe Finish.
Lathe Drill.
Lathe Groove.
Lathe Cutoff.

➲ **Inspect the toolpath using Mastercam's Verify and Backplot by:**
Launching the Verify function to machine the part on the screen.
Generating the NC- code.

LATHE - LESSON-6 DRAWING

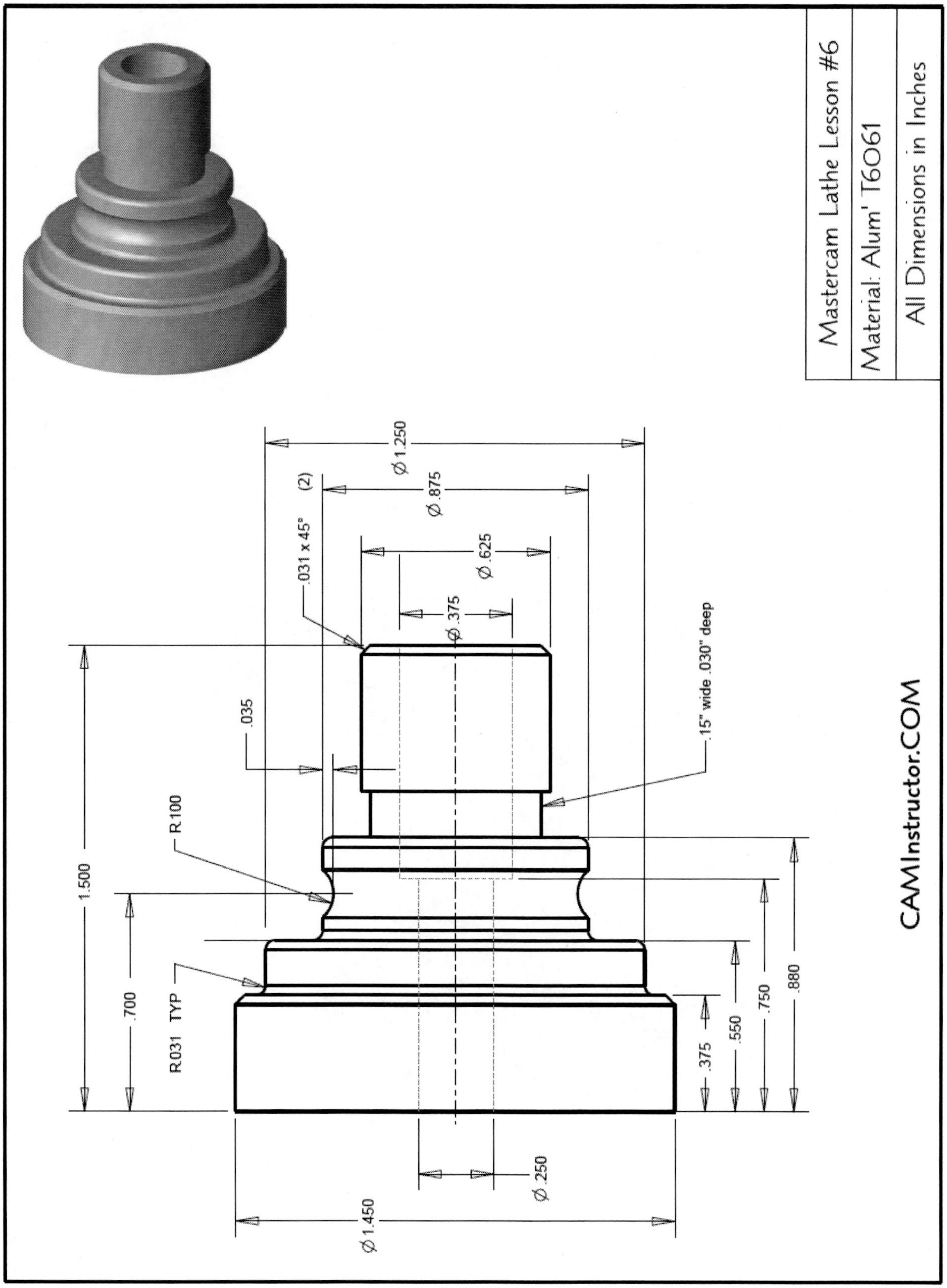

TOOL LIST

Six tools will be used to create this part.

- **Tool #1 Face, Rough and Finish the outside diameters**
  Holder: Outside Diameter Rough Right Hand - DCGNR-164D.
  Insert: 80 Degree Diamond Insert – CNMG-432

- Tool #2 Finish the 0.1 radius
  Holder: Offset Profiling.
  Insert: 0.1875 circular insert

- **Tool #3 Center drill**
  Centre Drill – body diameter 0.250”

- **Tool #4 0.250 diameter drill**
  Drill 0.25” diameter

- **Tool #5 0.375 End Mill**
  End Mill 0.375” diameter

- **Tool #6 Cutoff tool**
  Holder: Outside Diameter Groove Right Hand - Narrow.
  Insert: 0.125” Wide - GC-4125

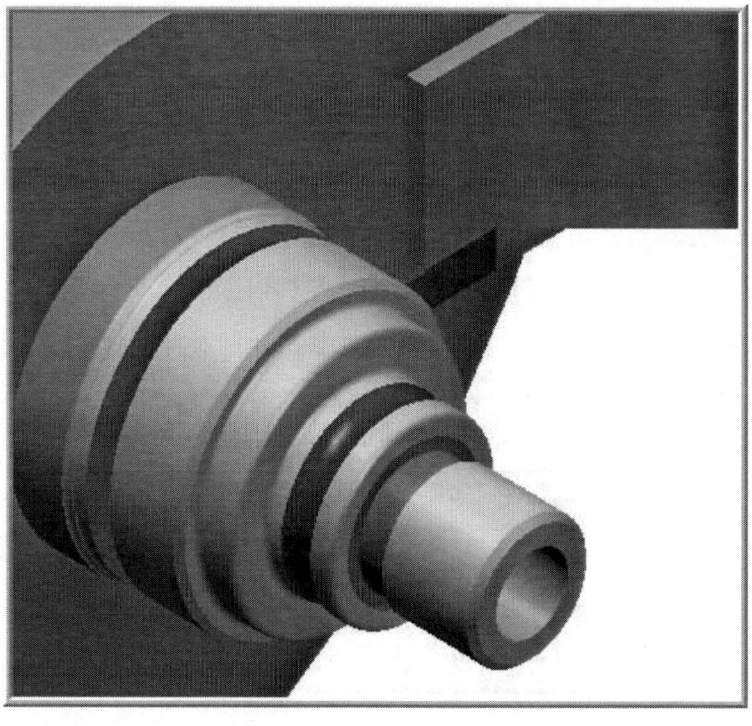

LESSON - 6 - THE PROCESS

Geometry Creation

TASK 1: Setting the environment
TASK 2: Setting the construction planes
TASK 3: Create the geometry
TASK 4: Create the 0.100" radius
TASK 5: Create the chamfers
TASK 6: Create the fillet radii
TASK 7: Create the geometry for the bore
TASK 8: Save the drawing

Toolpath Creation

TASK 9: Define the stock and chuck parameters
TASK 10: Face the front of the part
TASK 11: Rough the outside diameters
TASK 12: Finish the outside diameters
TASK 13: Finish the 0.1 radius
TASK 14: Center drill hole
TASK 15: Peck Drill the 0.250" Hole
TASK 16: Drill the 0.375" Hole
TASK 17: Cut the Groove
TASK 18: Cut off the part
TASK 19: Verify the toolpath
TASK 20: Save the updated Mastercam file
TASK 21: Post and create the cnc code file

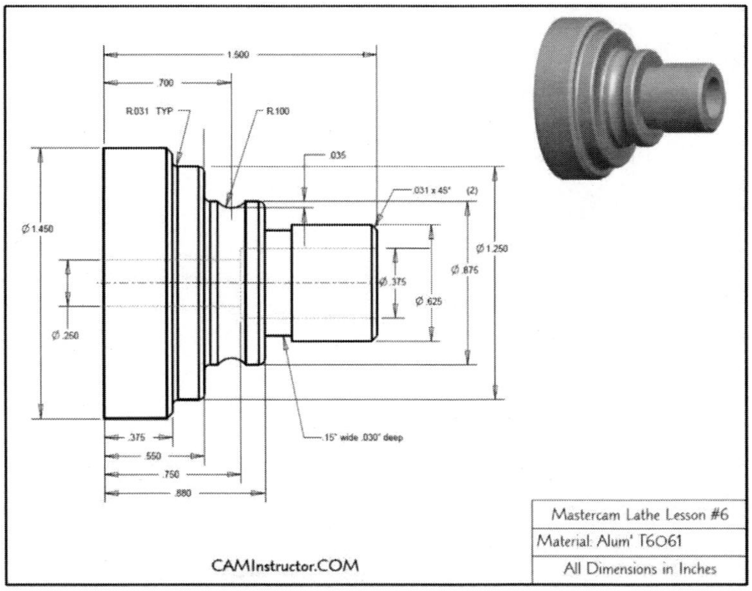

Geometry Creation

TASK 1:
SETTING THE ENVIRONMENT

Before starting the geometry creation you should set up the grid and toolbars as outlined in the **Setting the Environment** section at the beginning of this text:

1. Set up the Grid. This will help identify the location of the origin.
2. Load the Workspace – **SETTINGS>Load Workspace>Lathe** to machine a part on the Lathe.
3. Set the machine type to the default Lathe.

TASK 2:
SETTING THE CONSTRUCTION PLANES:

➲ **Set the Construction Plane to Lathe diameter +D +Z (WCS)**

1. Click on Planes at the bottom of the screen as shown below:

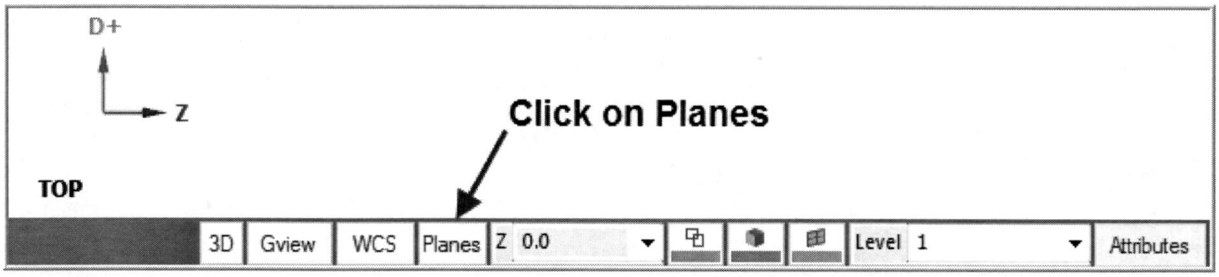

2. Click on Lathe diameter>+D +Z (WCS) as shown below:

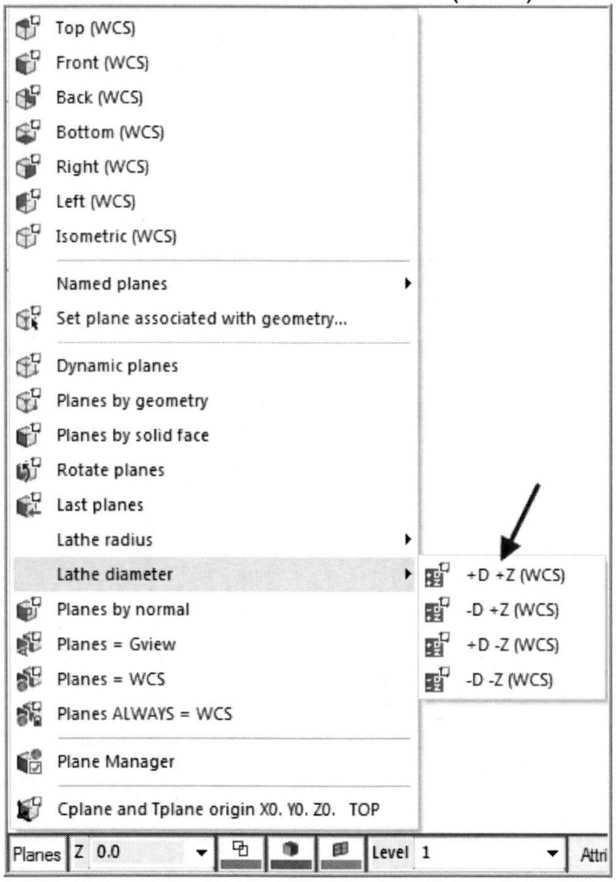

TASK 3:
CREATE THE GEOMETRY

1. This task explains how to create the geometry of this part. In this lathe part you only need to create **half of the geometry**, the geometry above the center line.
2. Lines 1 through 12 will be created first and then the radius and chamfer will be created.

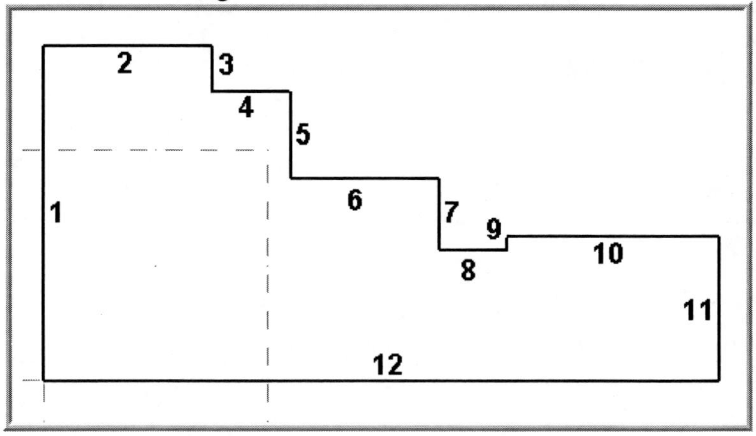

➲ **Create Line #1**

1. Select **Alt-O** on your keyboard to turn off the display of the Toolpaths Manager.
2. Select from the pull down menu **CREATE>Line>Endpoint…**

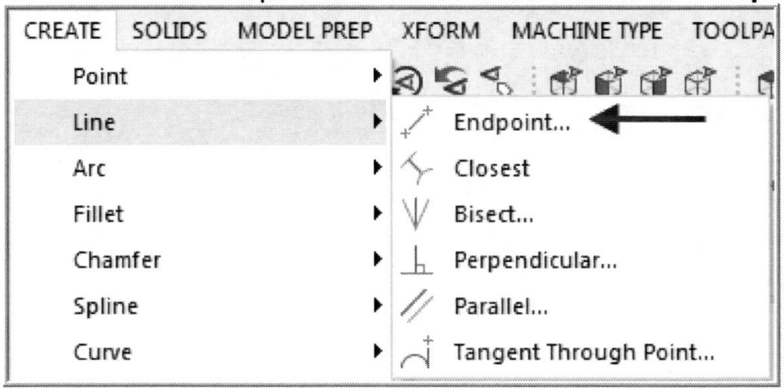

3. The Line ribbon bar appears:

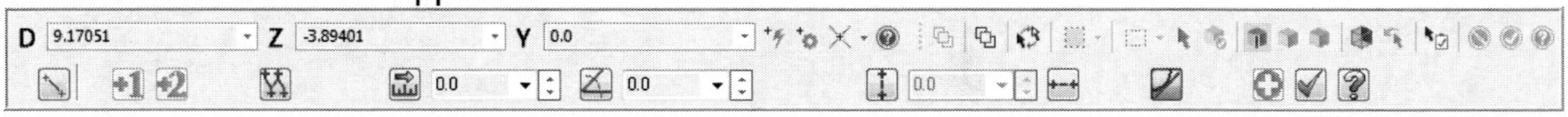

4. Move the cursor over the **center of the grid** and as you get close to the origin a visual cue appears.  This is the cue that will allow you to snap to the **origin**. With this visual cue highlighted pick the **origin.**

AutoCursor: Visual Cues detects and highlights endpoints and midpoints of curves, lines, arc center points, and point entities. In addition, AutoCursor can snap to angle, nearest, tangent, perpendicular, horizontal, and vertical conditions.

➲ The following are Mastercam Visual Cues:

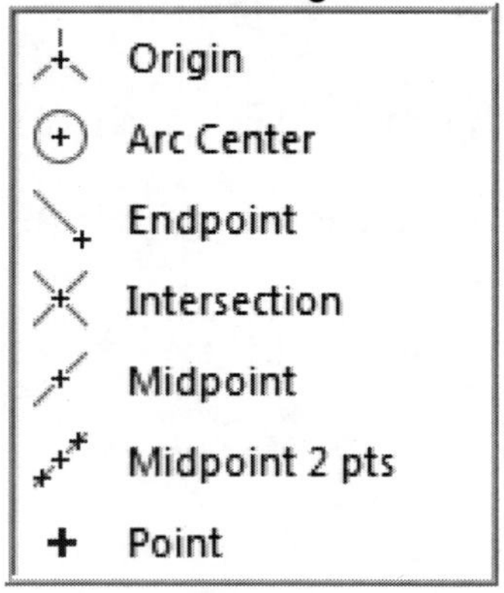

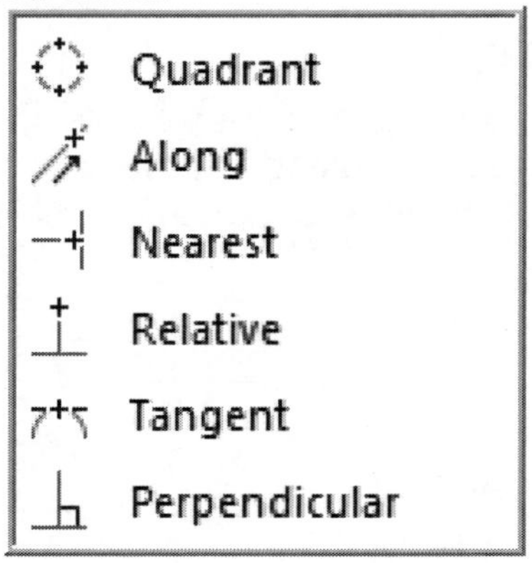

5. You are next prompted to **"Specify the second endpoint".** On the left hand side of the Line ribbon bar click on the **Multi-Line** button to activate it as shown below by the arrow:

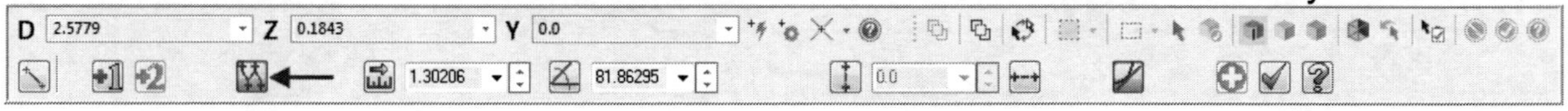

6. Click in the **D** value space (Diameter) and enter a value of **1.45**. Hit the Enter key and enter a value of **0 for the Z**, hit the Enter key again and enter a value of **0 for the Y** and hit Enter.

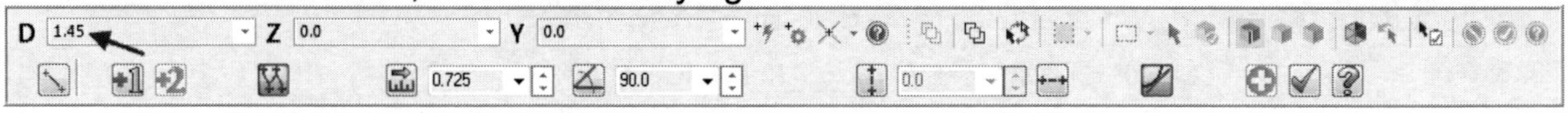

7. A vertical line should be visible as shown below:

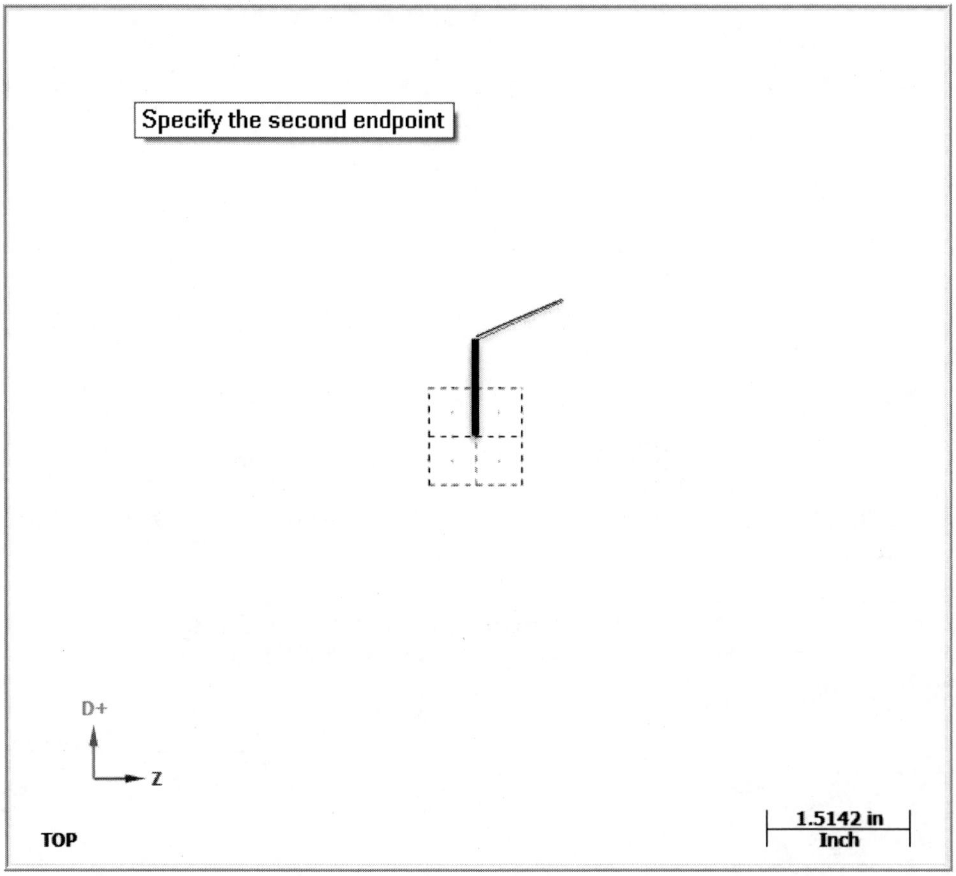

➲ **Create Line #2**

8. **"Specify the second endpoint";** Type in **1.45 in D** hit Enter, type in **0.375 in Z. Note** the value of Y is set to **Zero**, this does not need to be input. Hit the Enter key once again to complete this line.

➲ **Create Line #3**

9. **"Specify the second endpoint";** Type in **1.250 in D** hit Enter, type in **0.375 in Z.** Hit the Enter key once again to complete this line.

➲ **Create Line #4**

10. **"Specify the second endpoint";** Type in **1.250 in D** hit Enter, type in **0.550 in Z.** Hit the Enter key once again to complete this line.

➲ **Create Line #5**

11. **"Specify the second endpoint";** Type in **0.875 in D** hit Enter, type in **0.550 in Z.** Hit the Enter key once again to complete this line.

➲ **Create Line #6**

12. **"Specify the second endpoint";** Type in **0.875 in D** hit Enter, type in **0.880 in Z.** Hit the Enter key once again to complete this line.

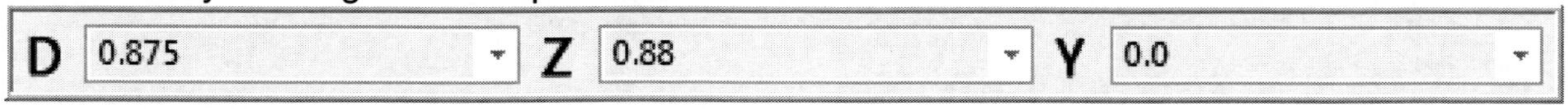

➲ **Create Line #7**

13. **"Specify the second endpoint";** Type in **0.625-0.06 in D** hit Enter, type in **0.880 in Z.** Hit the Enter key once again to complete this line.

➲ **Create Line #8**

14. **"Specify the second endpoint";** Type in **0.625-0.06 in D** hit Enter, type in **0.880+0.15 in Z.** Hit the Enter key once again to complete this line.

➲ **Create Line #9**

15. **"Specify the second endpoint";** Type in **0.625 in D** hit Enter, type in **0.880+0.15 in Z.** Hit the Enter key once again to complete this line.

➲ **Create Line #10**

16. **"Specify the second endpoint";** Type in **0.625 in D** hit Enter, type in **1.500 in Z.** Hit the Enter key once again to complete this line.

➲ **Create Line #11**

17. **"Specify the second endpoint";** Type in **0 in D** hit Enter, type in **1.500 in Z.** Hit the Enter key once again to complete this line.

➲ **Create Line #12**

18. **"Specify the second endpoint";** Move the cursor over the **center of the grid** and as you get close to the origin a visual cue appears.  Click on this point.
19. Click on the **OK** icon  to complete this feature.
20. Fit the image to the screen by clicking on the **Fit** icon as shown below:

21. Then unzoom by clicking on the **Un-Zoom Previous / .5** icon as shown below:

22. Your geometry should look like the figure below:

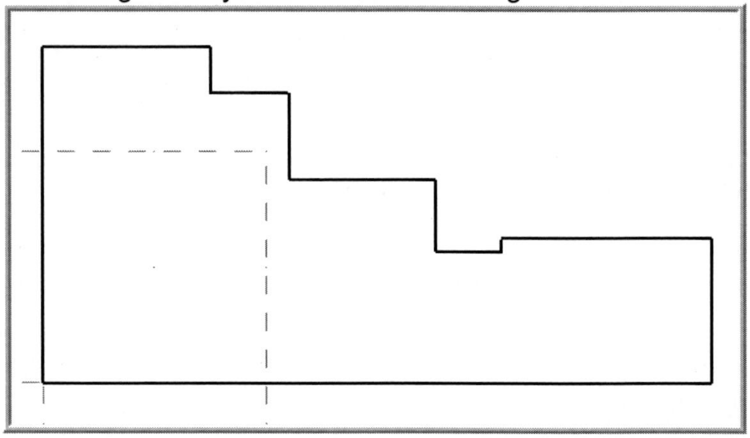

TASK 4:
CREATE THE 0.100" RADIUS

➲ In this task you will create the 0.100 arc. The center position and radius are known.

1. Select **CREATE>Arc>Arc Polar…**

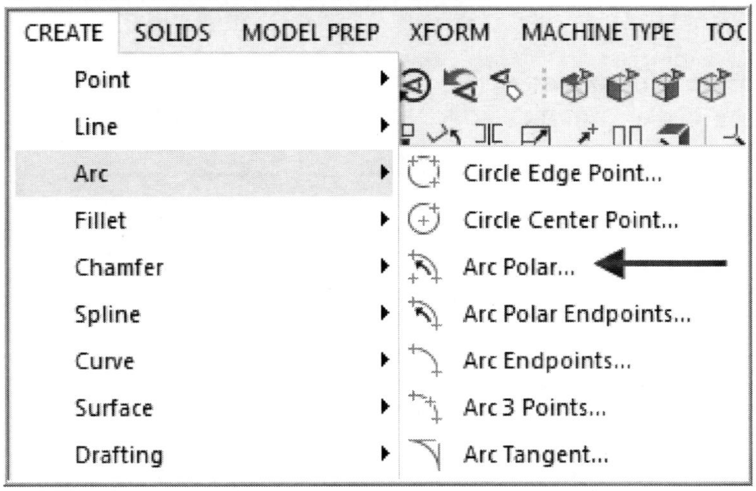

2. The **Arc Polar** ribbon bar appears and you are prompted to **Enter the center point**. Click on the **FastPoint** icon as shown below and enter the coordinates for the center of the arc **0.875-0.07+0.2 , 0.7** and then hit enter.

3. The prompt now changes to **Sketch the initial angle**. Click in the space for **radius** and enter **0.1** and then hit the **tab key twice** to move over to the start angle.
4. Input a **Start angle of 180** and hit the tab key.
5. For the **End angle** input **0** and then hit enter.

6. Click on the OK icon ✔ to complete this feature.
7. The completed arc is shown below:

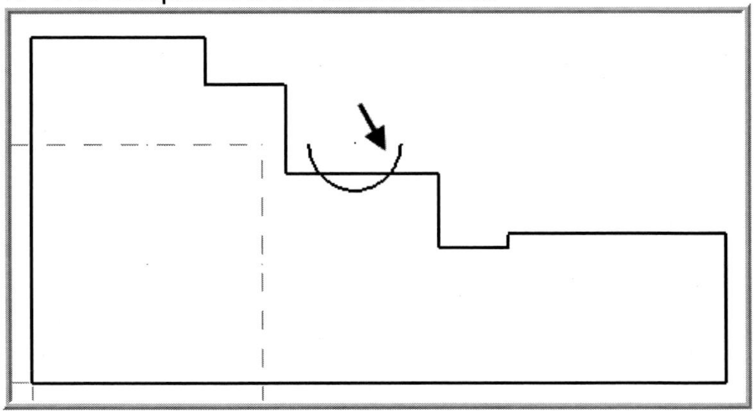

➲ **Trim the Arc**

8. Select **EDIT>Trim/Break>Trim/Break/Extend**
9. The Trim / Extend / Break ribbon bar appears and you are prompted to **Select the entity to trim/extend**.
10. Click on the **Trim 1 entity** button as shown below:

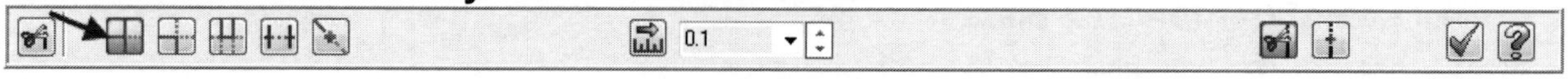

11. Now at the prompt **Select the entity to trim/extend** select the arc at position 1,
12. The prompt changes to **Select the entity to trim/extend** to, select the remaining entities in the order shown below.

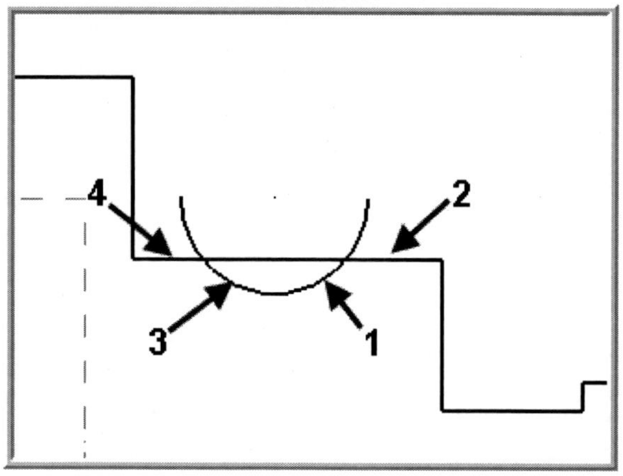

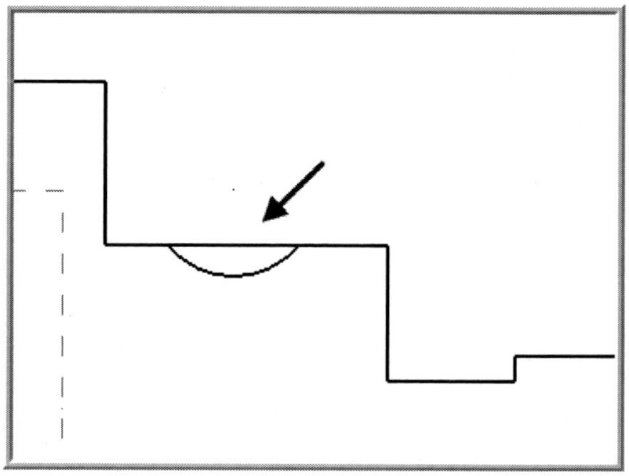

13. The entities are trimmed as shown above right.
14. Now click on the **Divide** icon.
15. The prompt changes to **Select the curve to divide.** Move the cursor over the line and select it as shown below left.

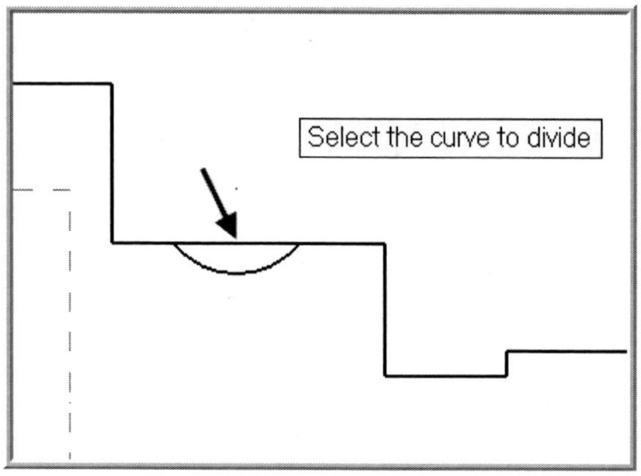

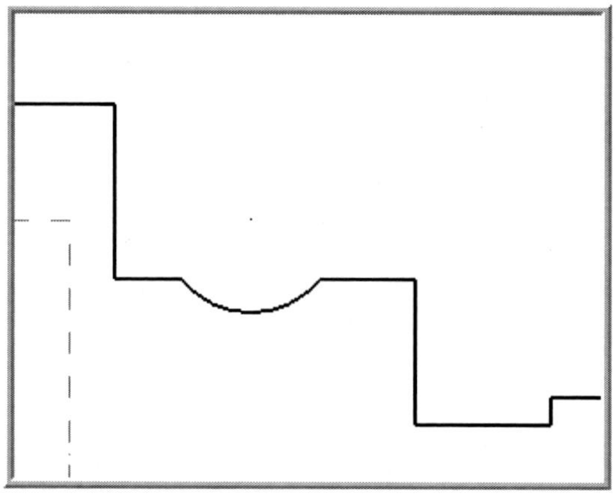

16. Click on the OK icon to complete this feature.

➲ The line is trimmed back to the two closest intersections as shown above right:

TASK 5:
CREATE THE CHAMFERS

➲ **Create the two chamfers 45 degrees x .031.**

1. Select **CREATE>Chamfer>Entities…**

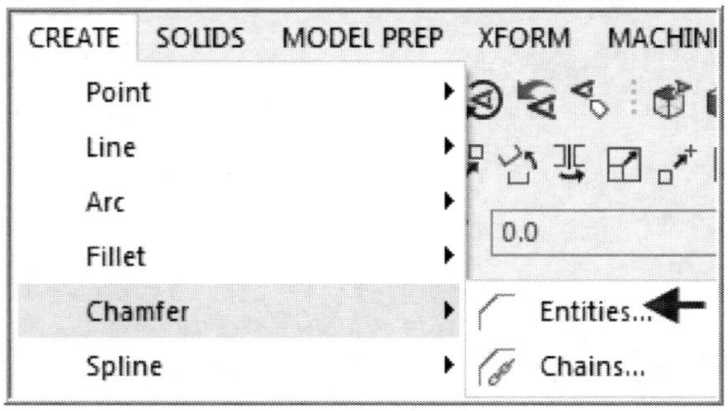

2. You are prompted to "Select line or arc".
3. Click in the **Distance** window as shown below and type in **0.031** and hit enter:

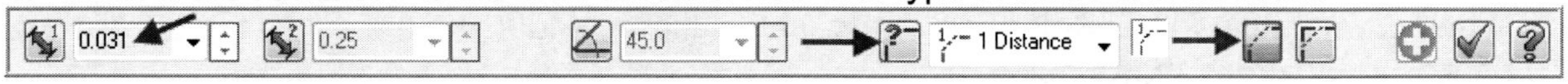

4. Ensure the **1 Distance** option is selected and **Trim is on** as shown above:
5. Click on line 1 and then line 2 as shown below. Next on line 3 and line 4.

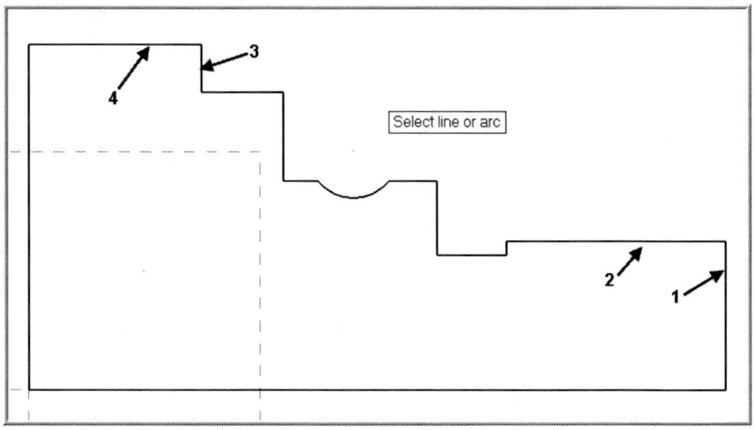

6. Click on the OK icon to complete this feature.
7. The completed geometry should look like the image below:

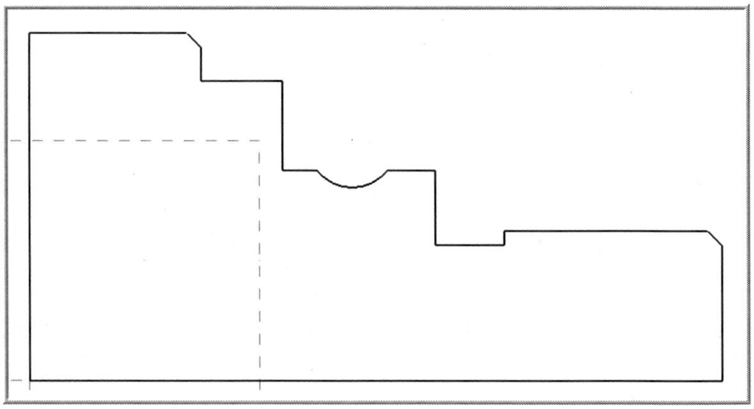

TASK 6:
CREATE THE FILLET RADII

➲ In this task you will create the 0.031 fillet radii in four places.

1. Select **CREATE>Fillet>Entities…**

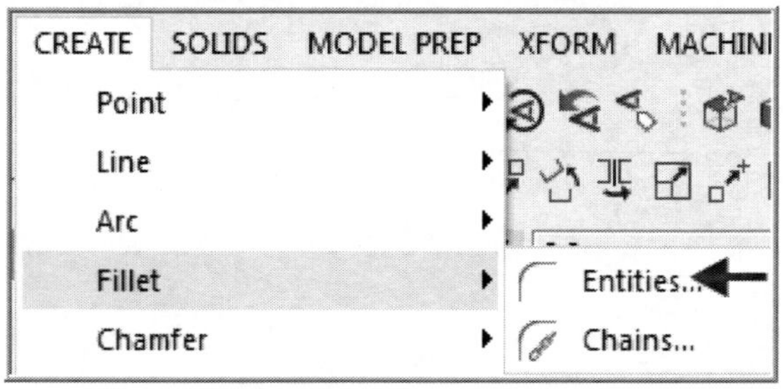

2. On the Fillet ribbon bar enter **0.031 for the radius** and hit enter. Ensure the **Style** of radius is set to **Normal** and the trim button is depressed to turn the **trim on**.

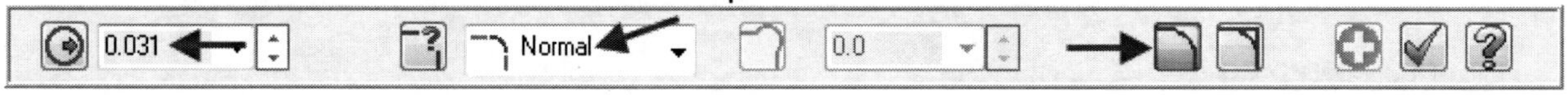

3. When prompted to **Fillet: Select an entity,** select Line 1 and 2 and the select the remaining entities in the order shown below:

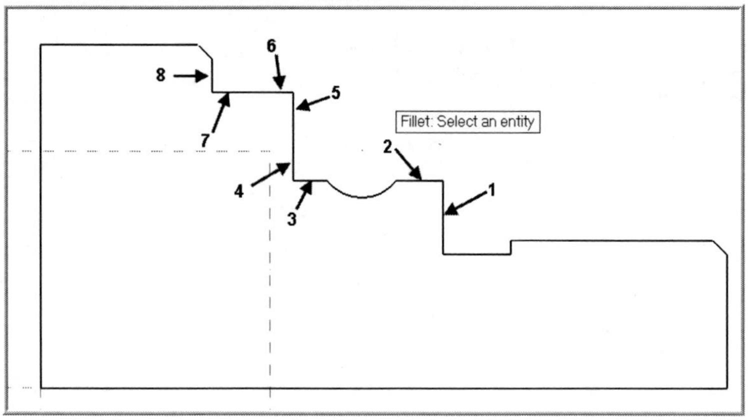

4. Click on the OK icon  to complete this feature. The completed geometry is shown below:

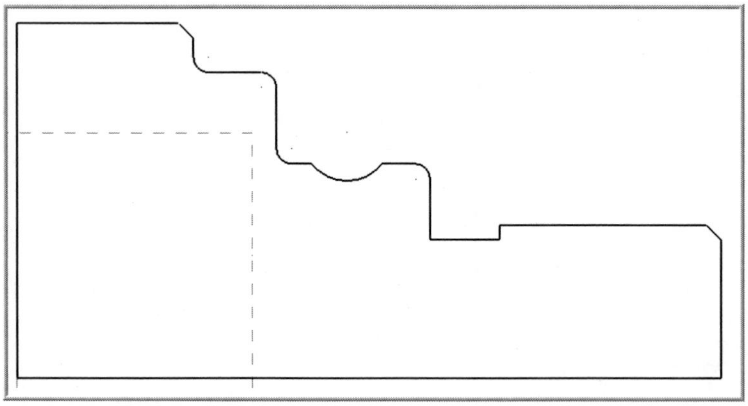

TASK 7:
CREATE THE GEOMETRY FOR THE BORE

➲ In this task you will create the geometry that make up the bore of this part

1. Select from the pull down menu: **CREATE>Line>Parallel....**
2. **On the graphics screen you are prompted**: **Select a line** and the Line Parallel ribbon bar appears.
3. To satisfy the prompt **Select a line**, select the line shown below.

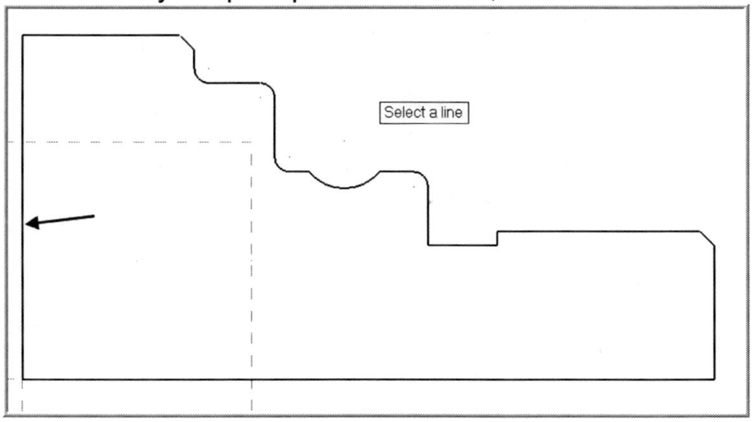

4. To satisfy the next prompt **Select the point to place a parallel line through** move the cursor to the right of the line and pick a point.
5. For the **Distance** input **0.750** then hit **enter**.
6. On the ribbon bar click on **Apply**  to fix the entity,
7. To satisfy the prompt **Select a line**, select the line shown below.

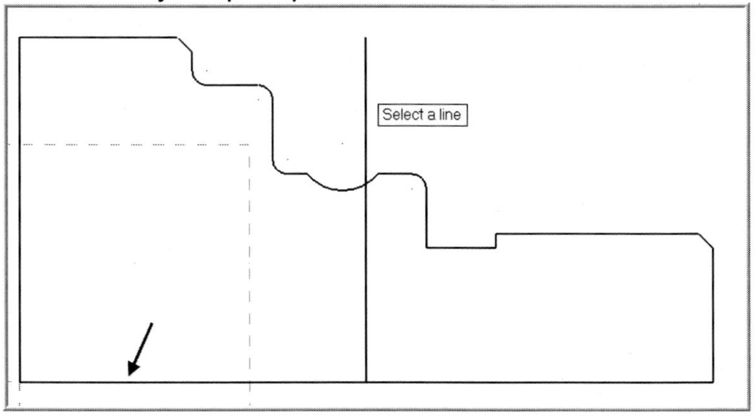

8. To satisfy the next prompt **Select the point to place a parallel line through** move the cursor above the line and pick a point.
9. For the **Distance** input **0.250/2** then hit **enter**
10. On the ribbon bar click on **Apply**  to fix the entity.

11. To satisfy the prompt **Select a line**, select the line shown below:

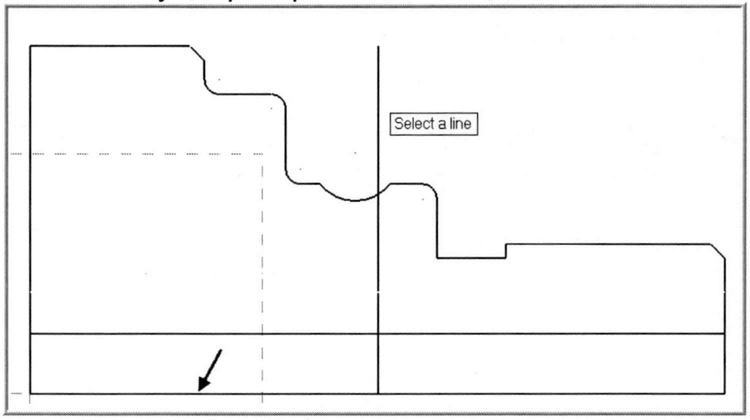

12. To satisfy the next prompt **Select the point to place a parallel line through** move the cursor above the line and pick a point.
13. For the **Distance** input **0.375/2** then hit **enter**
14. Click on the OK icon  to complete this feature. The completed geometry is shown below:

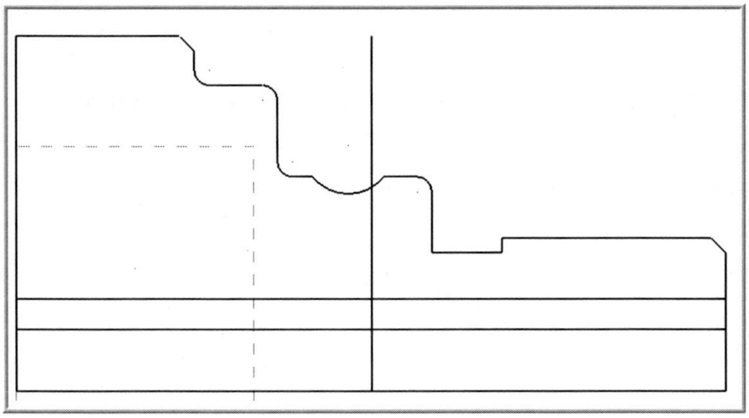

➲ Trim the bore

15. Select **EDIT>Trim/Break>Trim/Break/Extend**
16. The Trim / Extend / Break ribbon bar appears and you are prompted to **Select the entity to trim/extend**.
17. Click on the **Trim 2 entity** button as shown below:

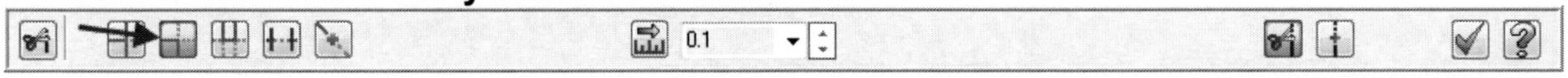

18. Now at the prompt **Select the entity to trim/extend** select the line at **position 1,**
19. The prompt changes to **Select the entity to trim/extend to**, select the line at **position 2**
20. Now at the prompt **Select the entity to trim/extend** select the line at **position 3,**
21. The prompt changes to **Select the entity to trim/extend to**, select the line at **position 4**

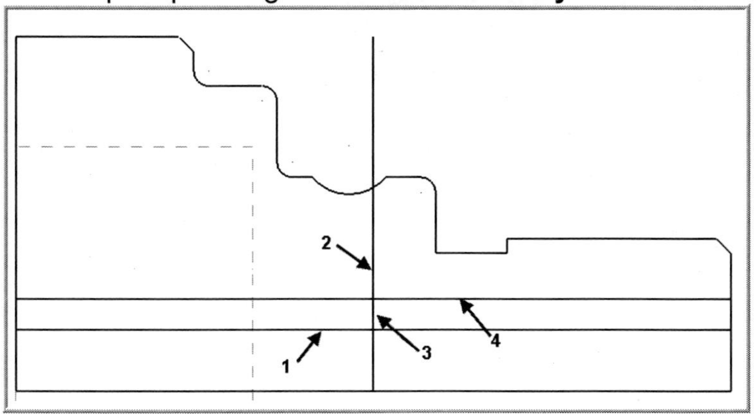

22. Click on the OK icon [✓] to complete this feature.

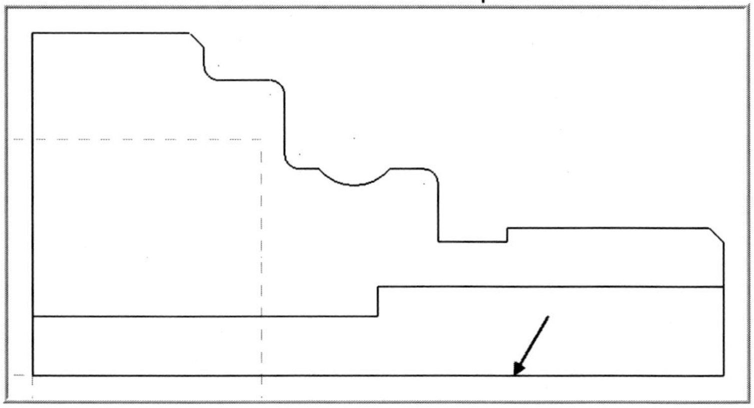

23. **Delete** the construction line shown above. Select the line and hit the delete key on your keyboard.

TASK 8:
SAVE THE DRAWING

1. Select **File.**
2. Select **Save as.**
3. In the **"File name"** box, type **"Lathe-Lesson-6".**
4. Save to an appropriate location.
5. Select the Save button to save the file and complete this function.

Toolpath Creation

TASK 9:
DEFINING THE STOCK AND CHUCK PARAMETERS

1. Fit the image to the screen by clicking on the Fit icon .
2. Ensure your screen looks like the image below:
   a. The Toolpaths Manager is open, if it is not Select Alt and O on your keyboard to open it.
   b. The properties icon displays Lathe Default. If it is not refer to **Setting the Environment** chapter at the beginning of the book.
   c. The Lathe Lesson-6 Geometry is displayed.

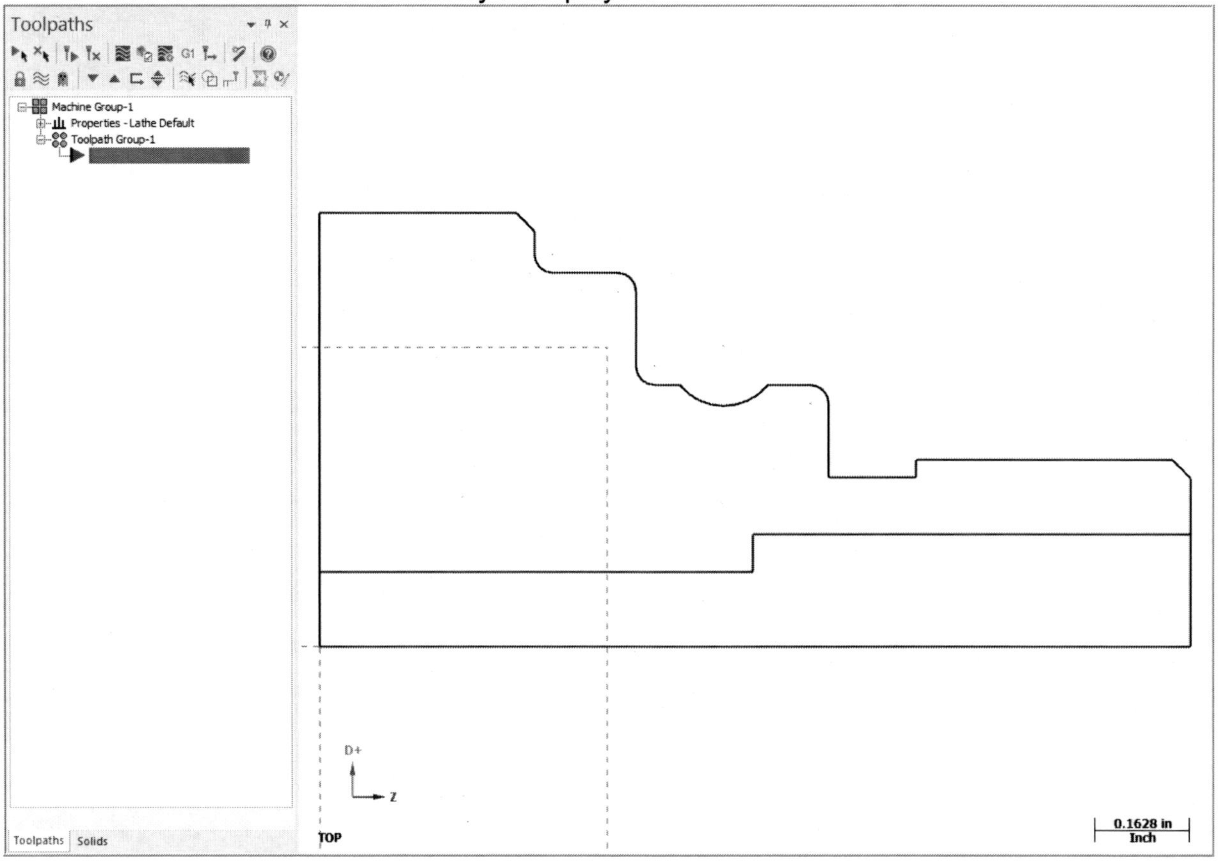

3. Select the plus in front of **Properties** to expand the Machine Group Properties.

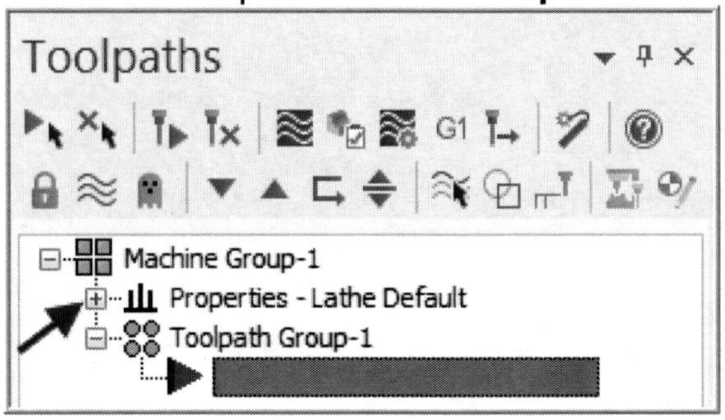

4. Select **Stock setup** in the Toolpaths Manager window.

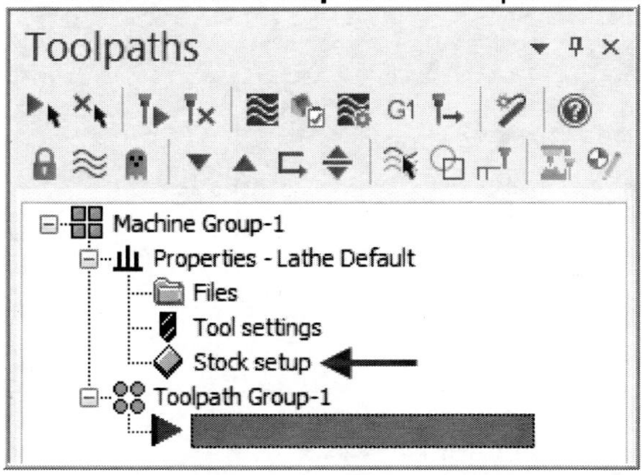

5. Select the **Stock Properties** button in the **Stock Setup** page as shown in the screenshot below:

Note: To learn more about Stock Setup refer to the Tips and Techniques section on the Mastercam Training Guide – Lathe DVD that accompanies this book.

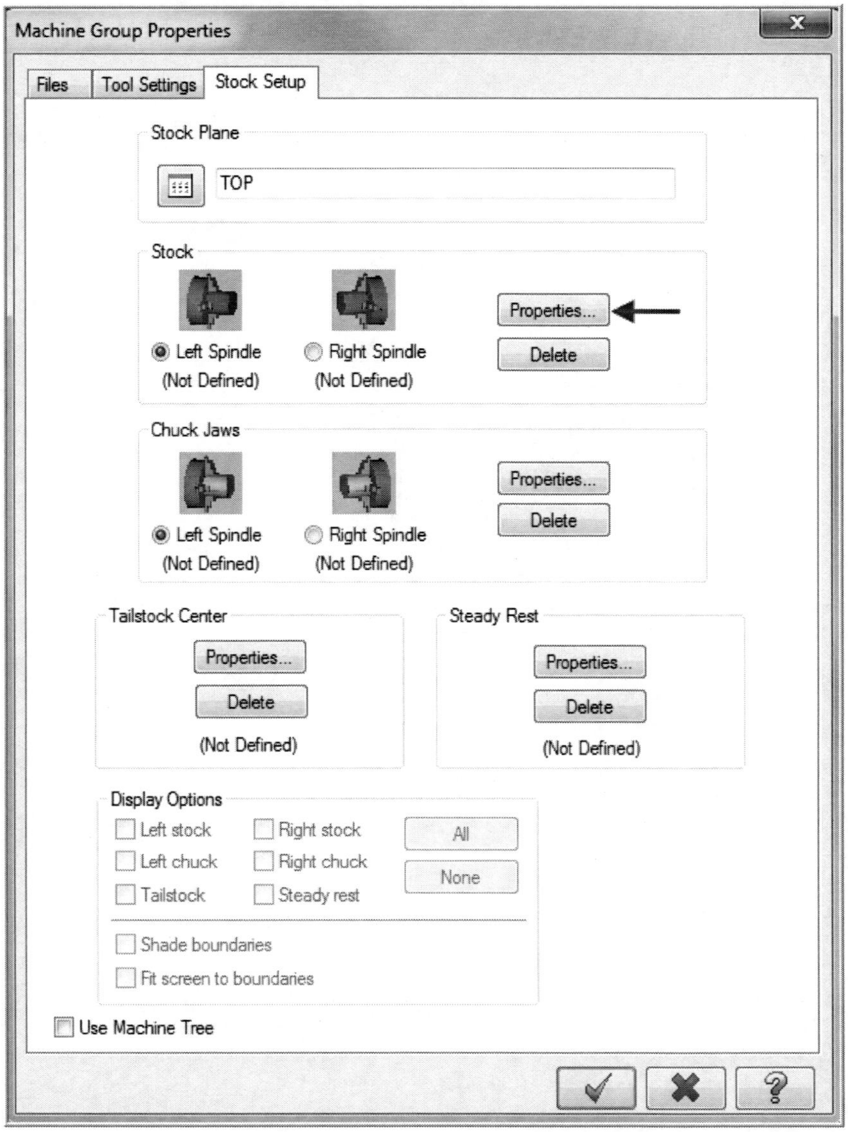

6. In the **Machine Component Manager-Stock** window click on the **Geometry** button and select **Cylinder** as shown below:

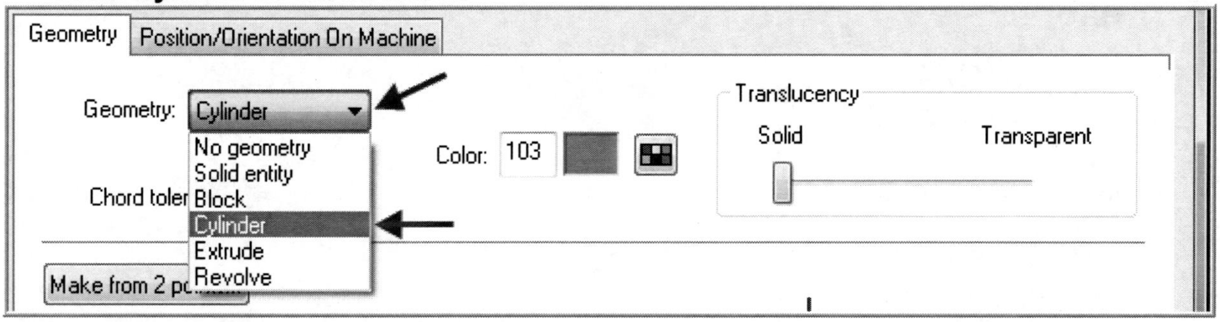

7. In the **Stock** setup set the values as shown below. **Axis is set to +Z**.

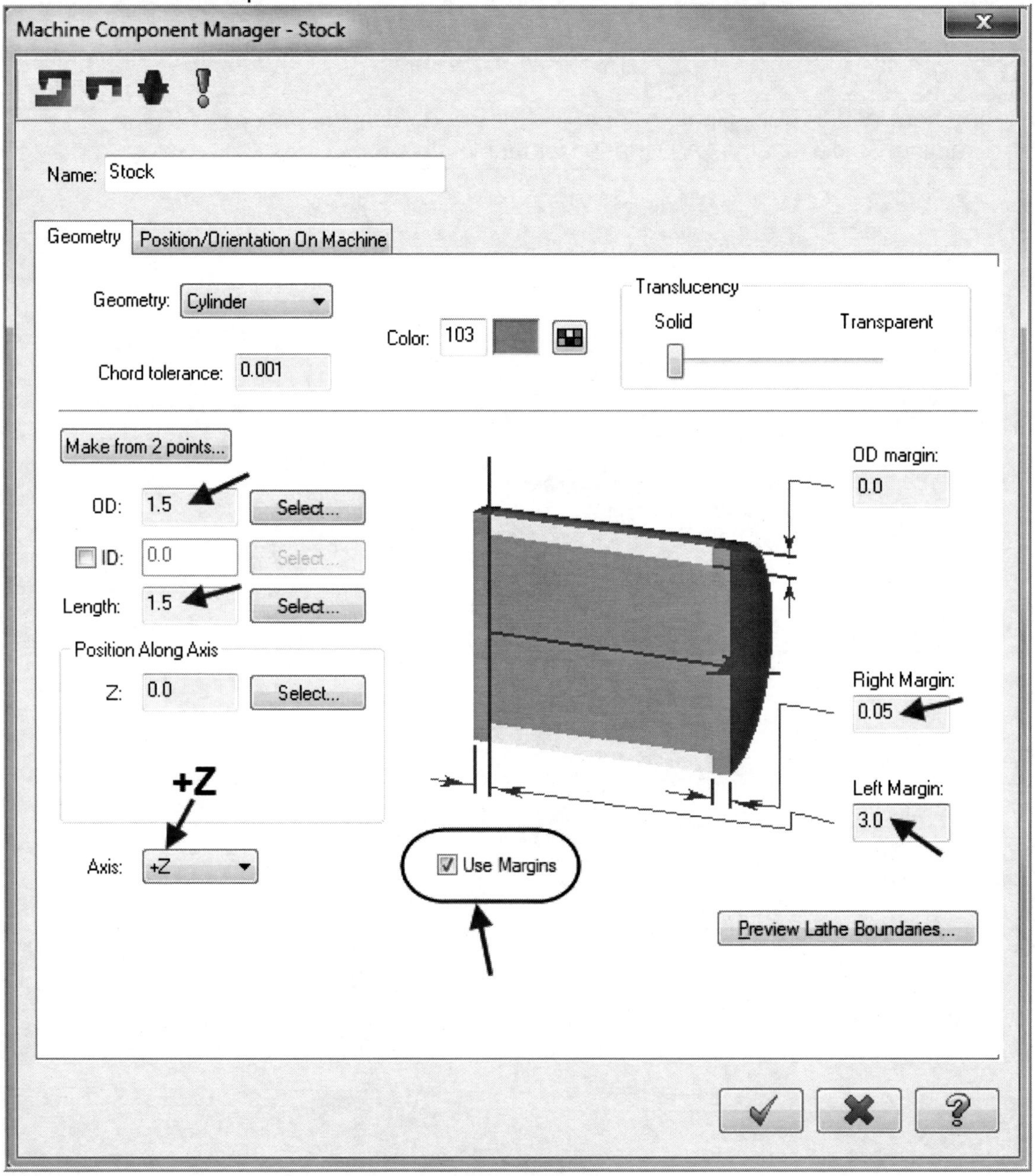

8. Click on the OK icon ✓ to complete this feature.

9. Still on the Stock Setup page activate **Fit screen to boundaries**.

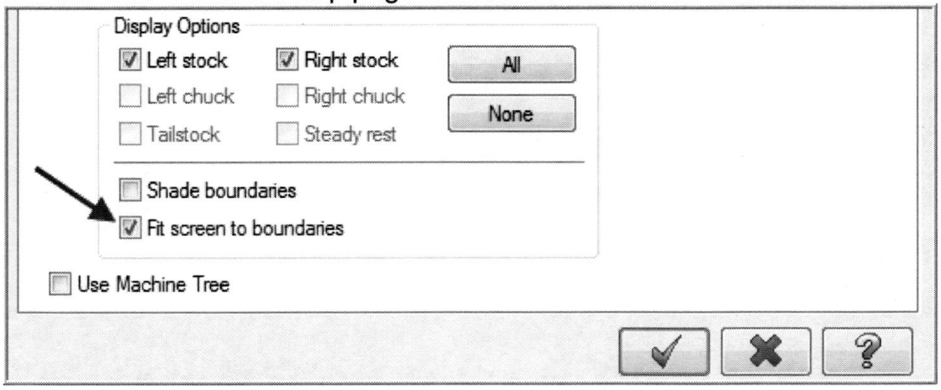

10. Select the **Chuck Properties** button in the **Stock Setup** page as shown in the screenshot below:

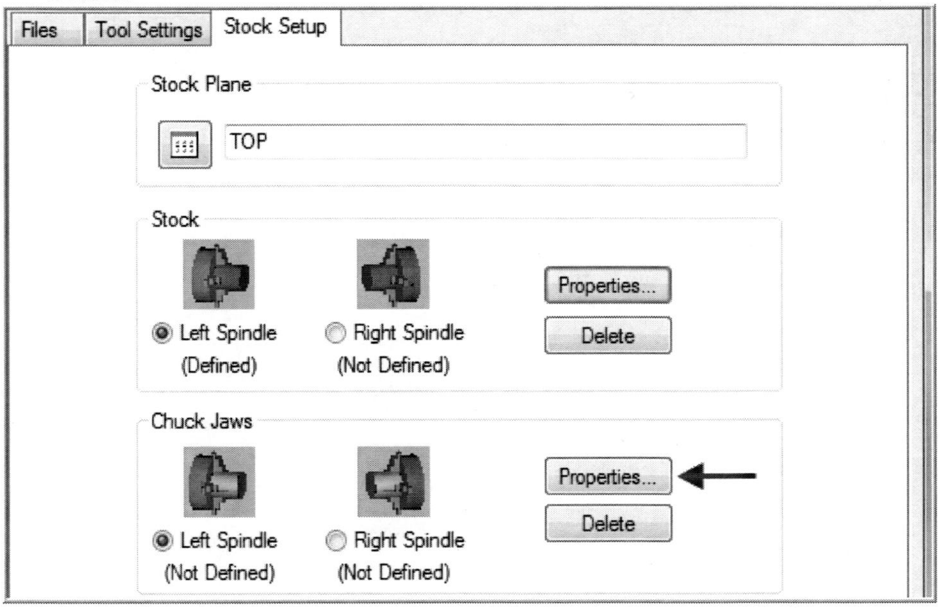

11. In the **Chuck Jaws** setup set the values as shown below:

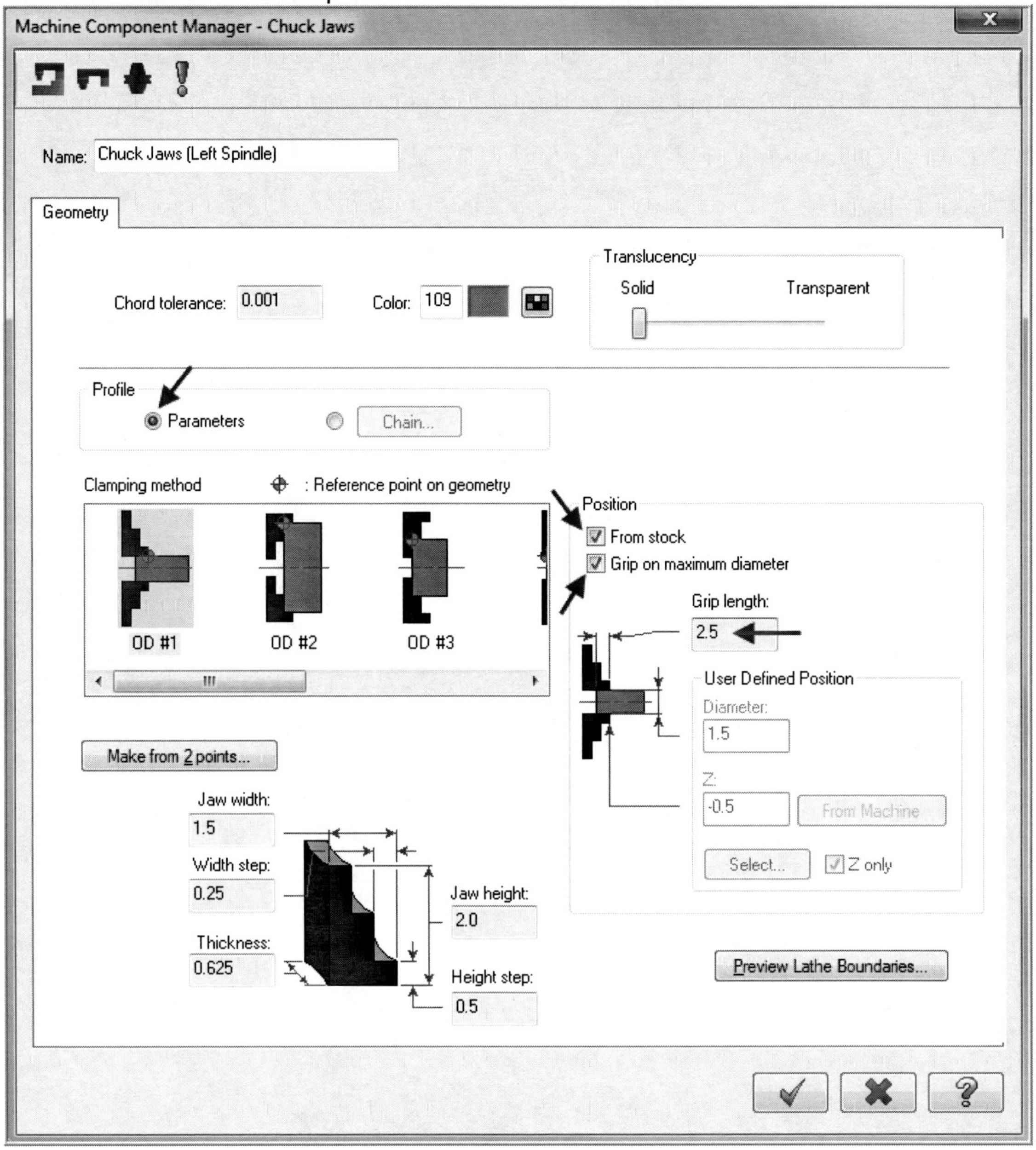

12. Click on the OK icon  to complete this feature.

13. Click on the **Tool Settings** page and make changes as shown below:

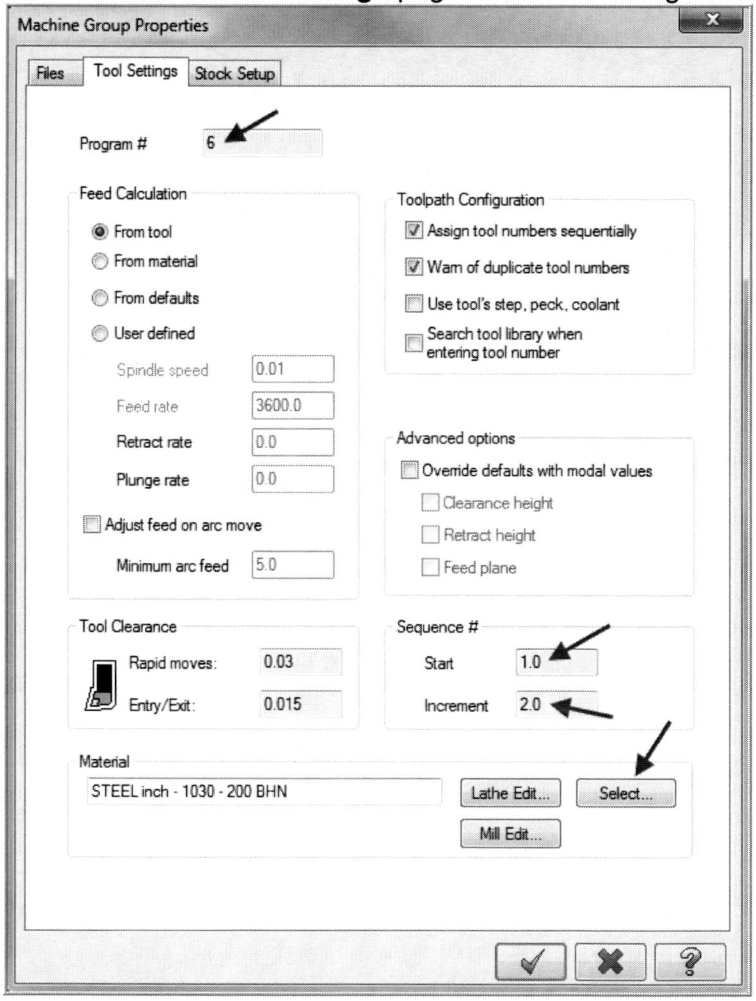

14. To change the **Material** type to Aluminum 6061 pick the **Select** button at the bottom of the Tool Settings page.
15. At the **Material List** dialog box open the Source drop down list and select **Lathe – library.**

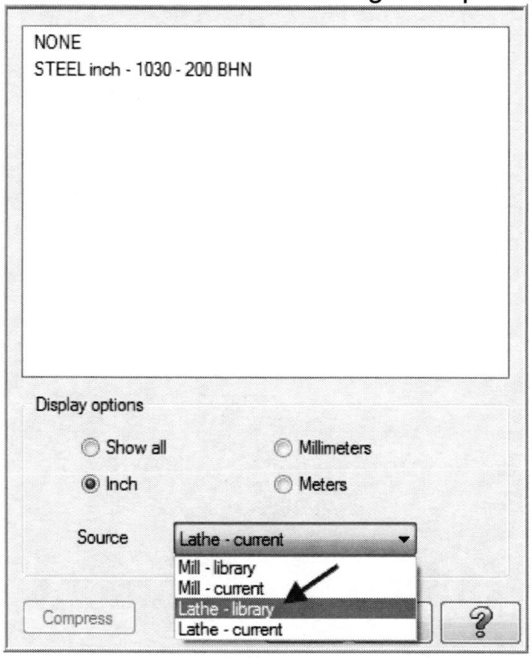

16. From the **Default Materials** list select **ALUMINUM inch - 6061** and then select .

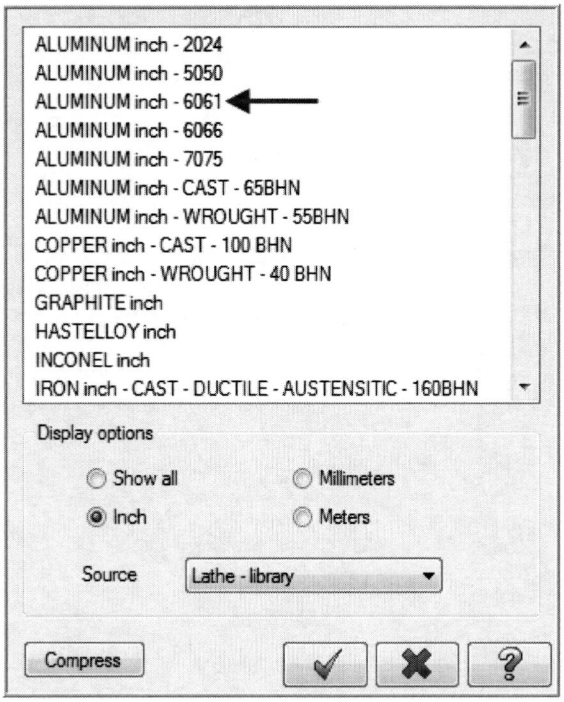

17. Select the OK button again to complete this Stock Setup function.

18. Select the **Screen Fit** icon to fit the part to the screen .
Notice the stock setup outline as indicated by broken lines as shown below:

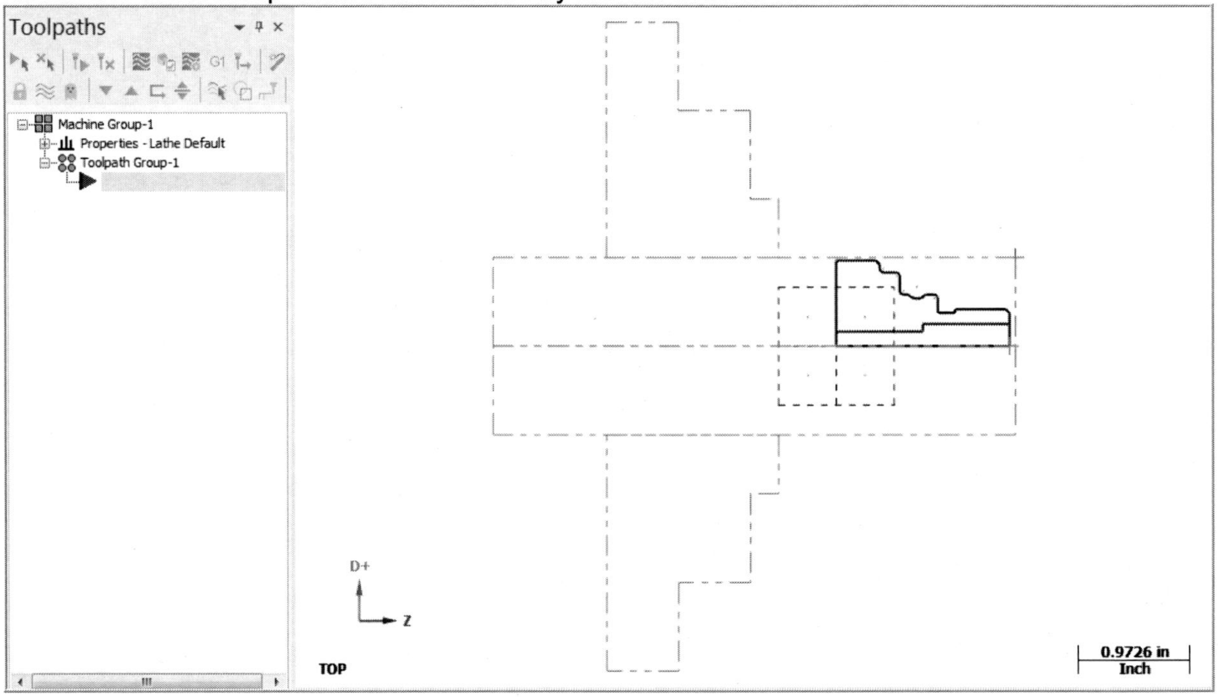

TASK 10:
FACE THE FRONT OF THE PART:

➲ In this task you will use a facing tool to face the front of the part in one cut.

1. Select the **Screen Fit** icon to fit the part to the screen if required.
2. From the menu bar select **TOOLPATHS>Face…**

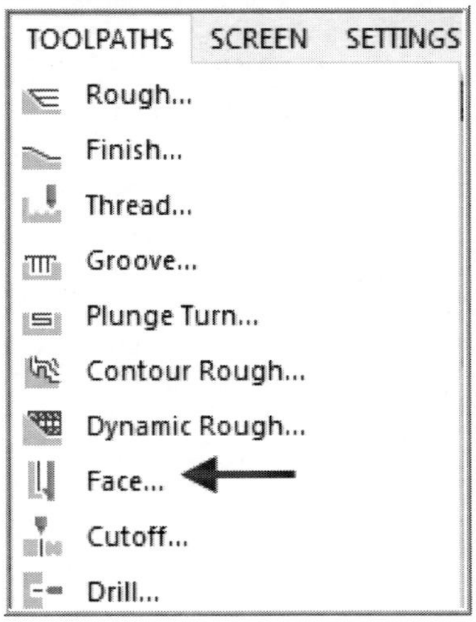

3. When prompted to **"Enter new NC name"** Ensure **LATHE-LESSON-6** is entered and then select the OK button .

➲ After selecting the OK button you are confronted with **Toolpath parameters** page. The first task here will be to select **Tool #1 a Roughing – 80 deg.**

4. Click on **Tool 0101 Roughing – 80 degree** and ensure the settings are the same as in the Toolpath parameters page as shown below:

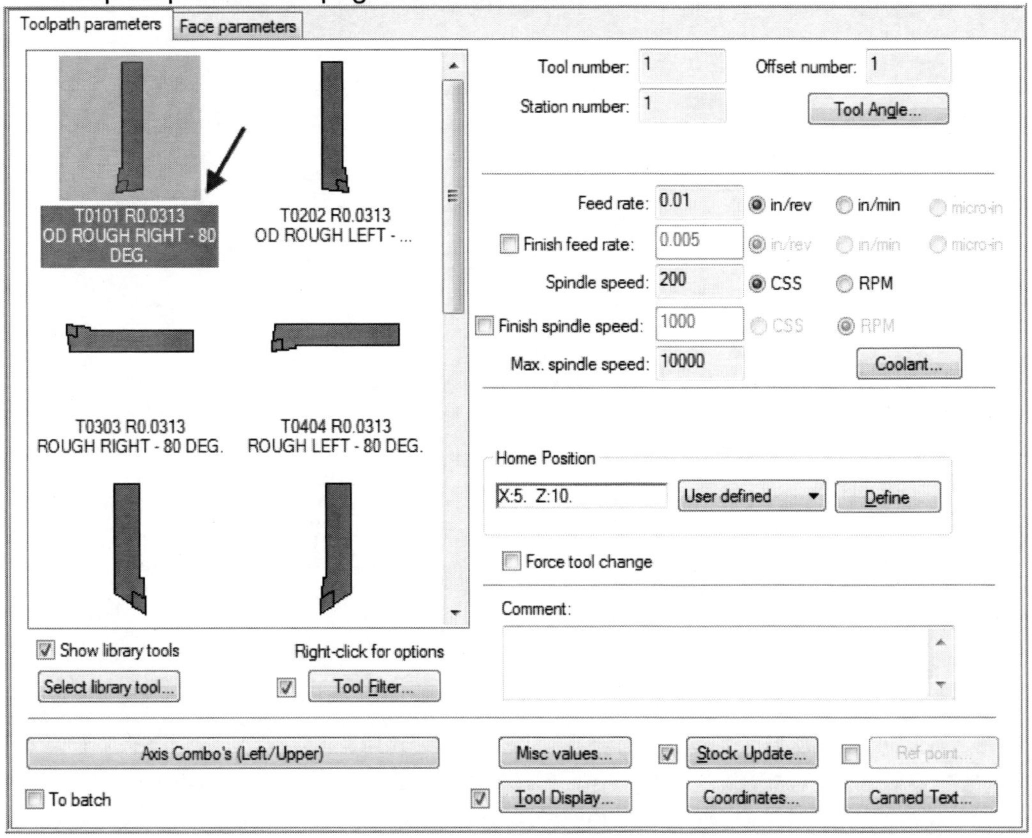

5. Select the **Face parameters** page and make changes as shown below:

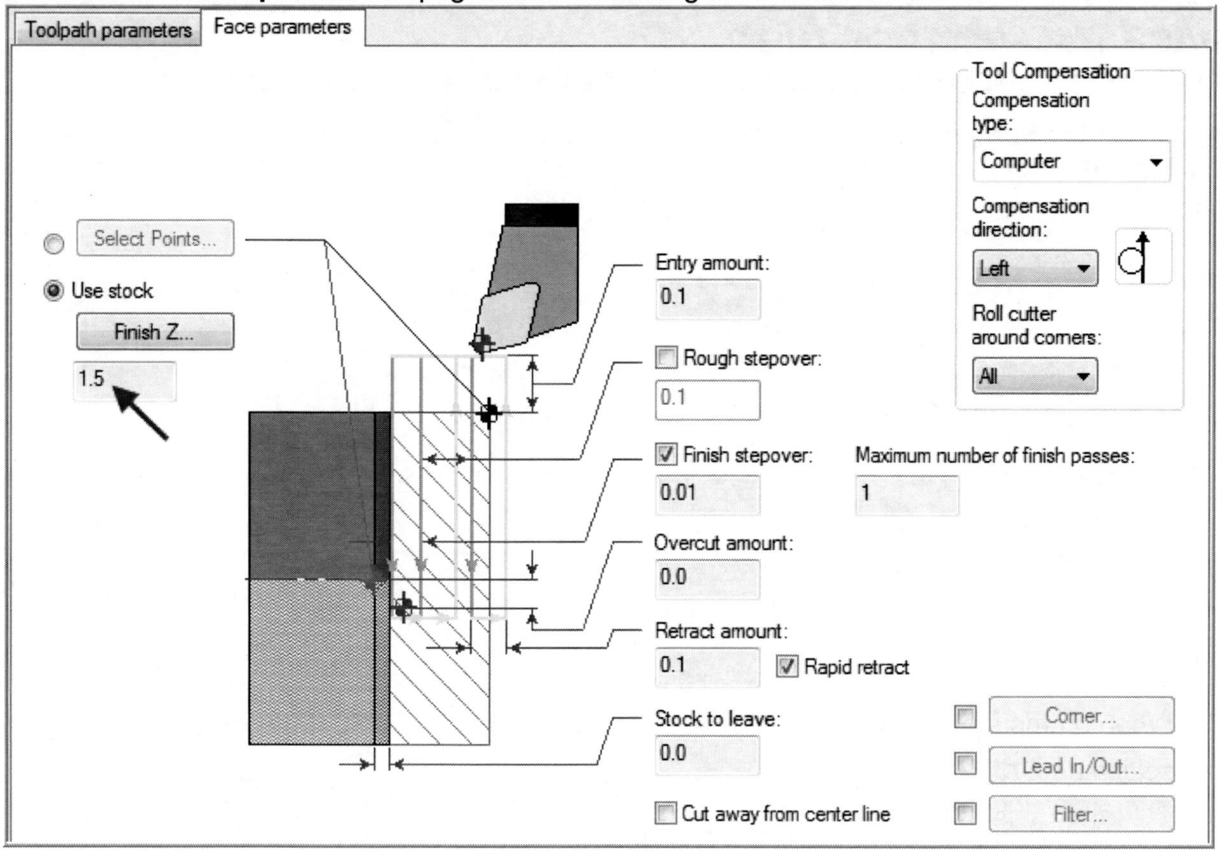

6. Select the OK button ✓ to complete this **Lathe Face** operation.

TASK 11:
ROUGH THE OUTSIDE DIAMETERS

➲ In this task you will use a Lathe toolpath called Lathe Quick Rough Toolpath.
➲ You will use the same tool as used for the previous facing operation **Tool #1 an OD Rough-Right – 80 deg.**

1. From the menu bar select **TOOLPATHS>Quick>Rough…**

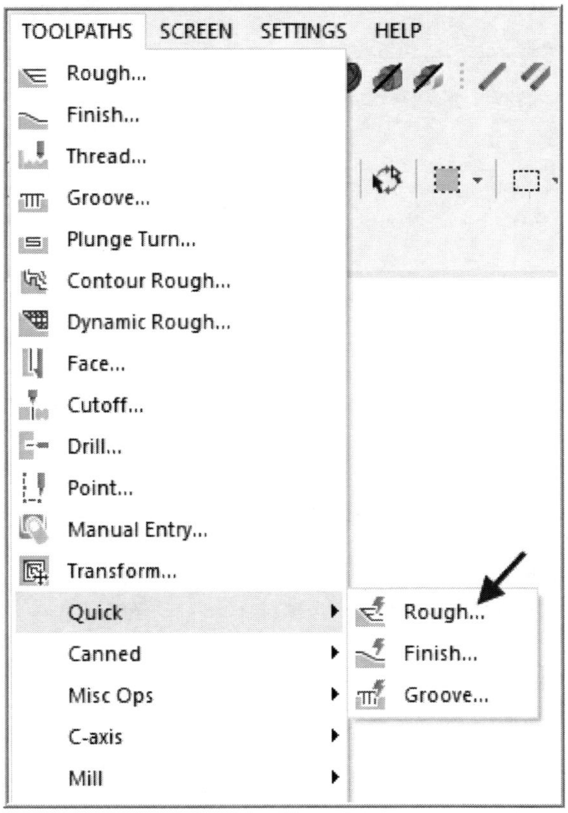

2. In the **Chaining** window Chaining mode is set to **Partial** by default.

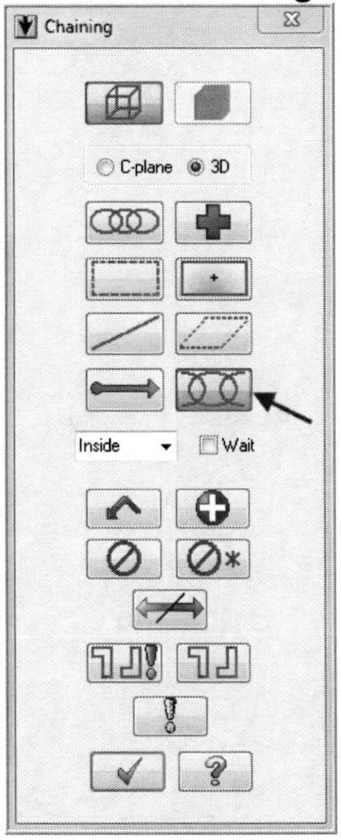

3. Select the chamfer, Line 1 as the start of the **Partial chain**.

After you have selected the chamfer **ensure** that the arrows are pointing up and to the left of the part. If it is not select the reverse button in the Chaining dialog box.

4. Then select Line 2 as the end entity in this chain.

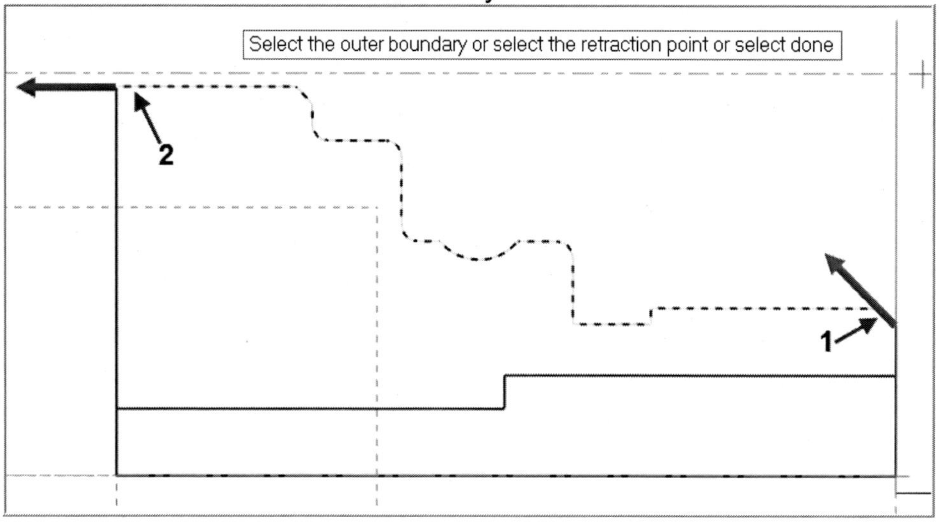

5. Select the OK button  to exit the Chaining dialog window.
6. In the **Quick Tool parameters** page select the **Tool #1 Roughing – 80 deg** and make any necessary changes as shown below:

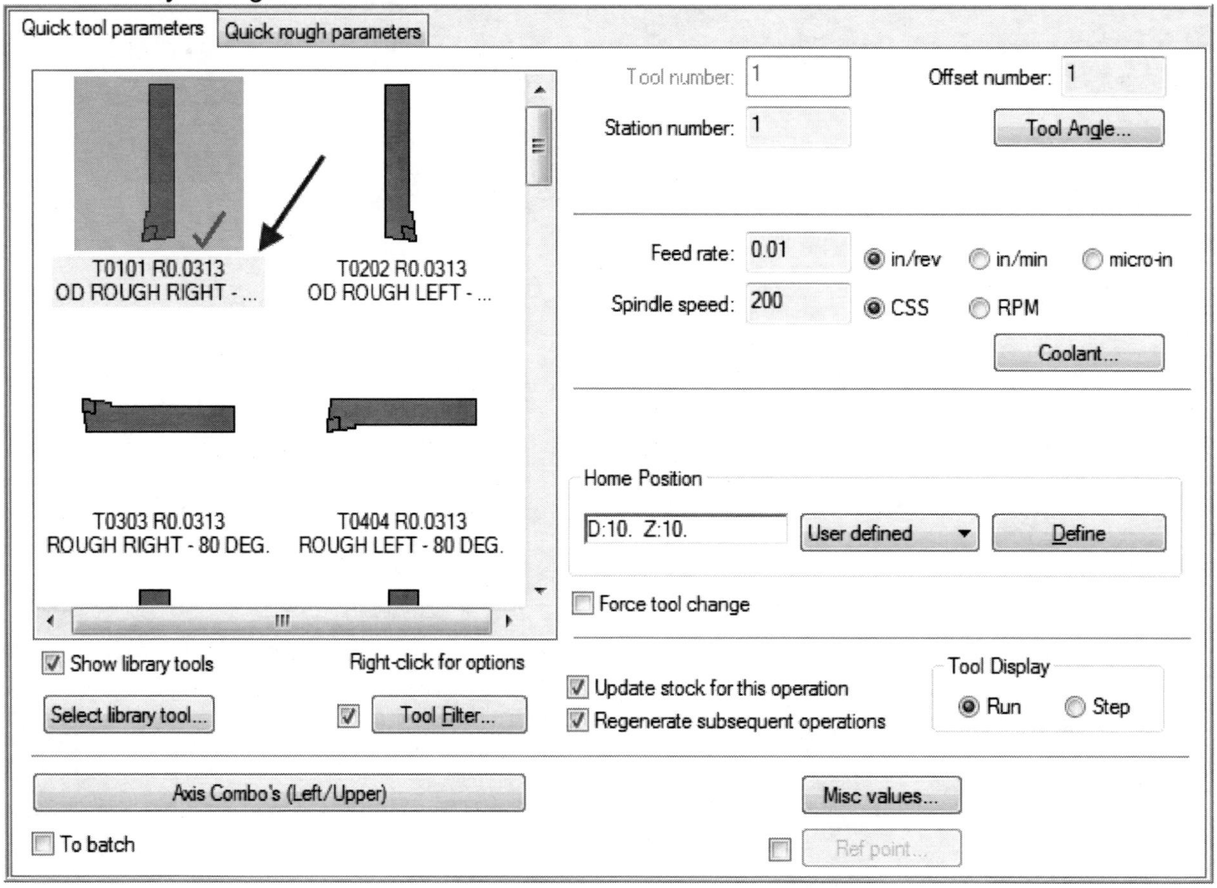

7. Select the **Quick Rough parameters** page and make any necessary changes as shown below:

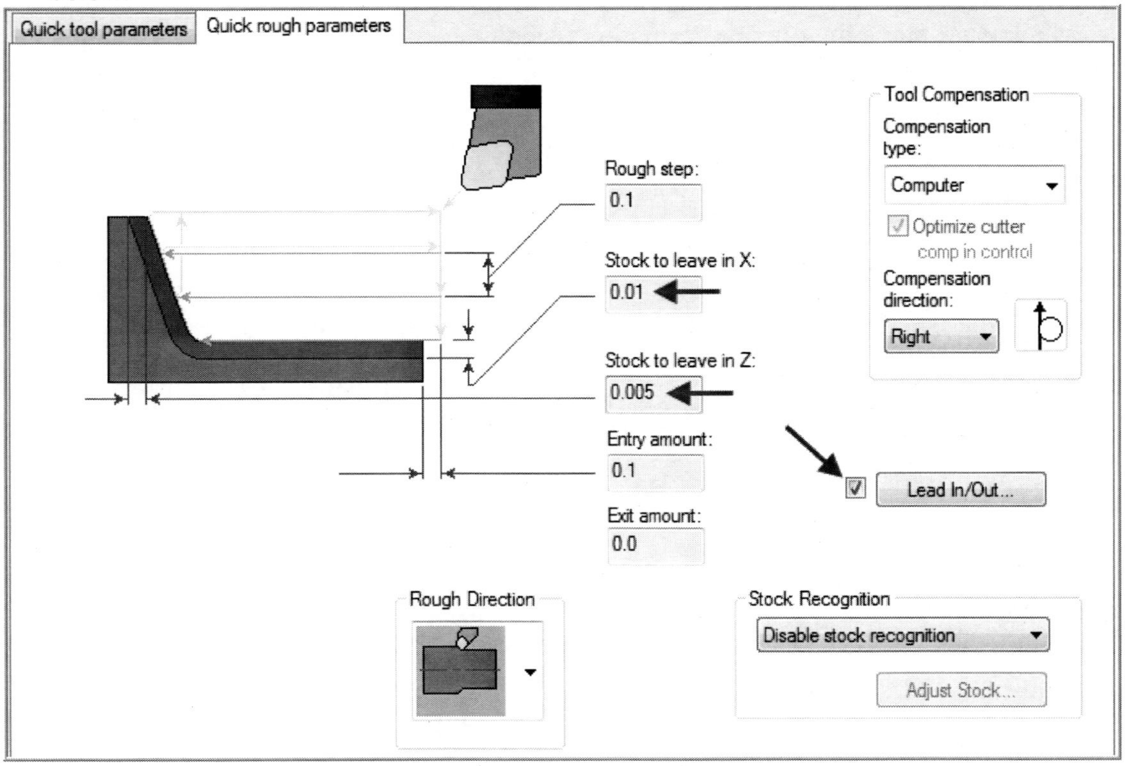

8. Select the **Lead In/Out** button, then select the **Lead out** page and extend the contour by .2 as shown below:

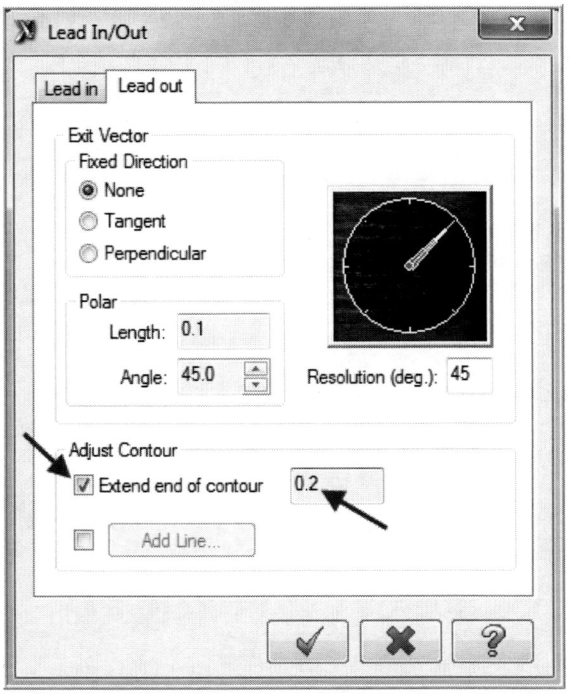

9. Select the OK button ✓ to exit this function.

10. Select the OK button ✓ to exit Quick Rough Parameters.

TASK 12:
FINISH THE OUTSIDE DIAMETERS

➲ In this task you will finish the outside diameters using Quick Finish. The tool you used for rouging will be used in this operation as well.

1. From the menu bar select **TOOLPATHS>Quick>Finish…**

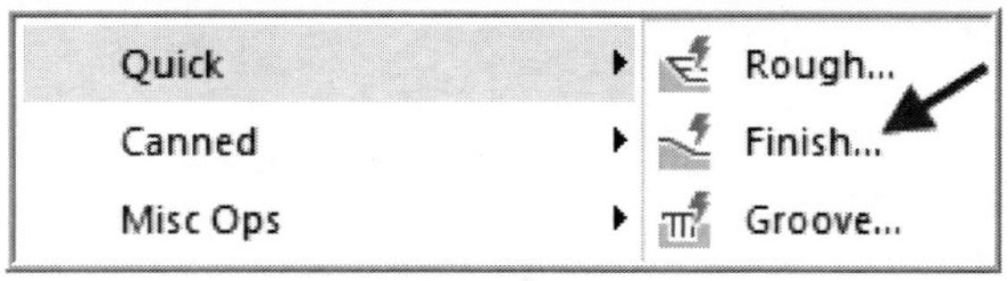

2. In the **Quick tool parameters** page select **Tool #1 Roughing – 80 deg** and make any necessary changes as shown below:

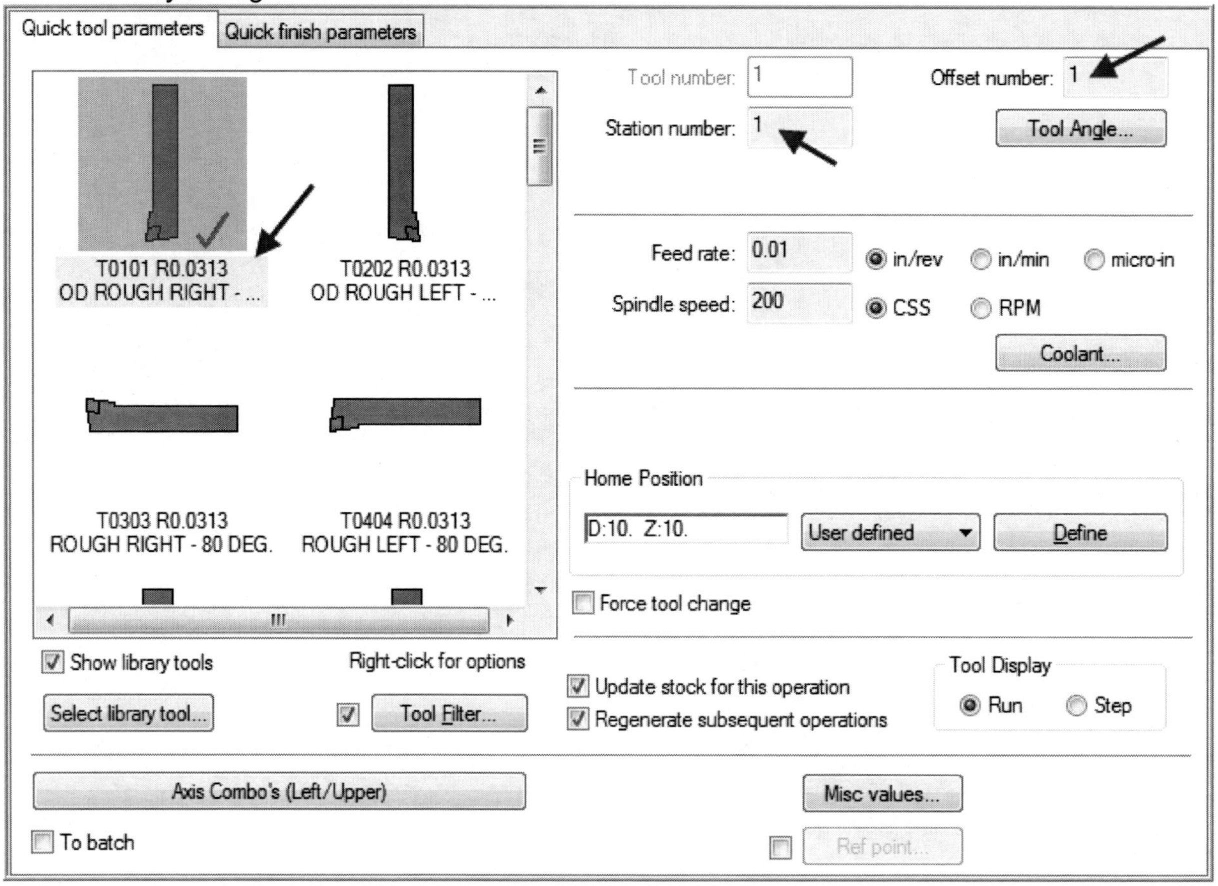

3. Select the **Quick finish parameters** page and make any necessary changes as shown below:

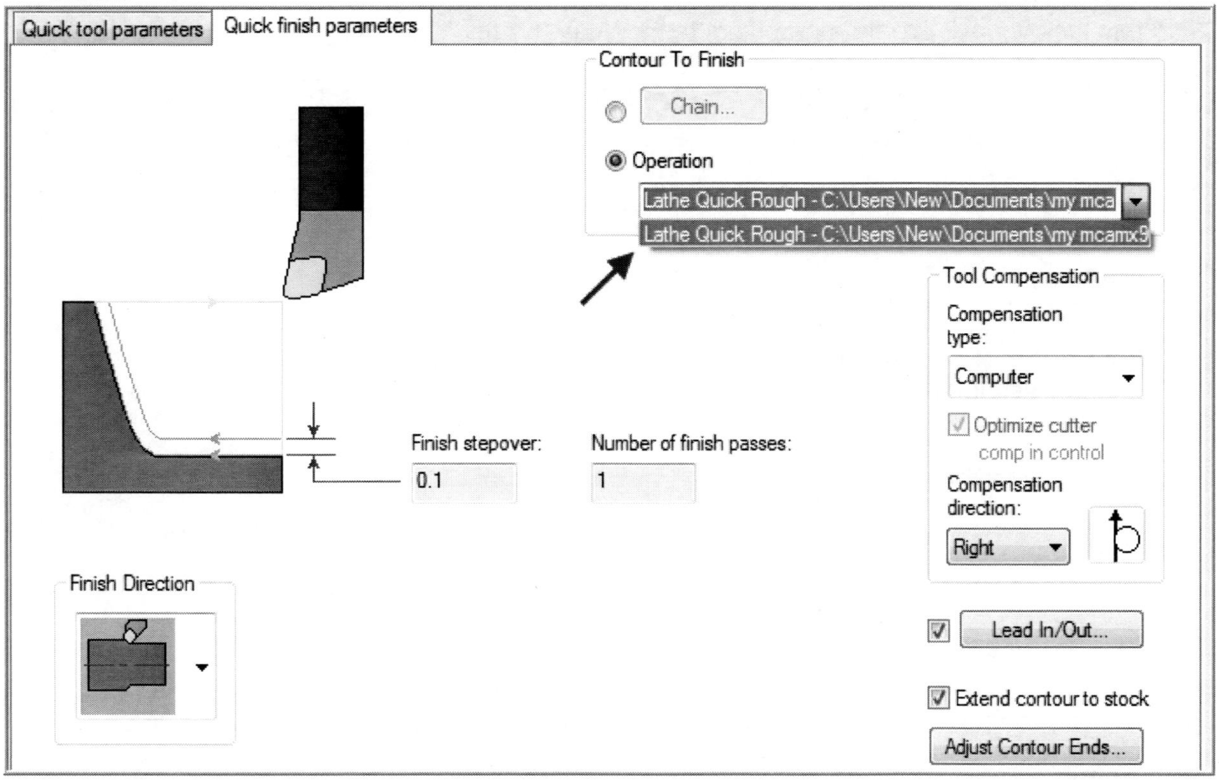

4. Select the **Lead In/Out** button select the Lead out page and extend the contour by **0.2** as shown below:

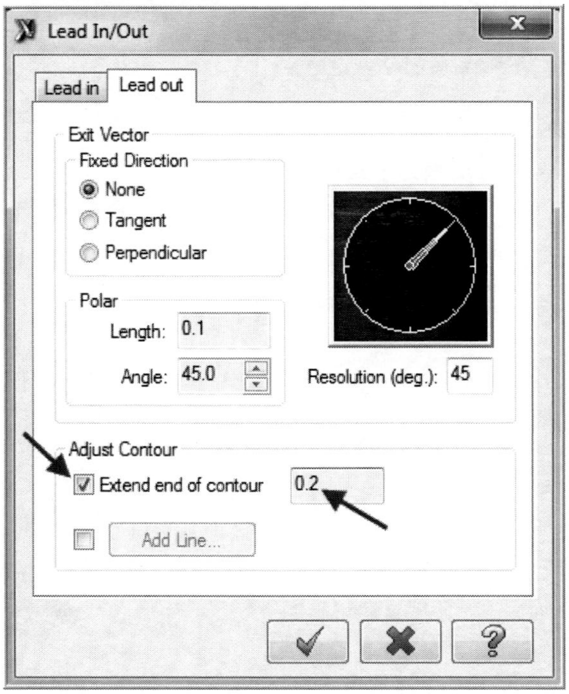

5. Select the OK button  to exit this function.
6. Select the OK button  to exit **Quick finish parameters**.

TASK 13:
FINISH THE 0.1 RADIUS

➲ In this task you will create a new Tool to machine the **0.1" Radius**.

1. From the menu bar select **TOOLPATHS>Finish…**

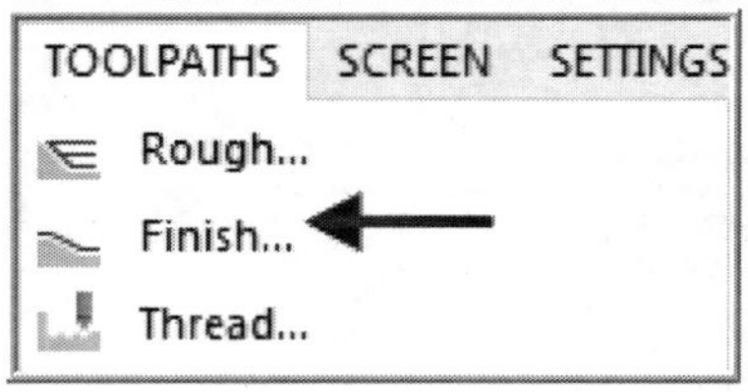

2. In the **Chaining** window click on the icon for Single 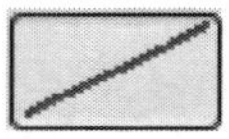
3. Select the **Arc** in the position shown below:

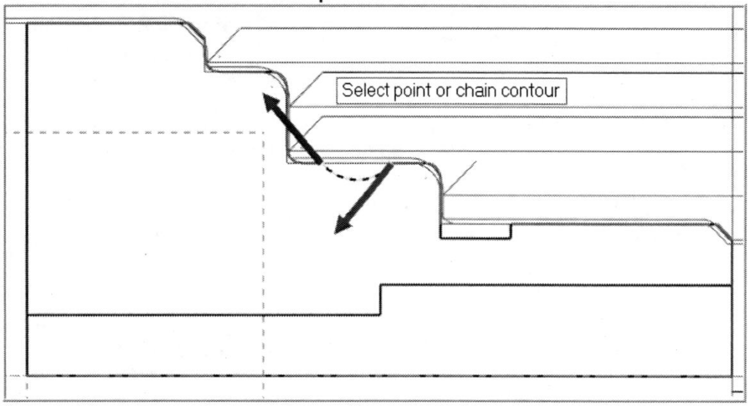

4. Select the OK button  to exit the **Chaining** dialog window.
5. Right Click the mouse in the space as indicated by **arrow # 1** shown below:
6. Click on **Create new tool…** as indicated by **arrow # 2** as shown below:

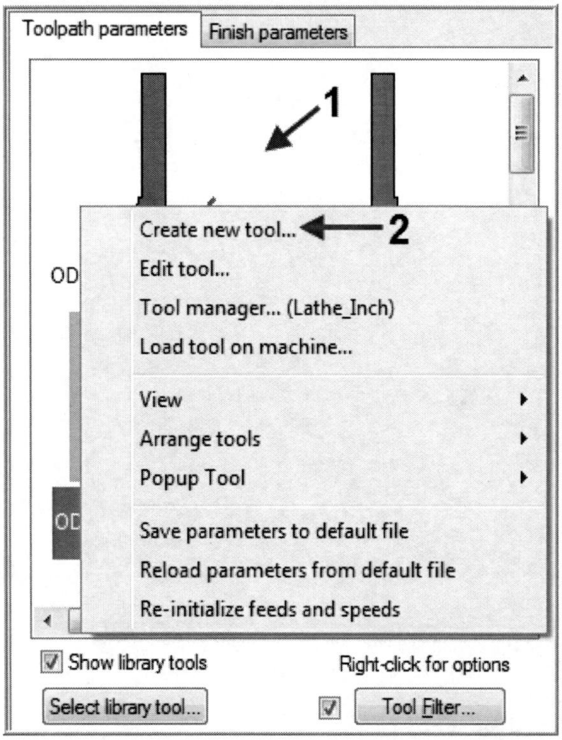

7. Click on the **General Turning** Button as shown below:

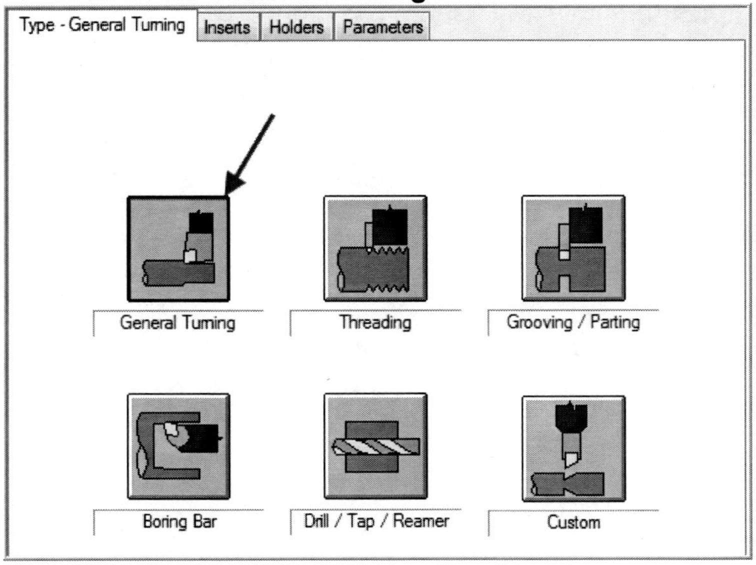

8. Click on the **Round** insert as shown below. Open up the drop down menu for **IC Dia / Length** and select **3/16**.

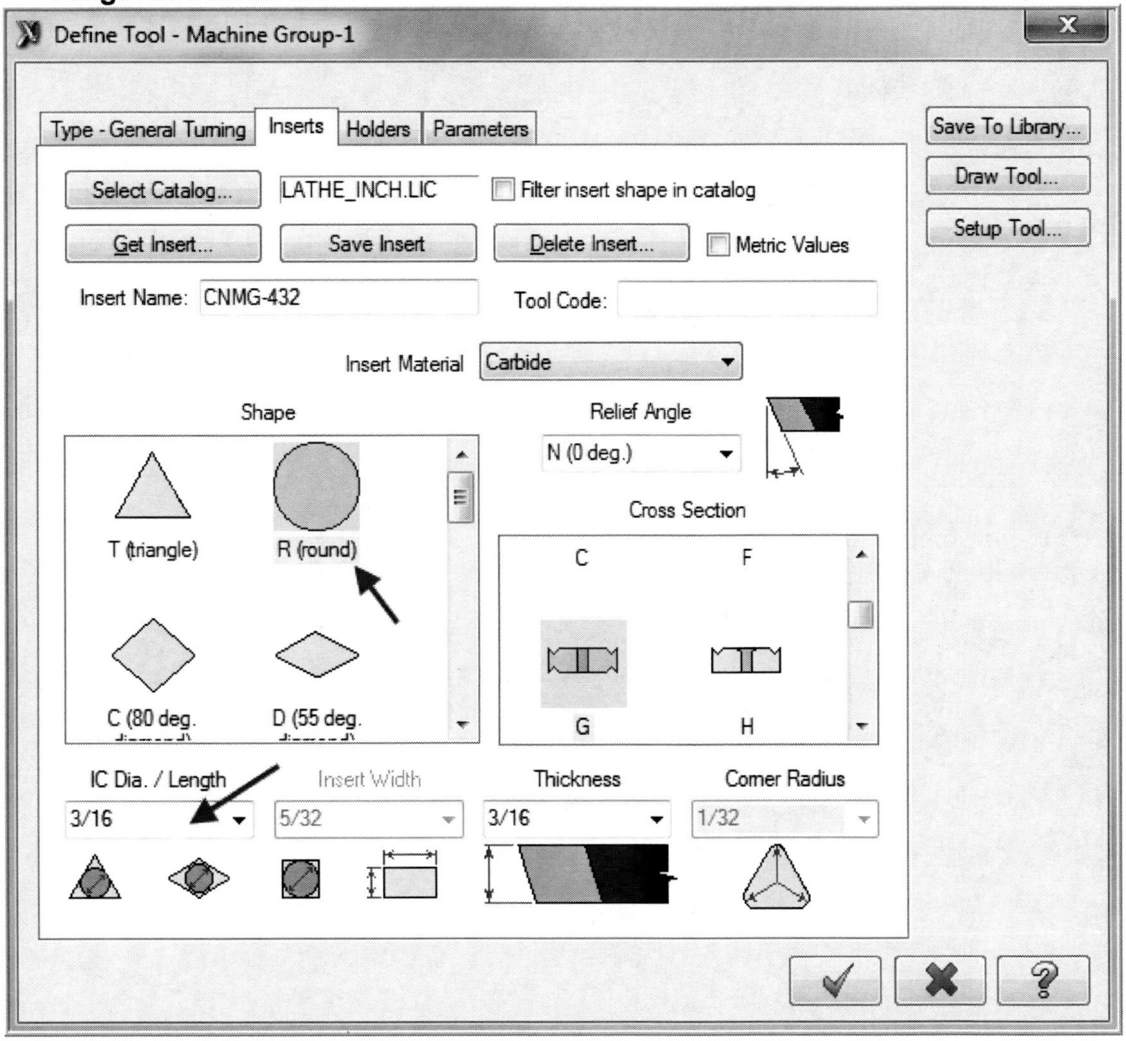

9. Click on the **Holders** Tab.
10. Scroll down and click on the **Offset Profiling** holder as shown below:

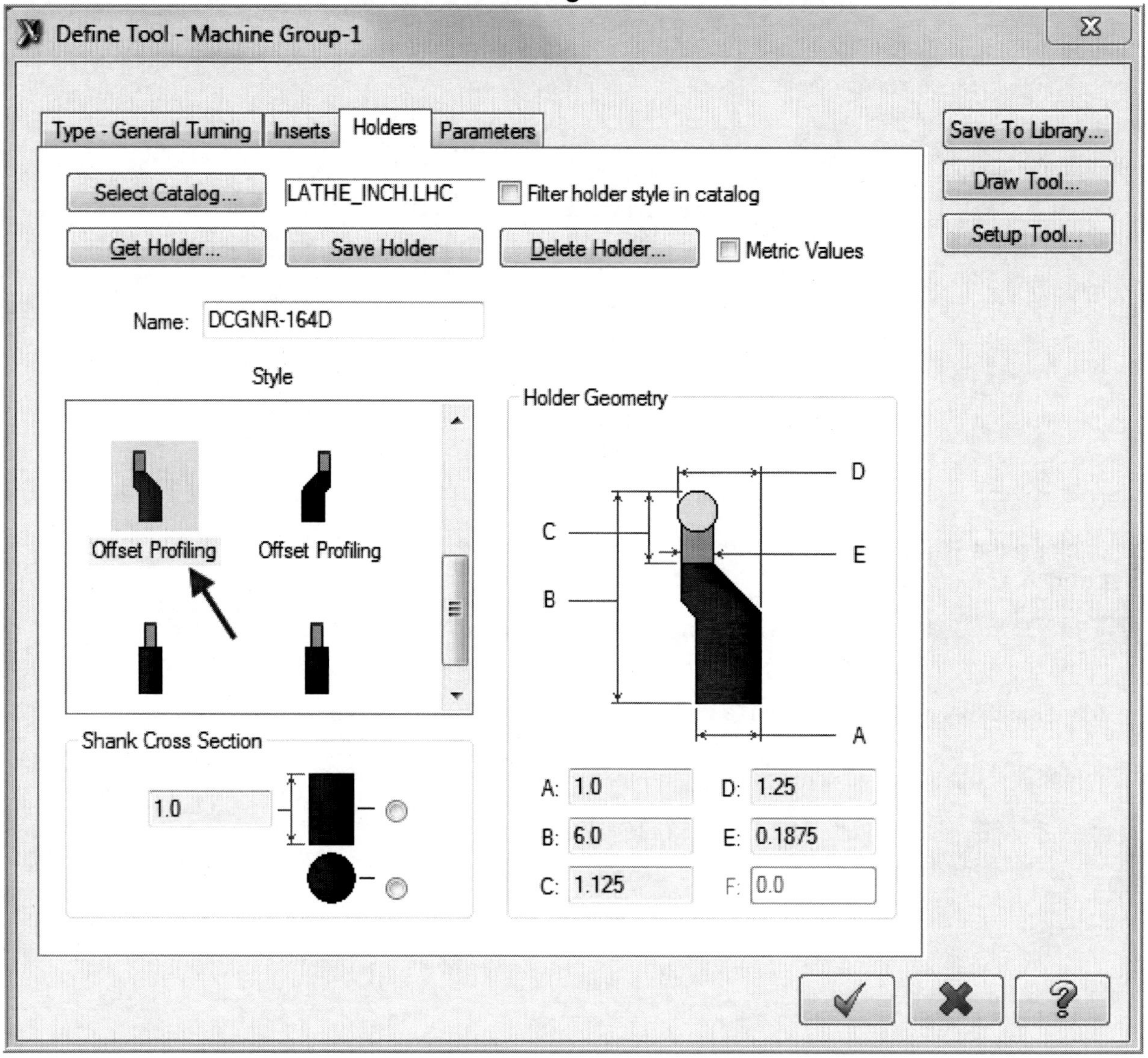

11. Click on the **Parameters** page and at the bottom of this page set the compensation for this tool as shown below:

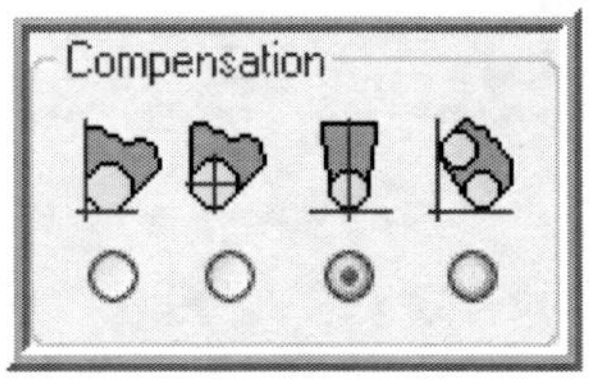

Compensation: Tip
The toolpath is programmed from the tip of the tool corner radius.

This is the only option available for threading tools, drills, taps, and reamers.

12. Click on the OK icon .

13. Make any necessary changes on the **Toolpath parameters** page as shown below:

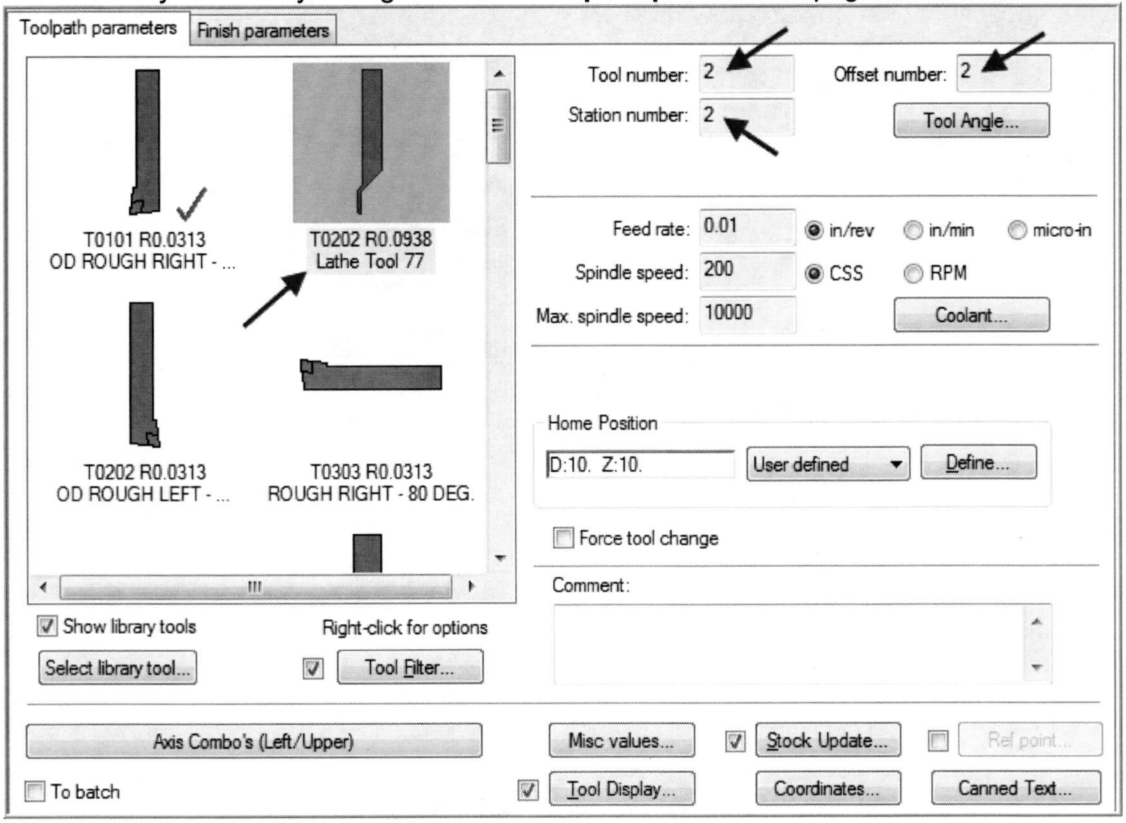

14. Click on the **Finish parameters** tab and make any necessary changes as shown below:

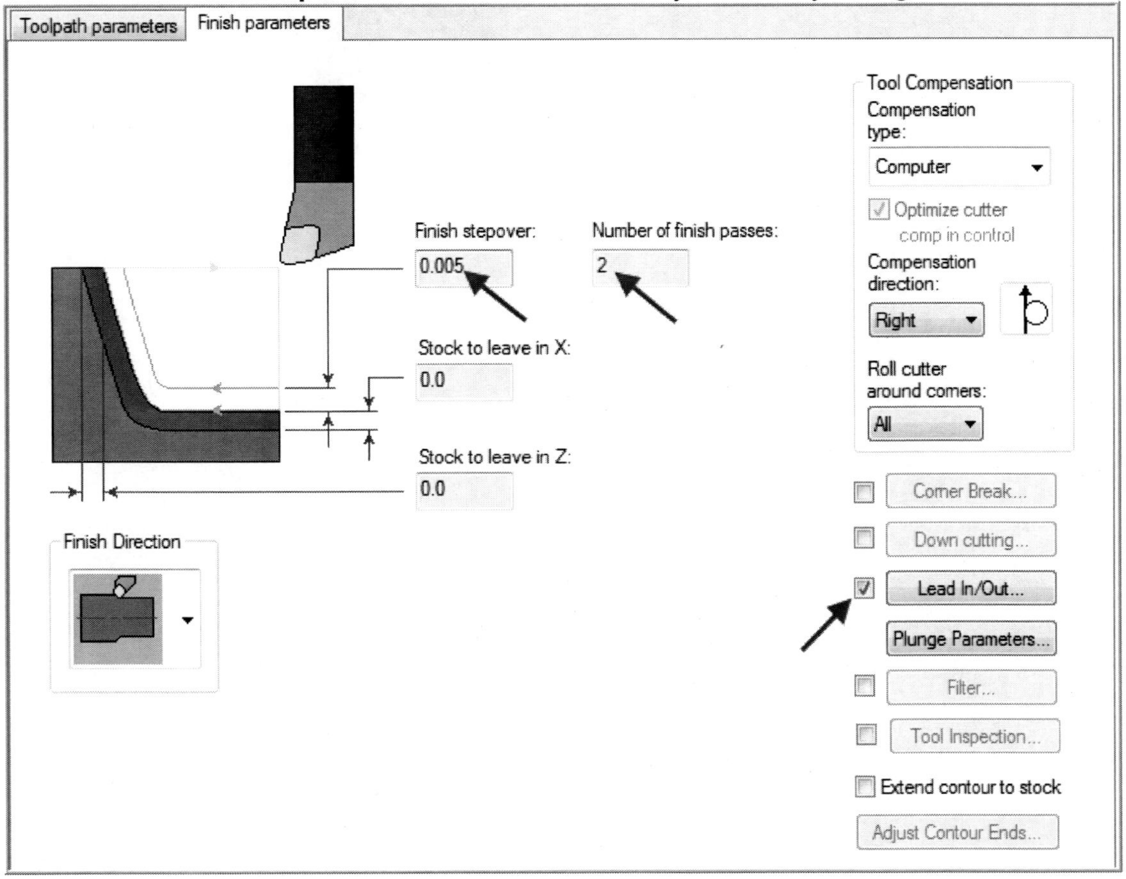

15. Click on the **Lead in/Out Button** as shown above:
16. Make the necessary changes as shown below on the **Lead In** page. In order to adjust the dial click on the desired location of the arrow:

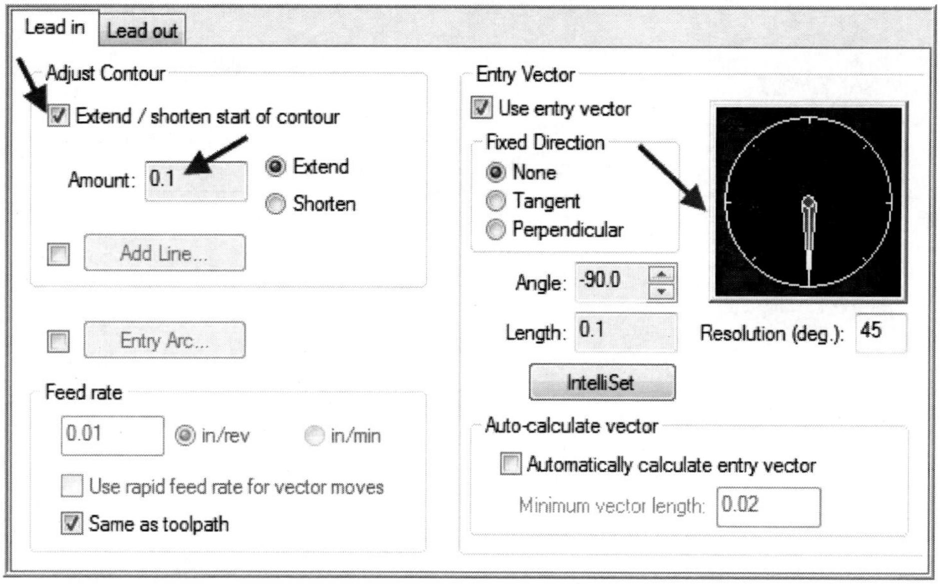

17. Click on the **Lead out** tab and make the necessary changes as shown below:

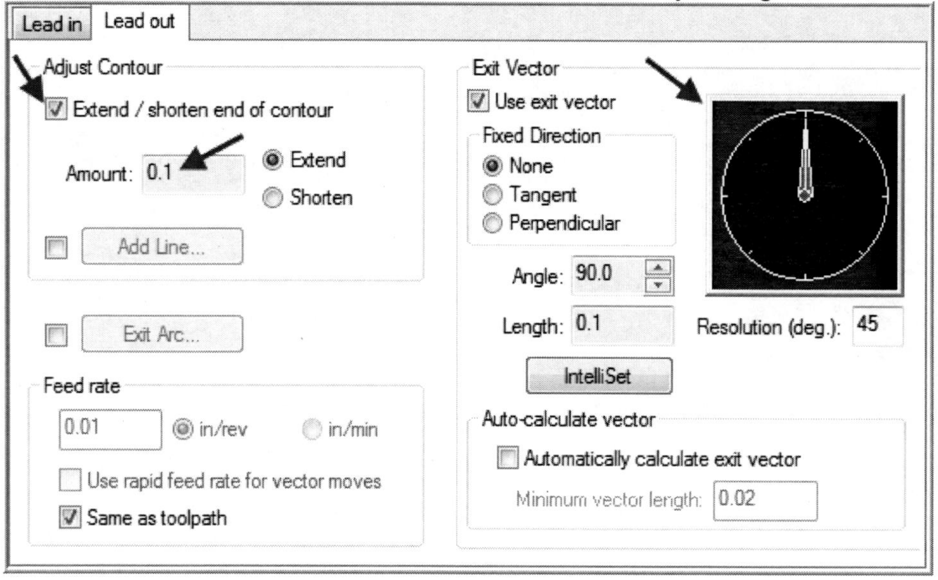

18. Click on OK  to exit the Lead In/out window.

19. Click on the **Plunge Parameters** button [Plunge Parameters...].
20. Make the necessary changes as shown below:

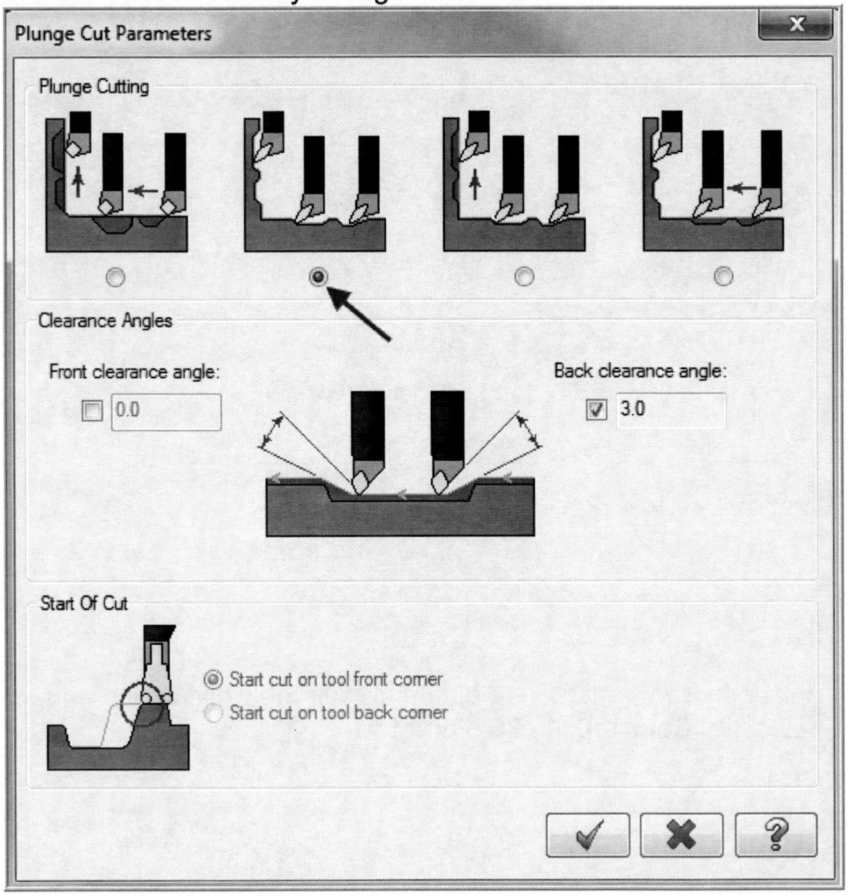

21. Click on Ok  to exit the Plunge Cut Parameters window.
22. Click on Ok  to exit the Lathe Finish parameters window.

TASK 14:
CENTER DRILL HOLE

➲ In this task you will center drill .2" depth using a **Centre Drill - .25 diameter.**

1. From the menu bar select **TOOLPATHS>Drill…**

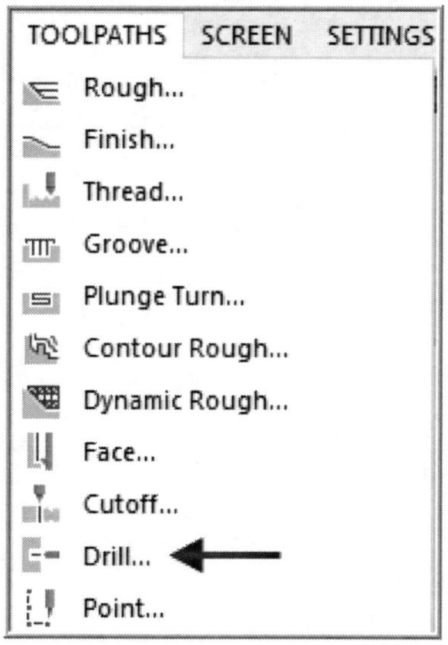

2. To achieve the tool list view shown below, right mouse button click in the white space and select **View>Details**. Then select the **Centre Drill .25 diameter.**

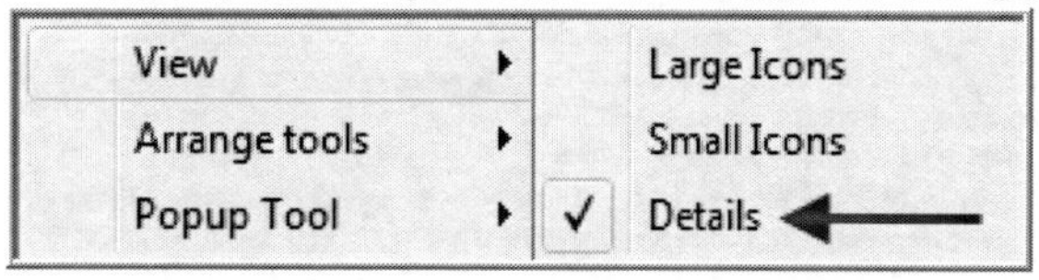

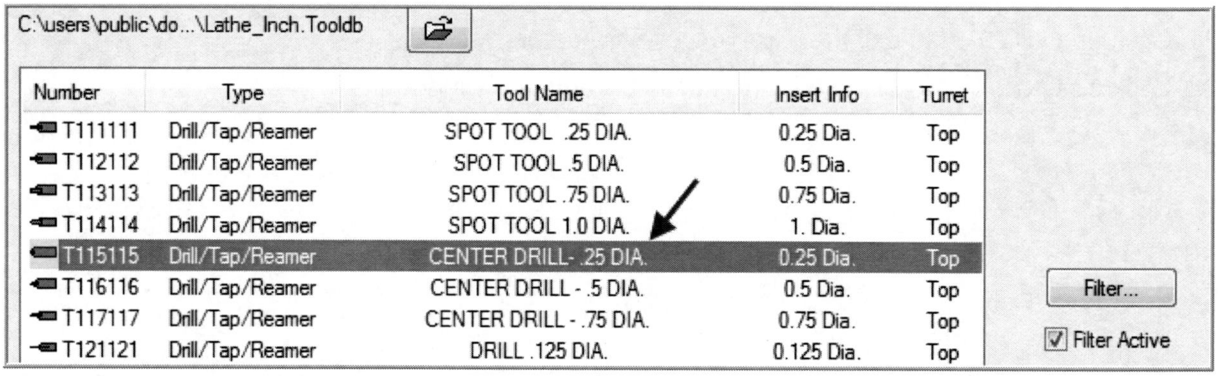

3. Select the OK button  to exit the tool selection.

4. Make changes as shown below:

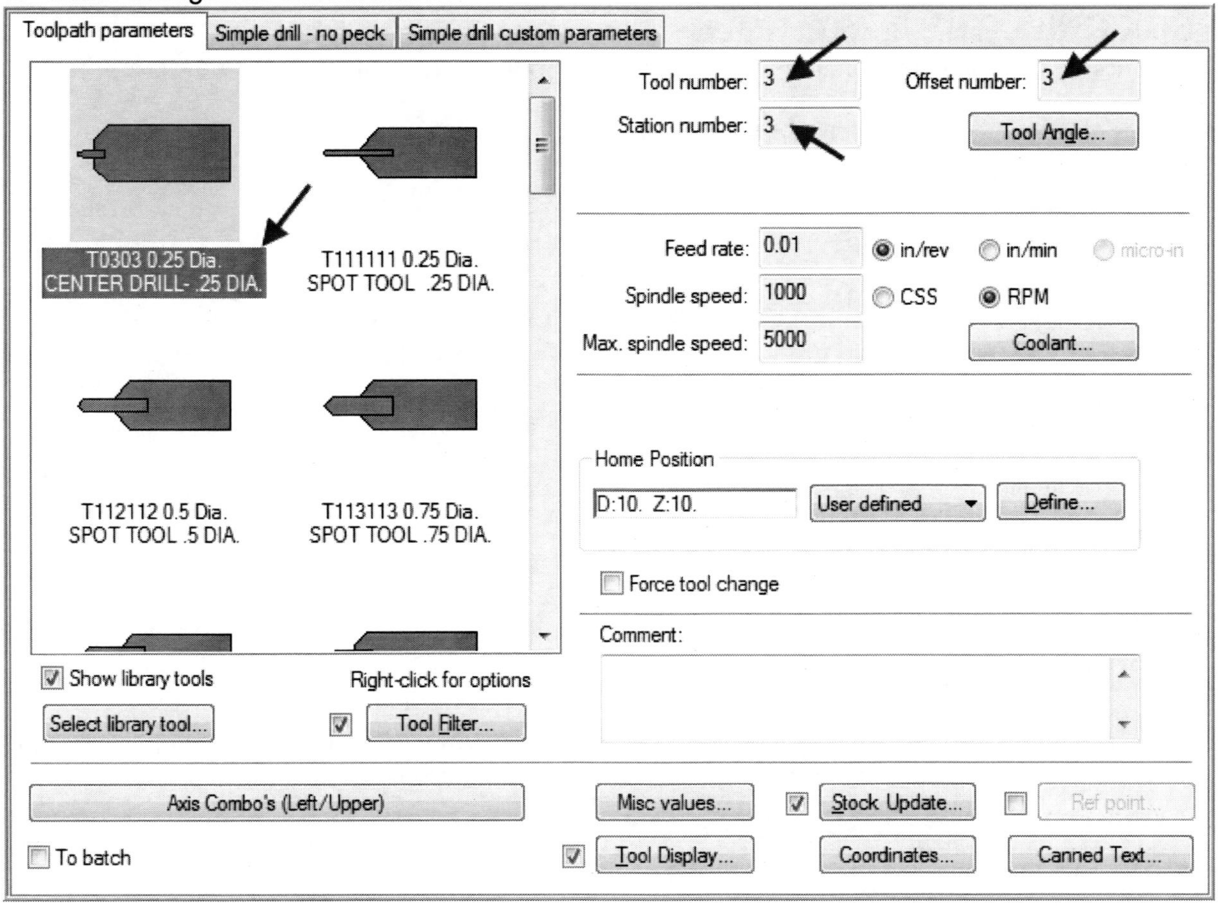

5. Select the **Simple drill** – no peck page and make changes as shown below:

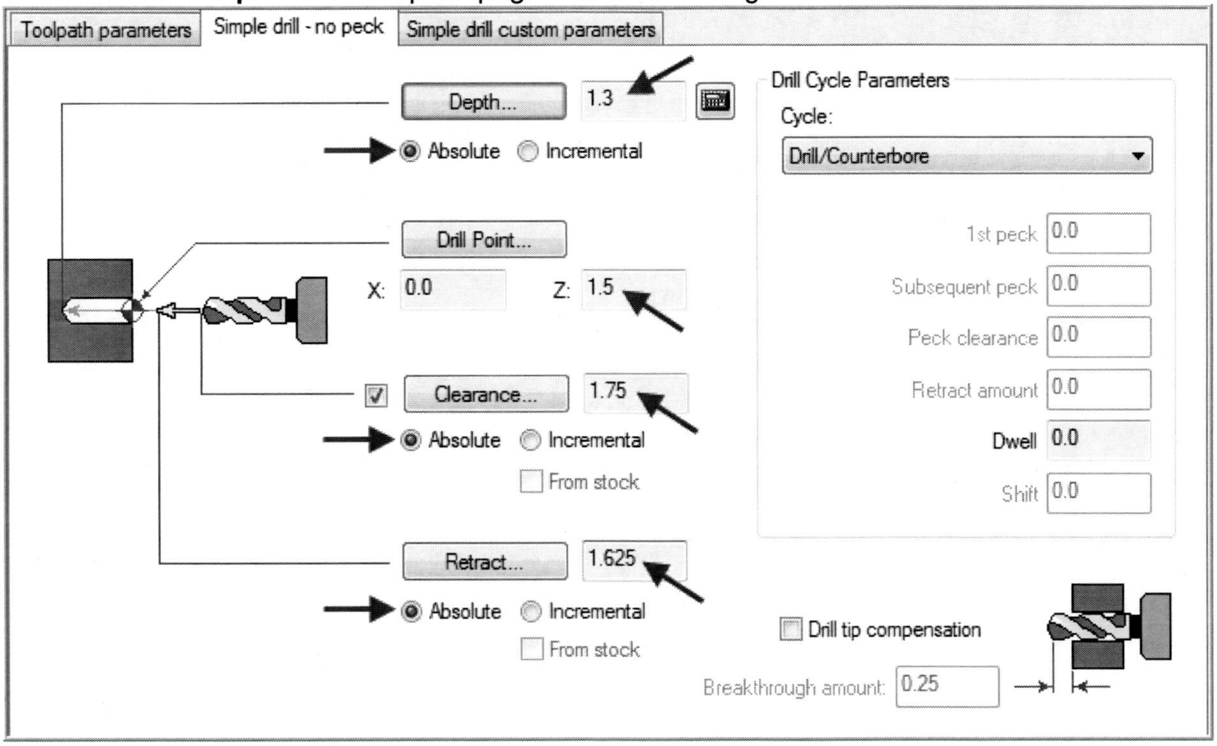

6. Select the OK button  to exit **Simple drill – no peck**.

TASK 15:
PECK DRILL THE 0.250" HOLE

➲ In this task you will peck drill the 0.25" hole through the part using **Drill - .250 diameter.**

1. From the menu bar select **TOOLPATHS>Drill…**

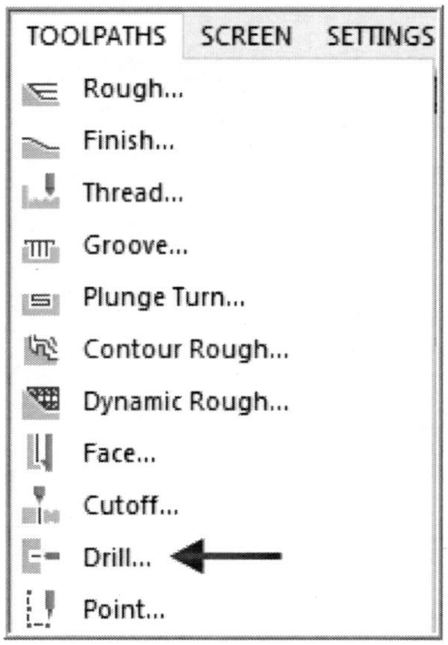

2. Right mouse button click in the white space and select **View>Icons.** Scroll down and select the **Drill - .250 diameter** tool from the tool list and make changes as shown below:

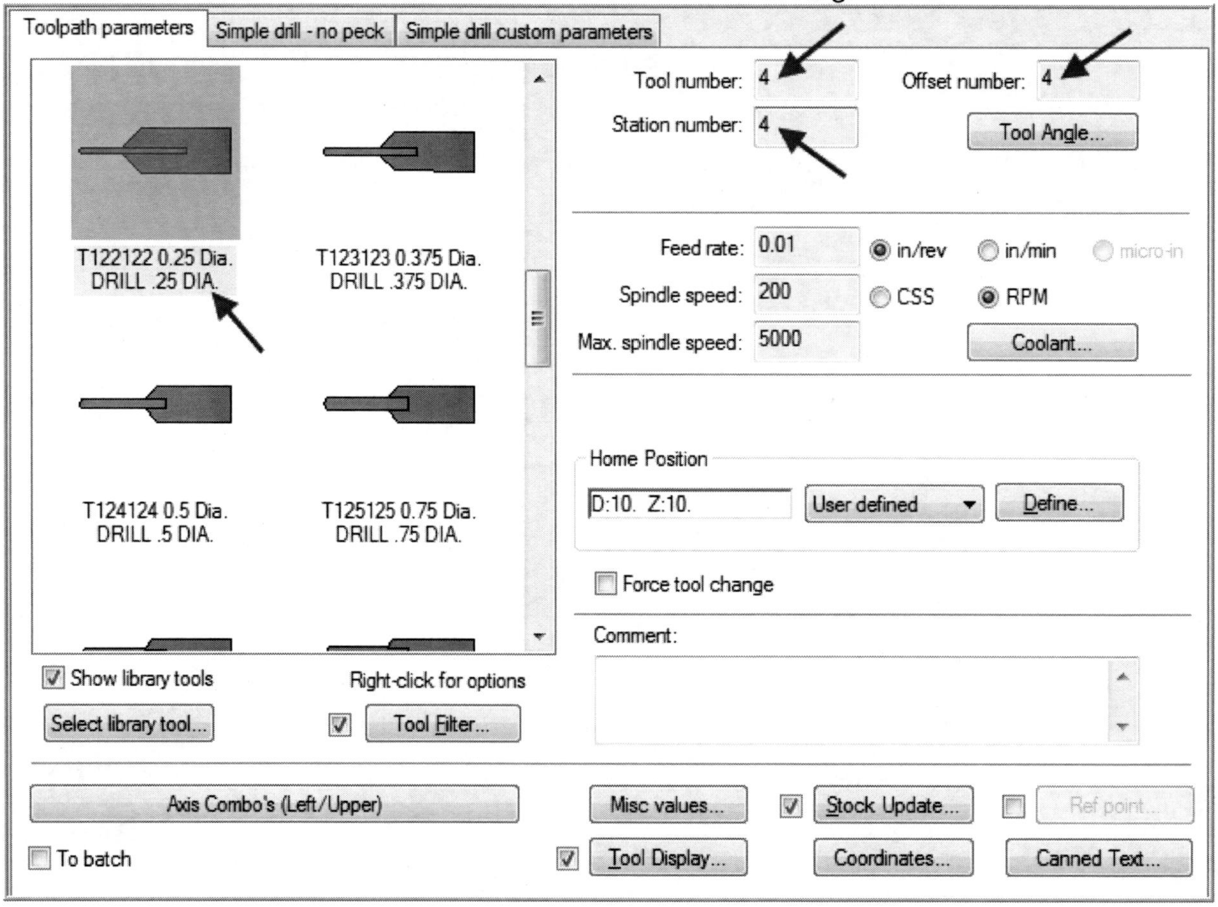

3. Select the **Simple drill – no peck** page and make changes as shown below. This hole will be **peck drilled through the part**. Make changes as shown below:

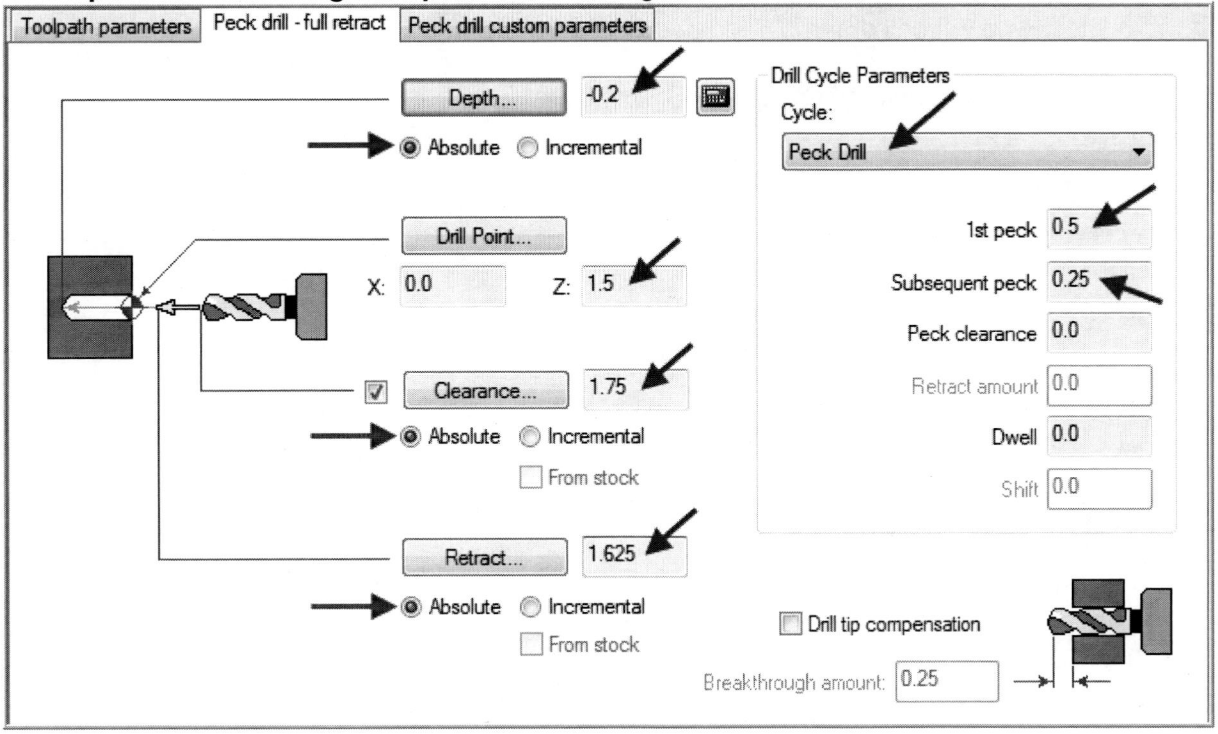

4. Select the OK button to exit Peck drill – full retract.

TASK 16:
DRILL THE 0.375" HOLE

➲ In this task you will drill the 0.375" hole using **0.375 diameter end mill.**

1. From the menu bar select **TOOLPATHS>Drill...**

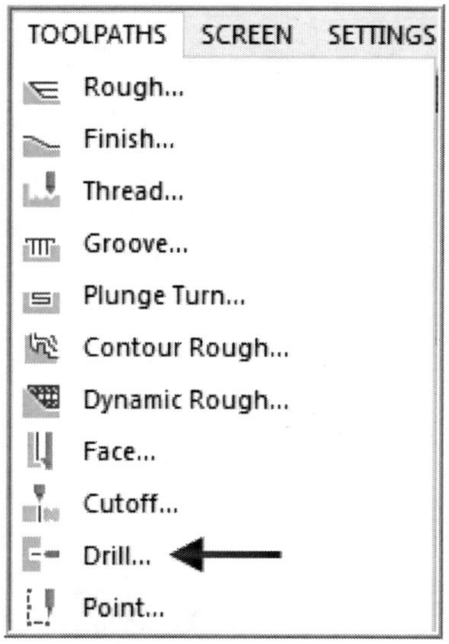

2. Scroll down and select the **0.375 DIA. - .007R diameter End Mill** tool from the tool list and make changes as shown below:

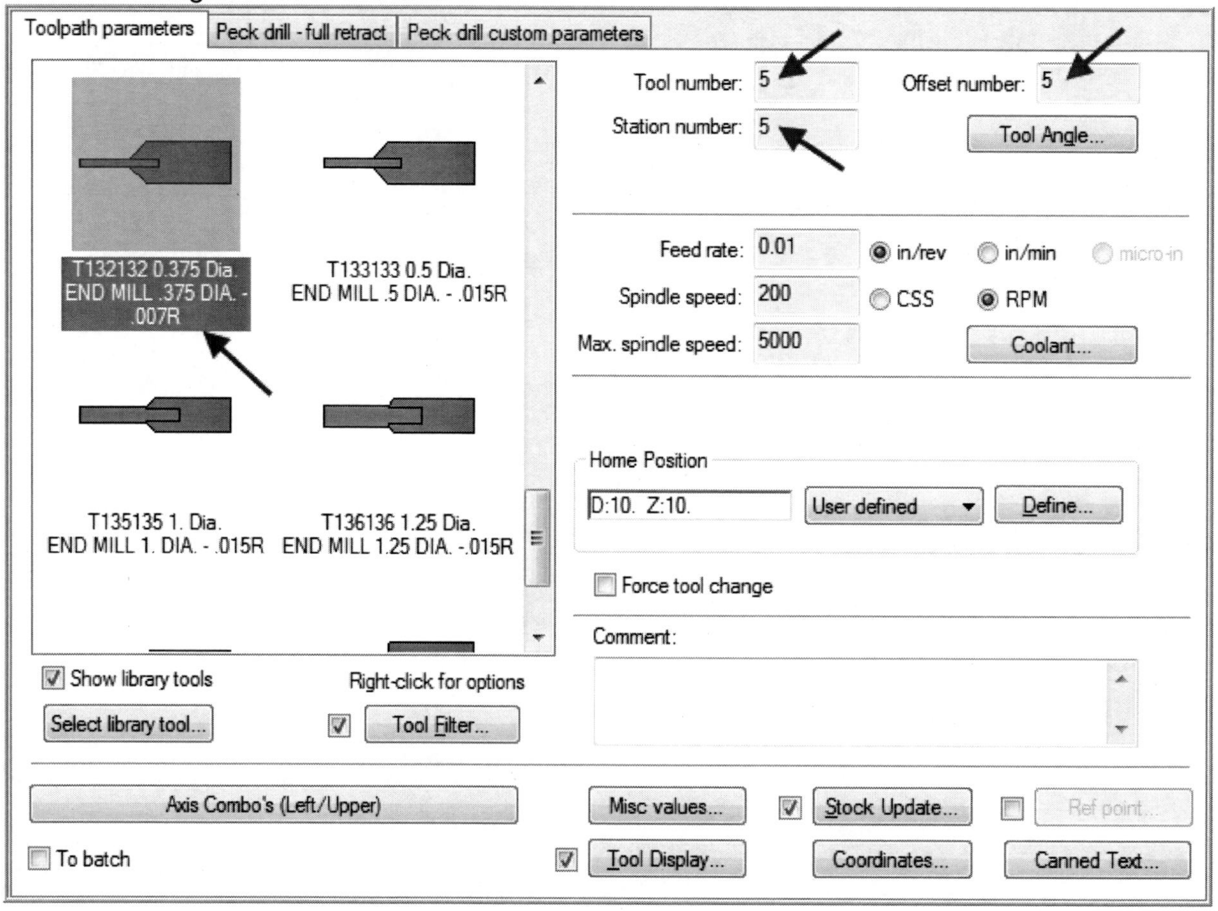

3. Select the second tab **Peck drill – full retract** and make changes as shown below. This is a **Simple drill – no peck** operation so change the **Cycle to Drill/Counterbore**.

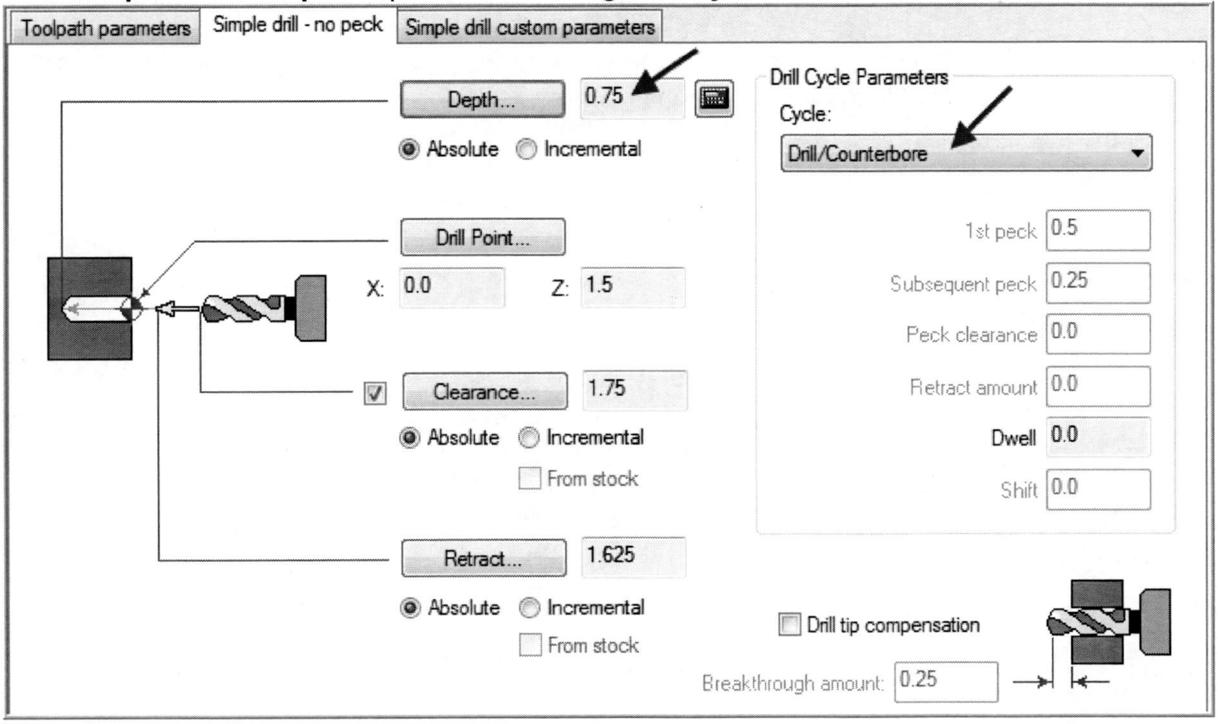

4. Select the OK button  to exit Simple drill – no peck.

TASK 17:
CUT THE GROOVE

➲ In this task you will use the Lathe Groove toolpath using an **OD Groove Right Width .125.**

1. From the menu bar select **TOOLPATHS>Groove…**

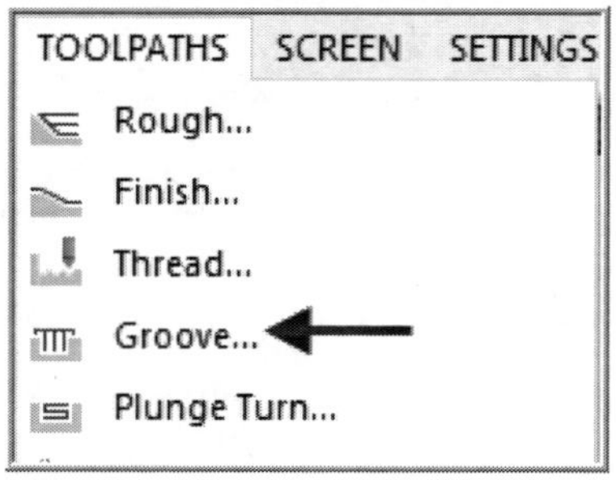

2. The Grooving Options window appears. Click on the **Chain** option as shown below:

3. Click on OK .
4. Select **Alt and T** on the keyboard to hide the toolpath.
5. Zoom in on the groove area as shown below:
6. In the **Chaining** window Chaining mode is set to **Partial** by default.
7. Select **Line 1** as the start of the **Partial chain.**

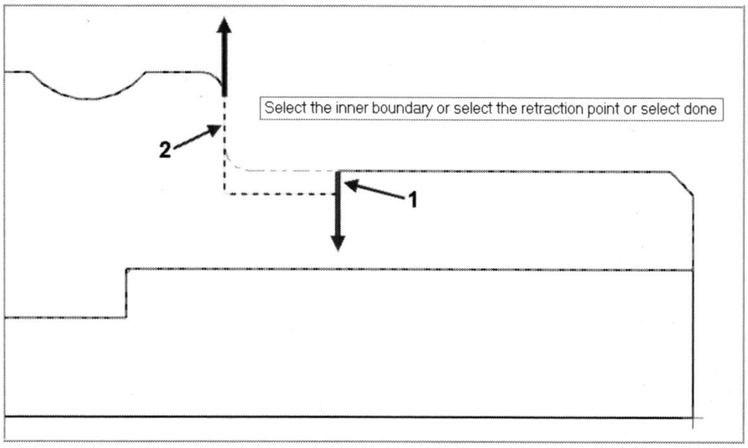

After you have selected line 1 **ensure** that the arrows are pointing downwards If it is not select the reverse button in the Chaining dialog box

8. Then select **Line 2** as the end entity in this chain.
9. Select the OK button  to exit the Chaining dialog window.

10. Select **OD Groove Right Width .125** tool from the tool list and make any necessary changes as shown below:

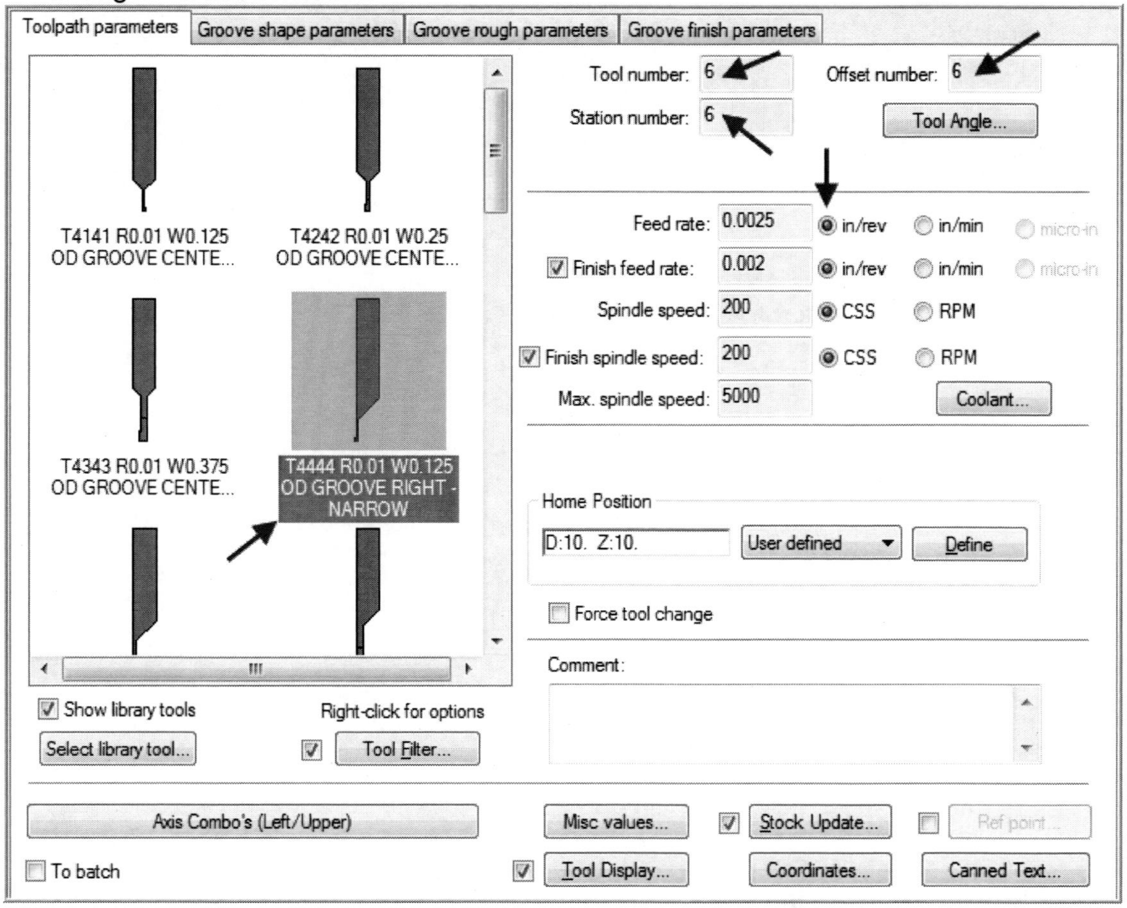

11. Select the **Groove finish parameters** page.

12. Click on the Lead **In** button  and make changes to the **Second pass Lead in** page as shown below.

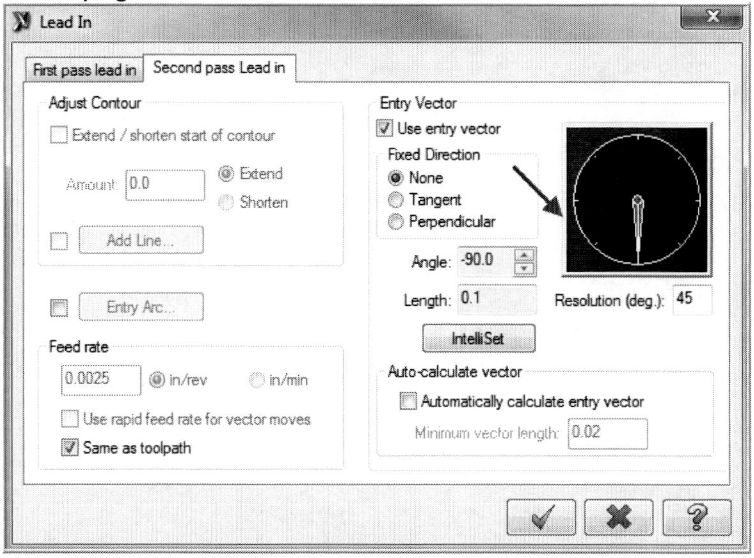

Note:
With grooving toolpaths, the tabs are called **1st Pass Lead In** or **2nd Pass Lead In**.

13. Select the OK button  to exit Lead in.

14. Select the OK button  to exit as no further changes are required.

TASK 18:
CUT OFF THE PART

➲ In this task you will cut off the part using **OD Groove Right Width .125** the same tool as the previous grooving operation.

1. Fit the image to the screen by clicking on the **Fit** icon as shown below:

2. From the menu bar select **TOOLPATHS>Cutoff…**

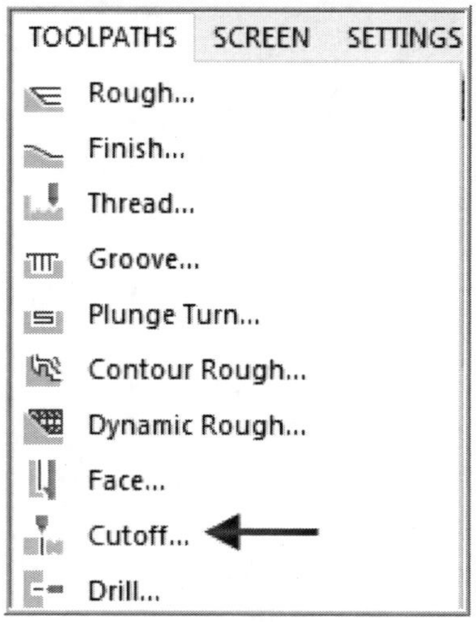

3. When prompted to **Select cutoff boundary point** pick the end point of the line shown below. Move the cursor over the corner until the visual cue for End point displays and then click on this point.

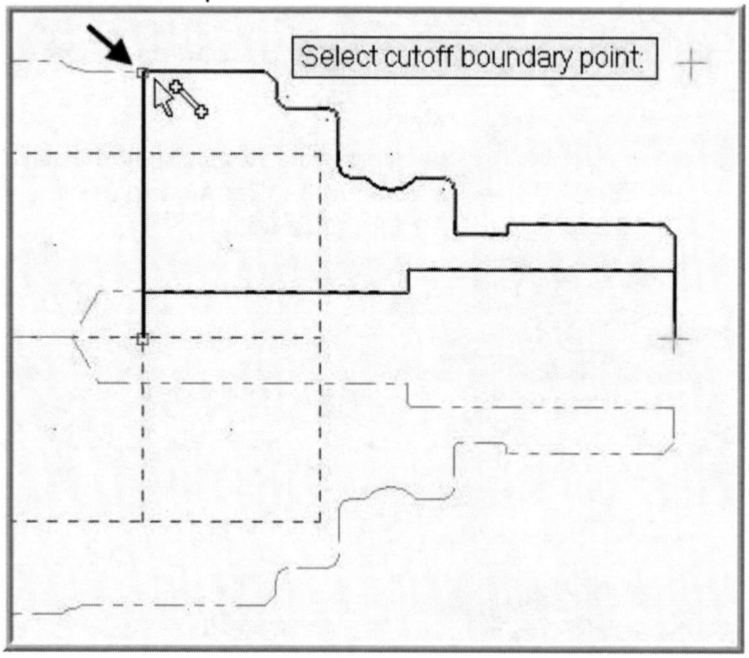

4. Select **OD GROOVE RIGHT WIDTH .125** tool from the tool list and make any necessary changes as shown below:

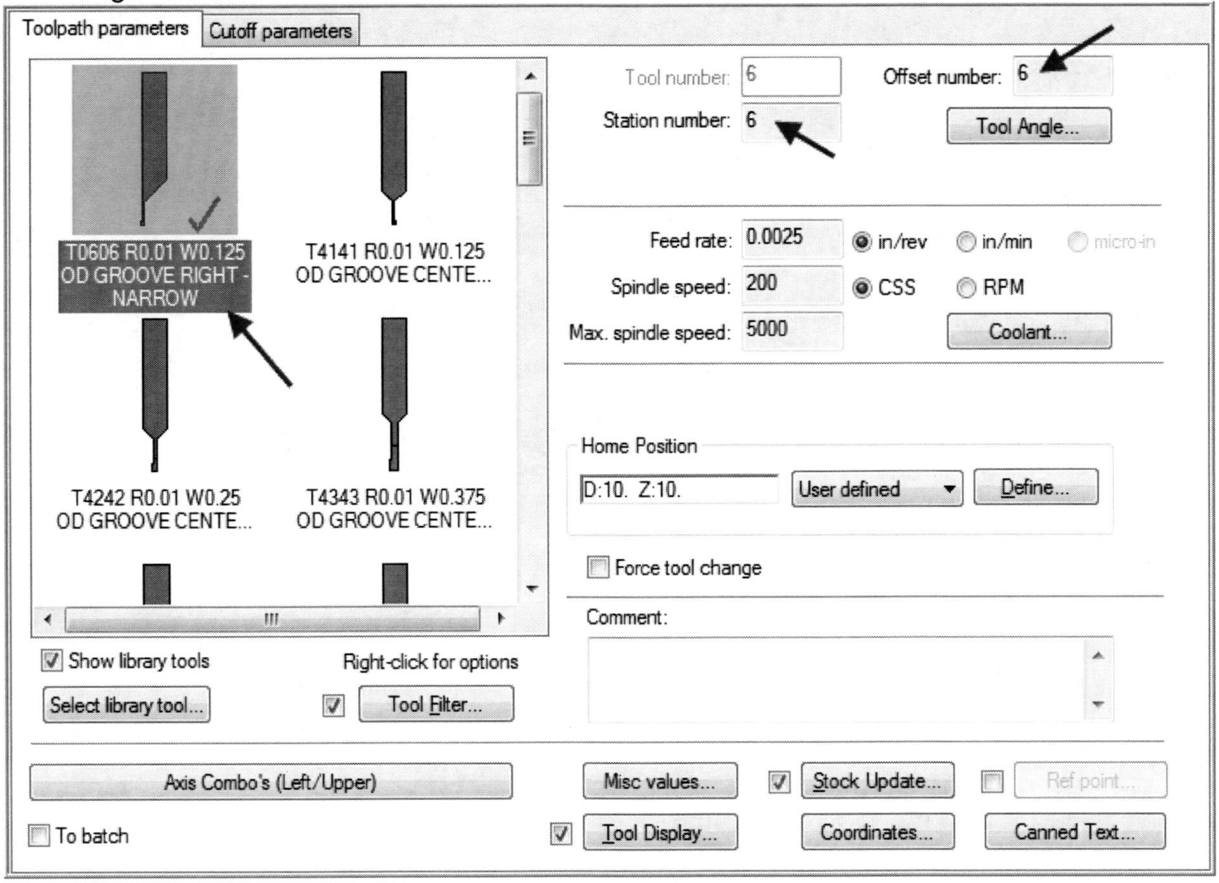

5. Still on the **Toolpath parameters** page click on the Stock Update button .

6. Ensure **Keep separated piece** is activated.

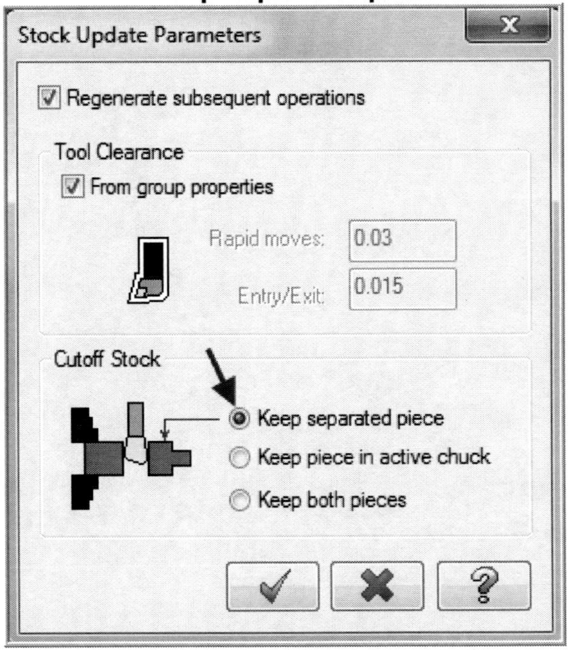

Stock Update Parameters
Use this dialog box to tell Mastercam to regenerate operations which follow the current operation when you finish editing it.
This lets you update those operations to take into account changes in the stock model caused by the current operation.
You can leave this option unselected if the only changes you are making to the operation don't affect the stock model—for example, changing the feed rate.
You can also use this dialog box to override the stock clearance values from the machine group properties, and, for cutoff operations, select whether the stock model will be based on the finished part or leftover stock.
Keep separated piece
Check to display the part boundary after the part is cut off. This option is available only with cutoff operations.

7. Select the **Cutoff parameters** page and make sure the settings are as shown below:

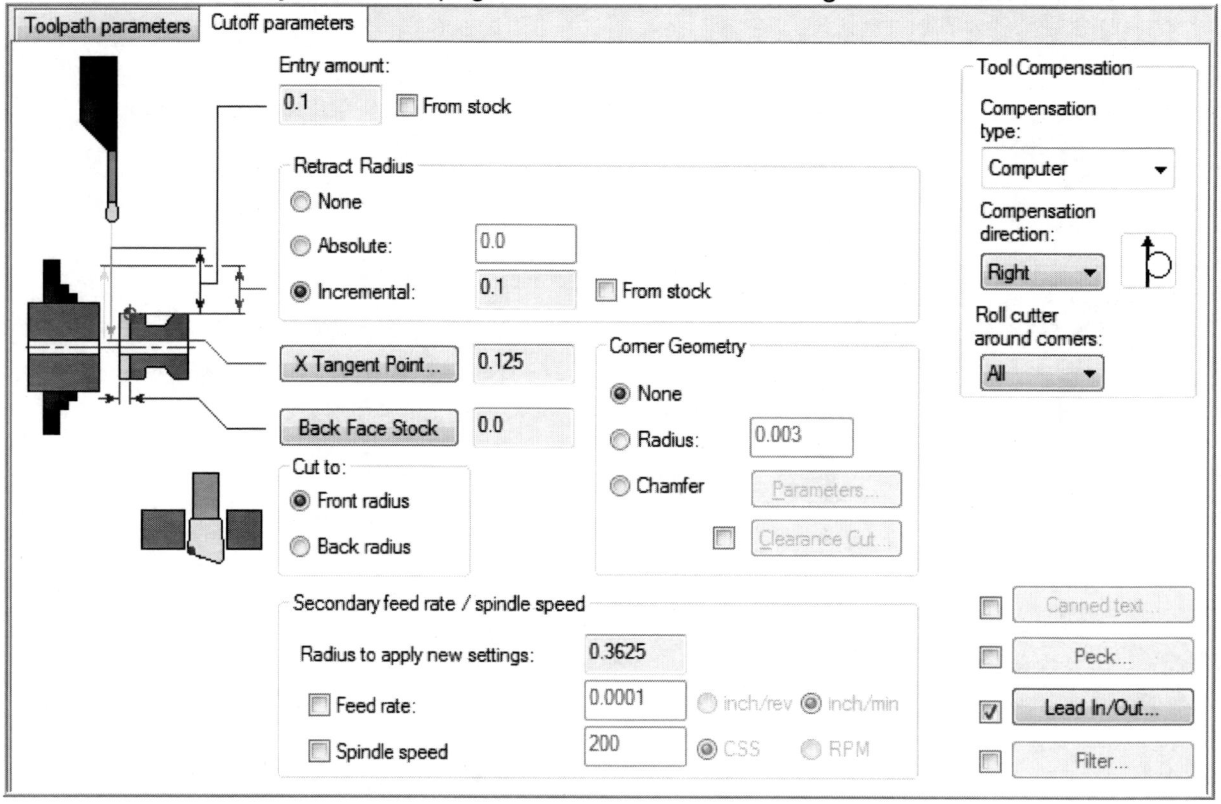

8. Select the OK button ✓ to exit **Lathe Cutoff parameters.**

TASK 19:
VERIFY THE TOOLPATH

➲ Mastercam's Verify utility allows you to use solid models to simulate the machining of a part. The model created by the verification represents the surface finish, and shows collisions, if any exist.

1. In the Toolpaths Manager pick all the operations to Verify by picking the **Select All** icon  .
2. Select the **Verify selected operations** icon shown below:

3. **Maximize** the Backplot/Verify window if required.
4. Now select the **Home** Tab if required.

5. Activate the options shown below in the **Visibility** section of the Home tab. **Initial Stock not** activated.

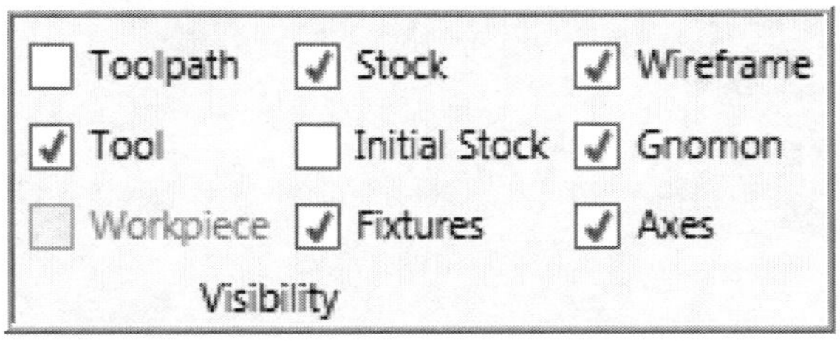

6. Activate the **Color Loop** to change the color of the tools for the verified part.

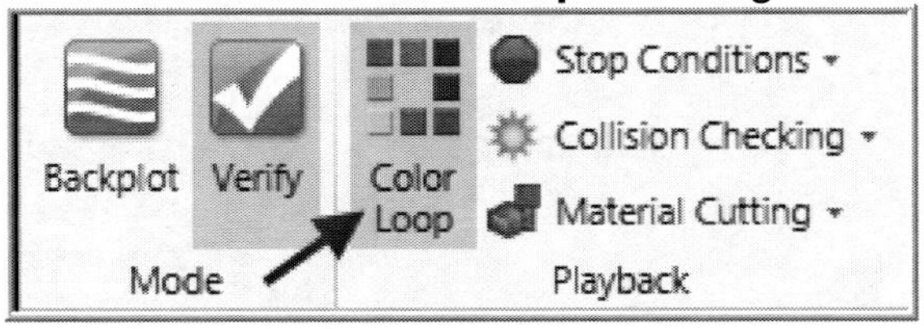

Color Loop
Changes the color of the toolpath or cut stock by operation or by tool change.

Choose **File Options** to set the colors.

7. At the top of the screen select the **View** tab, the **Isometric** icon and then select **Fit.**

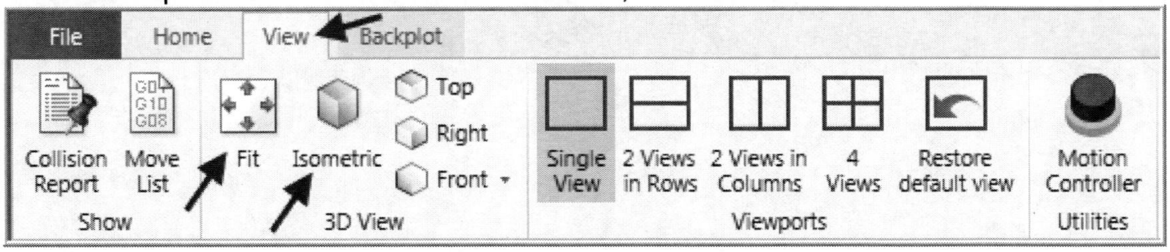

8. In the lower right corner of the screen now set the run **Speed** to slow by moving the slider bar pointer over to the left as shown below.

9. Now select the **Play Simulation** button to review the toolpaths.

10. Select the Close button  in the top right hand corner to exit Verify.

TASK 20:
SAVE THE UPDATED MASTERCAM FILE

1. Select the save icon from the toolbar .

TASK 21:
POST AND CREATE THE CNC CODE FILE

1. Ensure all the operations are selected by picking the **Select All** icon  from the Toolpaths manager.

2. Select the **Post selected operations** button from the Toolpaths manager.

➲ **Please Note:** If you cannot see **G1** click on the right pane of the Toolpaths manager window and expand the window to the right.

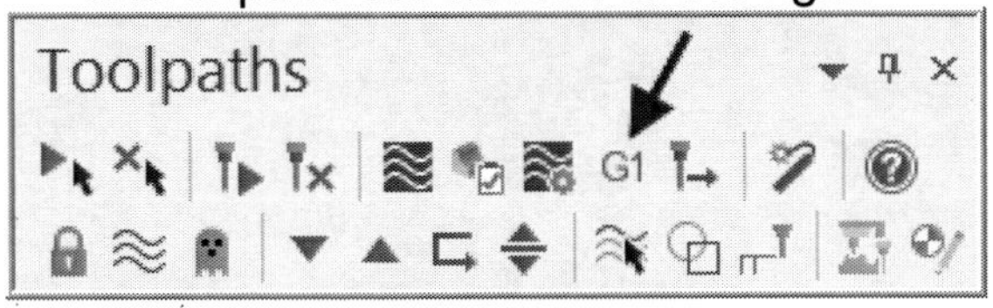

3. In the Post processing window, make the necessary changes as shown below:

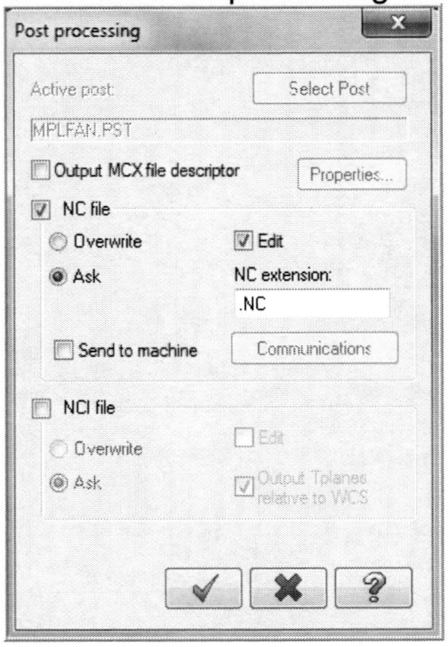

About Post Processing

NC file:
Select this option to save the NC file. The file name and extension are stored in the machine group properties for the selected operation. If you are posting operations from different machine groups or Mastercam files, or batch processing, Mastercam will create several files according to the settings for each machine group.

Edit:
When checked, automatically launches the default text editor with the file displayed so that you can review or modify it.

4. Select the OK button  to continue.

5. Ensure the same name as your Mastercam part file name is displayed in the **NC File name** field.
6. Select the **Save** button.
7. The CNC code file opens up in the default editor.

LATHE-LESSON-6.NC ×

```
(MATERIAL - ALUMINUM INCH - 6061)
G20
(TOOL - 1 OFFSET - 1)
(OD ROUGH RIGHT - 80 DEG.  INSERT - CNMG-432)
G0 T0101
G18
G97 S449 M03
G0 G54 X1.7 Z1.5
G50 S3600
G96 S200
G99 G1 X-.0625 F.01
G0 Z1.6
X1.2884
Z1.7
G1 Z1.6
Z.38
X1.3355
G18 G3 X1.3868 Z.3694 K-.0363
G1 X1.4488 Z.3384
G3 X1.47 Z.3127 I-.0257 K-.0257
G1 Z-.2313
```

8. Select the × in the top right corner to exit the CNC editor.
9. This completes LATHE-LESSON-6.

LATHE-LESSON-6 EXERCISE

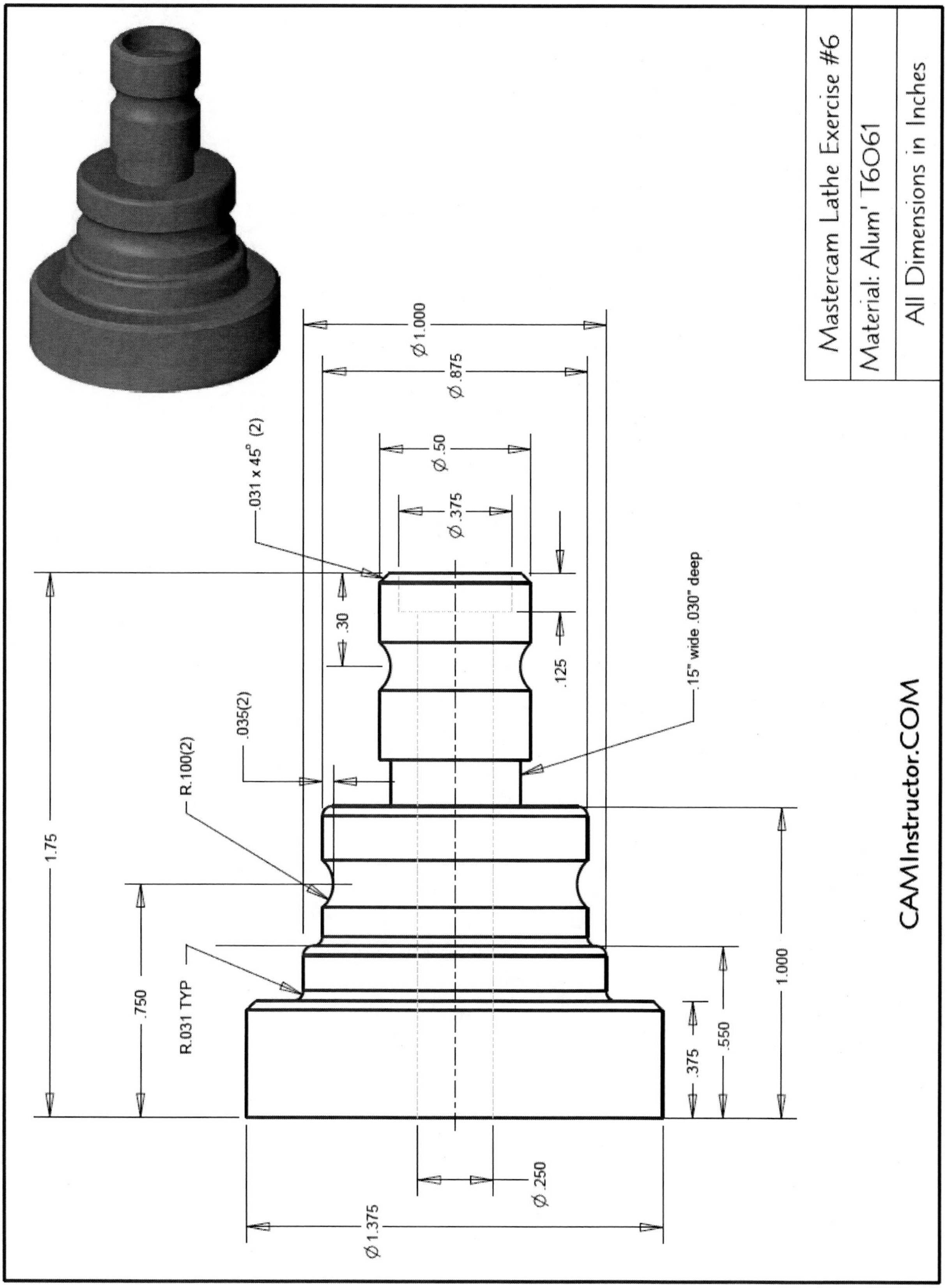

Mastercam® X[9]

TRAINING GUIDE

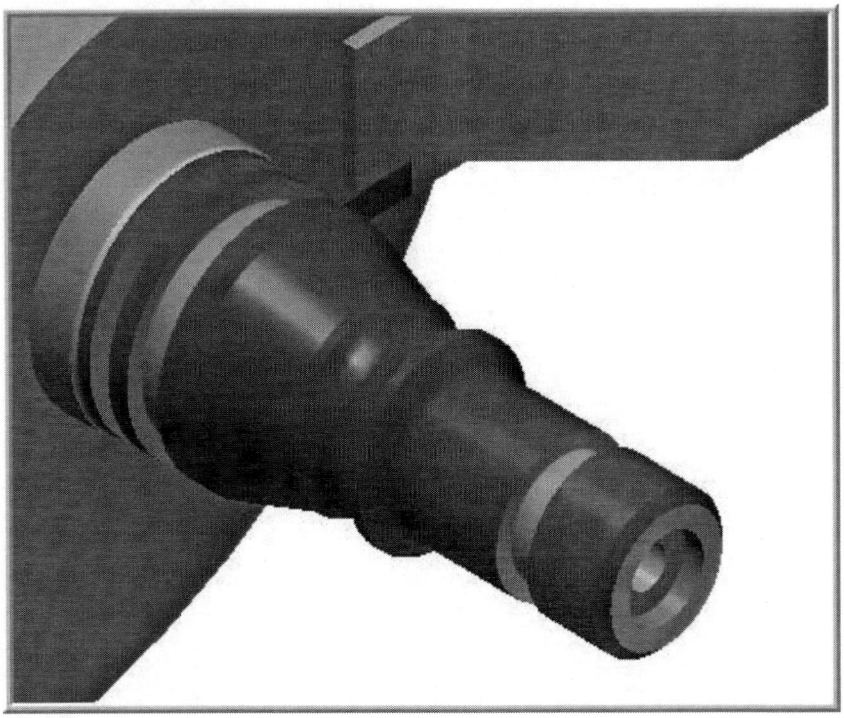

LATHE-LESSON-7

FACE, QUICK ROUGH AND FINISH, DRILL, TAP, GROOVE AND CUTOFF

camInstructor

Objectives

You will create the geometry for Lathe Lesson-7, and then generate a toolpath to machine the part on a CNC lathe. This lesson covers the following topics:

➲ **Create a 2-dimensional drawing by:**
Creating lines.
Creating fillets.
Creating chamfers.
Trimming geometry.

➲ **Establish Stock and Chuck Setup settings:**
Stock size.
Chuck Configuration.
Material for the part.
Feed calculation.

➲ **Generate a 2-dimensional lathe toolpath consisting of:**
Lathe Face.
Lathe Quick Rough.
Lathe Quick Finish.
Lathe Finish.
Lathe Drill.
Lathe Groove.
Lathe Cutoff.

➲ **Inspect the toolpath using Mastercam's Verify and Backplot by:**
Launching the Verify function to machine the part on the screen.
Generating the NC- code.

LATHE - LESSON-7 DRAWING

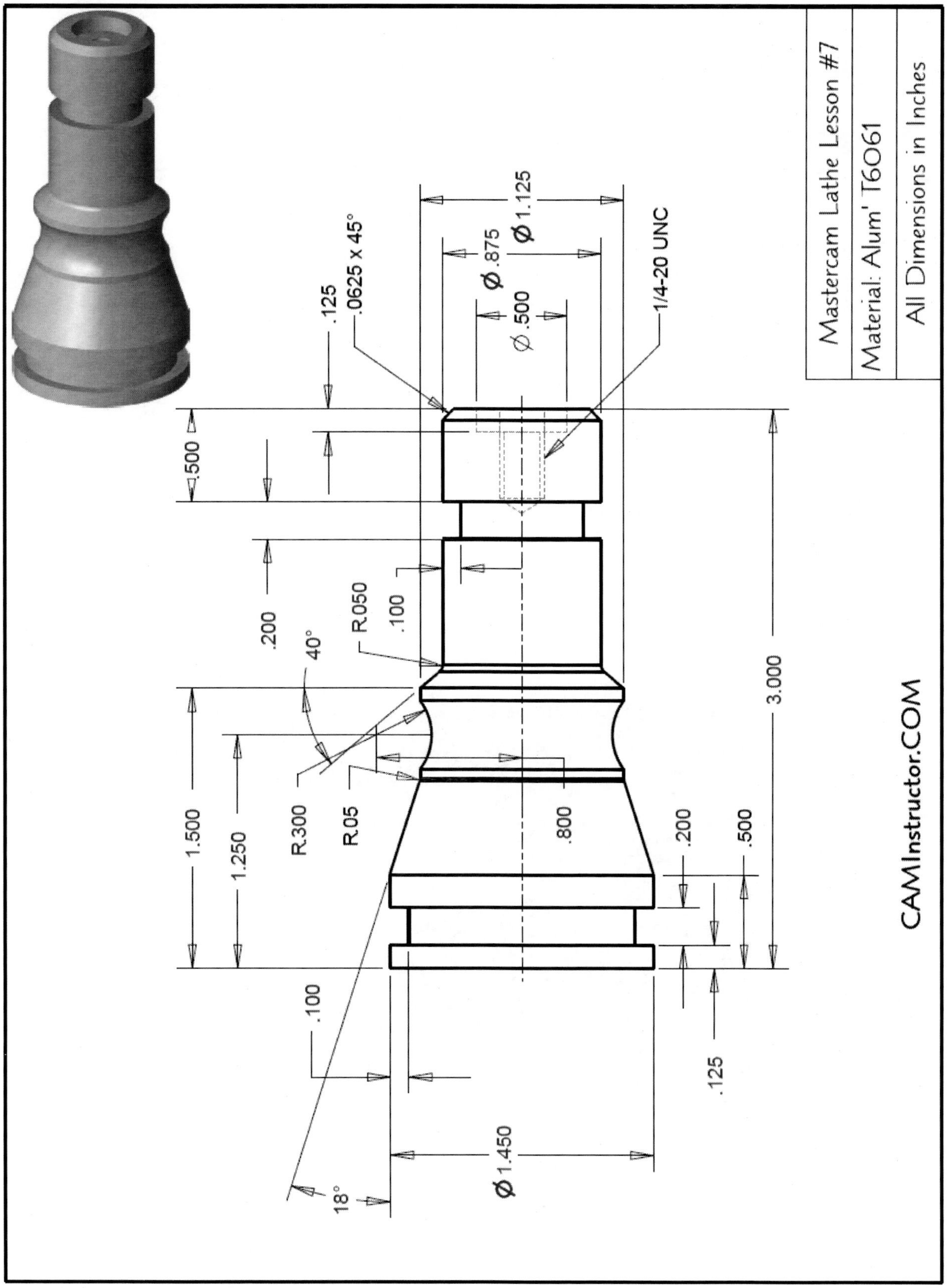

TOOL LIST

Seven tools will be used to create this part.

- **Tool #1 Face, Rough the outside diameters**
  Holder: Outside Diameter Rough Right Hand - DCGNR-164D.
  Insert: 80 Degree Diamond Insert – CNMG-432

- **Tool #2 Finish the outside diameters**
  Holder: Outside Diameter Finish Right Hand - MVJNR-164D.
  Insert: 35 Degree Diamond Insert – VNMG-431.

- **Tool #3 Center drill**
  Centre Drill – body diameter 0.250"

- **Tool #4 13/64 diameter drill**
  Drill 13/64" (0.2031)" diameter

- **Tool #5 ¼-20 UNC tap**
  Tap ¼"-20 UNC

- **Tool #6 Boring tool**
  Holder: Boring Bar – minimum diameter 0.1875".
  Insert: 75 Degree Diamond Insert

- **Tool #7 Cutoff tool**
  Holder: Outside Diameter Groove Right Hand - Narrow.
  Insert: 0.125" Wide - GC-4125

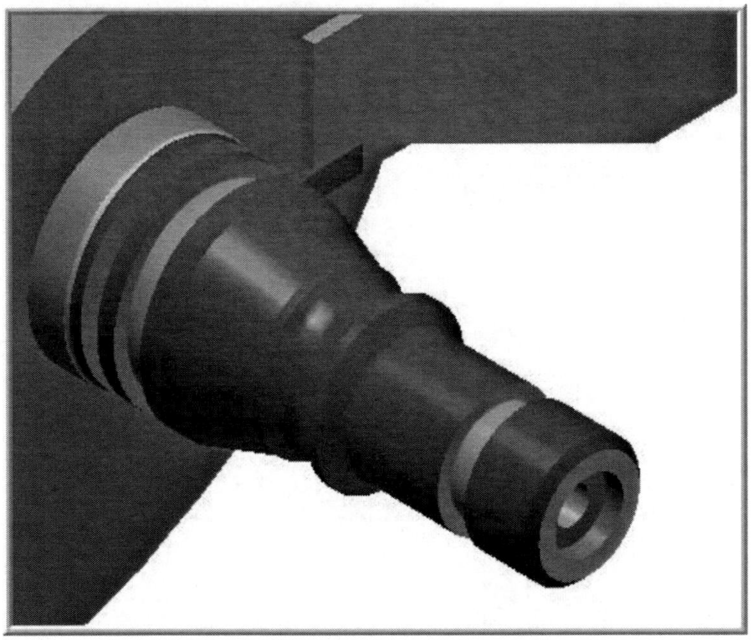

LESSON - 7 - THE PROCESS

Geometry Creation

TASK 1: Setting the environment
TASK 2: Setting the construction planes
TASK 3: Create the geometry – Part 1
TASK 4: Create the geometry – Part 2
TASK 5: Create the 40 degree line and 0.050 fillets
TASK 6: Create the chamfer on right side of part
TASK 7: Create the 0.300" Radius
TASK 8: Trim the Geometry
TASK 9: Create the geometry for the bore
TASK 10: Trim the geometry for the bore
TASK 11: Save the drawing

Toolpath Creation

TASK 12: Define the stock and chuck parameters
TASK 13: Face the front of the part
TASK 14: Rough the outside diameters
TASK 15: Finish the outside diameters
TASK 16: Finish the 0.3 radius
TASK 17: Center drill hole
TASK 18: Tap Drill 13/64" diameter
TASK 19: Tap the ¼-20 UNC Hole
TASK 20: Rough the bore
TASK 21: Finish the bore
TASK 22: Cut the Grooves
TASK 23: Cut off the part
TASK 24: Verify the toolpath
TASK 25: Save the updated Mastercam file
TASK 26: Post and create the cnc code file

Geometry Creation

TASK 1:
SETTING THE ENVIRONMENT

Before starting the geometry creation you should set up the grid and toolbars as outlined in the **Setting the Environment** section at the beginning of this text:

1. Set up the Grid. This will help identify the location of the origin.
2. Load the Workspace – **SETTINGS>Load Workspace>Lathe** to machine a part on the Lathe.
3. Set the machine type to the default Lathe.

TASK 2:
SETTING THE CONSTRUCTION PLANES:

➲ **Set the Construction Plane to Lathe diameter +D +Z (WCS)**

1. Click on Planes at the bottom of the screen as shown below:

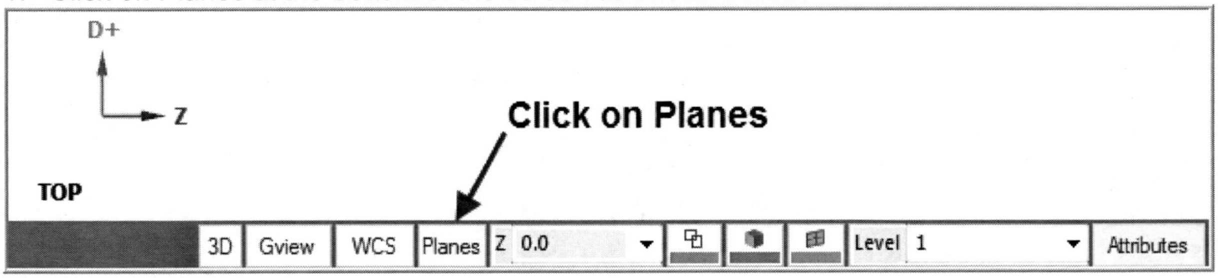

2. Click on Lathe diameter>+D +Z (WCS) as shown below:

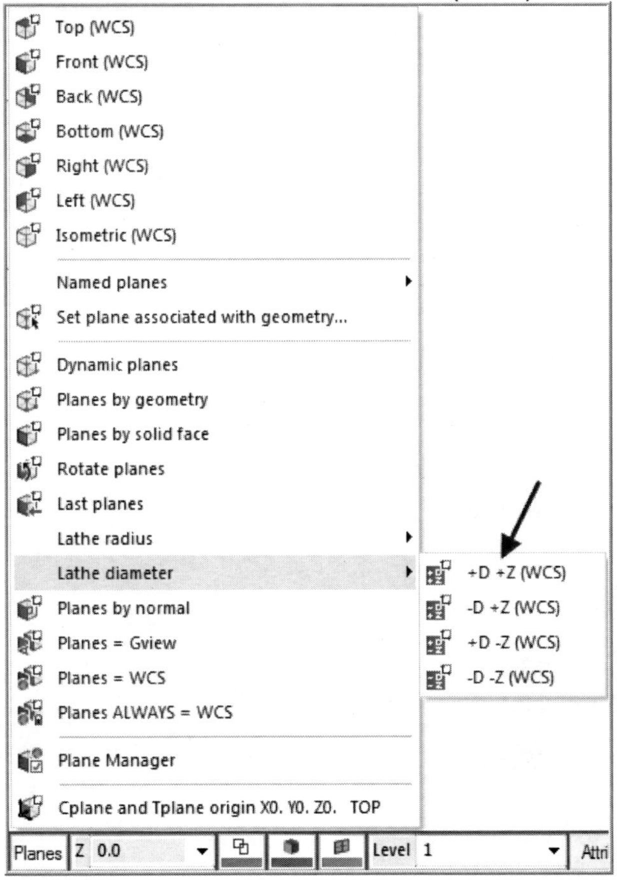

TASK 3:
CREATE THE GEOMETRY – PART 1

➲ This task explains how to create the geometry of this part. In this lathe part you only need to create half of the geometry, the geometry above the center line.

➲ Lines 1 through 8 will be created in this task.

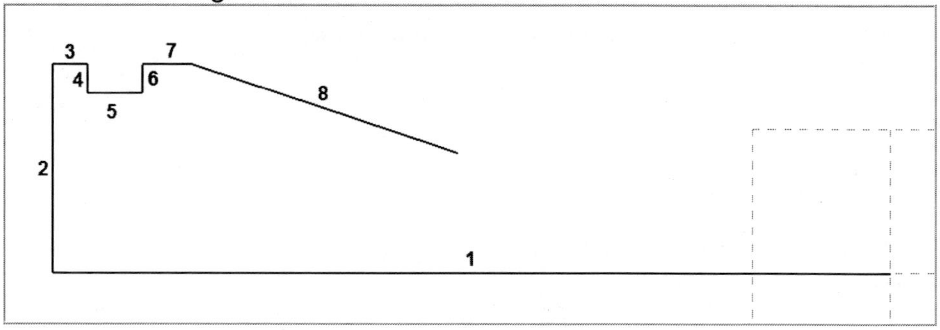

➲ **Create Line #1**

1. Select **Alt-O** on your keyboard to turn off the display of the Toolpaths Manager.
2. Select from the pull down menu **CREATE>Line>Endpoint…**

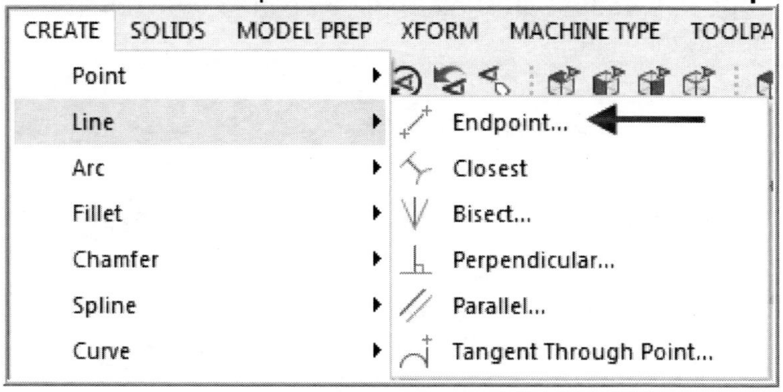

3. The Line ribbon bar appears:

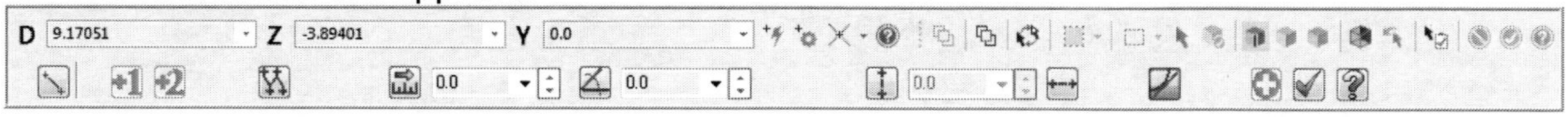

4. Move the cursor over the **center of the grid** and as you get close to the origin a visual cue appears.  This is the cue that will allow you to snap to the **origin**. With this visual cue highlighted pick the **origin**.
5. You are next prompted to **"Specify the second endpoint"**. On the left hand side of the Line ribbon bar click on the **Multi-Line** button to activate it as shown below by the arrow:

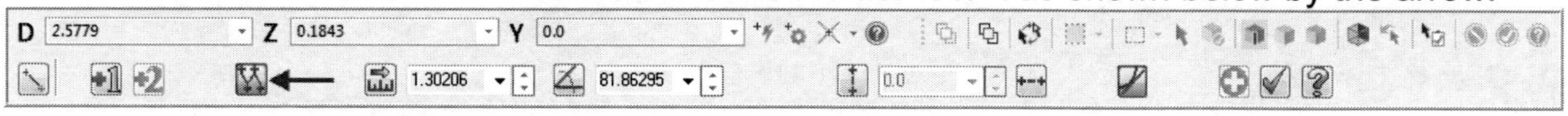

6. Click in the **D** value space (Diameter) and enter a value of **0**. Hit the Enter key and enter a value of **-3.0 for the Z**. **Note** the value of Y is set to Zero, this does not need to be input. Hit the Enter key once again to complete this line.

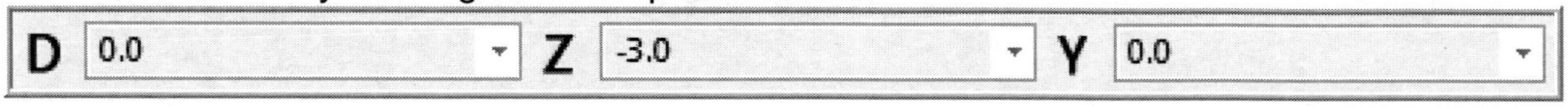

➲ **Create Line #2**

7. Click in the D value space (Diameter) and enter a value of **1.45**. Hit the Enter key and enter a value of **-3.0 for the Z**. Hit the Enter key once again to complete this line.

| D | 1.45 | ▾ | Z | -3.0 | ▾ | Y | 0.0 | ▾ |

8. Fit the image to the screen by clicking on the **Fit** icon as shown below:

➲ **Create Line #3**

9. "**Specify the second endpoint**"; Type in **1.45 in D** hit Enter, type in **-3.0+0.125 in Z**. Hit the Enter key once again to complete this line.

| D | 1.45 | ▾ | Z | -2.875 | ▾ | Y | 0.0 | ▾ |

➲ **Create Line #4**

10. "**Specify the second endpoint**"; Type in **1.450-0.2 in D** hit Enter, type in **-3.0+0.125 in Z**. Hit the Enter key once again to complete this line.

| D | 1.25 | ▾ | Z | -2.875 | ▾ | Y | 0.0 | ▾ |

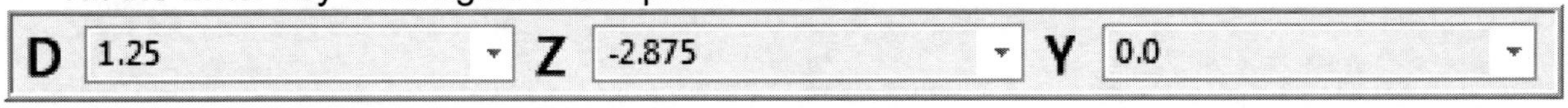

➲ **Create Line #5**

11. "**Specify the second endpoint**"; Type in **1.450-0.2 in D** hit Enter, type in **-3.0+0.125+0.2 in Z**. Hit the Enter key once again to complete this line.

| D | 1.25 | ▾ | Z | -2.675 | ▾ | Y | 0.0 | ▾ |

➲ **Create Line #6**

12. "**Specify the second endpoint**"; Type in **1.45 in D** hit Enter, type in **-3.0+0.125+0.2 in Z**. Hit the Enter key once again to complete this line.

| D | 1.45 | ▾ | Z | -2.675 | ▾ | Y | 0.0 | ▾ |

➲ **Create Line #7**

13. "**Specify the second endpoint**"; Type in **1.45 in D** hit Enter, type in **-3.0+0.500 in Z**. Hit the Enter key once again to complete this line.

| D | 1.45 | ▾ | Z | -2.5 | ▾ | Y | 0.0 | ▾ |

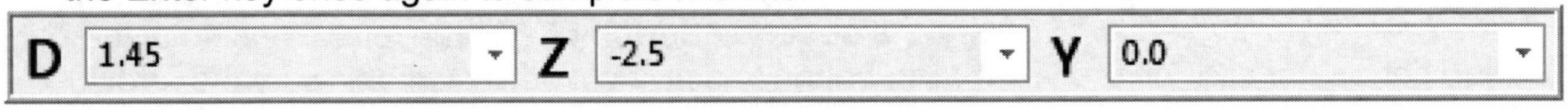

➲ **Create Line #8**

14. Now click in the space for **Length** and enter a value of **1.0** and hit the tab key to move over to Angle.

15. In the space for **Angle** enter a value of **-18.0** and hit the enter key.

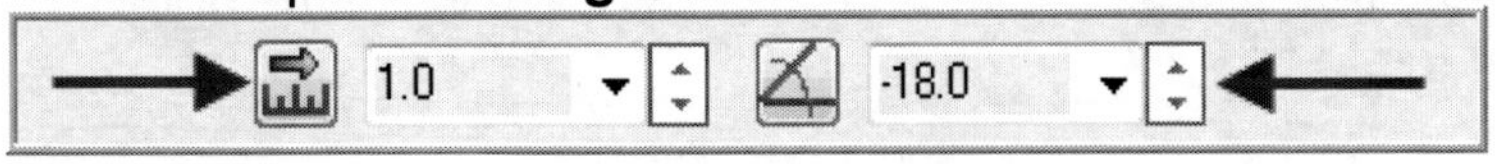

16. Click on the OK icon [✓] to complete this feature.

TASK 4:
CREATE THE GEOMETRY – PART 2

➲ This task explains how to create the geometry of this part.
➲ Lines 9 through 15 will be created using **Line>Parallel**.

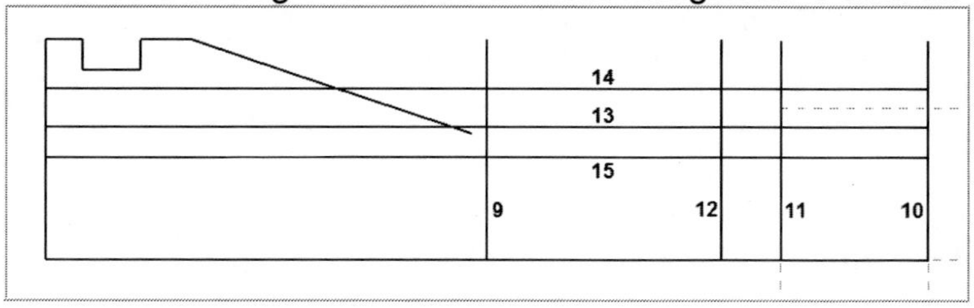

1. Fit the image to the screen by clicking on the **Fit** icon as shown below:

2. Your geometry should look like the figure below:

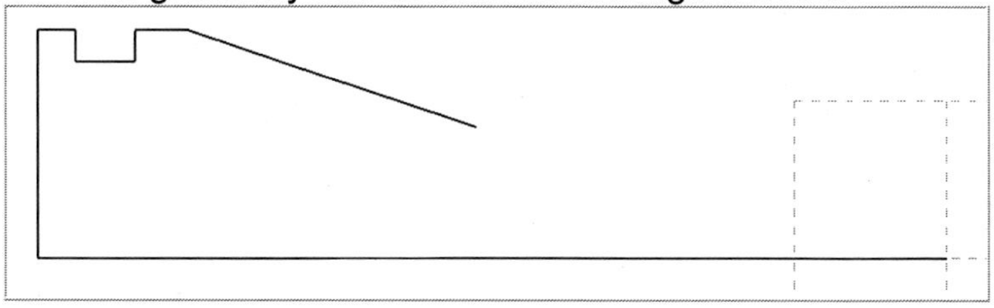

➲ **Create Line #9**

3. Select from the pull down menu: **CREATE>Line>Parallel….**
4. On the graphics screen you are prompted **"Select a line"** and the Line Parallel ribbon bar appears.
5. To satisfy the prompt **Select a line**, select the line shown below:

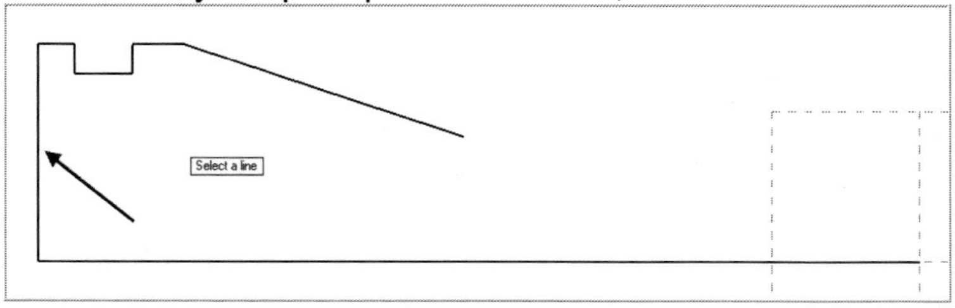

6. To satisfy the next prompt **Select the point to place a parallel line through** move the cursor to the right of the line and pick a point.
7. For the **Distance** input **1.500** then hit **enter**.
8. On the ribbon bar click on **Apply** to fix the entity.

➲ **Create Line #10**

9. To satisfy the prompt **Select a line**, select the line shown below:

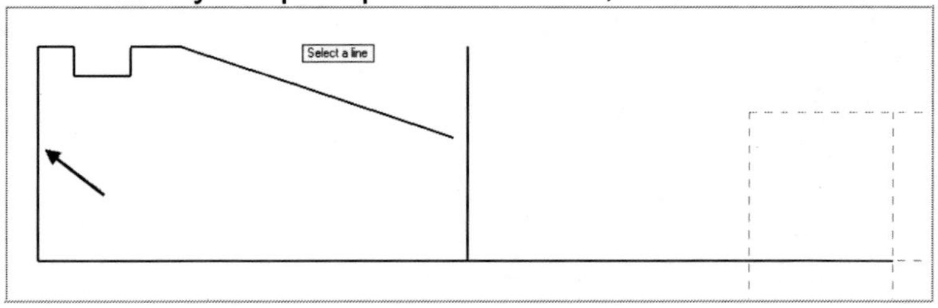

10. To satisfy the next prompt **Select the point to place a parallel line through** move the cursor to the right of the line and pick a point.
11. For the **Distance** input **3.0** then hit **enter.**
12. On the ribbon bar click on **Apply** to fix the entity.

➲ **Create Line #11**

13. To satisfy the prompt **Select a line**, select the line shown below:

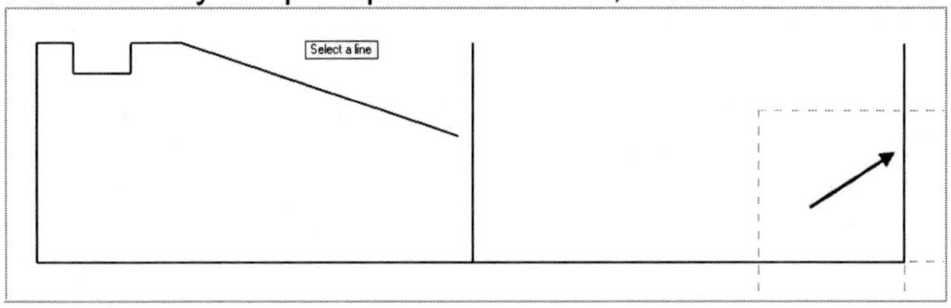

14. To satisfy the next prompt **Select the point to place a parallel line through** move the cursor to the left of the line and pick a point.
15. For the **Distance** input **0.500** then hit **enter**
16. On the ribbon bar click on **Apply** to fix the entity.

➲ **Create Line #12**

17. To satisfy the prompt **Select a line**, select the line shown below:

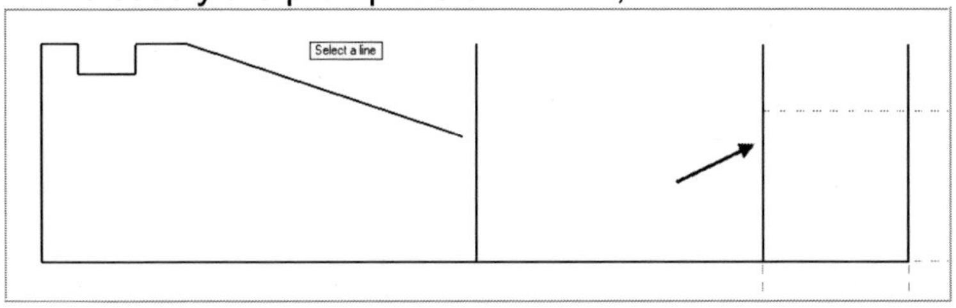

18. To satisfy the next prompt **Select the point to place a parallel line through** move the cursor to the left of the line and pick a point.
19. For the **Distance** input **0.200** then hit **enter.**
20. On the ribbon bar click on **Apply** to fix the entity.

➲ **Create Line #13**

21. To satisfy the prompt **Select a line**, select the line shown below:

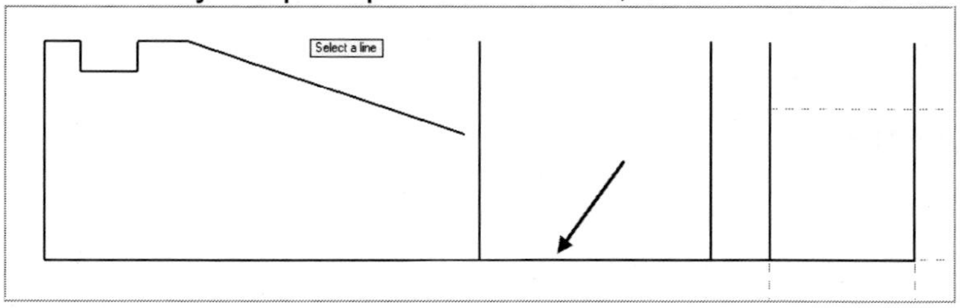

22. To satisfy the next prompt **Select the point to place a parallel line through** move the cursor above the line and pick a point.
23. For the **Distance** input **0.875/2** then hit **enter.**
24. On the ribbon bar click on **Apply** to fix the entity.

➲ **Create Line #14**

25. To satisfy the prompt **Select a line**, select the line shown below:

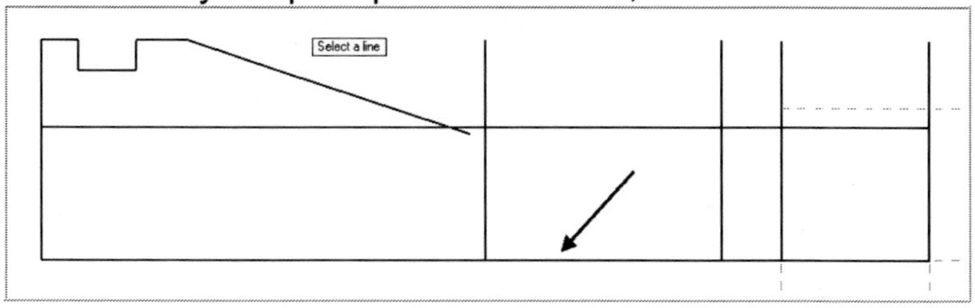

26. To satisfy the next prompt **Select the point to place a parallel line through** move the cursor above the line and pick a point.
27. For the **Distance** input **1.125/2** then hit **enter.**
28. On the ribbon bar click on **Apply** to fix the entity.

➲ **Create Line #15**

29. To satisfy the prompt **Select a line**, select the line shown below:

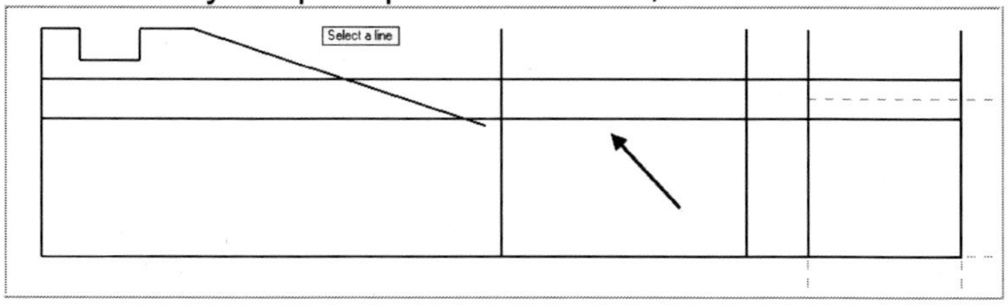

30. To satisfy the next prompt **Select the point to place a parallel line through** move the cursor below the line and pick a point.
31. For the **Distance** input **0.1** then hit **enter.**
32. Click on the **OK** icon to complete this feature. Completed geometry is shown below:

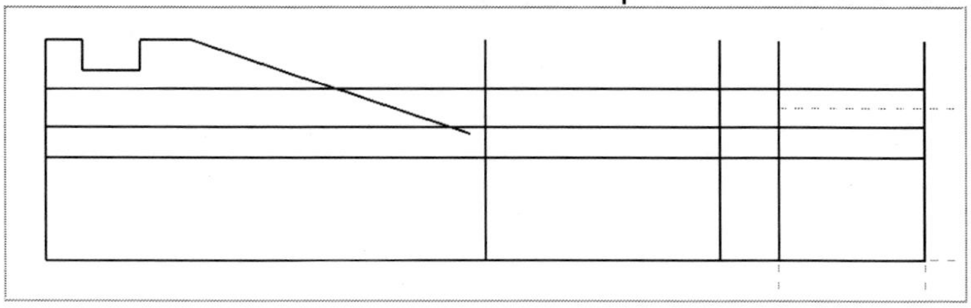

TASK 5:
CREATE THE 40 DEGREE LINE AND 0.050 FILLETS

1. Select from the pull down menu **CREATE>Line>Endpoint…**

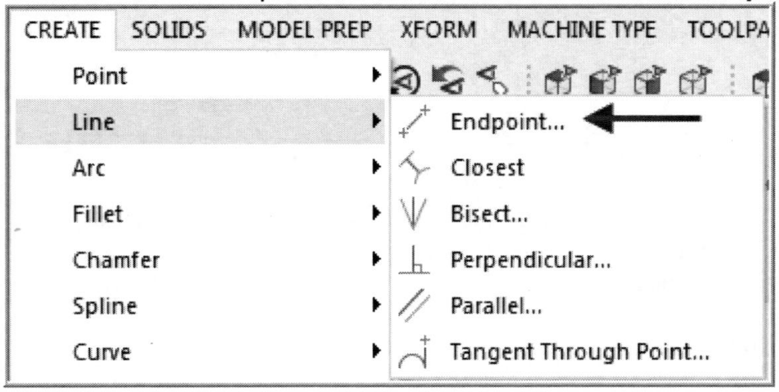

2. You are next prompted to **"Specify the first endpoint".** Move the cursor over the intersection of the two lines shown below and when the visual cue for intersection  appears pick this point.

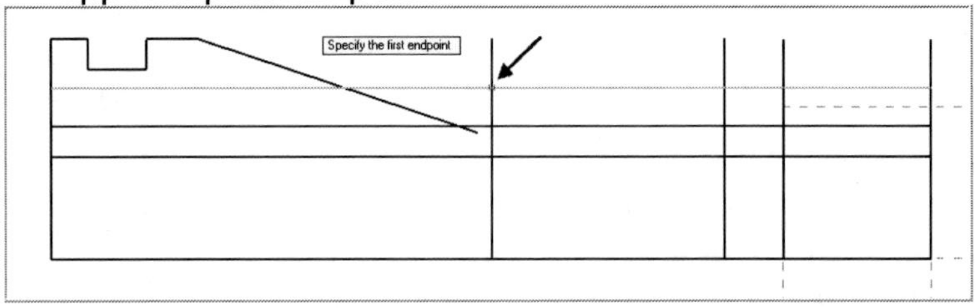

3. Now click in the space for **Length** and enter a value of **0.25** and hit the tab key to move over to Angle value.
4. For **Angle** enter a value of **-50.0 (90-40 degrees)** and hit the enter key.

5. Click on the **OK** icon  to complete this feature.

Your geometry should look like the figure below:

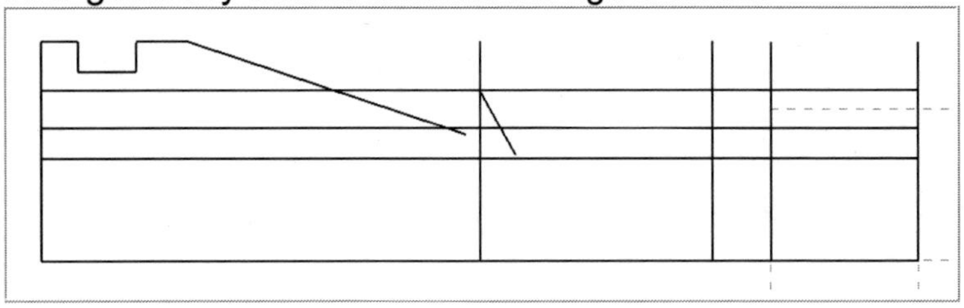

➲ **Create 0.050 fillet**

6. Select **CREATE>Fillet>Entities…**

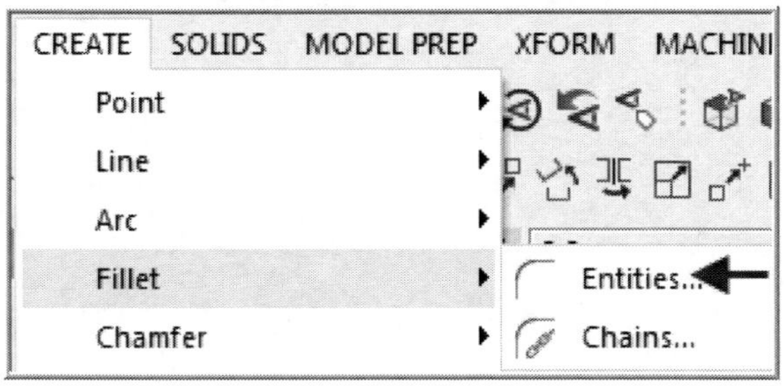

7. On the Fillet ribbon bar enter **0.050 for the radius** and hit enter. Ensure the **Style** of radius is set to **Normal** and the trim button is depressed to turn the **trim on**.

8. When prompted to **Fillet: Select an entity,** select Line 1 and 2 as shown below:
9. When prompted to **Fillet: Select an entity,** select Line 3 and 4 as shown below:

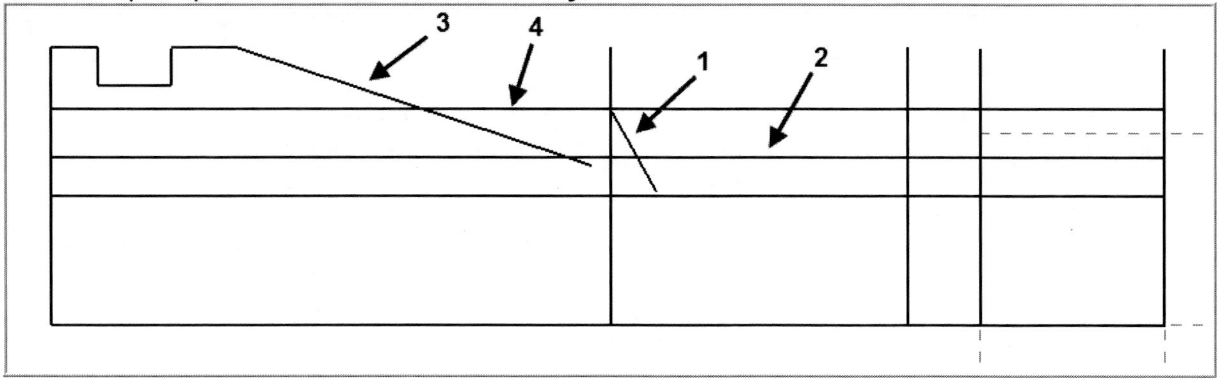

10. Click on the **OK** icon ✔ to complete this feature. The completed geometry is shown below:

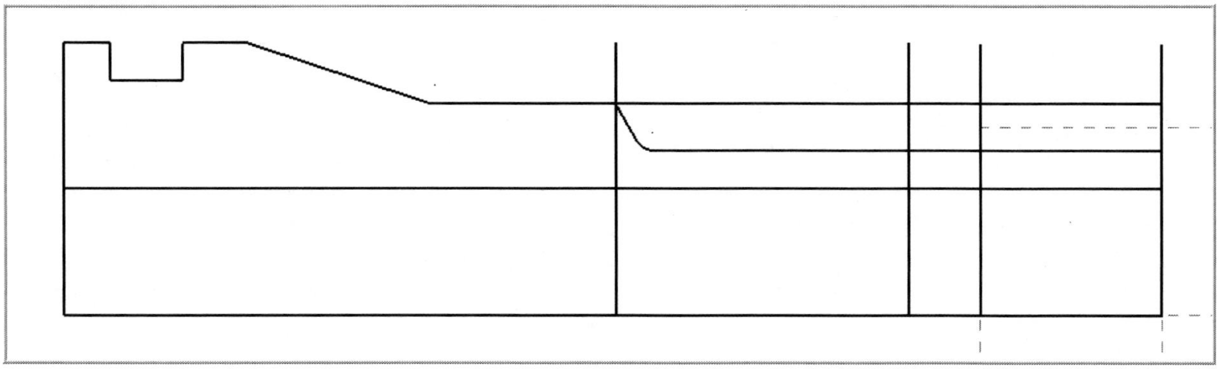

TASK 6:
CREATE THE CHAMFER ON RIGHT SIDE OF PART

➲ Create the chamfer 45 degrees x .0625.

1. Select **CREATE>Chamfer>Entities…**

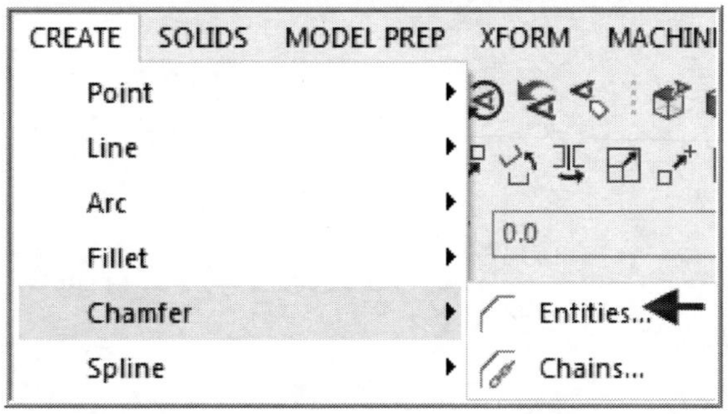

2. You are prompted to Select line or arc.
3. Click in the **Distance** window as shown below and type in **0.0625** and hit enter:

4. Ensure the **1 Distance** option is selected and **Trim is on** as shown above:
5. Click on line 1 and then line 2 as shown below on the right side of the part.

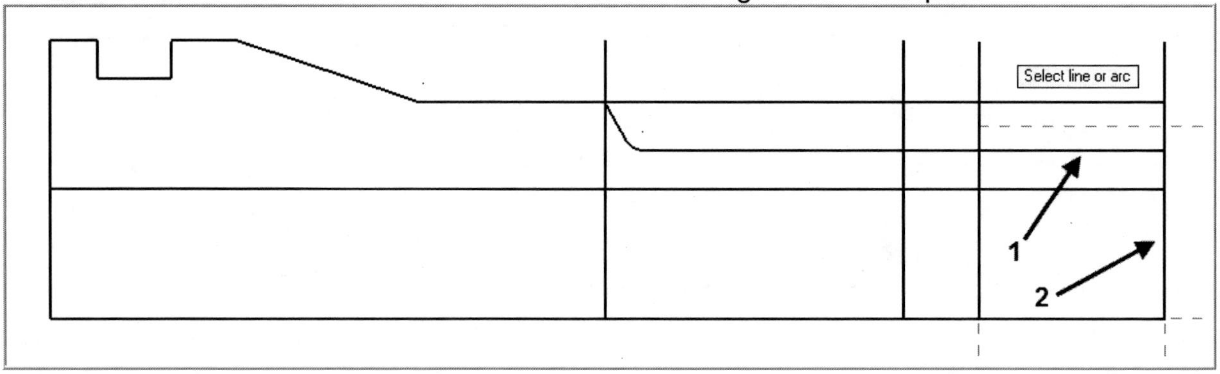

6. Click on the **OK** icon  to complete this feature.
7. The completed geometry should look like the image below:

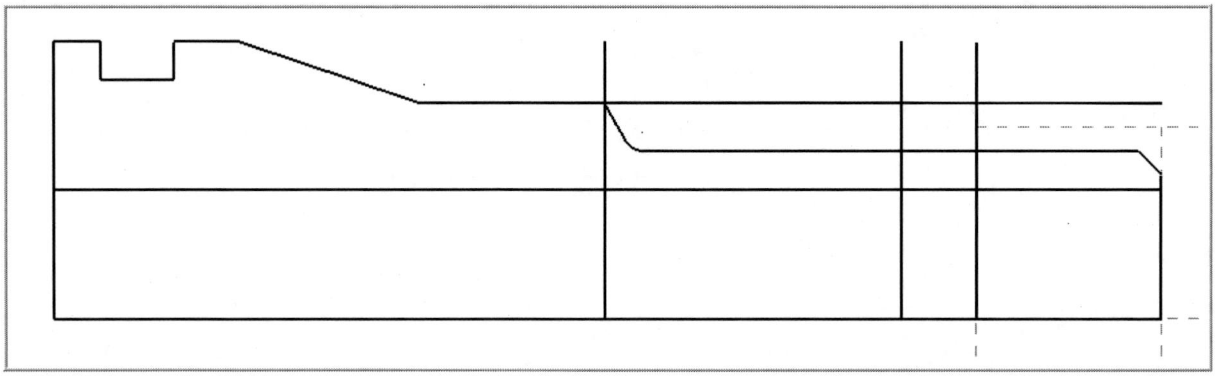

TASK 7:
CREATE THE 0.300" RADIUS

➲ In this task you will create the 0.300 arc. The center position and radius are known.

1. Select **CREATE>Arc>Arc Polar…**

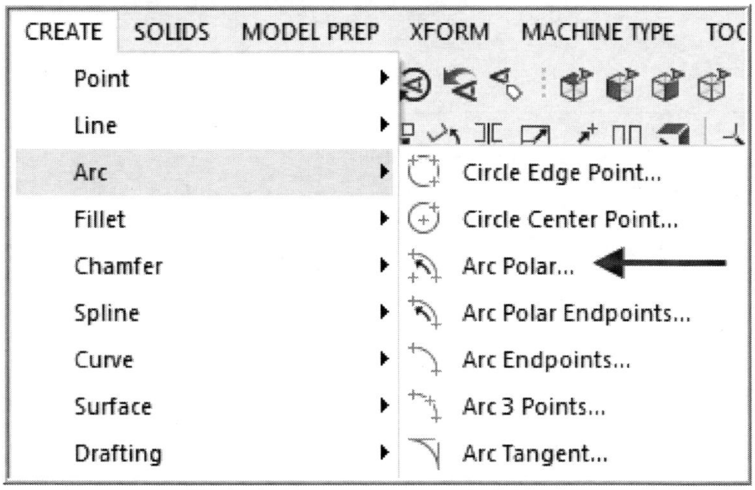

2. The **Arc Polar** ribbon bar appears and you are prompted to **Enter the center point** click on the **FastPoint** icon as shown below and enter the coordinates for the center of the arc **1.600 , -1.75** and then hit enter.

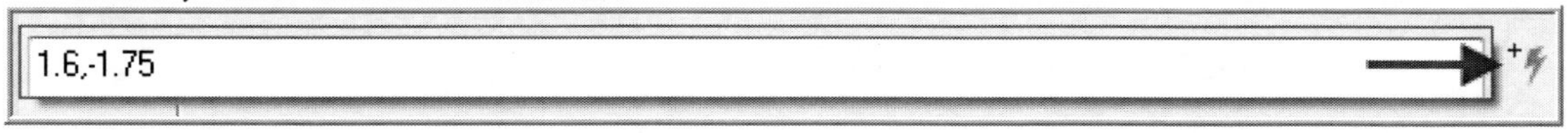

3. The prompt now changes to **Sketch the initial angle**. Click in the space for **radius** and enter **0.3** and then hit the **tab key twice** to move over to the start angle.
4. Input a **Start angle of 0** and hit the tab key.
5. For the **End angle** input **180** and then hit enter. Use the **Flip** button to place the arc in the desired position as shown below.

6. Click on the **OK** icon  to complete this feature.
7. The completed arc is shown below:

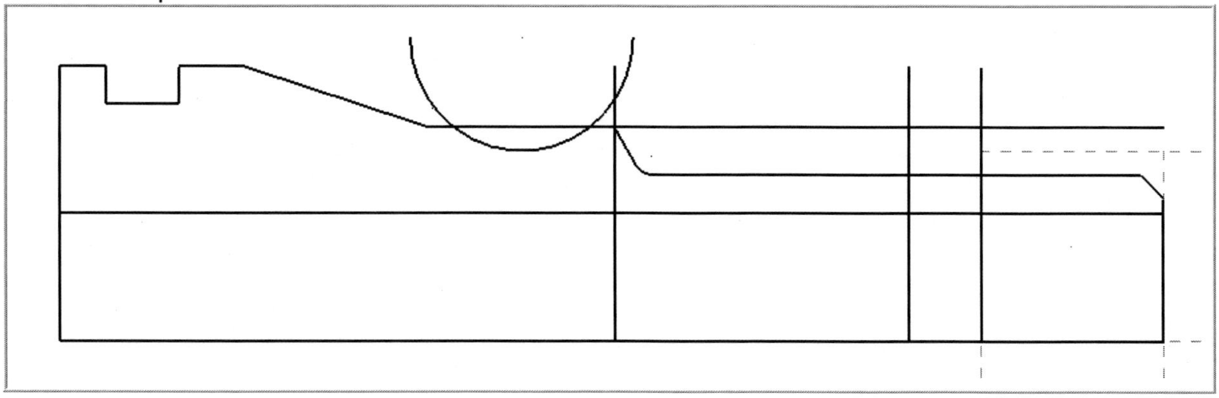

TASK 8:
TRIM THE GEOMETRY

➲ In this task you will use **Divide** to trim the entities.

1. **Delete** the line shown below: Select the line and hit the delete key on your keyboard.

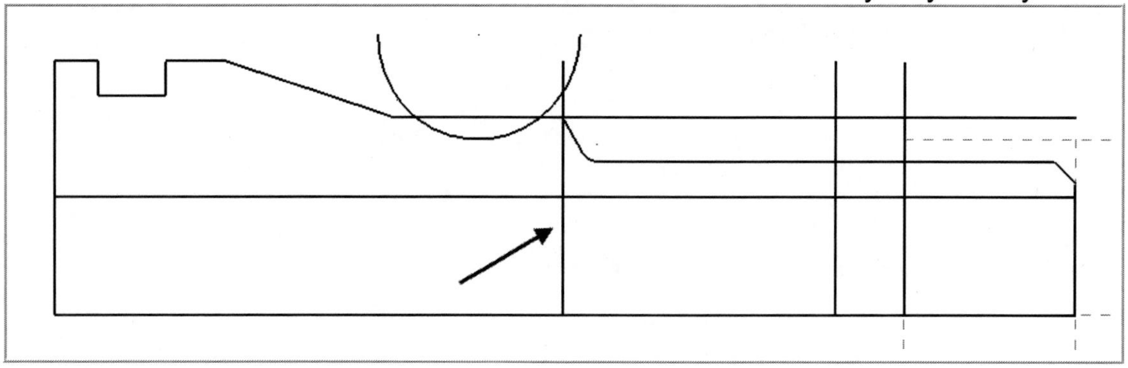

2. Select **EDIT>Trim/Break>Trim/Break/Extend**
3. The Trim / Extend / Break ribbon bar appears and you are prompted to **Select the entity to trim/extend**.
4. Now click on the **Divide** icon .
5. The prompt changes to **Select the curve to divide.** Move the cursor over the various entities and select in the order and position shown below:

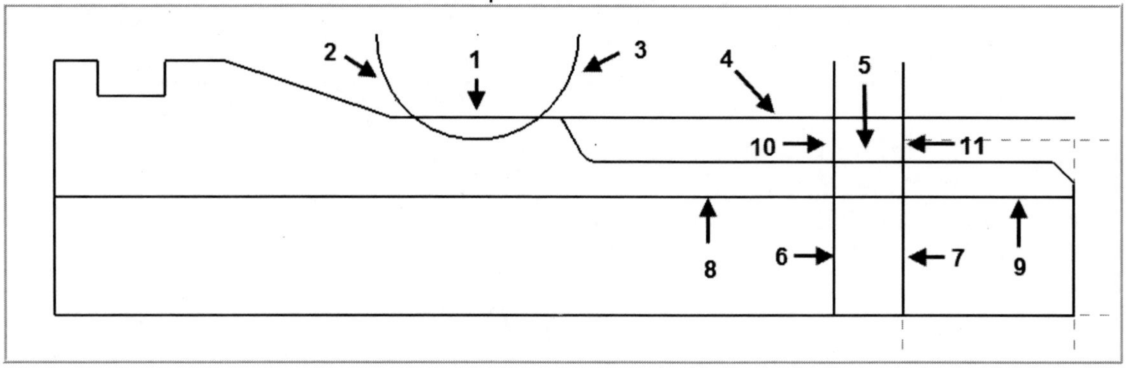

6. Click on the **OK** icon  to complete this feature.
7. **Delete** the three lines shown below: Select the three lines and then hit the delete key on your keyboard.

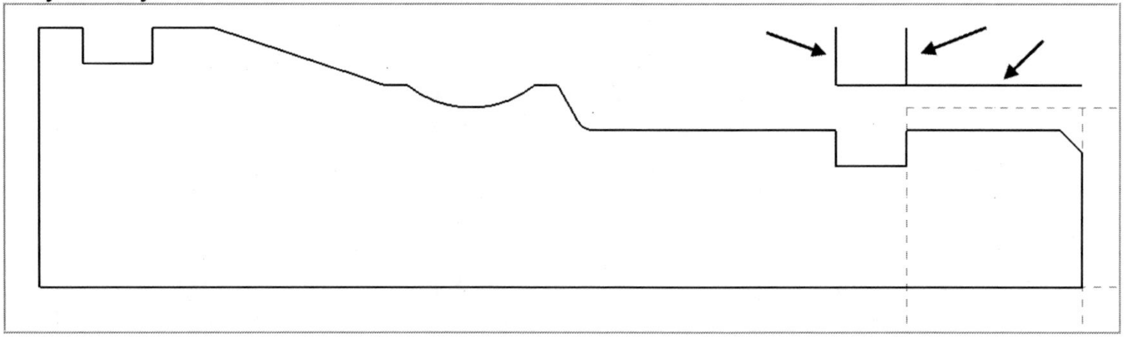

TASK 9:
CREATE THE GEOMETRY FOR THE BORE

➲ In this task you will create the geometry that make up the bore of this part

1. Select from the pull down menu: **CREATE>Line>Parallel….**
2. On the graphics screen you are prompted **"Select a line"** and the Line Parallel ribbon bar appears.
3. To satisfy the prompt **Select a line**, select the line shown below:

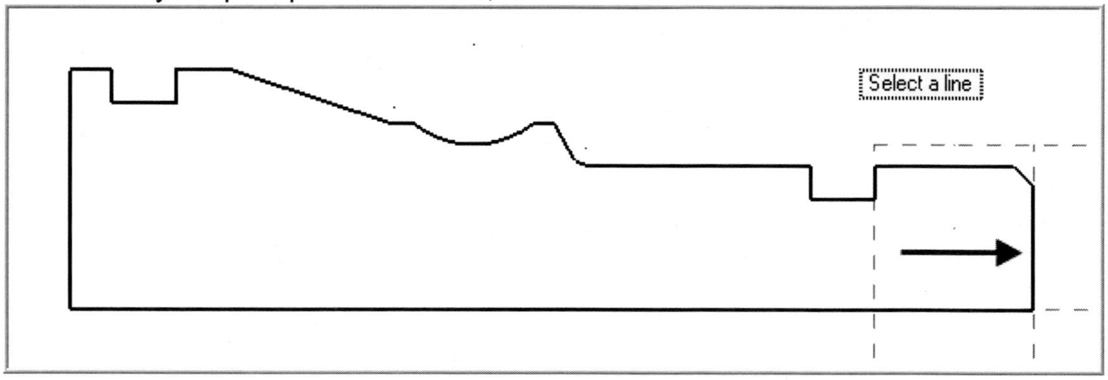

4. To satisfy the next prompt **Select the point to place a parallel line through** move the cursor to the left of the line and pick a point.
5. For the **Distance** input **0.125** then hit **enter**.
6. On the ribbon bar click on **Apply**  to fix the entity.
7. To satisfy the prompt **Select a line**, select the line shown below:

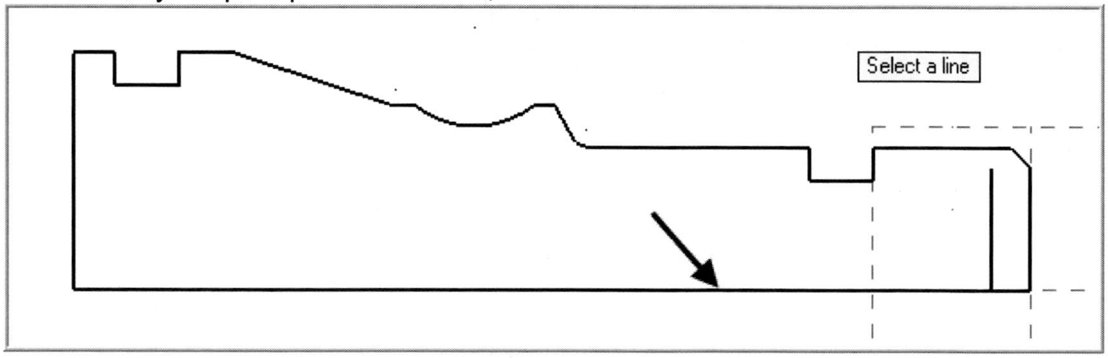

8. To satisfy the next prompt **Select the point to place a parallel line through** move the cursor above the line and pick a point.
9. For the **Distance** input **0.500/2** then hit **enter.**
10. On the ribbon bar click on **Apply**  to fix the entity,
11. To satisfy the prompt **Select a line**, select the line shown below:

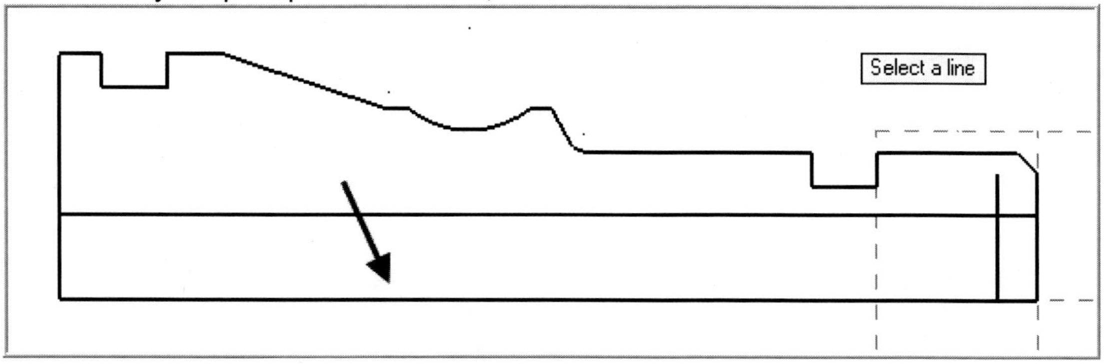

12. To satisfy the next prompt **Select the point to place a parallel line through** move the cursor above the line and pick a point.
13. For the **Distance** input **0.250/2** then hit **enter.**
14. Click on the **OK** icon ☑ to complete this feature. The completed geometry is shown below:

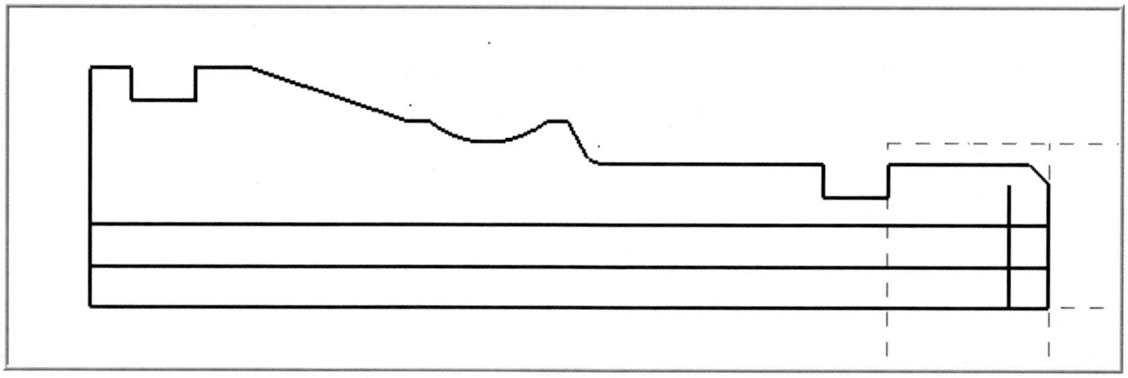

TASK 10:
TRIM THE GEOMETRY FOR THE BORE

1. Select **EDIT>Trim/Break>Trim/Break/Extend**
2. The Trim / Extend / Break ribbon bar appears and you are prompted to **Select the entity to trim/extend.**
3. Now click on the **Divide** icon [+·+].
4. The prompt changes to **Select the curve to divide.** Move the cursor over the various entities and select in the order and position shown below:

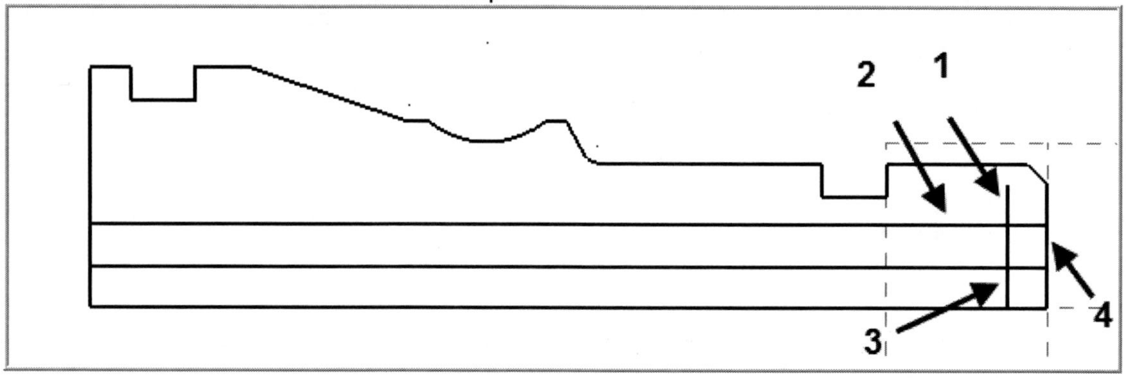

5. Click on the **OK** icon ☑ to complete this feature.
6. **Delete** the three lines shown below: Select the three lines and then hit the delete key on your keyboard.

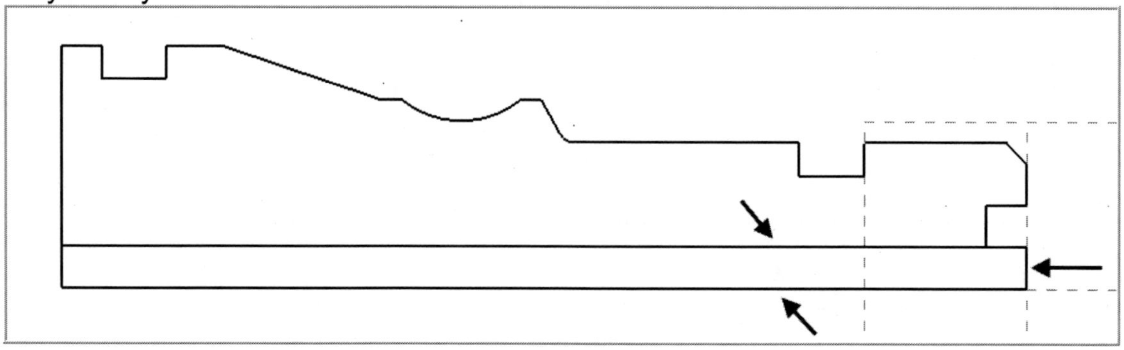

7. The completed geometry is shown below:

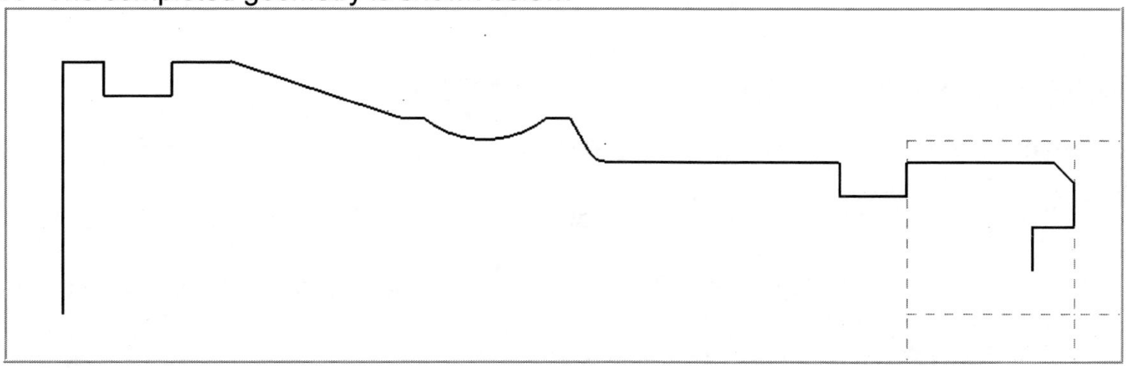

TASK 11:
SAVE THE DRAWING

1. Select **File.**
2. Select **Save as.**
3. In the **"File name"** box, type **"Lathe-Lesson-7".**
4. Save to an appropriate location.
5. Select the Save button to save the file and complete this function.

Toolpath Creation

TASK 12:
DEFINING THE STOCK AND CHUCK PARAMETERS

1. Fit the image to the screen by clicking on the **Fit** icon.
2. Ensure your screen looks like the image below:
   a. The **Toolpaths Manager** is open, if it is not Select **Alt and O** on your keyboard to open it.
   b. The properties icon displays Lathe Default. If it is not refer to **Setting the Environment** chapter at the beginning of the book.
   c. The **Lathe Lesson-7** Geometry is displayed.

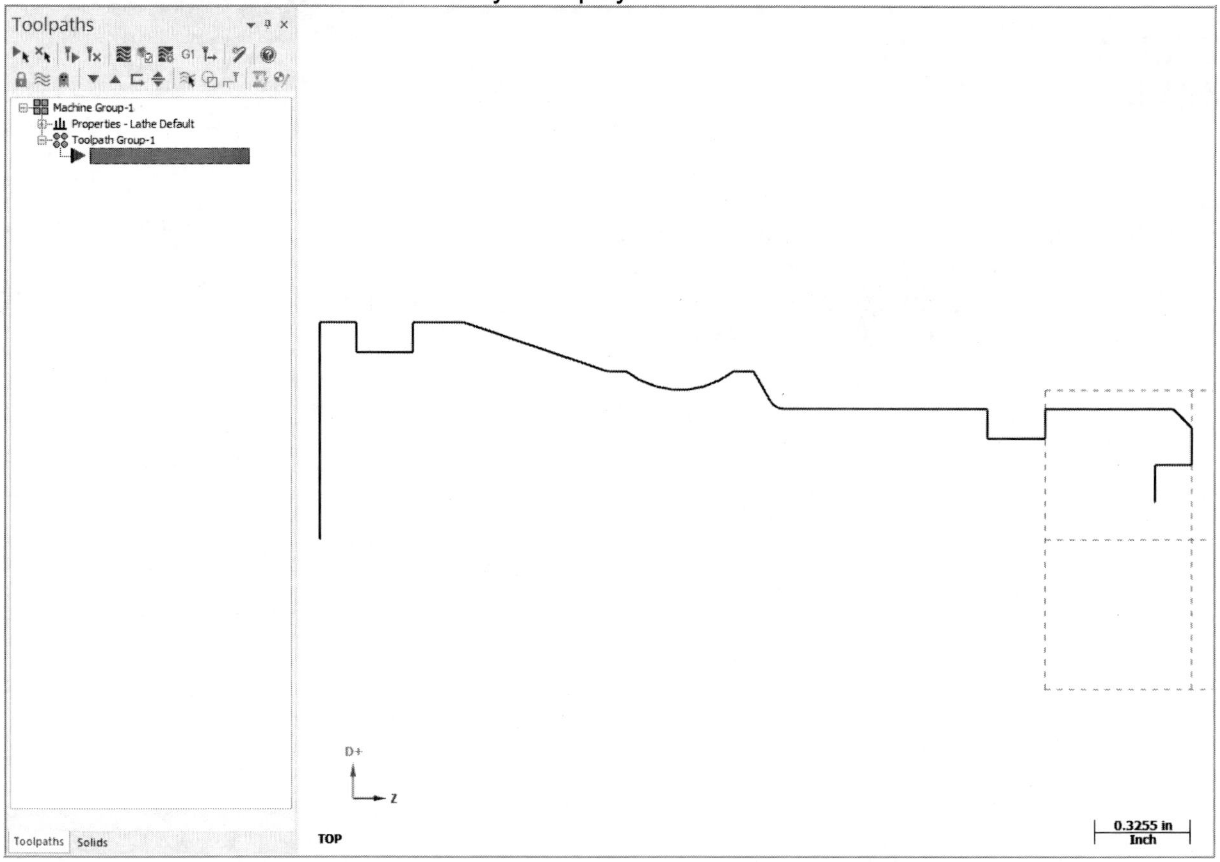

3. Select the plus in front of **Properties** to expand the Machine Group Properties.

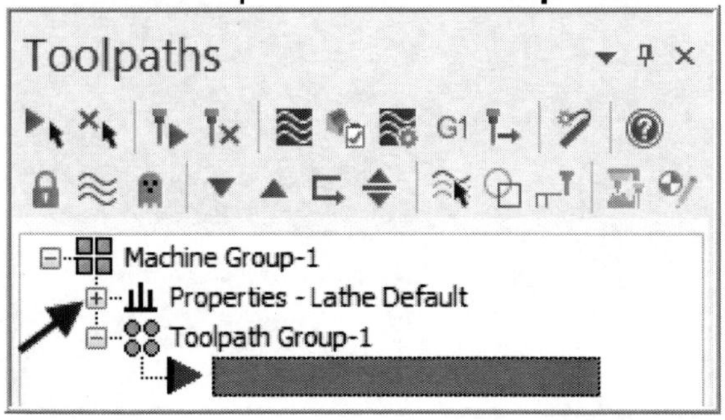

4. Select **Stock setup** in the Toolpaths Manager window.

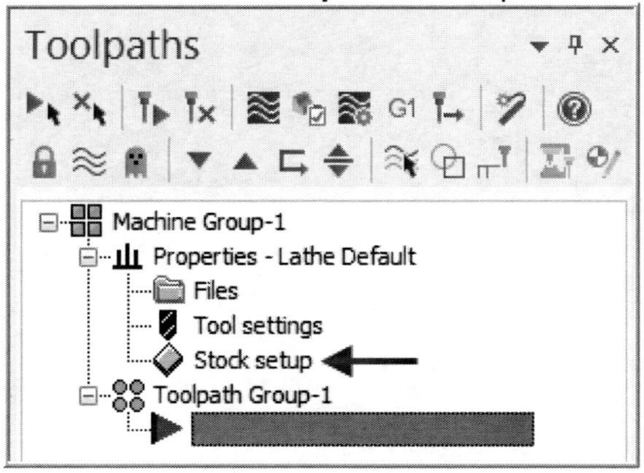

5. Select the **Stock Properties** button in the **Stock Setup** page as shown in the screenshot below:

Note: To learn more about Stock Setup refer to the Tips and Techniques section on the Mastercam Training Guide – Lathe DVD that accompanies this book.

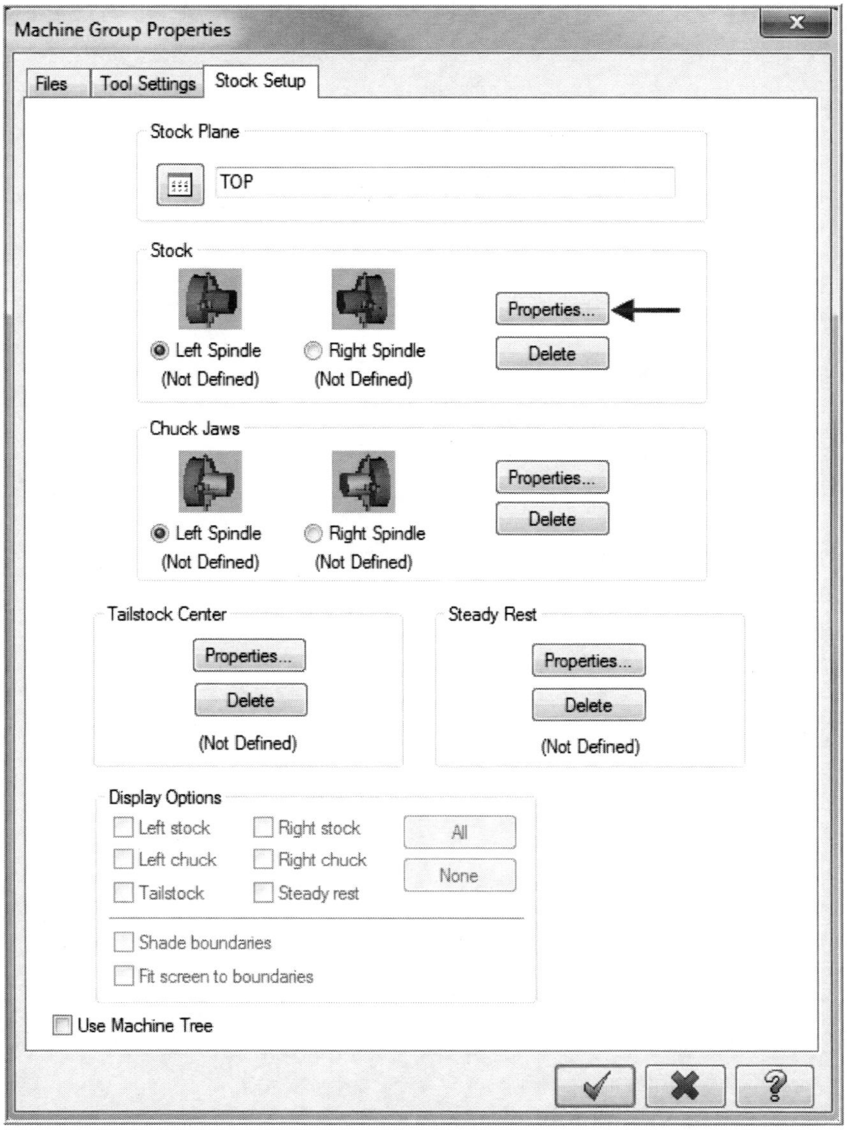

6. In the **Machine Component Manager-Stock** window click on the **Geometry** button and select **Cylinder** as shown below:

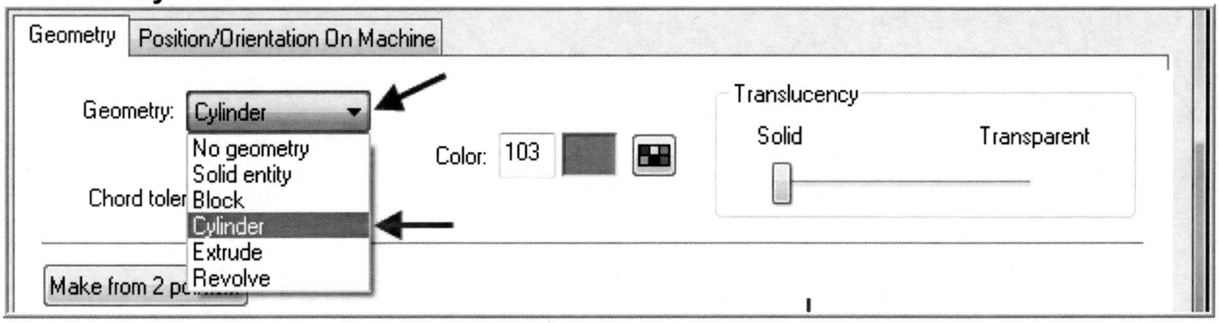

7. In the **Stock setup** set the values as shown below. **Axis is set to -Z**.

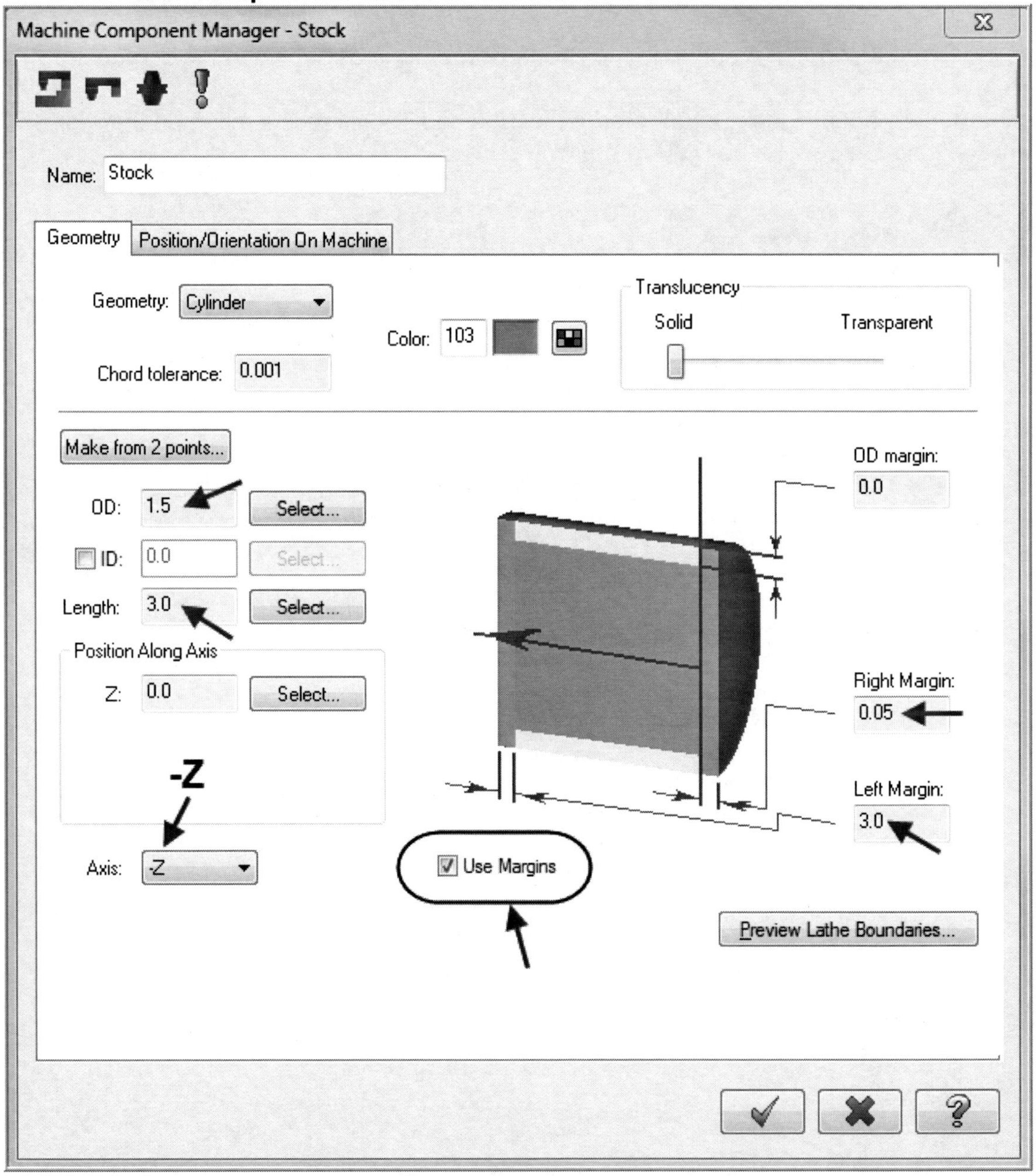

8. Click on the OK icon  to complete this feature.

9. Still on the Stock Setup page activate **Fit screen to boundaries**.

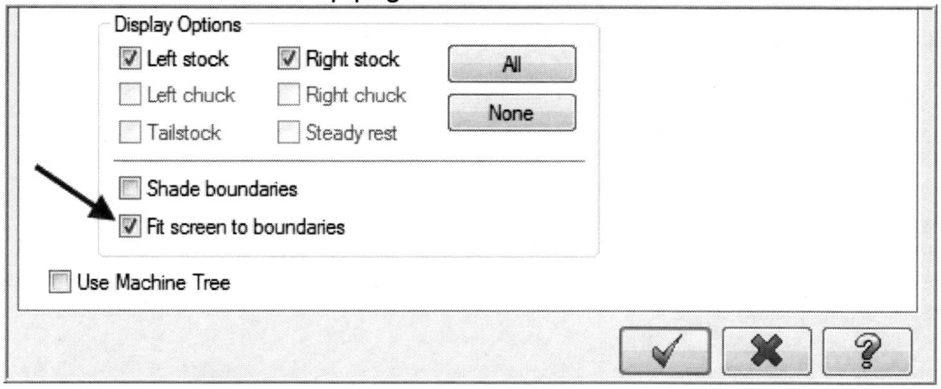

10. Select the **Chuck Properties** button in the **Stock Setup** page as shown in the screenshot below:

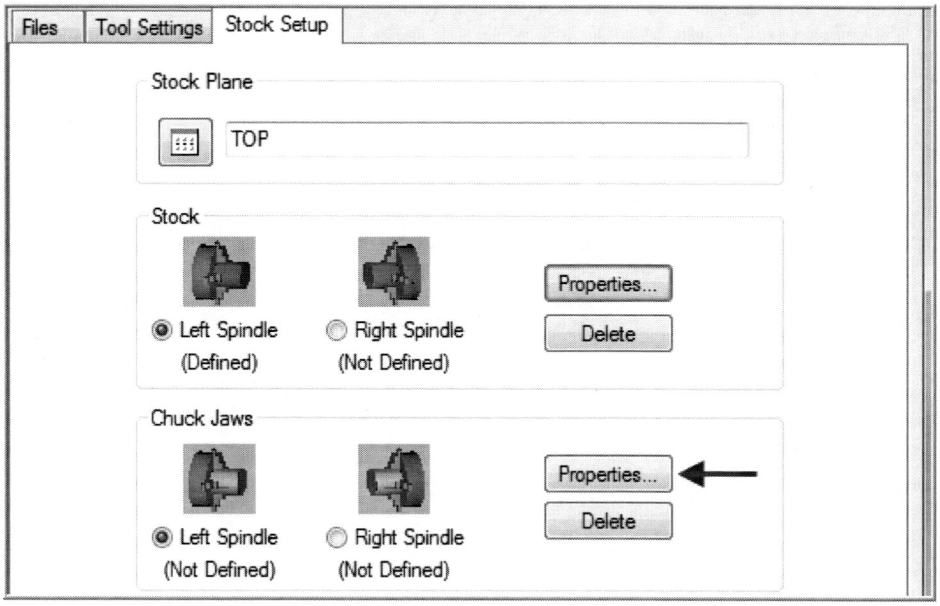

11. In the **Chuck Jaws** setup set the values as shown below:

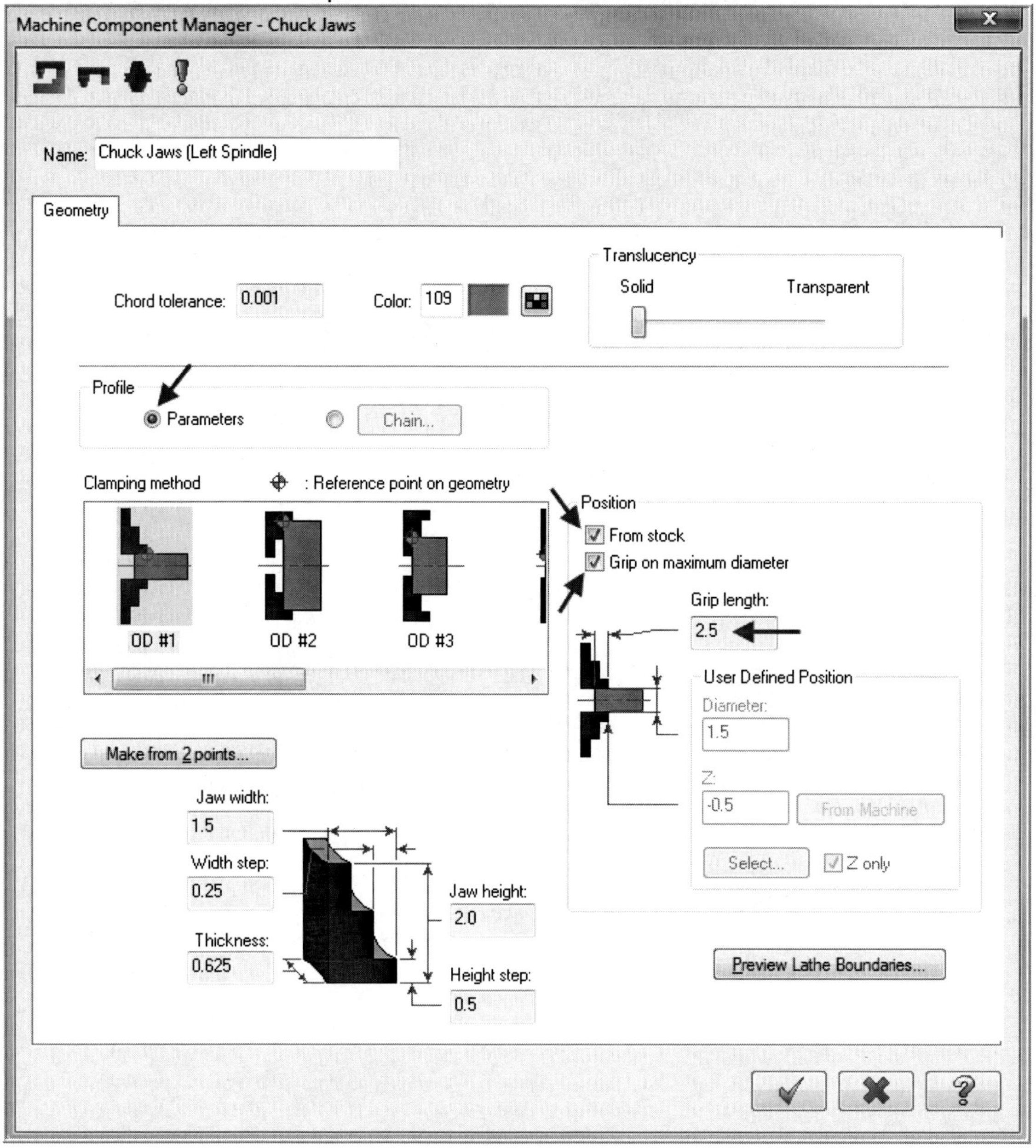

12. Click on the OK icon  to complete this feature.

13. Click on the **Tool Settings** page and make changes as shown below:

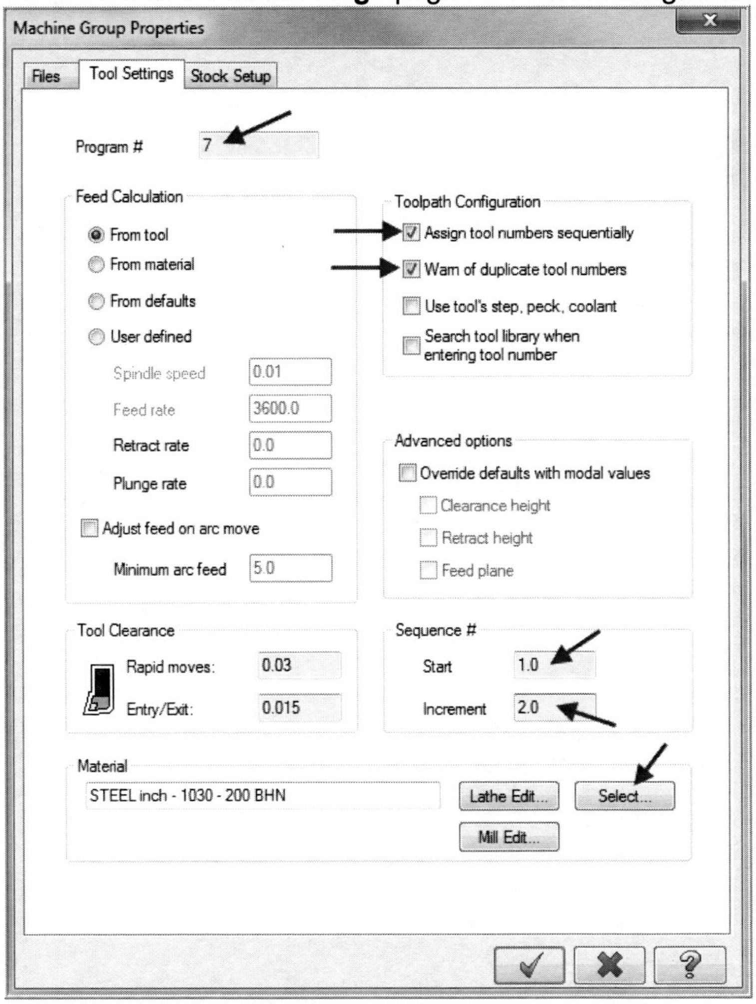

14. To change the **Material** type to Aluminum 6061 pick the **Select** button at the bottom of the Tool Settings page.
15. At the **Material List** dialog box open the Source drop down list and select **Lathe – library.**

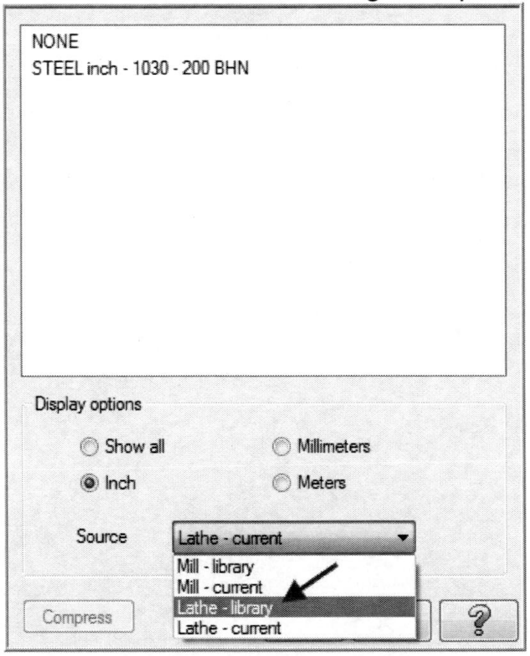

16. From the **Default Materials** list select **ALUMINUM inch - 6061** and then select ✓.

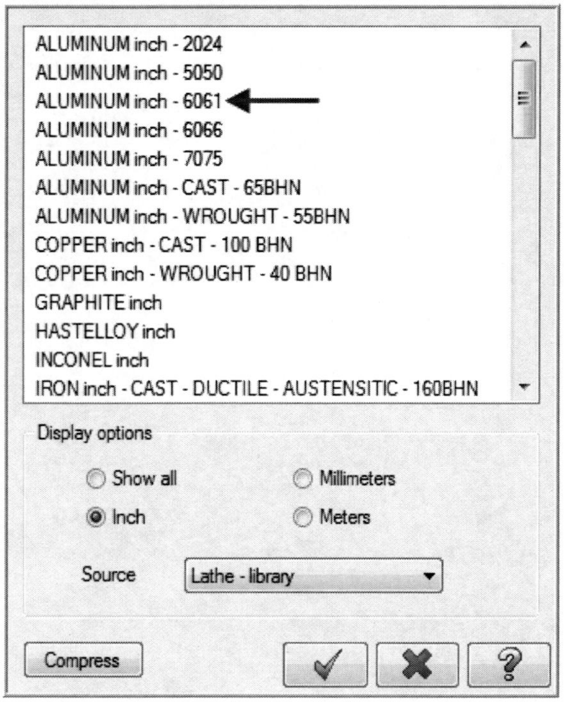

17. Select the **OK** button ✓ again to complete this Stock Setup function.

18. Select the **Screen Fit** icon to fit the part to the screen.
Notice the stock setup outline as indicated by broken lines as shown below:

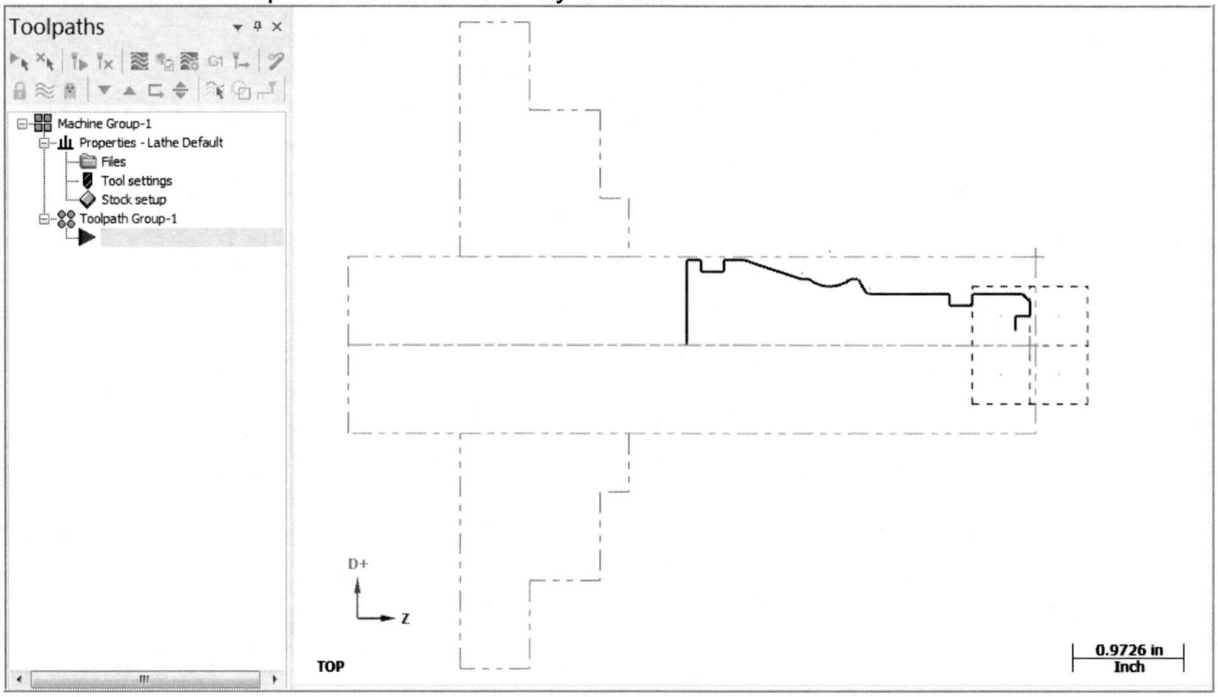

TASK 13:
FACE THE FRONT OF THE PART:

➲ In this task you will use a facing tool to face the front of the part in one cut.

1. Select the **Screen Fit** icon to fit the part to the screen.
2. From the menu bar select **TOOLPATHS>Face…**

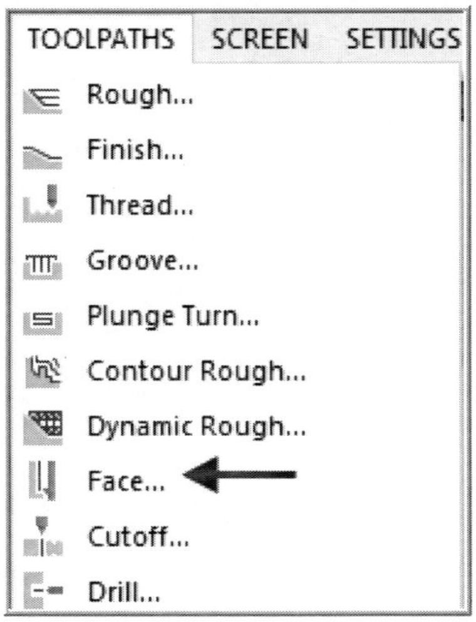

3. When prompted to **"Enter new NC name"** Ensure **LATHE-LESSON-7** is entered and then select the **OK** button.

➲ After selecting the **OK** button you are confronted with **Toolpath parameters** page. The first task here will be to select **Tool #1 a Roughing – 80 deg.**

4. Click on **Tool 0101 Roughing – 80 degree** and ensure the settings are the same as in the Toolpath parameters page as shown below:

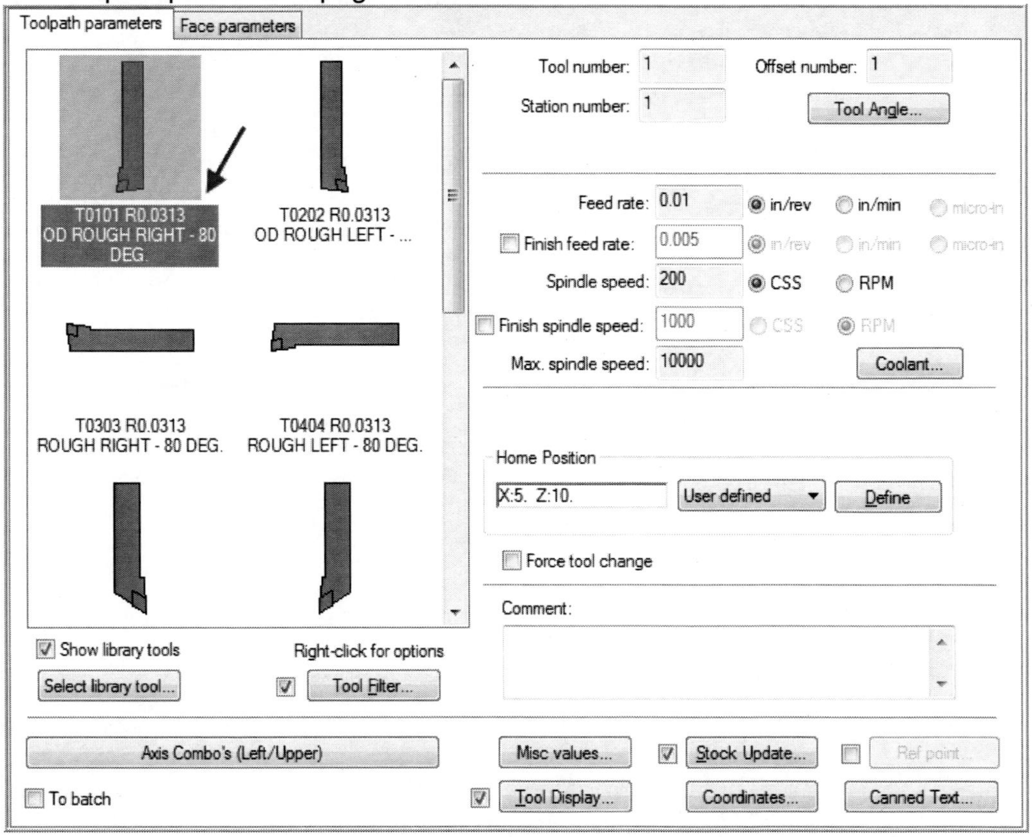

5. Select the **Face parameters** page and make changes as shown below:

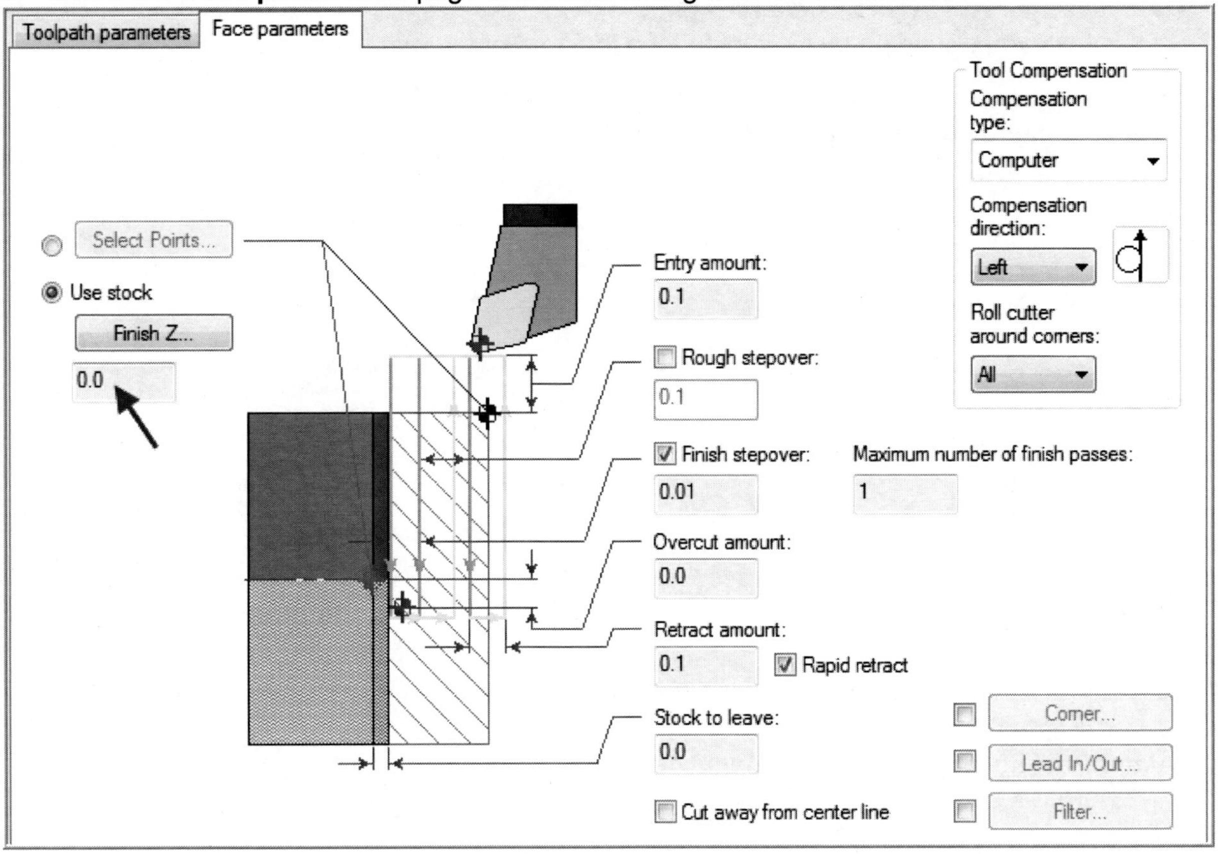

6. Select the **OK** button [✓] to complete this **Lathe Face** operation.

TASK 14:
ROUGH THE OUTSIDE DIAMETERS

➲ In this task you will use Lathe Quick Rough Toolpath to rough the outside diameters.

➲ You will use the same tool as used for the previous facing operation Tool #1 an OD Rough-Right – 80 deg.

1. From the menu bar select **TOOLPATHS> Quick> Rough…**

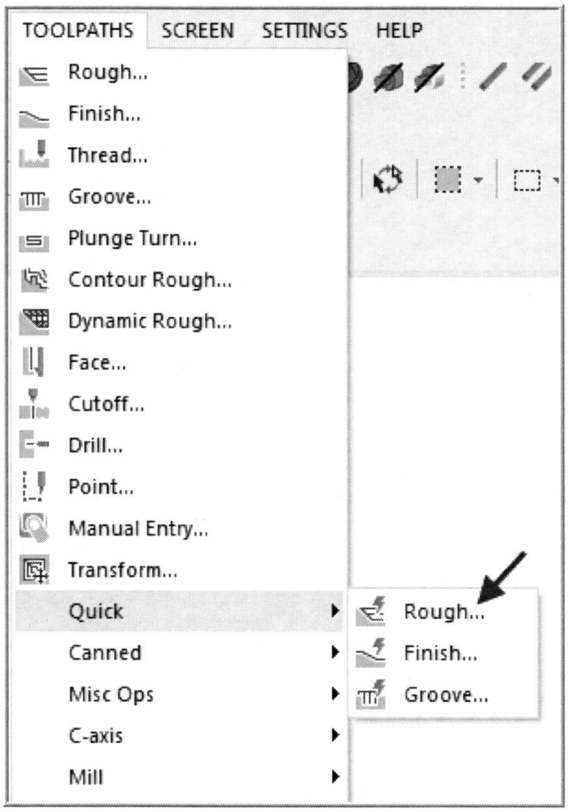

2. In the Chaining window Chaining mode is set to Partial by default.

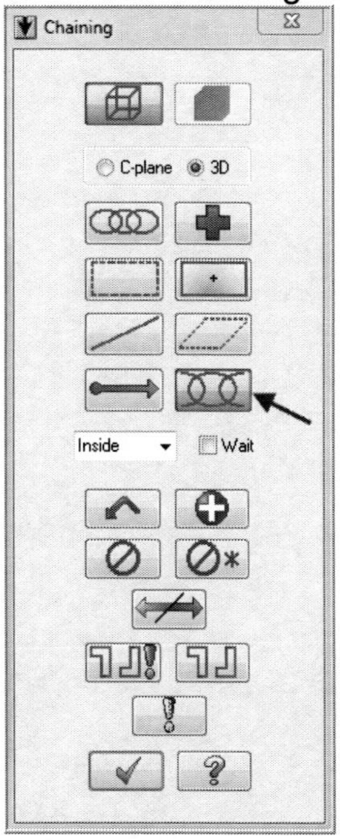

3. Select the chamfer, Line 1 as the start of the Partial chain.

After you have selected the chamfer **ensure** that the arrows are pointing up and to the left of the part. If it is not select the reverse button in the Chaining dialog box.

4. Then select Line 2 as the end entity in this chain.

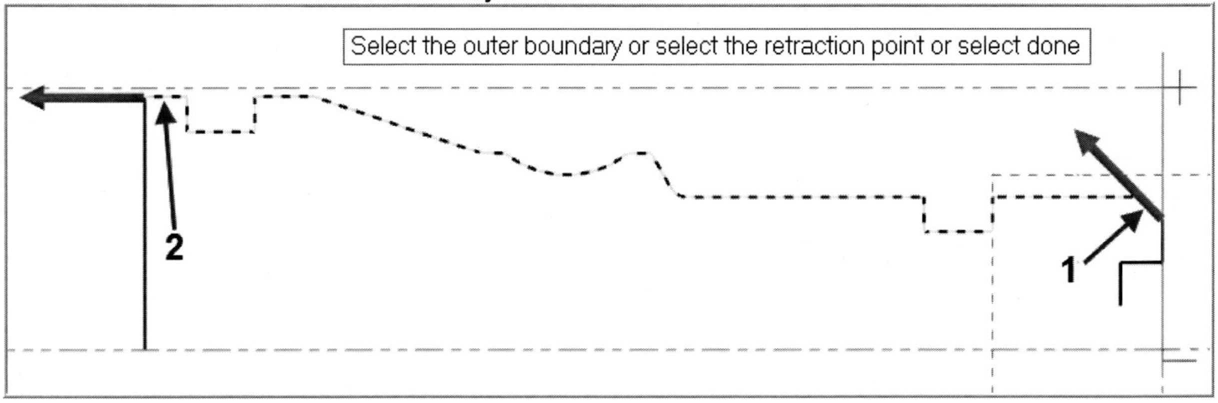

5. Select the OK button  to exit the Chaining dialog window.
6. In the Quick Toolpath parameters page select the Tool #1 Roughing – 80 deg and make any necessary changes as shown below:

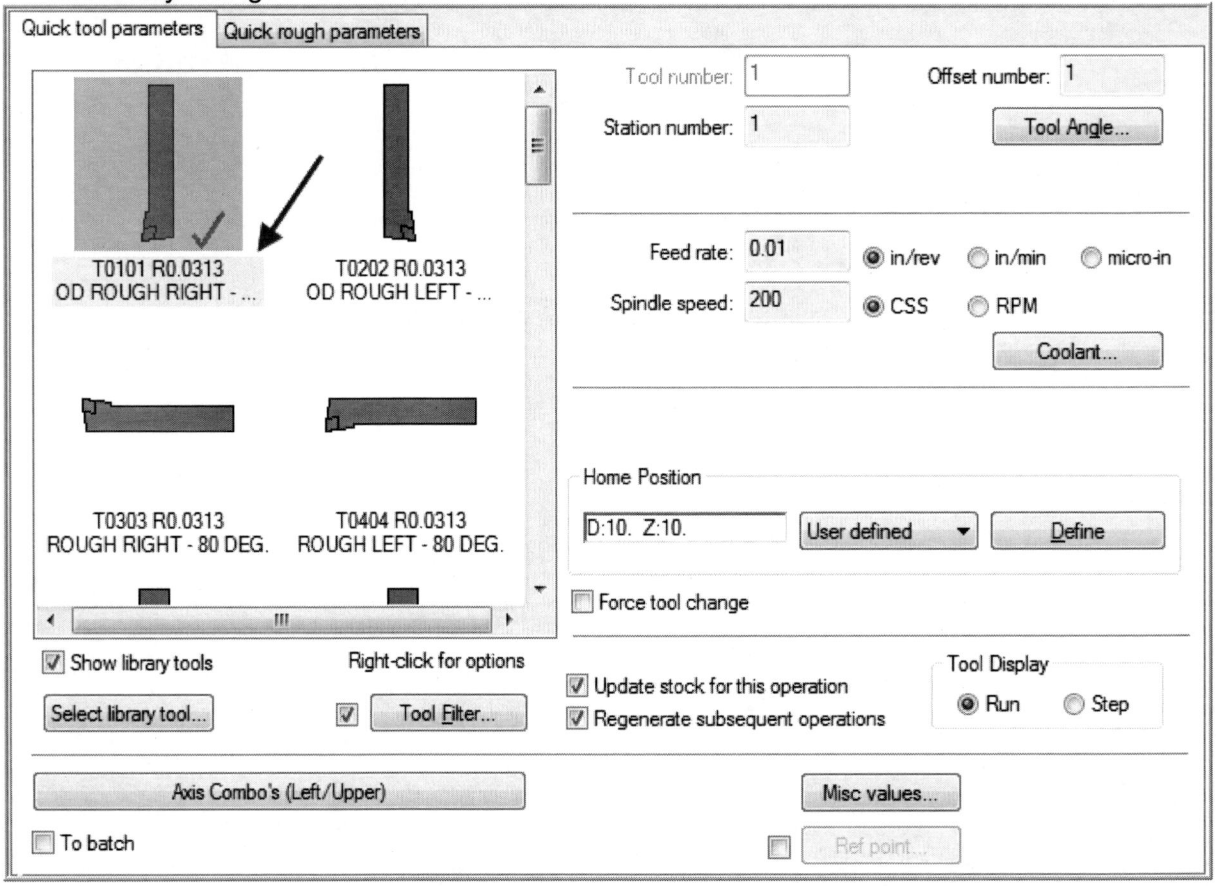

7. Select the **Quick Rough** parameters page and make any necessary changes as shown below:

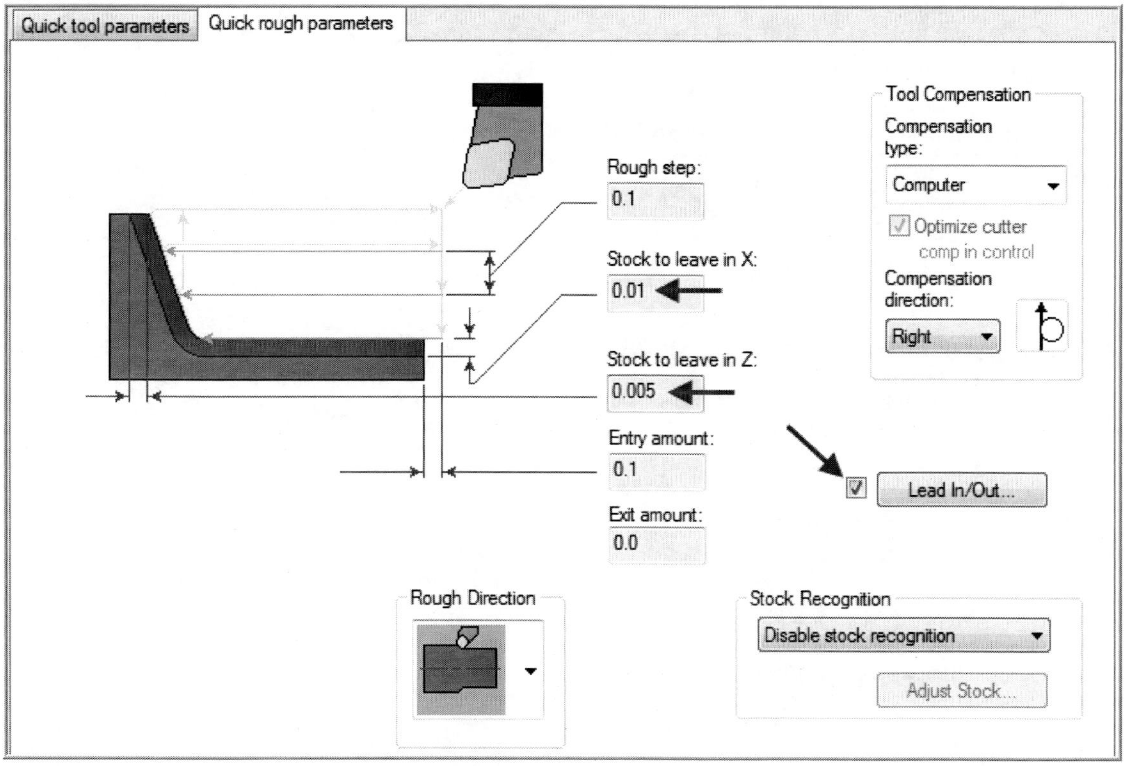

8. Select the **Lead In/Out** button, then select the **Lead out** page and extend the contour by .2 as shown below:

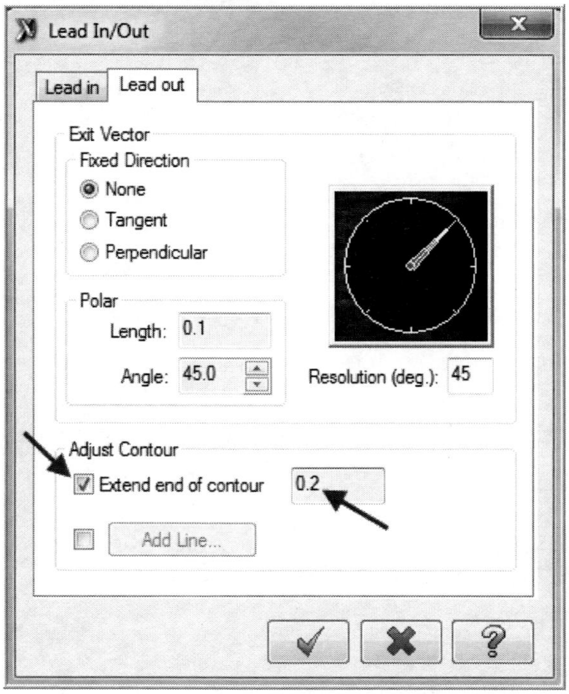

9. Select the **OK** button [✓] to exit this function.
10. Select the **OK** button [✓] to exit Quick Rough Parameters.

TASK 15:
FINISH THE OUTSIDE DIAMETERS

➲ In this task you will finish the outside diameters using Lathe Quick Finish Toolpath. The tool will be Tool #2 Finish – 35 deg.

1. From the menu bar select **TOOLPATHS>Quick>Finish…**

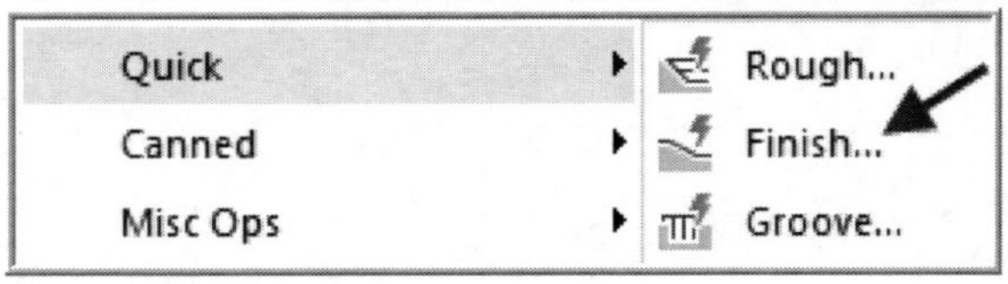

2. In the Quick tool parameters page **scroll down and locate the tool: OD Finish Right – 35 deg**. **<u>Then double click on this tool.</u>**

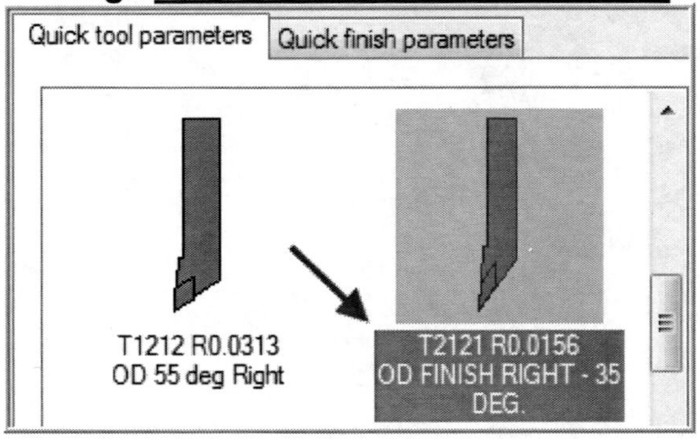

3. Click on the **Parameters** page and at the bottom of this page set the compensation for this tool as shown below:

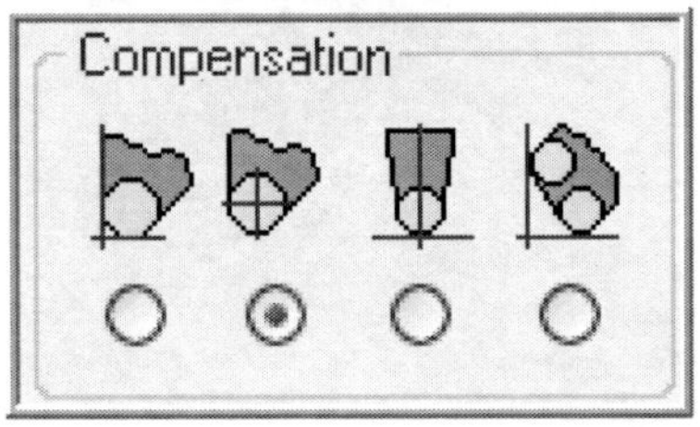

4. Click on the **OK** icon .

5. Back in the **Toolpath parameters** page make any necessary changes as shown below:

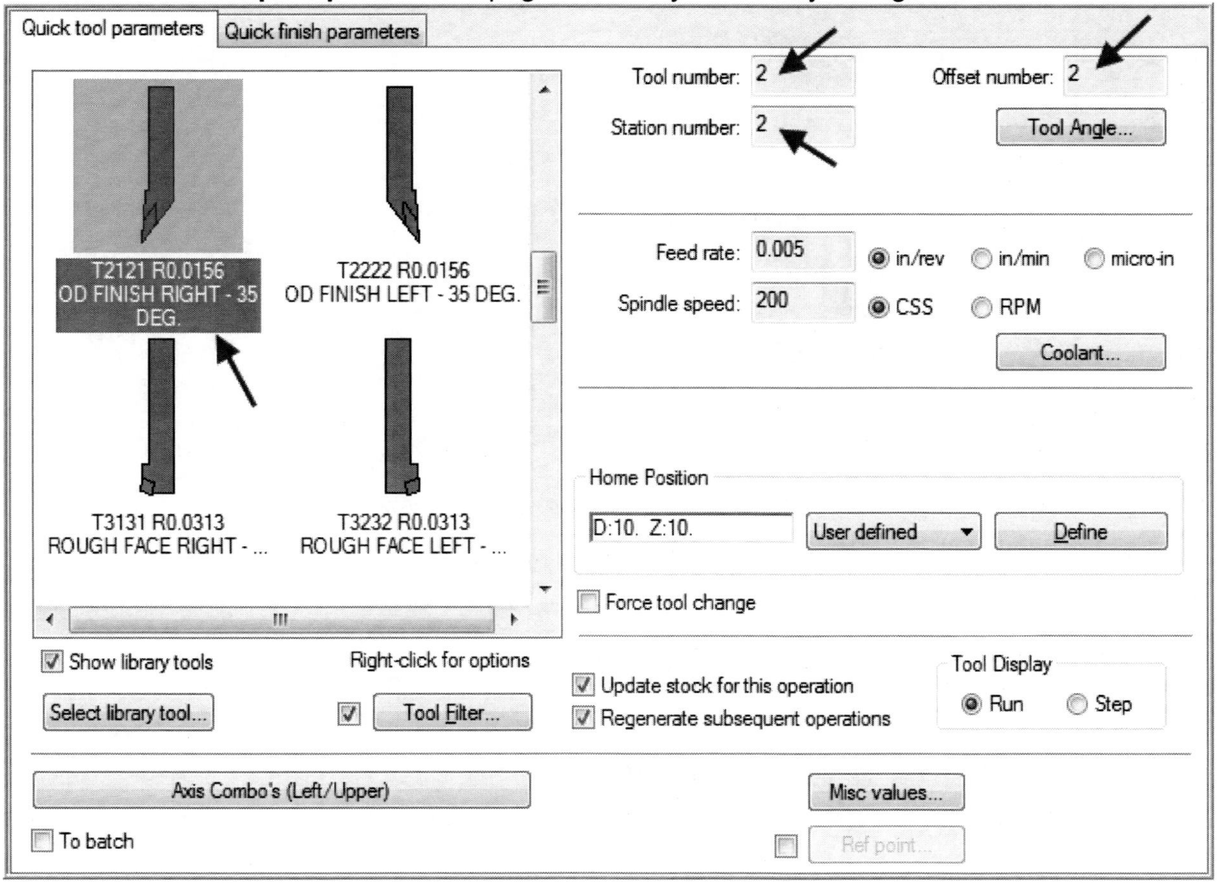

6. Select the **Quick Finish** parameters page and make any necessary changes as shown below:

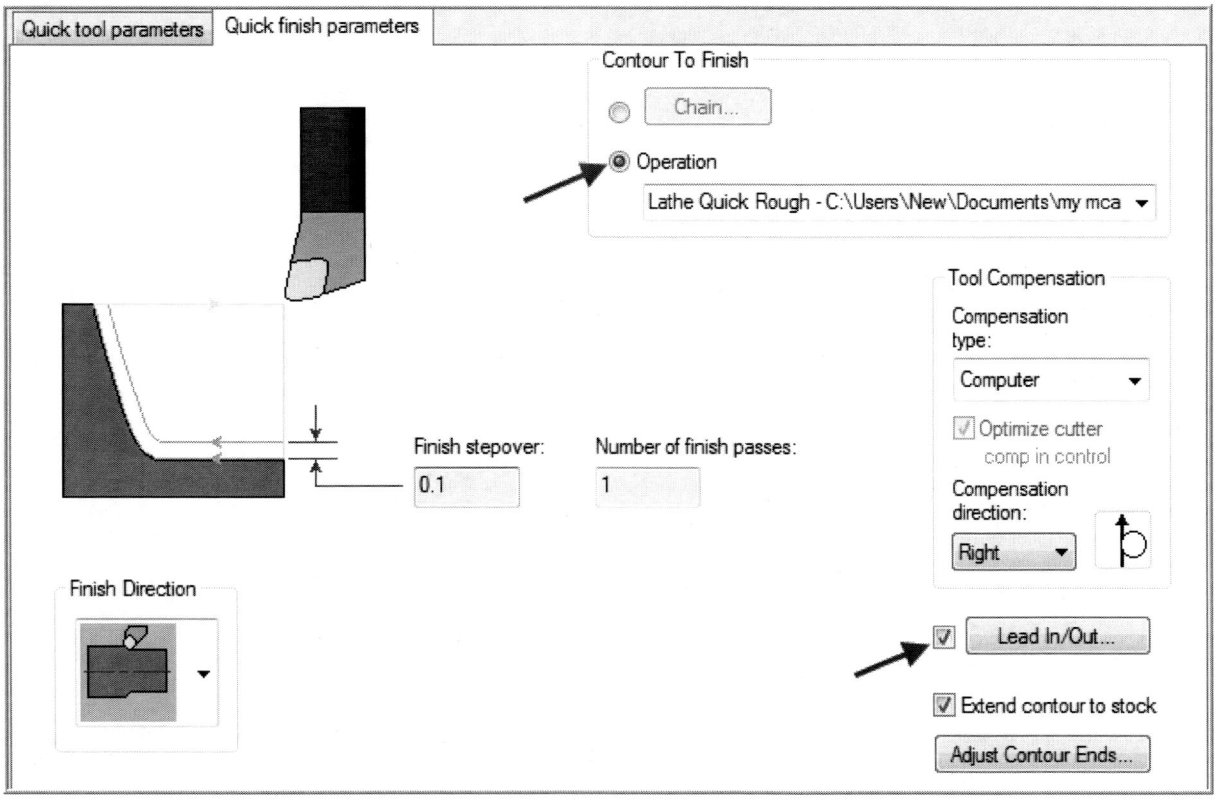

7. Select the **Lead In/Out** button select the **Lead out** page and extend the contour by .2 as shown below:

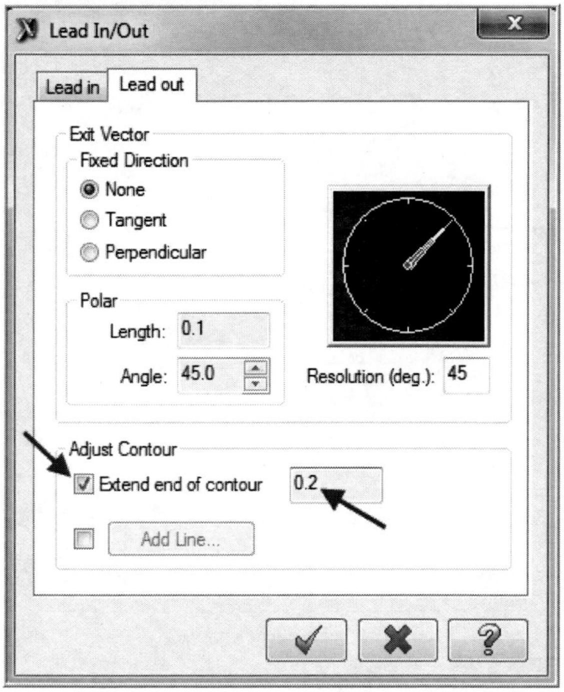

8. Select the **OK** button  to exit this function.
9. Select the **OK** button  to exit **Quick finish parameters**.

TASK 16:
FINISH THE 0.3 RADIUS

➲ In this task you will finish the 0.3 radius using the same tool you used for finishing a **Tool #2 Finish – 35 deg**.

1. From the menu bar select **TOOLPATHS>Finish…**

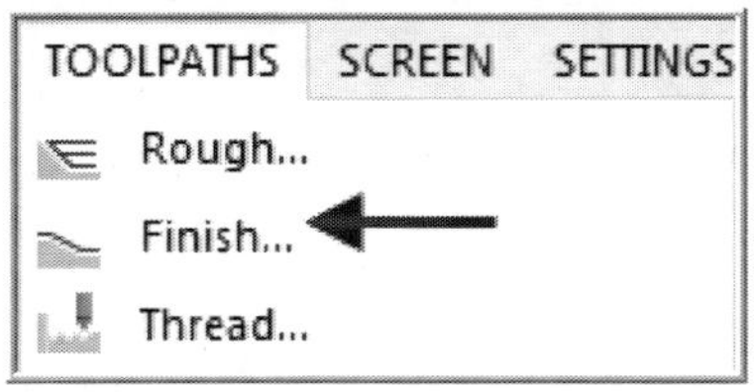

2. In the **Chaining** window click on the icon for **Single** 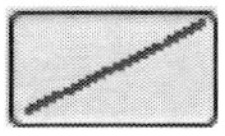
3. Select the Arc in the position shown below

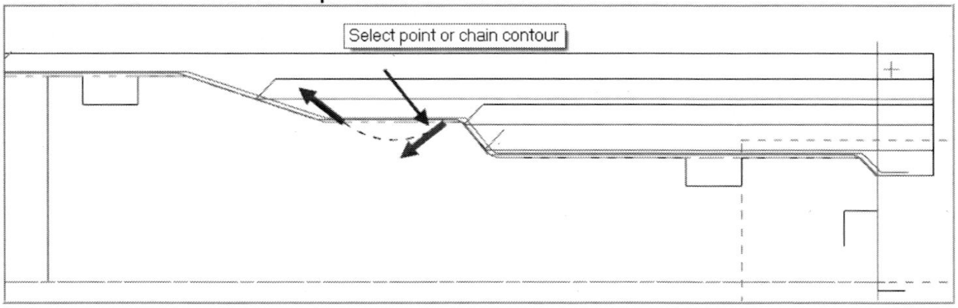

4. Select the **OK** button  to exit the Chaining dialog window.
5. In the **Toolpath parameters** page select **Tool #2 Finish – 35 deg** and make any necessary changes as shown below:

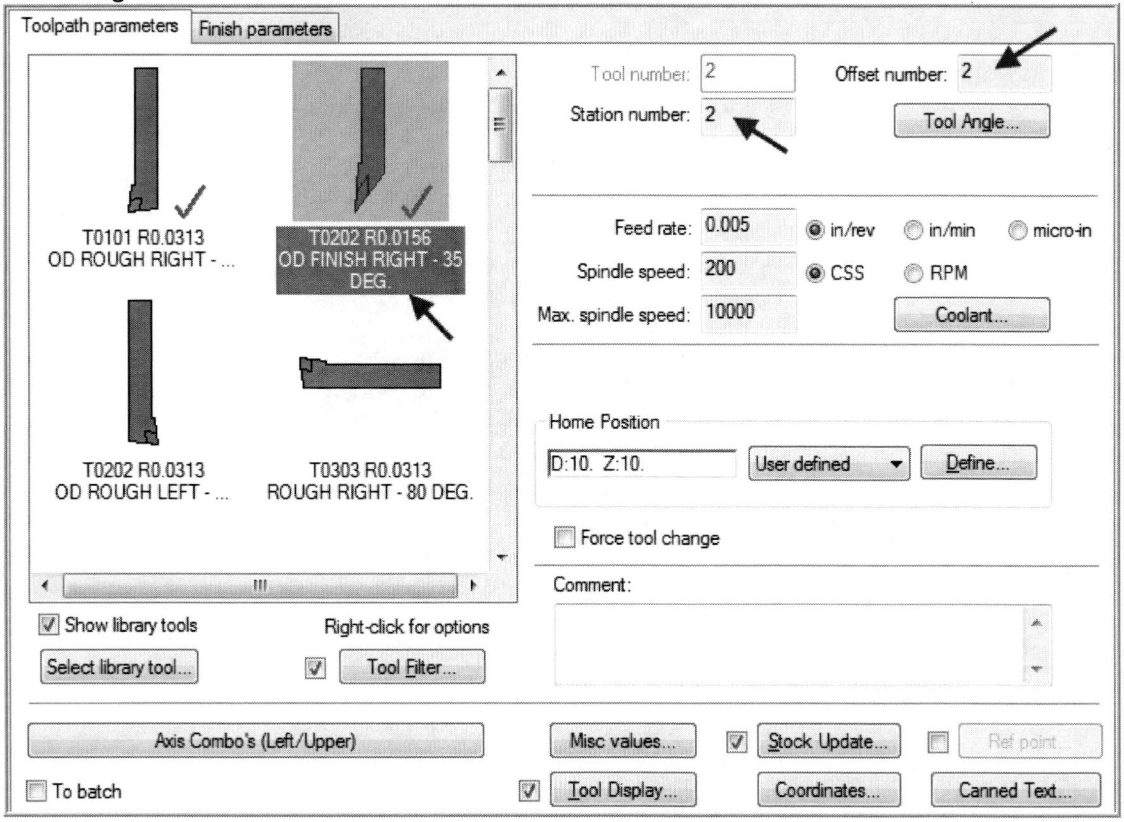

6. Click on the **Finish parameters** tab and make any necessary changes as shown below:

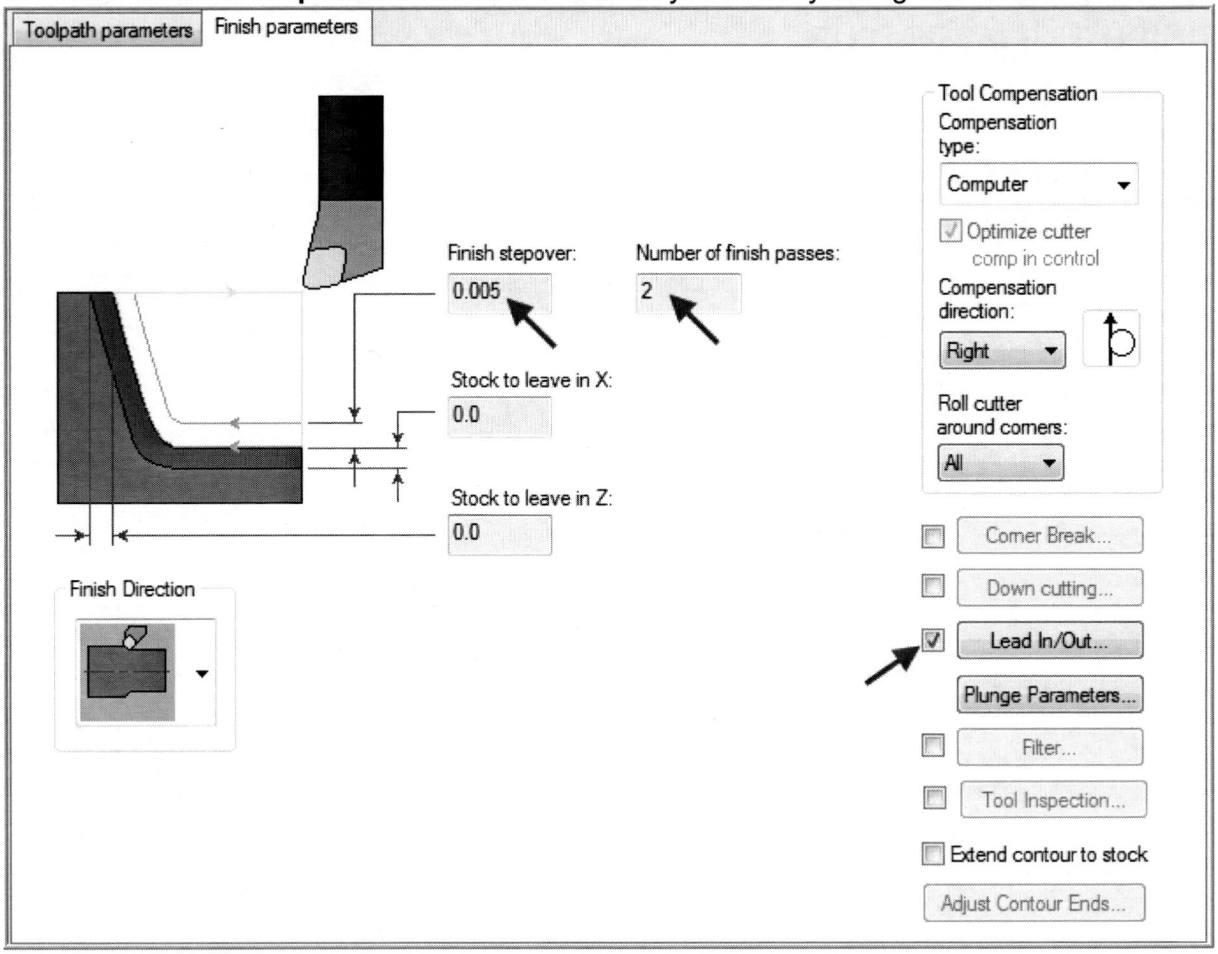

7. Click on the **Lead in/Out** button as shown above:
8. Make the necessary changes as shown below on the **Lead In** page. In order to adjust the dial click on the desired location of the arrow:

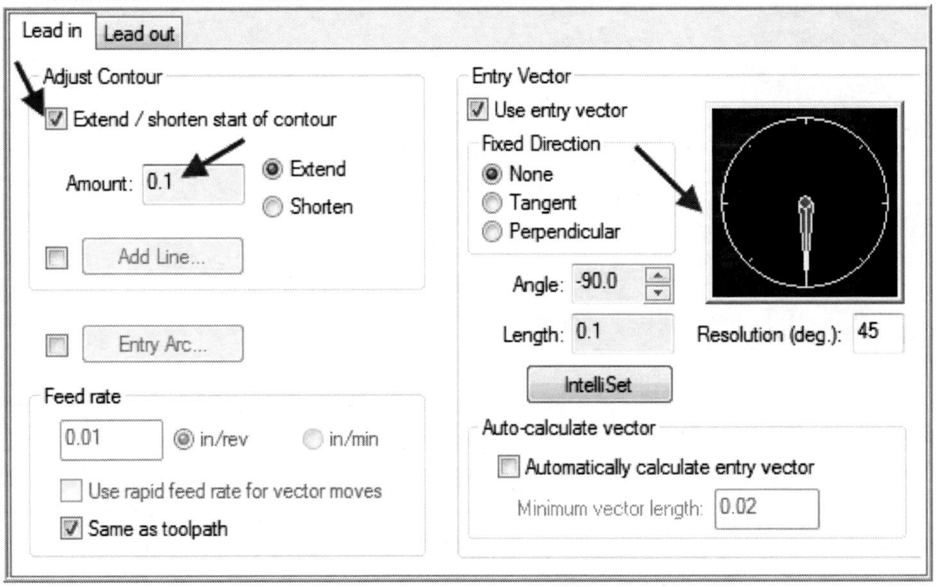

9. Click on the **Lead out** tab and make the necessary changes as shown below:

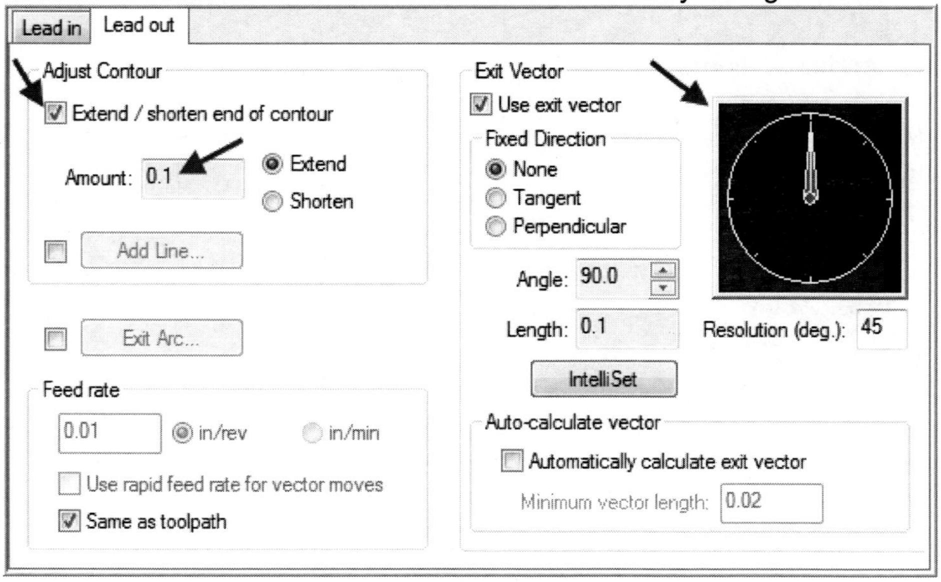

10. Click on **OK** to exit the Lead In/out window.

11. Click on the **Plunge Parameters** button Plunge Parameters... .

12. Make the necessary changes as shown below:

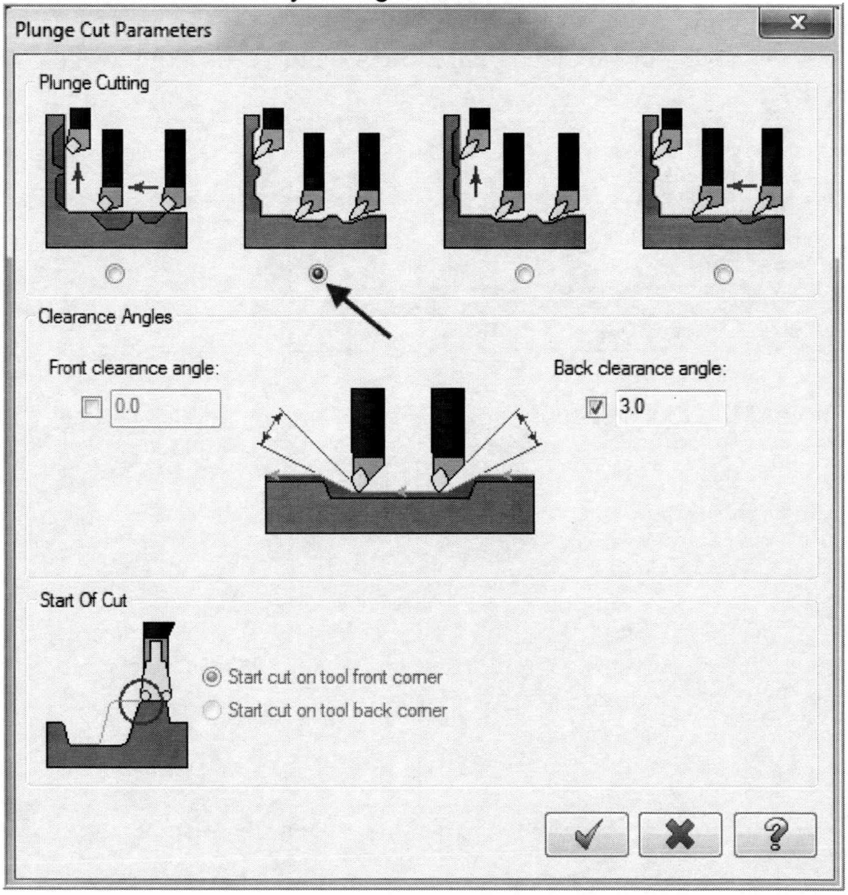

13. Click on Ok to exit the **Plunge Cut** Parameters window.

14. Click on Ok to exit the **Lathe Finish** parameters window.

TASK 17:
CENTER DRILL HOLE

➲ In this task you will center drill .2" depth using a **Centre Drill - .25 diameter.**

1. From the menu bar select **TOOLPATHS>Drill…**

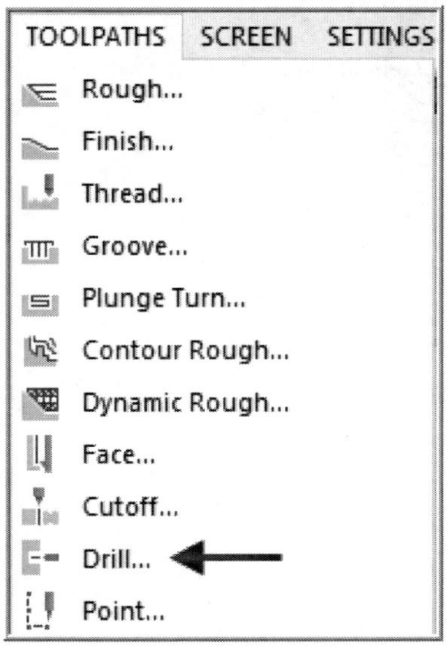

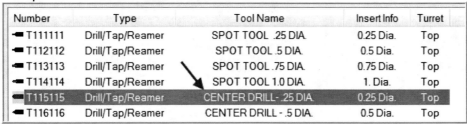

2. Click on the **Select library tool** button Select library tool... and then select the **Centre Drill .25 diameter.** To achieve the tool list view shown below, right mouse button click in the white space and select **View>Details**.

Number	Type	Tool Name	Insert Info	Turret
T111111	Drill/Tap/Reamer	SPOT TOOL .25 DIA.	0.25 Dia.	Top
T112112	Drill/Tap/Reamer	SPOT TOOL .5 DIA.	0.5 Dia.	Top
T113113	Drill/Tap/Reamer	SPOT TOOL .75 DIA.	0.75 Dia.	Top
T114114	Drill/Tap/Reamer	SPOT TOOL 1.0 DIA.	1. Dia.	Top
T115115	Drill/Tap/Reamer	CENTER DRILL - .25 DIA.	0.25 Dia.	Top
T116116	Drill/Tap/Reamer	CENTER DRILL - .5 DIA.	0.5 Dia.	Top

3. Select the **OK** button to exit the tool selection.

4. Make changes as shown below:

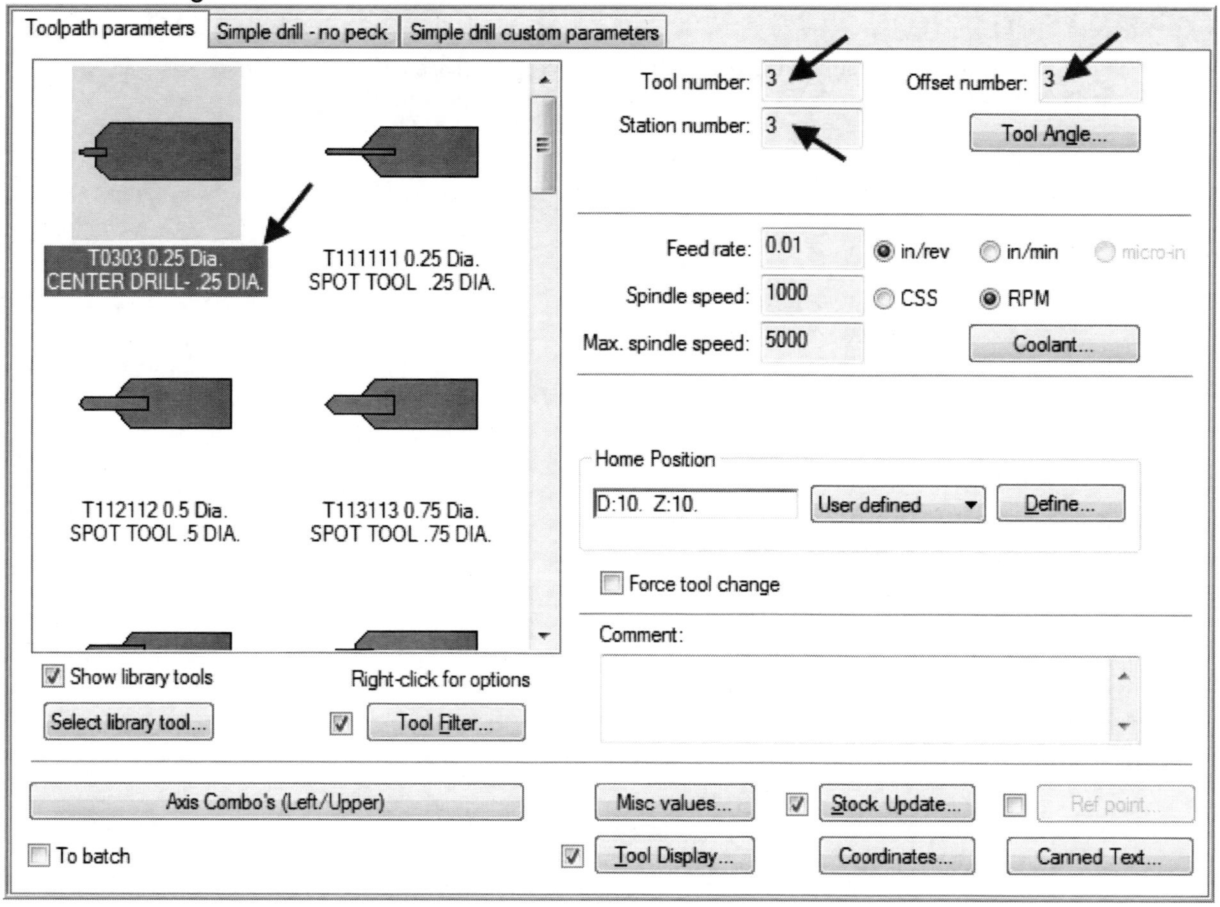

5. Select the **Simple drill – no peck** tab and make changes as shown below:

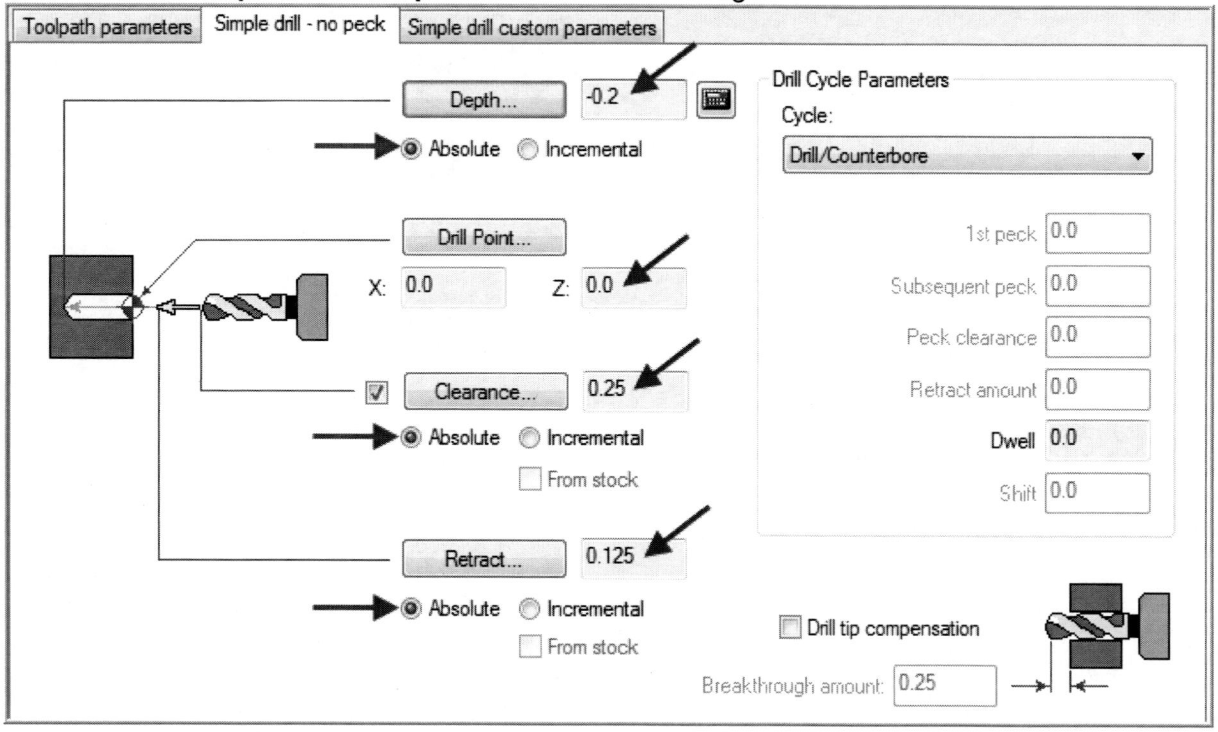

6. Select the **OK** button ✓ to exit **Simple drill – no peck**.

TASK 18:
TAP DRILL THE 0.25-20 UNC TAPPED HOLE 13/64 DIAMETER

➲ In this task you will tap drill the 0.25-20 UNC hole using **13/64 diameter drill** this will be a peck drill operation.

1. From the menu bar select **TOOLPATHS>Drill…**

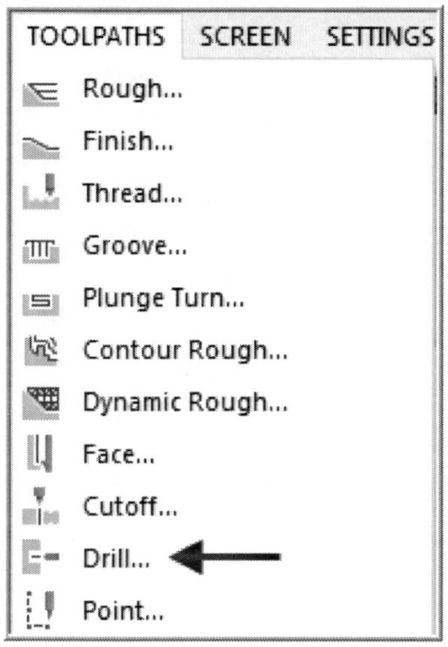

2. At the **Toolpath** parameters page click on the Select library tool button .
3. At the top left of this dialog box open up the Select new folder icon  to show the library tools list and select **LDRILLS.**

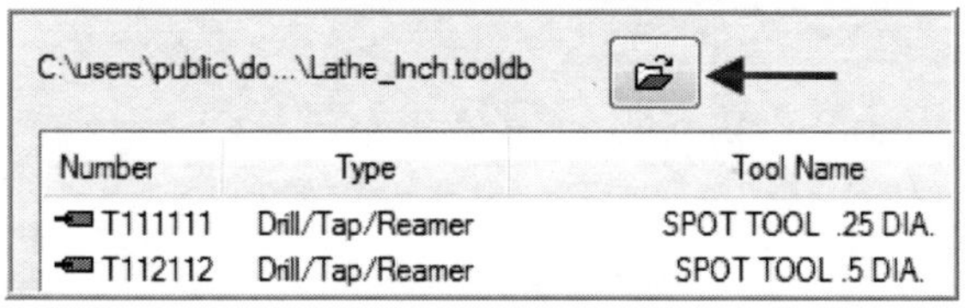

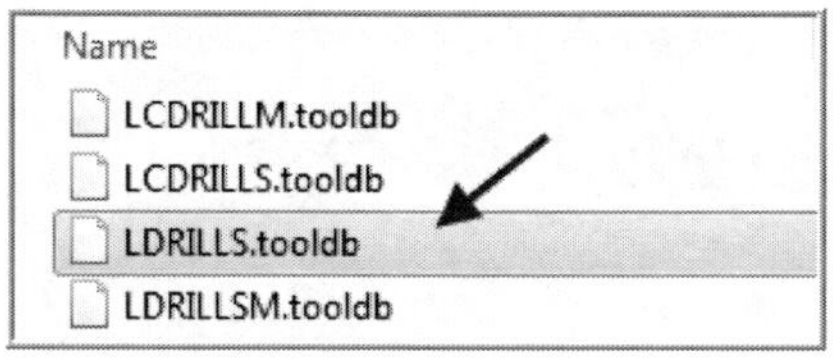

4. Scroll down and select the **13/64 drill** from the list:

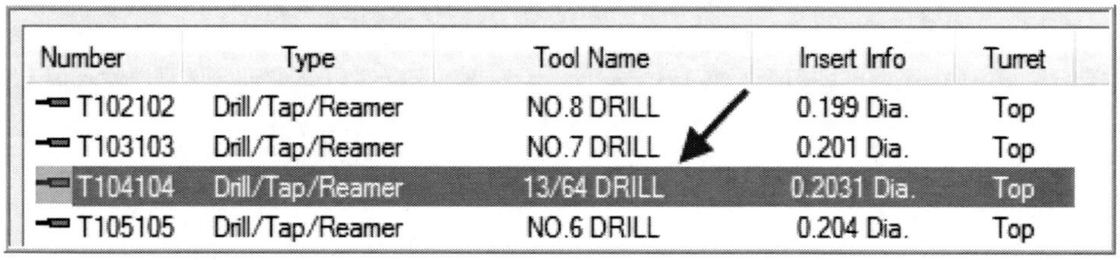

5. Select the **OK** button  to exit the tool selection.
6. Select the **Yes/OK** button for the Duplicate tool numbers warning if it appears.

7. Make changes as shown below:

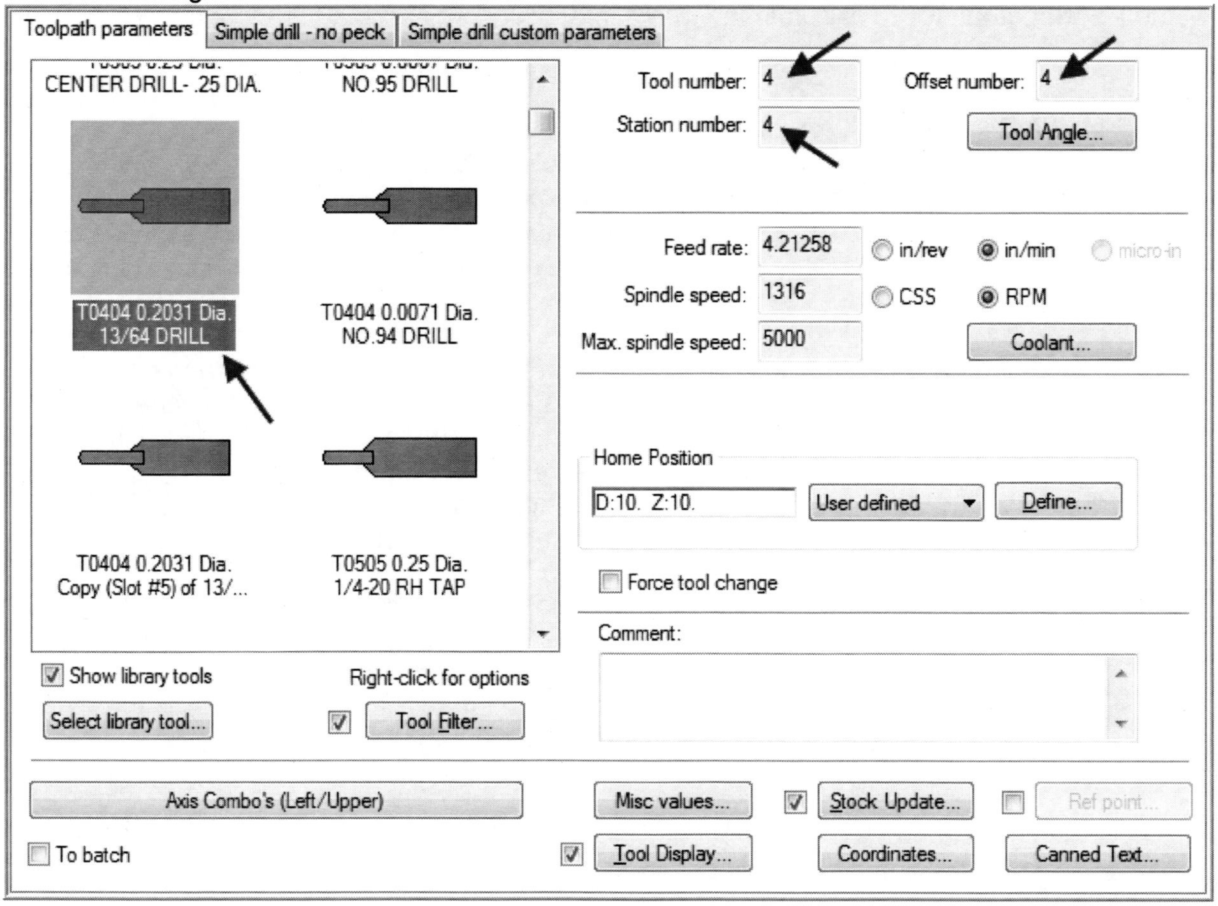

8. Select the **Simple drill – no peck** page and make changes as shown below: This hole will be peck drilled so **select the Cycle as Peck Drill** Make changes as shown below:

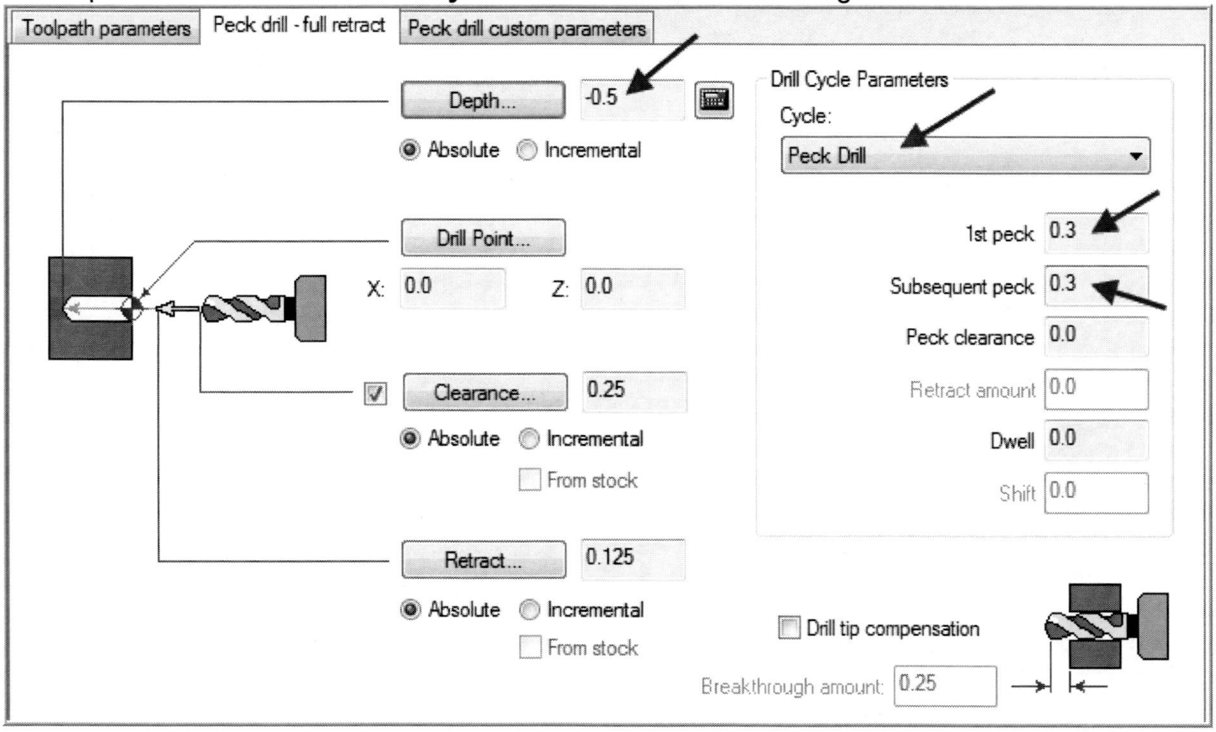

➲ As the drawing specifies the depth of 0.5 from the front face at full diameter you will now use the **Depth calculator** to calculate the true depth, taking into account the tip angle of this drill.

9. Click on the **Depth calculator** icon. 

10. At the Depth Calculator dialog box activate the radio button for **Add to depth**.

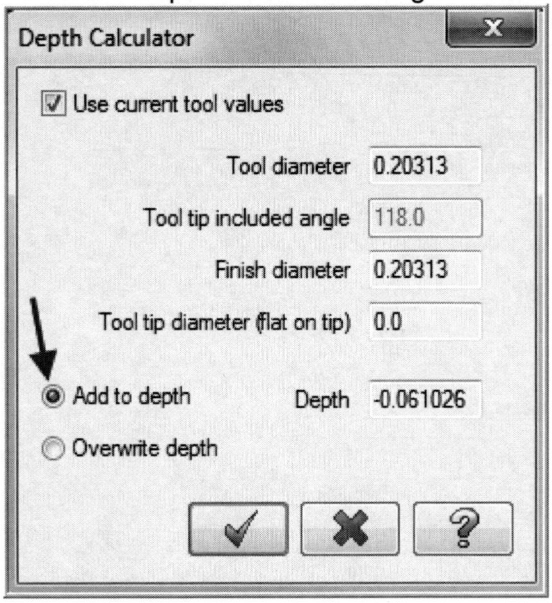

Use the **Depth Calculator** to calculate the proper drilling depth when the finish diameter of the hole is different from the drill diameter—for example, when countersinking a hole. Mastercam automatically displays the **Tool diameter**, **Tool tip included angle**, and **Tool tip diameter** for the drill that has been selected for the operation. Deselect **Use current tool values** to specify different values for these parameters.
Once you calculate the depth, you have two options:
Choose **Overwrite depth** to replace the existing depth value on the parameter page.
Choose **Add to depth** to add the calculated depth to the existing depth value on the parameter page.

11. Select the **OK** button  to exit Depth Calculator.
12. Notice how now the depth has been changed,

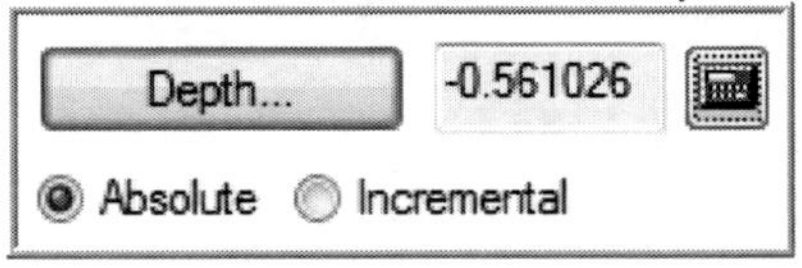

13. Select the **OK** button  to exit Peck drill – full retract.

TASK 19:
TAP THE 0.25-20 UNC TAPPED HOLE

➲ In this task you will tap the 0.25-20 hole.

1. From the menu bar select **TOOLPATHS>Drill...**

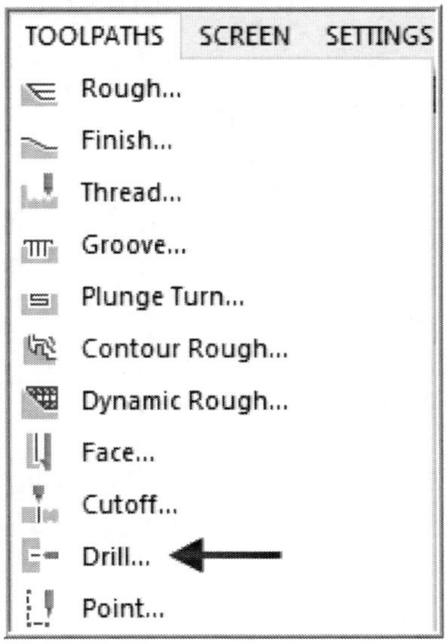

2. At the Toolpath parameters page click on the **Select library** tool button 

.

3. Select the **select new folder** icon  at the top of the dialog box and then the **LTAPS** from the list as shown below:

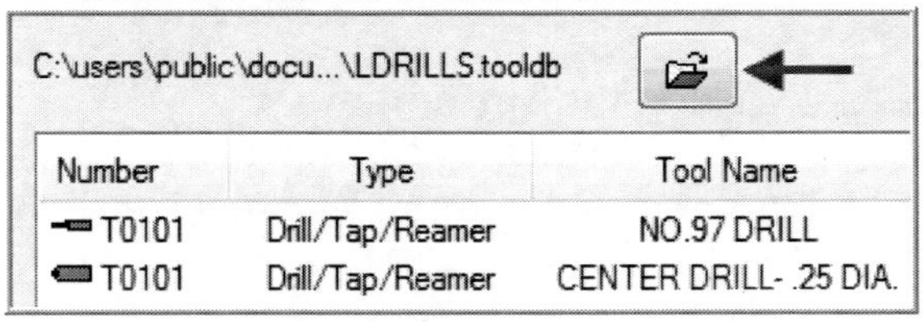

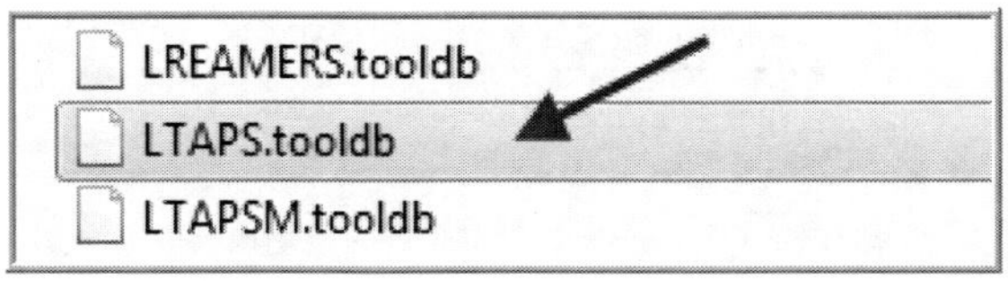

4. Select the **1/4-20 RH TAP** from the list:

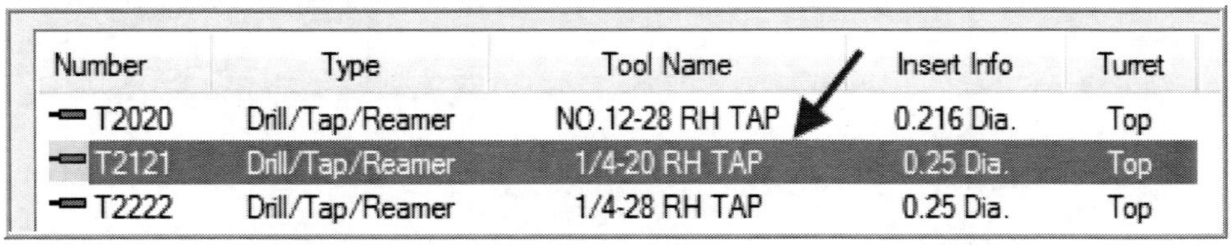

5. Select the **OK** button  to exit the tool selection.

6. **Double click** on the **1/4-20 tap** in the **Tool parameters** page.

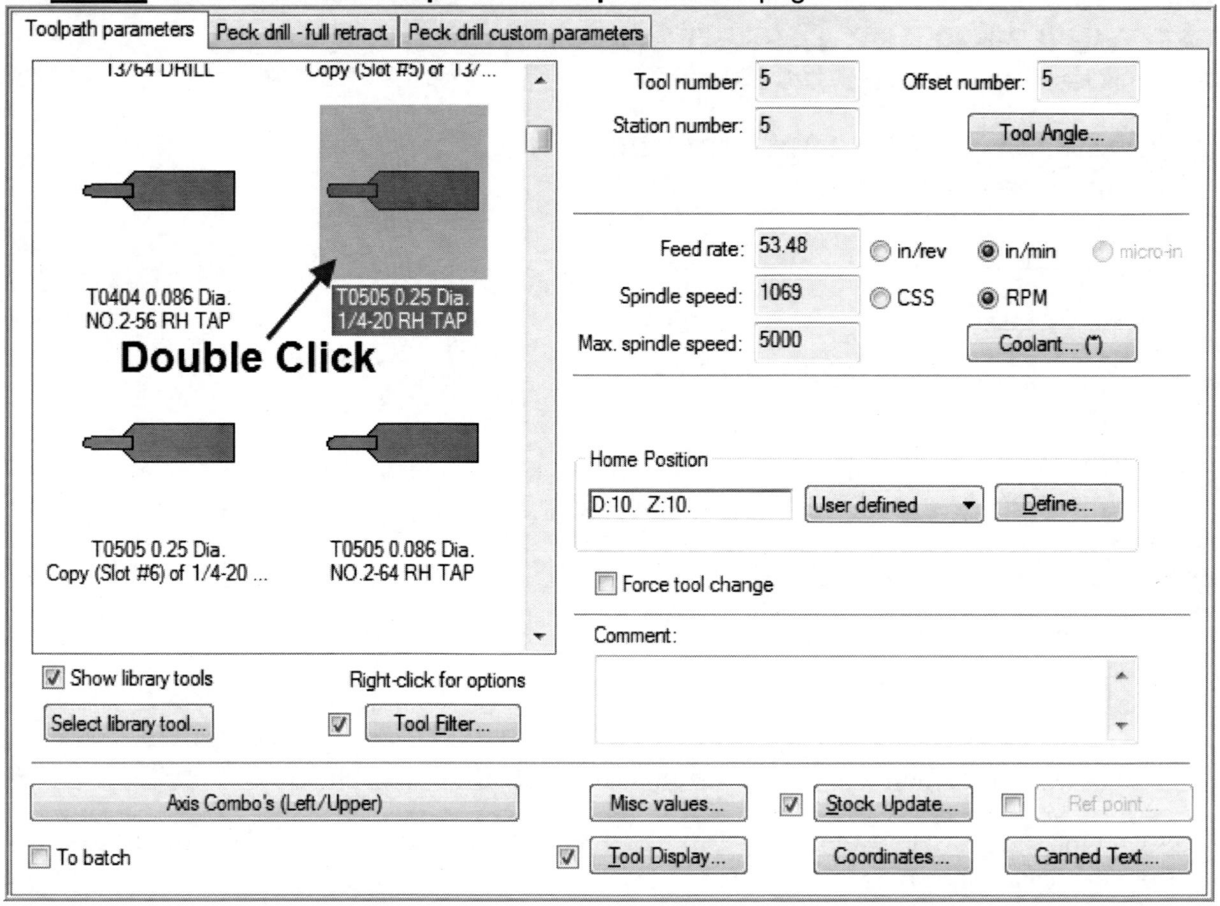

7. At the lower right corner of the screen activate the radio button for **Bottoming**.

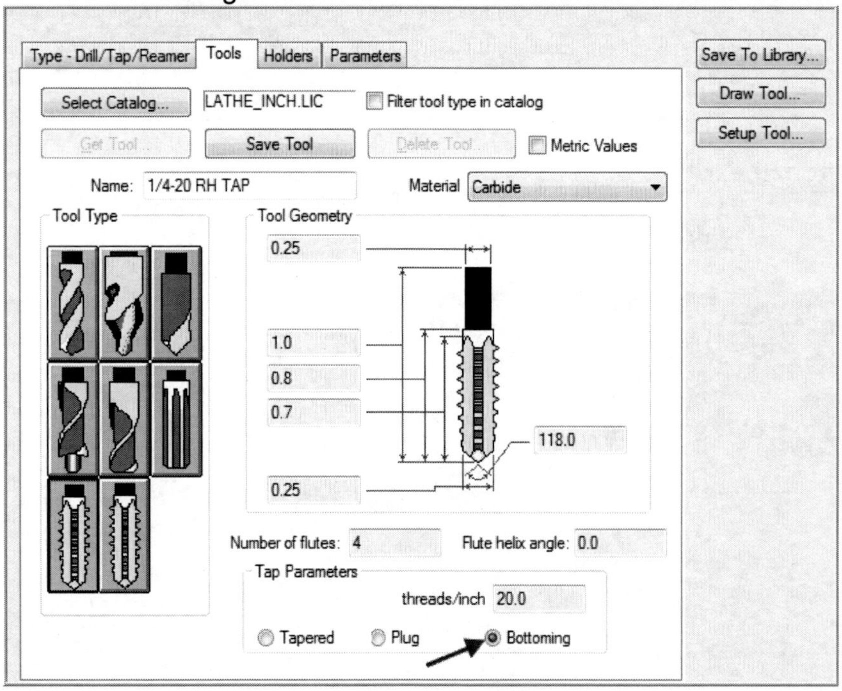

Bottoming
Select this option if you want the tap to have the same diameter all the way down.

This type of tap is used to cut threads through the bottom of the hole.

8. Select the **OK** button  to exit the Tools page.

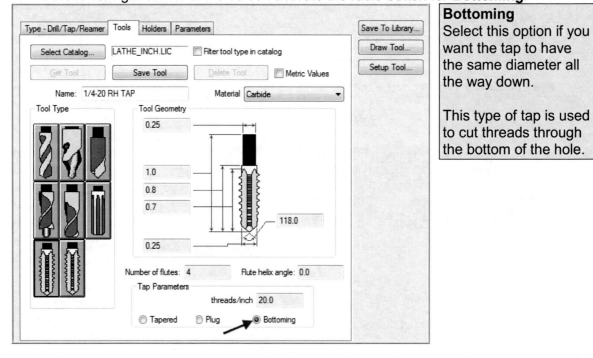

9. Make changes as shown below: The **Spindle Speed** and **Feedrate** are synchronized for a **1/40-20 tap**.

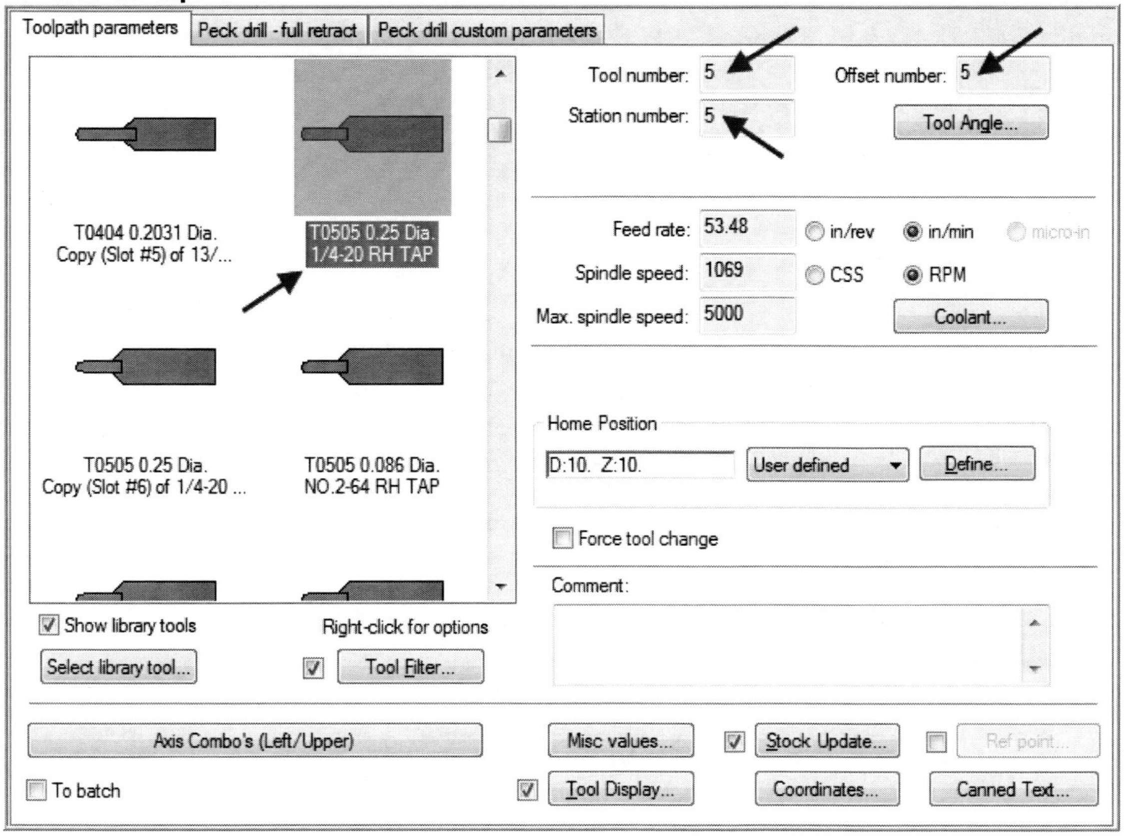

10. Select the **Peck drill – full retract** page and make changes as shown below: This hole will be tapped so **select the Cycle as Tap(G32)** Make changes as shown below:

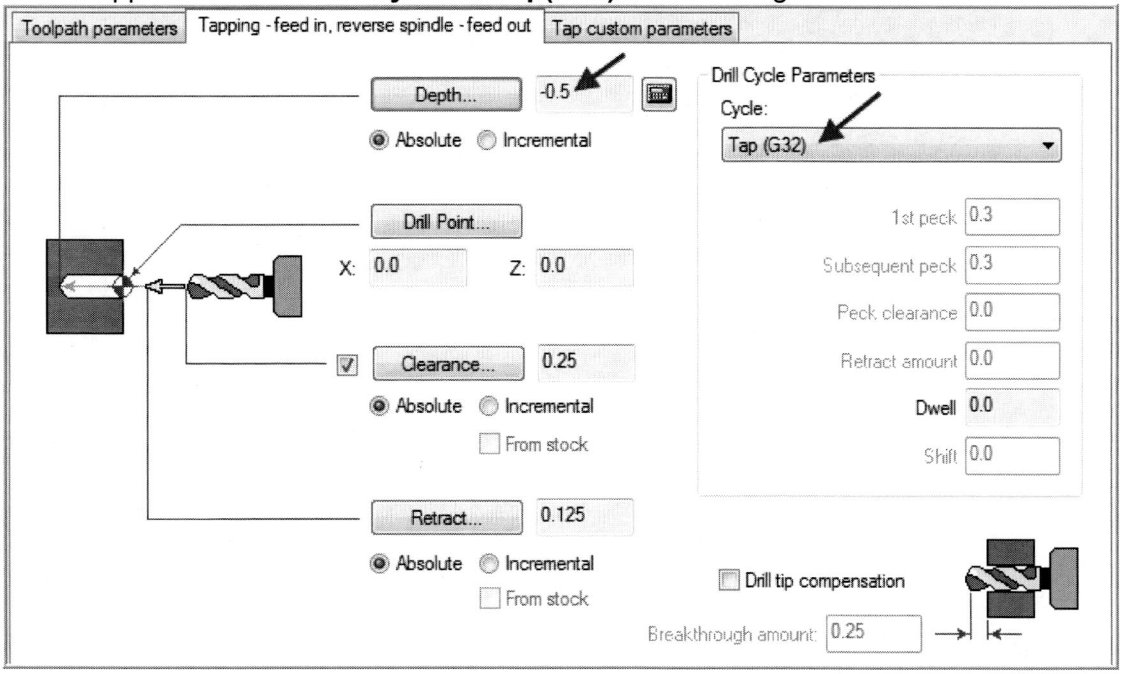

11. Select the **OK** button  to exit Tapping – feed in, reverse spindle – feed out.

TASK 20:
ROUGH THE BORE

➲ In this task you will use a boring tool to rough out the 0.500 diameter bore.

1. Select **Alt-T** on your keyboard to turn of the display of toolpaths.
2. From the menu bar select **TOOLPATHS>Quick>Rough …**

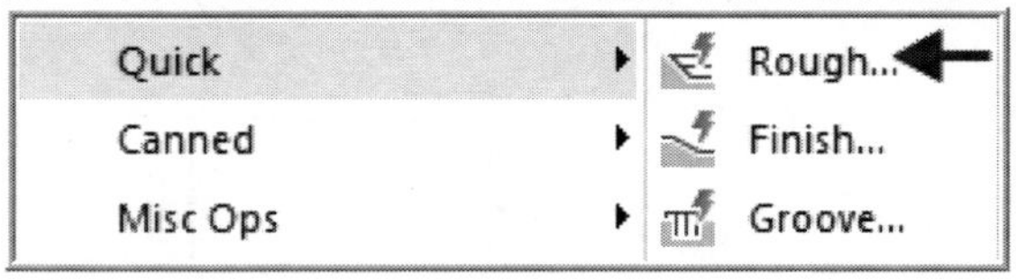

3. In the **Chaining window** Chaining mode is set to Partial by default.
4. Select **Line 1** as the **start** of the Partial chain.

After you have selected the first line **ensure** that the arrows are pointing towards the part as shown below: If it is not select the reverse button in the Chaining dialog box

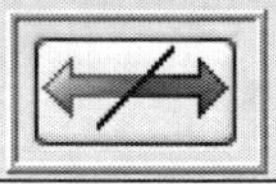

5. Then select **Line 2** as the **end** entity in this chain.

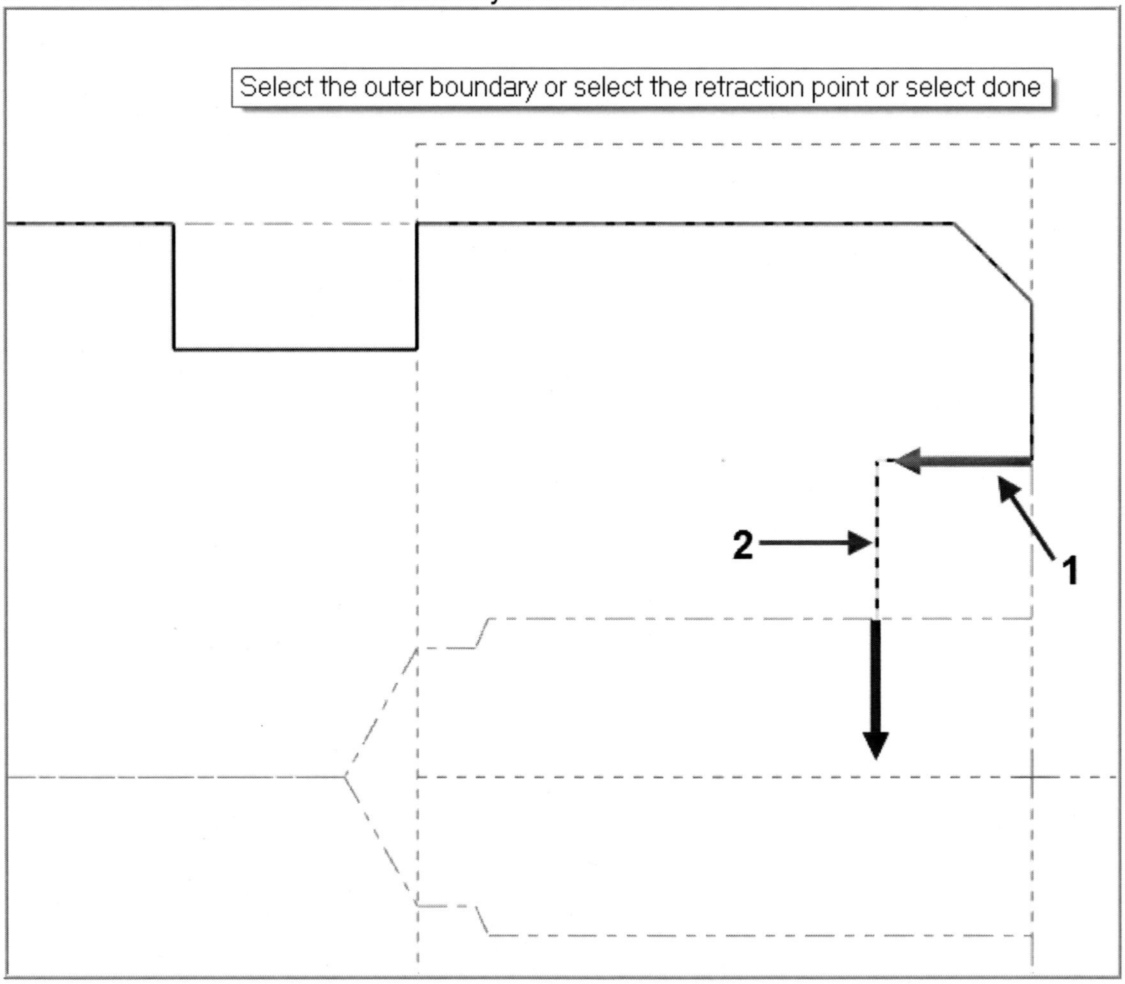

6. Select the **OK** button  to exit the Chaining dialog window.

7. At the **Toolpath parameters** page click on the **Select library tool** button [Select library tool...].
8. At the top left of this dialog box open up the Select new folder icon to show the library tools list and select **Lathe_Inch.**

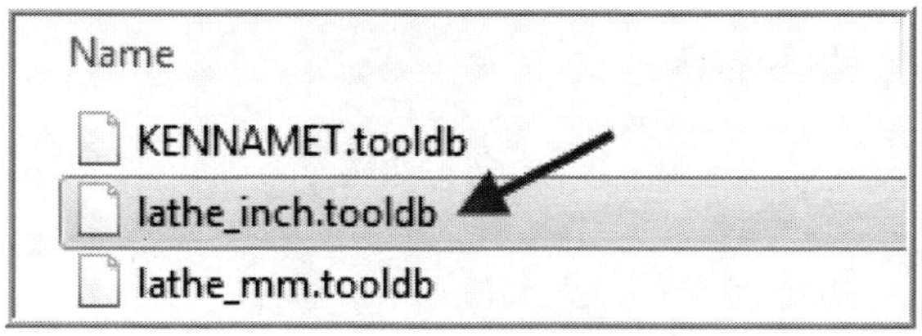

9. Select the boring bar **ID ROUGH MIN .1875 – 75 DEGREE**.

Number	Type	Tool Name	Insert Info	Turret
T0101	General Turning	OD ROUGH RIGHT - 80 DEG.	R0.0313	Top
T0202	General Turning	OD ROUGH LEFT - 80 DEG.	R0.0313	Top
T0303	General Turning	ROUGH RIGHT - 80 DEG.	R0.0313	Top
T0404	General Turning	ROUGH LEFT - 80 DEG.	R0.0313	Top
T1111	General Turning	OD 55 deg Left	R0.0313	Top
T1212	General Turning	OD 55 deg Right	R0.0313	Top
T2121	General Turning	OD FINISH RIGHT - 35 DEG.	R0.0156	Top
T2222	General Turning	OD FINISH LEFT - 35 DEG.	R0.0156	Top
T3131	General Turning	ROUGH FACE RIGHT - 80 DEG.	R0.0313	Top
T3232	General Turning	ROUGH FACE LEFT - 80 DEG.	R0.0313	Top
T7171	Boring bar	ID ROUGH MIN. .1875 DIA. - 75 DEG.	R0.0078	Top
T7272	Boring bar	ID ROUGH MIN. .25 DIA. - 75 DEG.	R0.0078	Top

10. Select the **OK** button to exit the selection of this tool.
11. Select the **OK/Yes** button for the Duplicate tool numbers warning if it appears.

12. Make any necessary changes as shown below:

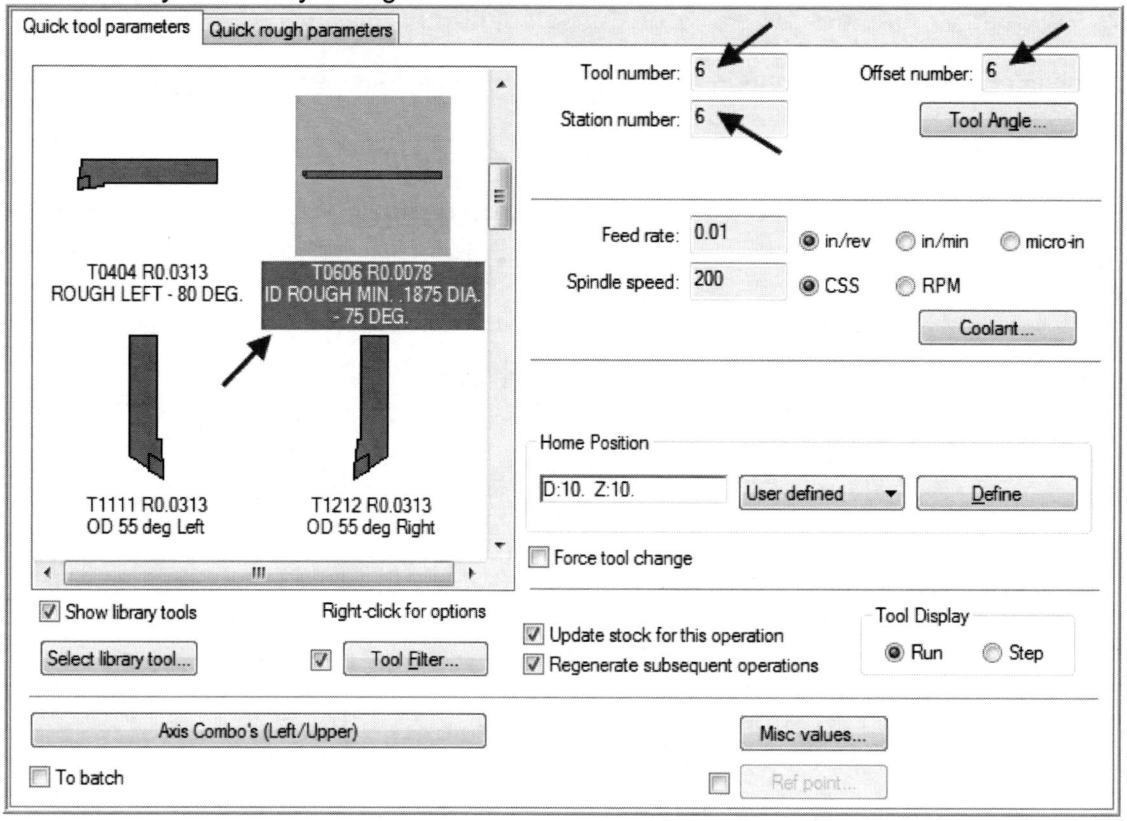

13. Select the **Quick rough parameters** page and make any necessary changes as shown below:

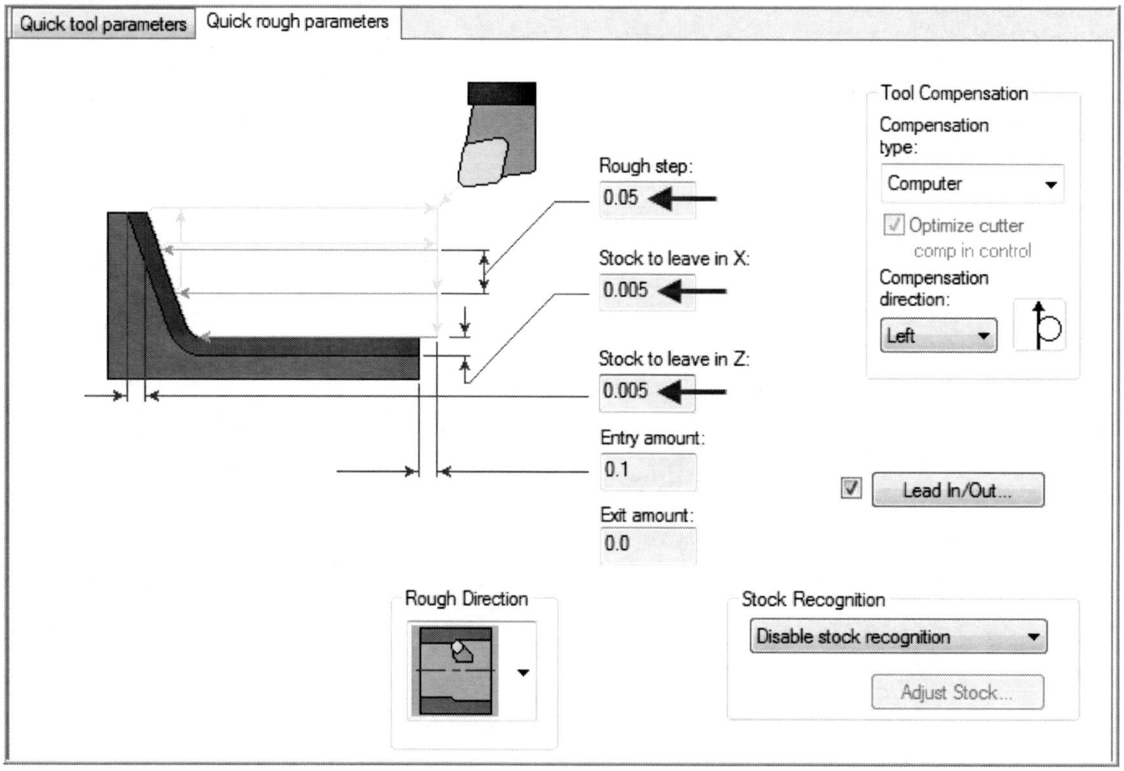

14. Select the **OK** button ✓ to exit Rough Parameters.

TASK 21:
FINISH THE BORE

➲ In this task you will use the same boring tool as used for the previous rouging operation.

1. From the menu bar select **TOOLPATHS> Quick> Finish …**

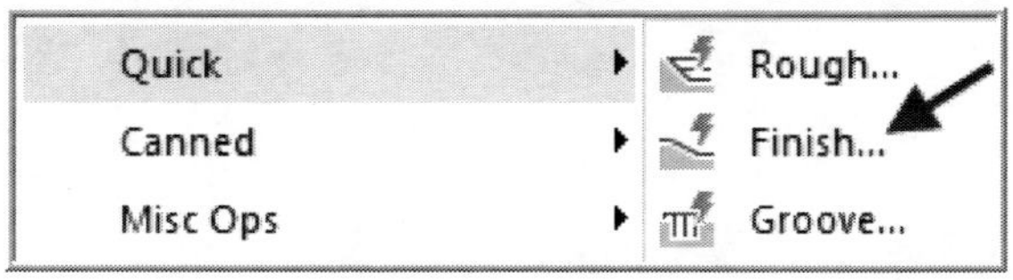

2. In the Quick Toolpath parameters page select **Tool #6 a boring tool ID ROUGH MIN .1875 DIA – 75 deg** and make any necessary changes as shown below:

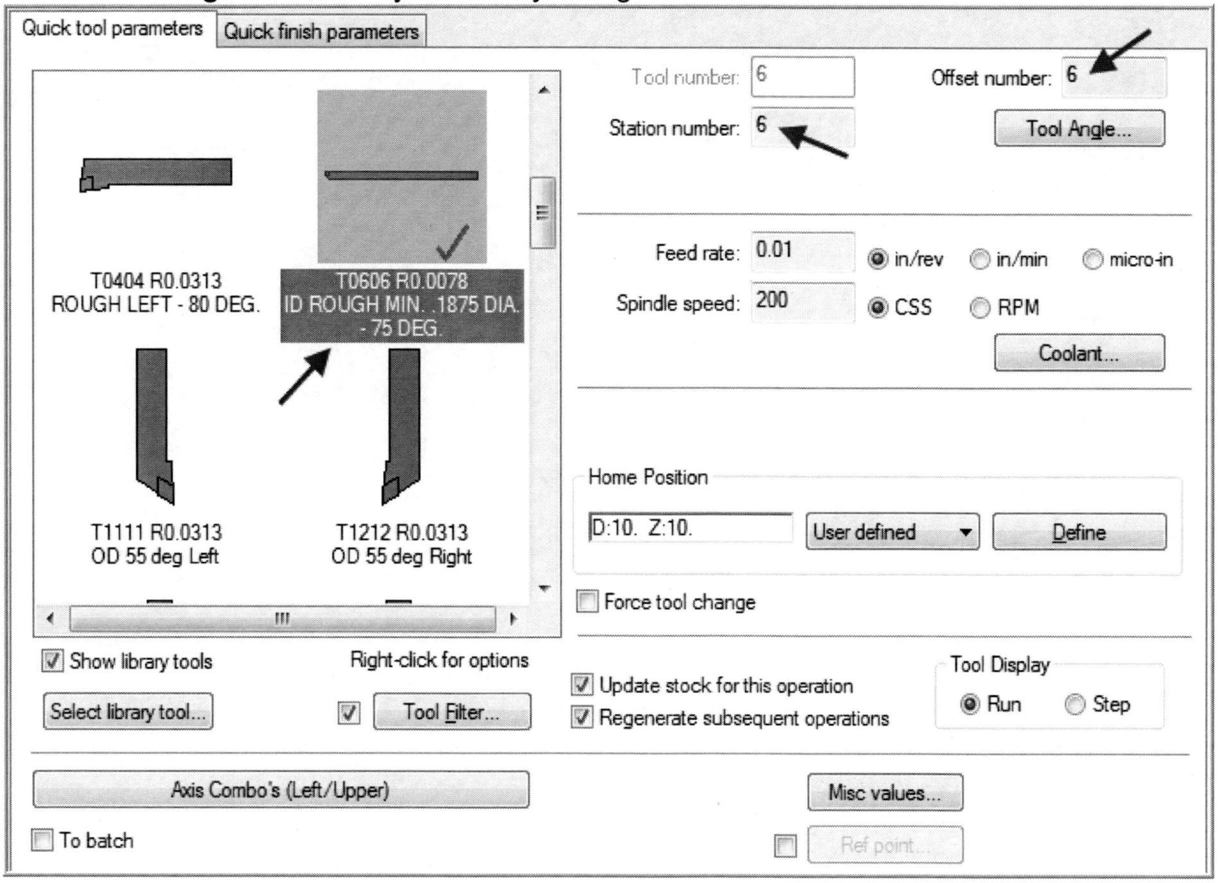

3. Select the **Quick finish parameters** page and make any necessary changes as shown below: Open up the drop down menu for operation and select the operation at the **bottom of the list**, this is the previous rough boring operation.

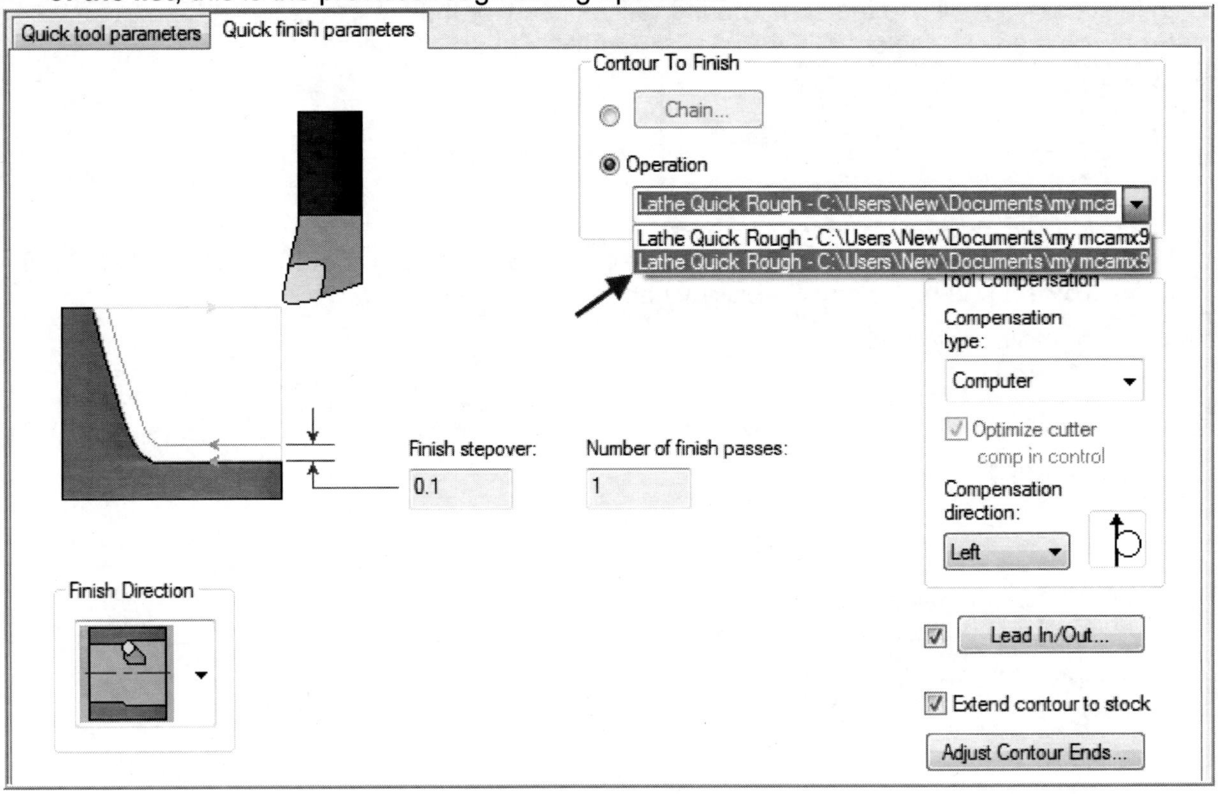

4. Select the **OK** button  to exit Quick finish parameters.

TASK 22:
CUT THE GROOVES

➲ In this task you will use the Lathe Quick Groove toolpath using an **OD Groove Right Width .125.**

Quick groove toolpaths
Lathe Quick groove toolpaths are useful when you need to create simple, symmetrical grooves. Quick groove toolpaths offer you a subset of Mastercam's grooving options.

Some of the differences between quick groove and regular groove toolpaths include:

- **No options** for chaining geometry or window chaining points. Your grooves must be defined by one, two, or three points.
- **Symmetrical grooves only**; no ability to individually set the chamfer or radius for each corner independently.
- **No tapered walls** or groove orientation options.
- **Fewer options** for roughing the groove walls, such as smoothing, separate stock to leave amounts for X and Z, and simpler pecking options.
- **Simpler lead in/out** and retract options.

If you need to use any of these features, consider creating a standard groove toolpath instead.

To create a quick groove toolpath, choose Toolpaths, Quick, Groove from the menu. You will be prompted to select the corner points of the grooves (you can select multiple sets of points to define several grooves). Press Enter when you have identified all the grooves. Use the Lathe Quick groove dialog box to select a tool and enter the quick groove parameters.

1. Select **Alt and T** on the keyboard to hide the toolpath.
2. From the menu bar select **TOOLPATHS> Quick>Groove …**

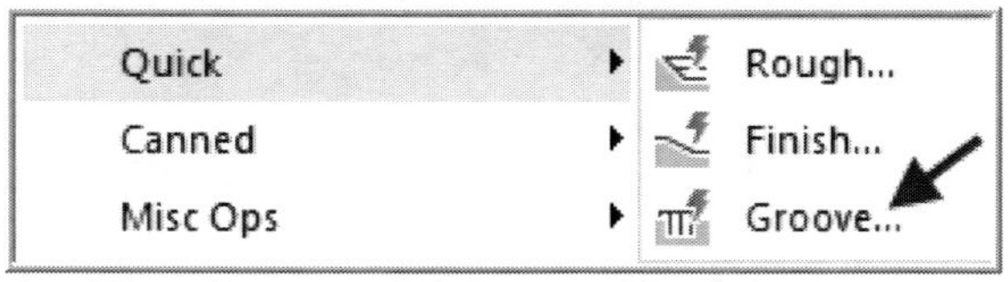

3. The **Groove Options** window appears. Click on the **2 Points** option as shown below:

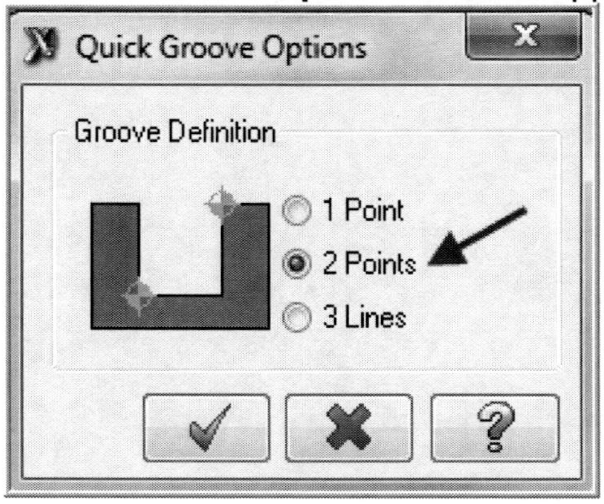

4. Click on **OK** .

5. Zoom in on the groove areas as shown below:
6. Select **Point 1 and Point 2** for the first groove. Move the cursor over the corner until the visual cue for End point displays and then click on the various points.
7. Then Select **Point 3 and Point 4** for the second groove.

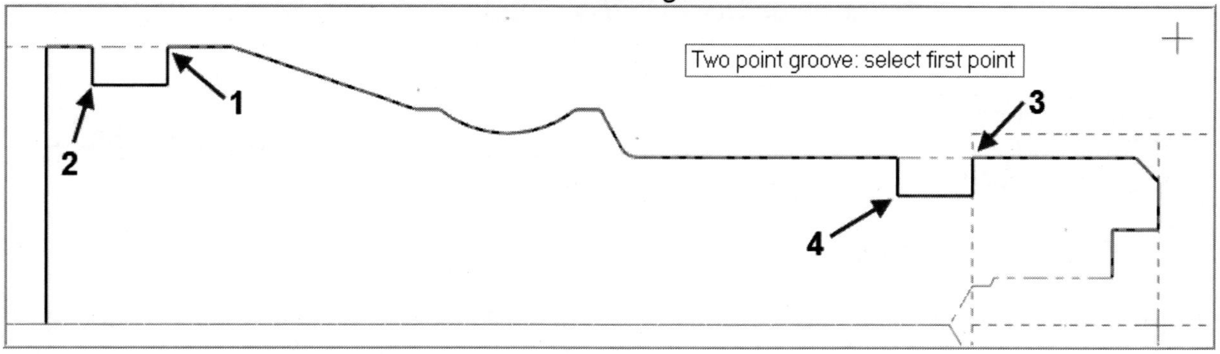

8. Press the **Enter** key when done.
9. Select **OD Groove Right Width .125** tool from the tool list and make any necessary changes as shown below:

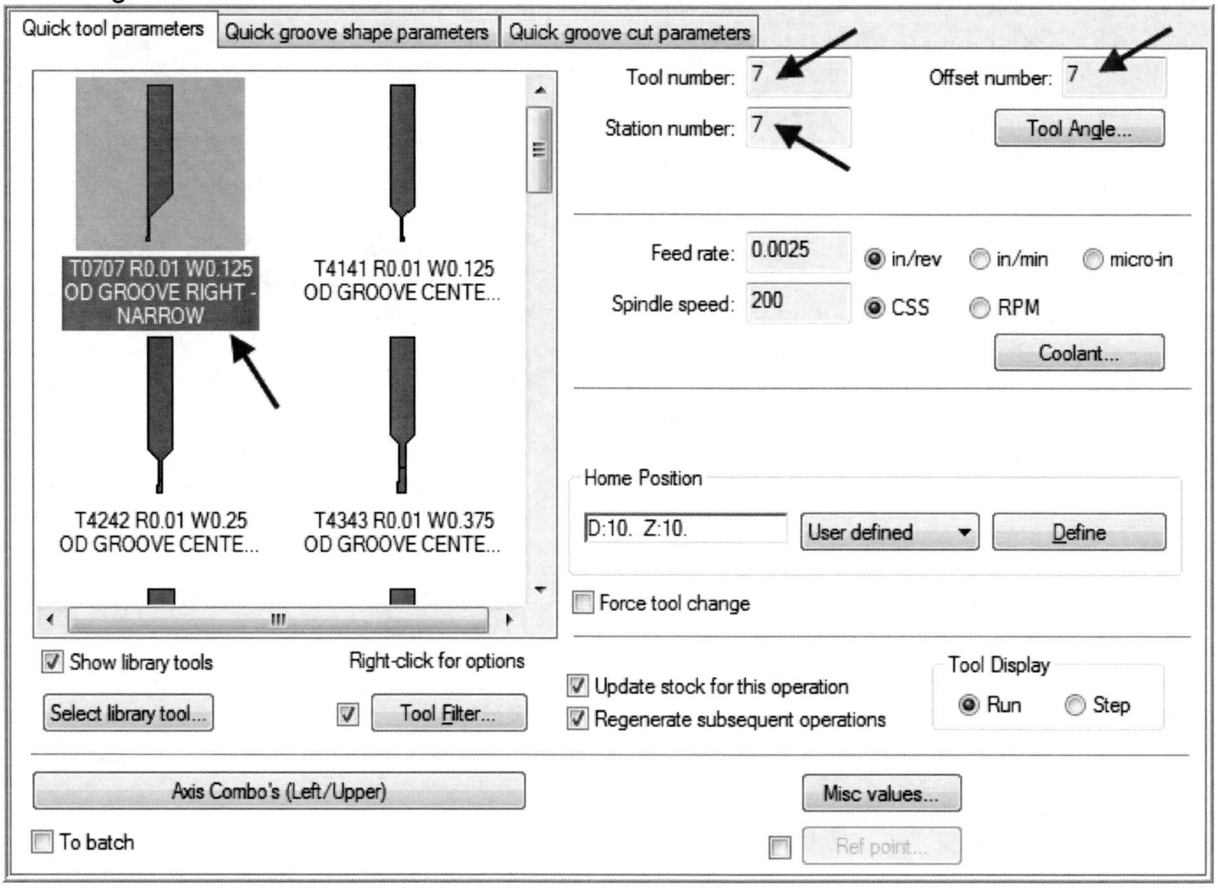

10. Select the **OK** button to exit as no further changes are required.

TASK 23:
CUT OFF THE PART

➲ In this task you will cut off the part using **OD Groove Right Width .125** the same tool as the previous grooving operation.

1. Fit the image to the screen by clicking on the **Fit** icon as shown below:

2. From the menu bar select **TOOLPATHS>Cutoff…**

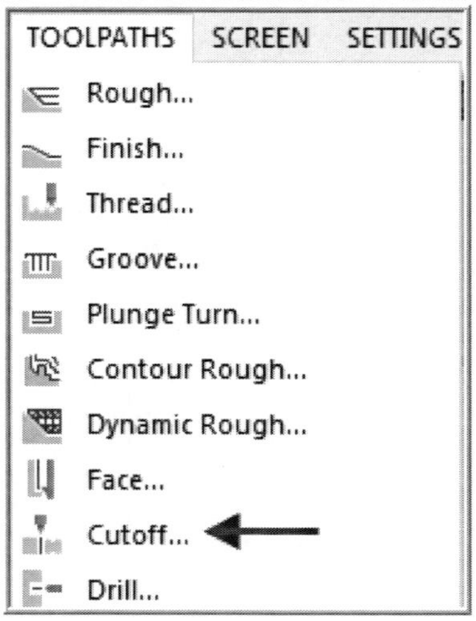

3. When prompted to **Select cutoff boundary point** pick the end point of the line shown below: Move the cursor over the corner until the visual cue for End point displays and then click on this point.

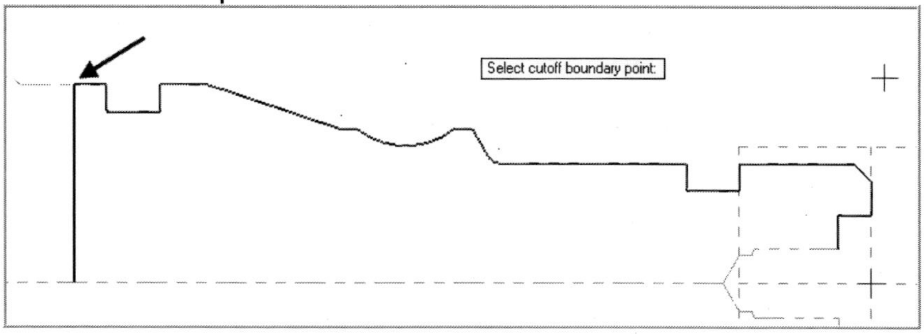

4. Select **OD GROOVE RIGHT WIDTH .125** tool from the tool list and make any necessary changes as shown below:

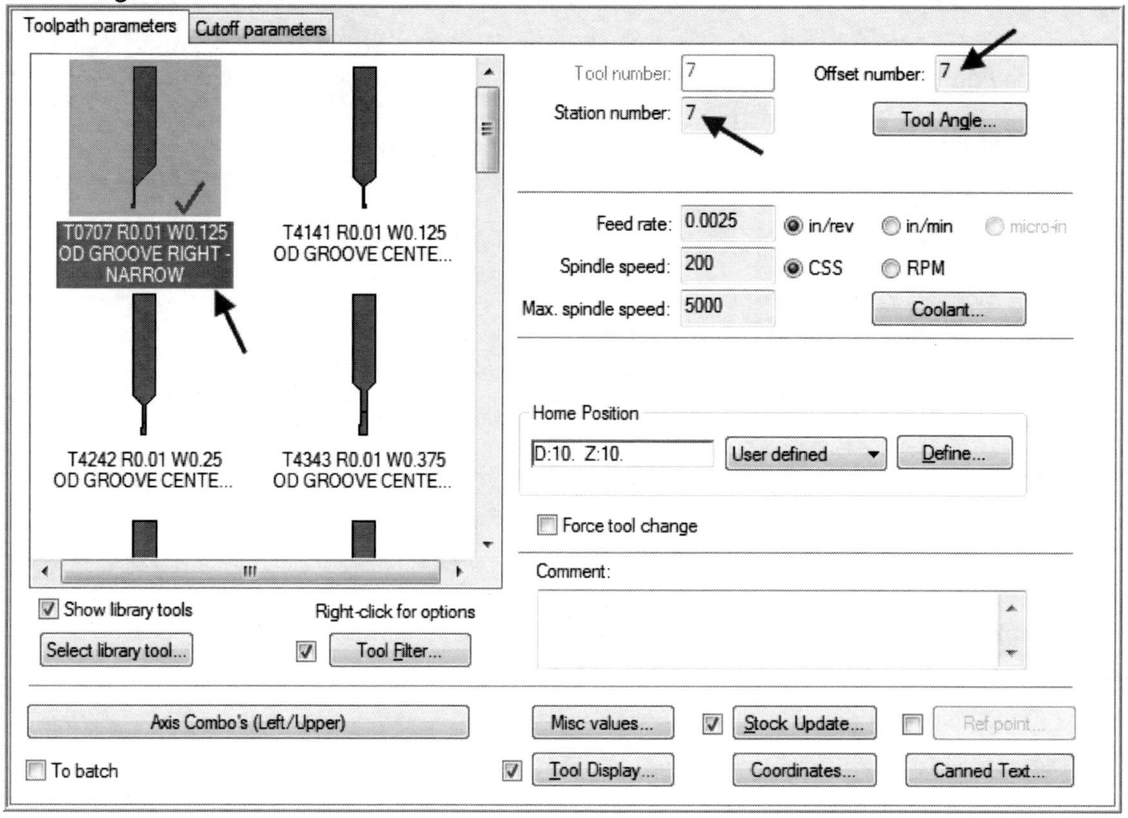

5. Select the **Cutoff parameters** page and make sure the settings are as shown below:

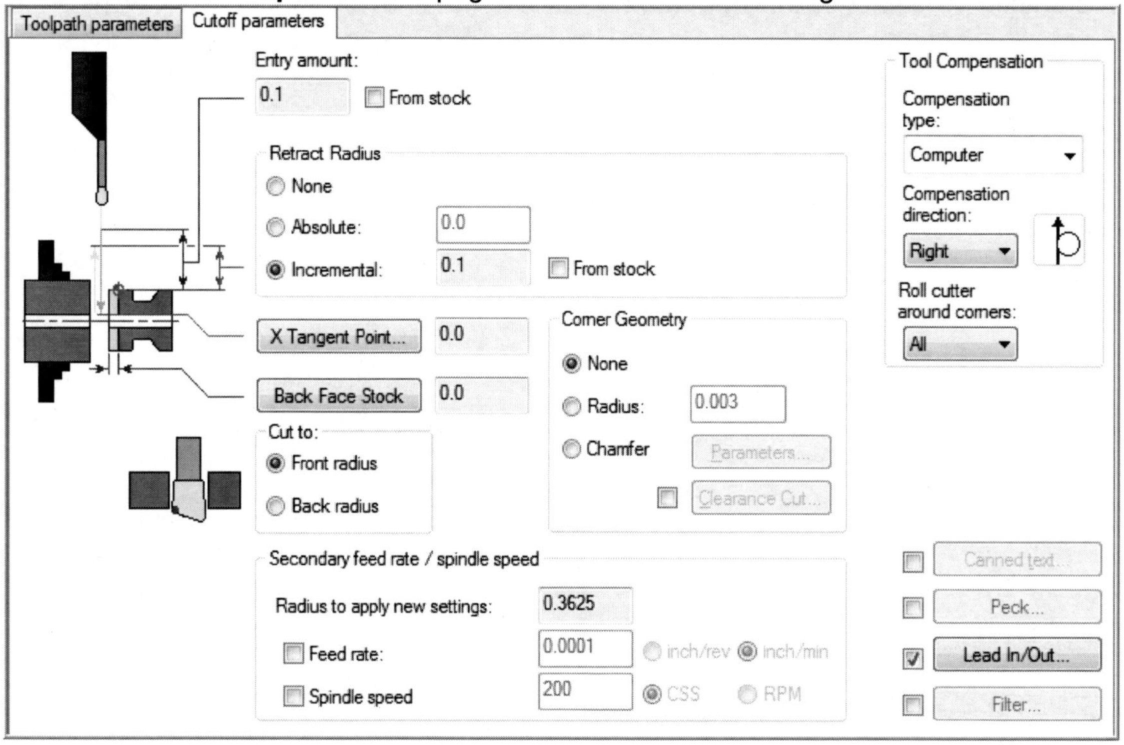

6. Select the **OK** button to exit **Lathe Cutoff parameters.**

TASK 24:
VERIFY THE TOOLPATH

➲ Mastercam's Verify utility allows you to use solid models to simulate the machining of a part. The model created by the verification represents the surface finish, and shows collisions, if any exist.

1. In the Toolpaths Manager pick all the operations to Verify by picking the Select All icon

.
2. Select the **Verify selected operations** icon shown below:

3. **Maximize** the Backplot/Verify window if required.
4. Now select the **Home** Tab if required.

5. Activate the options shown below in the **Visibility** section of the Home tab. **Initial Stock not activated.**
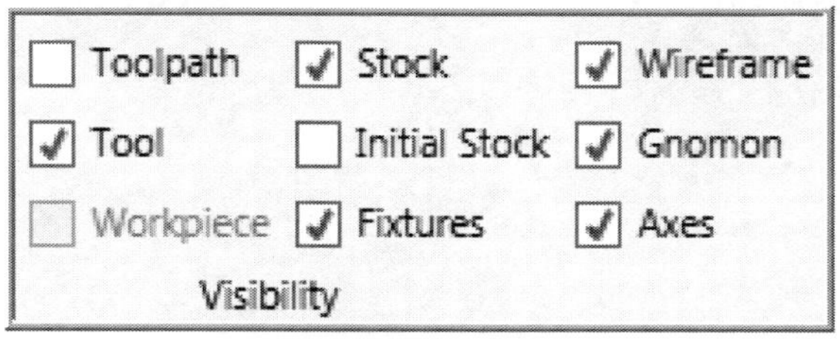

6. Activate the **Color Loop** to change the color of the tools for the verified part.
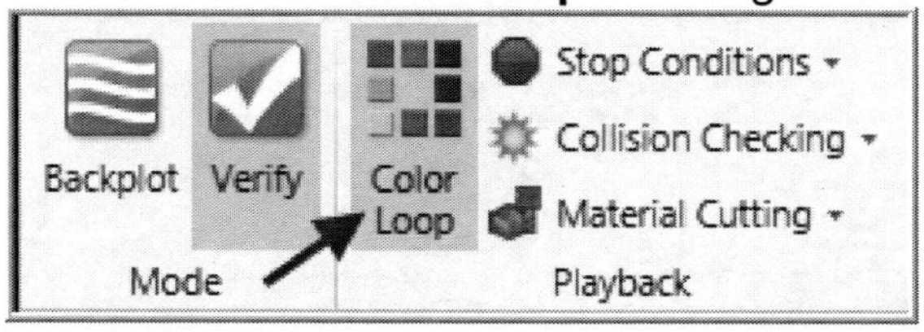

7. At the top of the screen select the **View** tab, the **Isometric** icon and then select **Fit**.
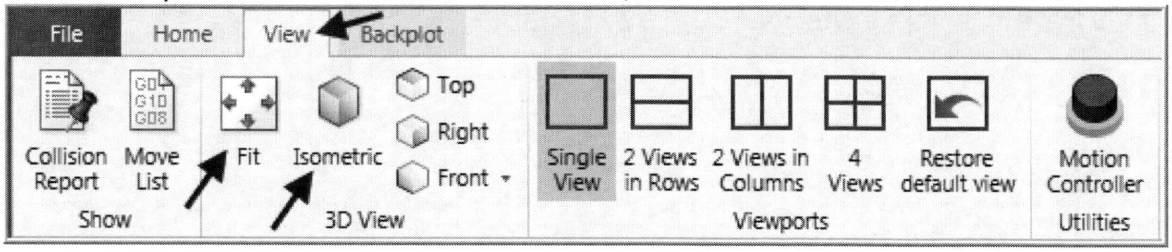

8. In the lower right corner of the screen now set the run **Speed** to slow by moving the slider bar pointer over to the left as shown below.

9. Now select the **Play Simulation** button to review the toolpaths.

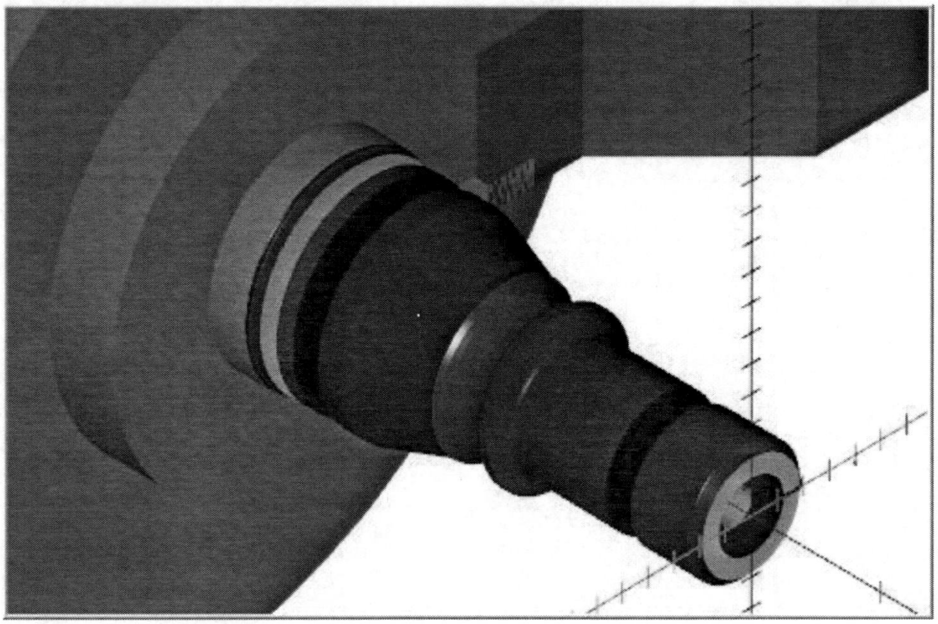

10. Select the **Close** button  in the top right hand corner to exit Verify.

TASK 25:
SAVE THE UPDATED MASTERCAM FILE

1. Select the Save icon from the toolbar .

TASK 26:
POST AND CREATE THE CNC CODE FILE

1. Ensure all the operations are selected by picking the **Select All** icon  from the Toolpaths manager.

2. Select the **Post selected operations** button from the Toolpaths manager.

➲ **Please Note:** If you cannot see **G1** click on the right pane of the Toolpaths manager window and expand the window to the right.

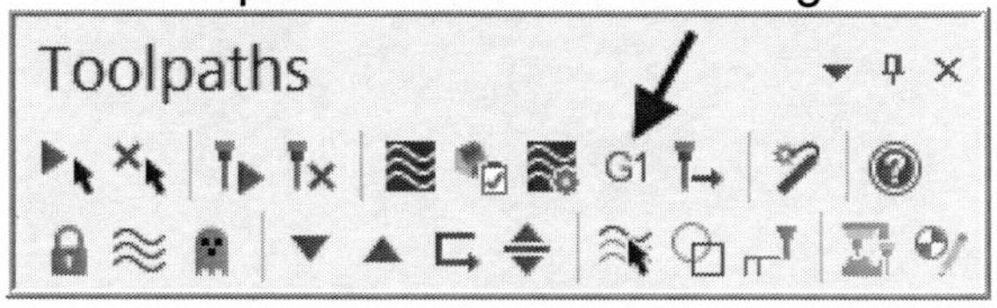

3. In the Post processing window, make the necessary changes as shown below:

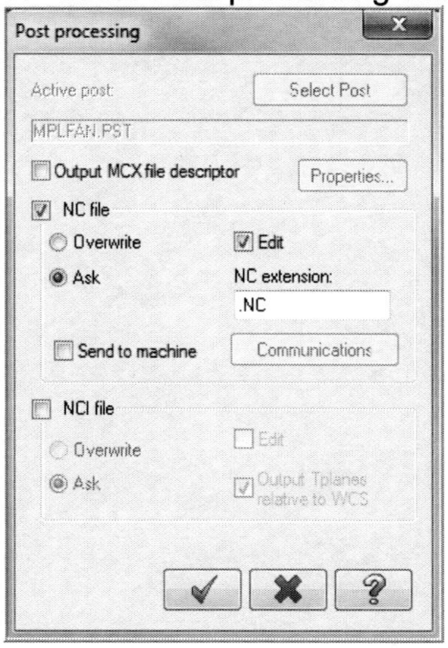

About Post Processing

NC file:
Select this option to save the NC file. The file name and extension are stored in the machine group properties for the selected operation. If you are posting operations from different machine groups or Mastercam files, or batch processing, Mastercam will create several files according to the settings for each machine group.

Edit:
When checked, automatically launches the default text editor with the file displayed so that you can review or modify it.

4. Select the OK button  to continue.

5. Ensure the same name as your Mastercam part file name is displayed in the **NC File name** field.
6. Select the **Save** button.
7. The CNC code file opens up in the default editor.

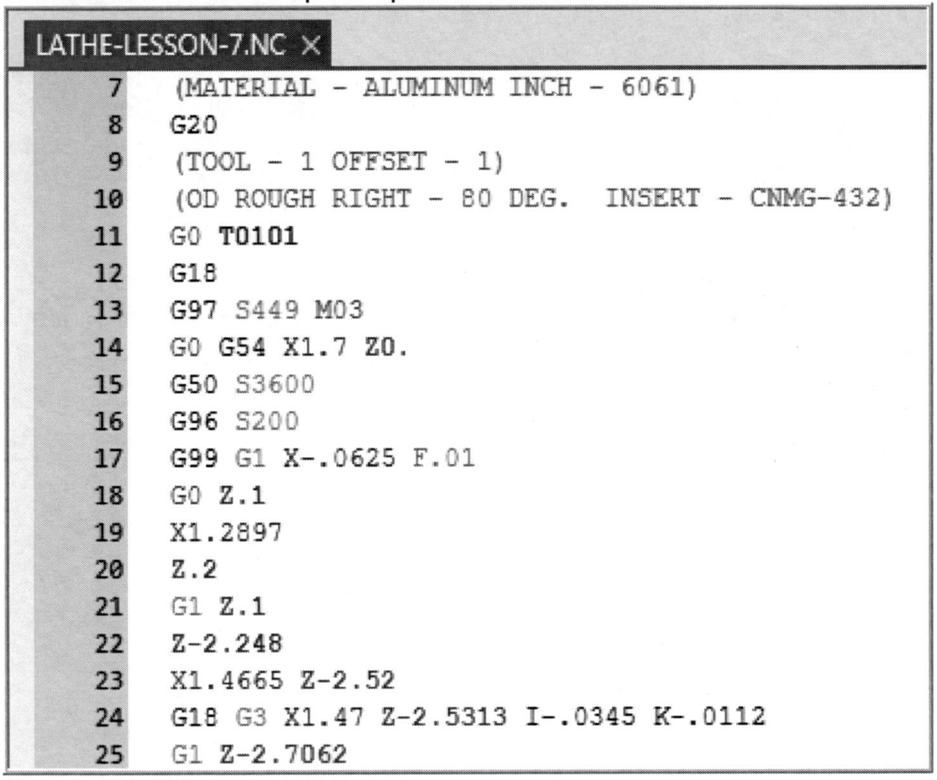


```
(MATERIAL - ALUMINUM INCH - 6061)
G20
(TOOL - 1 OFFSET - 1)
(OD ROUGH RIGHT - 80 DEG.  INSERT - CNMG-432)
G0 T0101
G18
G97 S449 M03
G0 G54 X1.7 Z0.
G50 S3600
G96 S200
G99 G1 X-.0625 F.01
G0 Z.1
X1.2897
Z.2
G1 Z.1
Z-2.248
X1.4665 Z-2.52
G18 G3 X1.47 Z-2.5313 I-.0345 K-.0112
G1 Z-2.7062
```

8. Select the × in the top right corner to exit the CNC editor.
9. This completes LATHE-LESSON-7.

LATHE-LESSON-7 EXERCISE

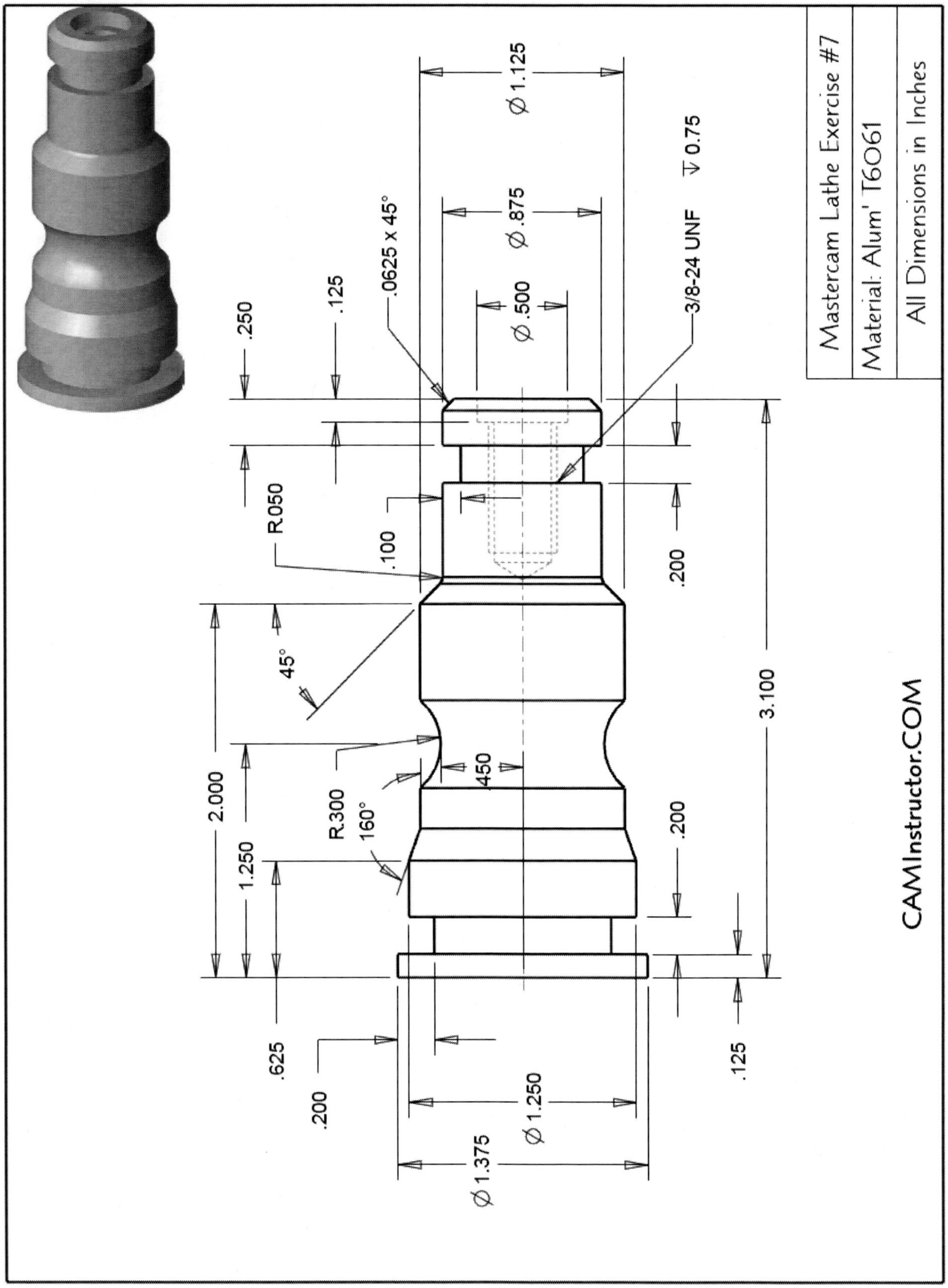

Mastercam® X9

TRAINING GUIDE

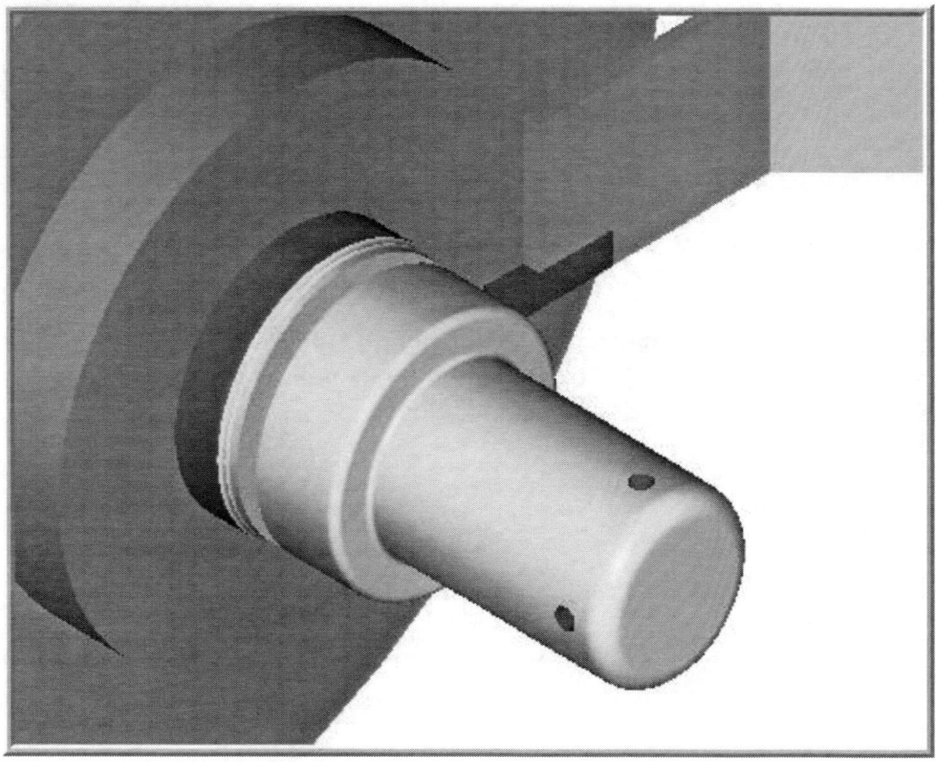

LATHE-LESSON-8

C-AXIS PART

camInstructor

Objectives

You will open an existing file: Lathe Lesson 1 and create the geometry for Lathe-Lesson-8. If you do not have the Mastercam file for Lathe Lesson 1 it is available on the DVD that came with this textbook in the folder **Sample-Files**. The geometry creation for this part will involve the creation of a series of points that will be used to machine the four holes using the C-Axis.

You will then generate a toolpath to machine the part on a CNC lathe. This lesson covers the following topics:

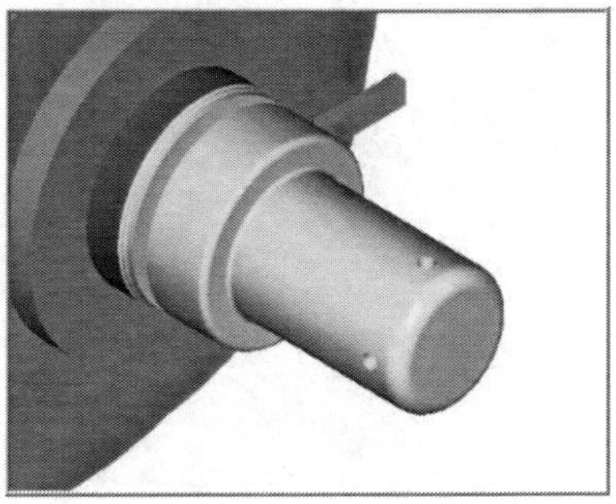

➲ **Create a 2-dimensional drawing by:**
Creating points.

➲ **Establish Stock and Chuck settings:**
Stock size.
Chuck Configuration.
Material for the part.
Feed calculation.

➲ **Generate a C-Axis lathe toolpath consisting of:**
C-Axis Drill.

➲ **Inspect the toolpath using Mastercam's Verify and Backplot by:**
Launching the Verify function to machine the part on the screen.
Using Backplot to identify the correctness of the toolpaths.
Generating the NC- code.

LATHE-LESSON-8 DRAWING

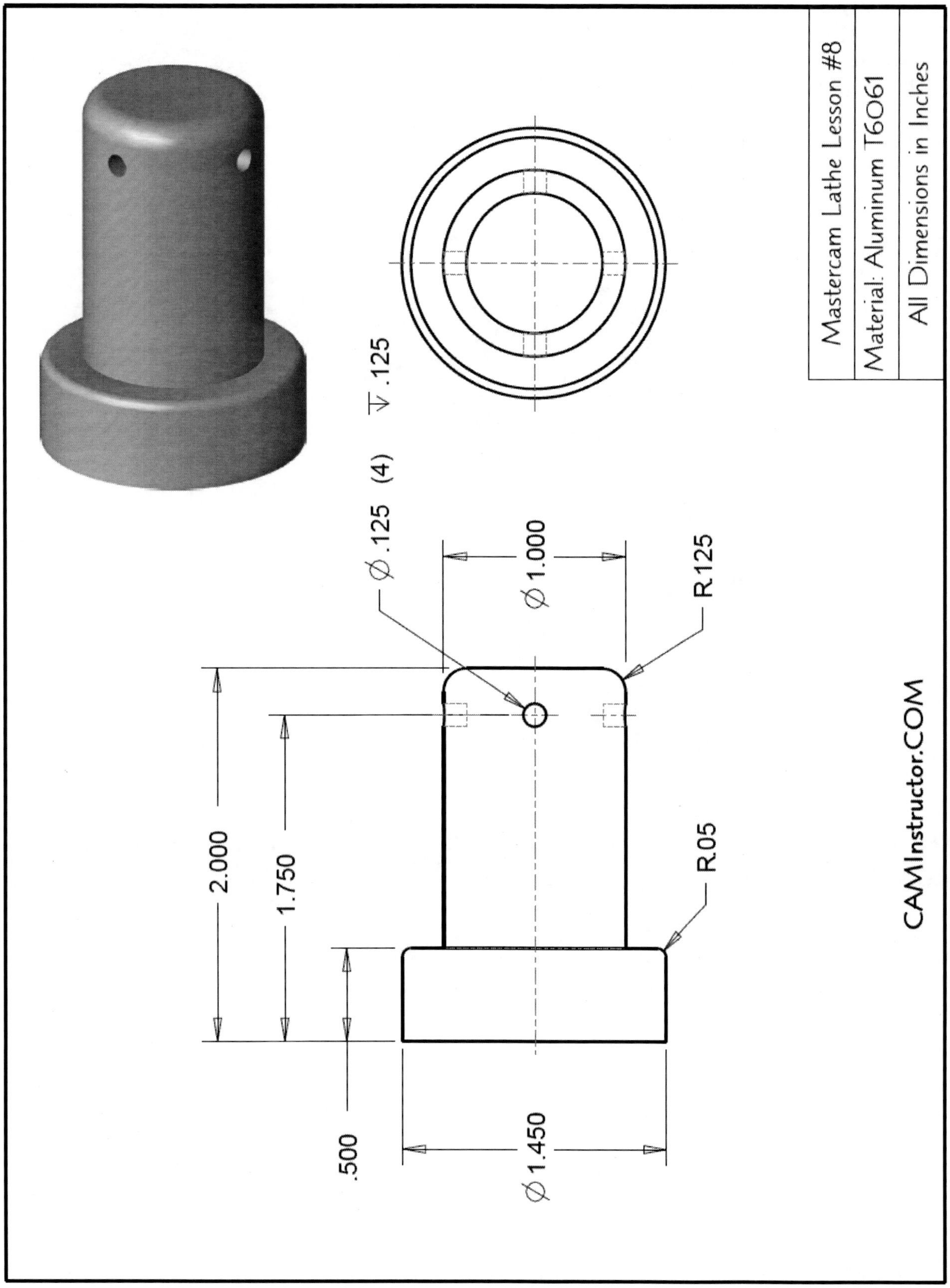

TOOL LIST

Three tools will be used to create this part.

- **Tool #1 Face, Rough and Finish the outside diameters**
  Holder: Outside Diameter Rough Right Hand - DCGNR-164D.
  Insert: 80 Degree Diamond Insert – CNMG-432.

- **Tool #2 Cutoff the part**
  Holder: Outside Diameter Cut-off Right Hand.
  Insert: 0.125" Wide.

- **Tool #3 Drill the part**
  Center cutting End Mill 0.125" diameter

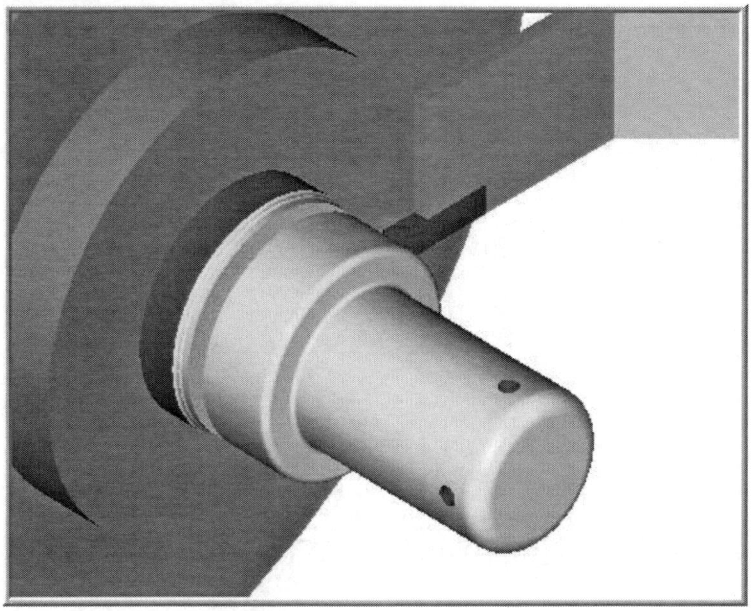

LATHE - LESSON - 8 - THE PROCESS

Geometry Creation

TASK 1: Duplicate Lathe-Lesson-1 for Lathe-Lesson-8
TASK 2: Setting the Environment
TASK 3: Create the Points
TASK 4: Save the Drawing

Toolpath Creation

TASK 5: Drill the Points using C-Axis toolpath
TASK 6: Backplot the Toolpath
TASK 7: Verify the Toolpath
TASK 8: Save the Updated Mastercam File
TASK 9: Post and Create the CNC Code File

Geometry Creation

TASK 1:
DUPLICATE LESSON-1 FOR LESSON-8

In this lesson you will use Lathe-Lesson-1 to complete Lathe-Lesson-8. If you do not have the Mastercam file for Lathe Lesson 1 it is available on the DVD that came with this textbook in the folder **Sample-Files**.

1. Click on **File>Open>Lathe-Lesson-1.**
2. The screen should look like the one below:

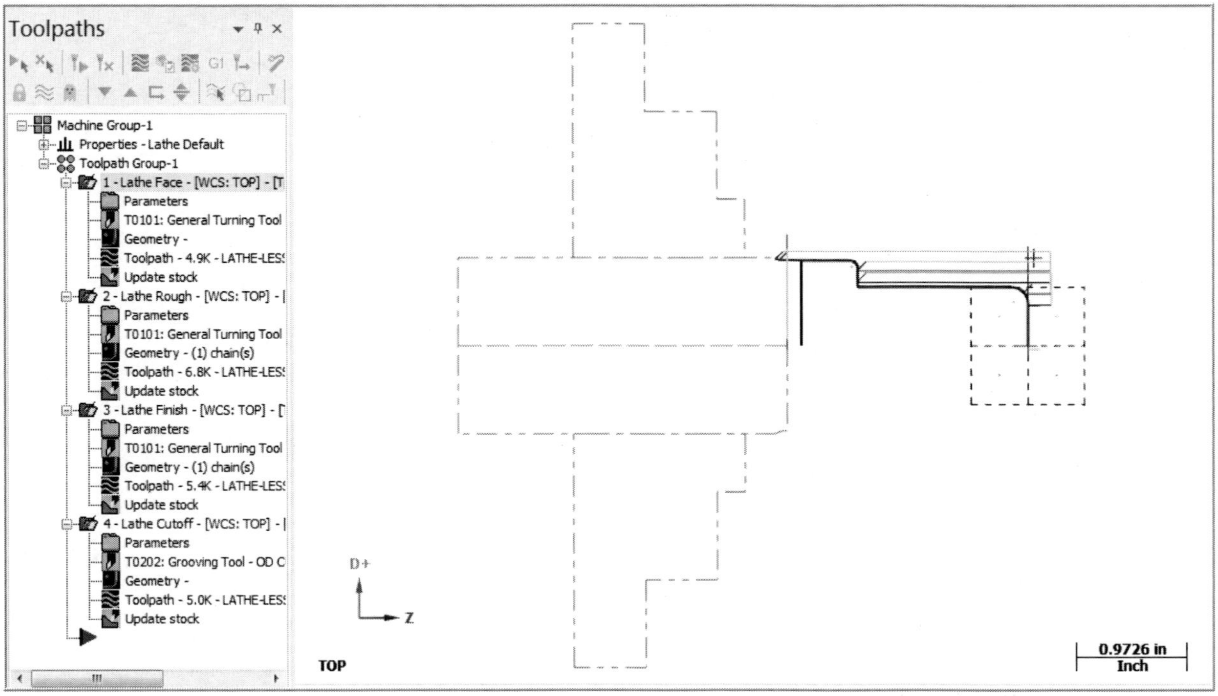

3. Select **File>Save as…**
4. In the File name box, type **Lathe-Lesson-8.**
5. Save to an appropriate location**.**
6. Select the Save button to save the file and complete this function.

TASK 2:
SETTING THE ENVIRONMENT

Before starting the geometry creation you should set up the grid and toolbars as outlined in the **Setting the Environment** section at the beginning of this text:

1. Set up the Grid. This will help identify the location of the origin.
2. Load the Workspace – **SETTINGS>Load Workspace>Lathe** to machine a part on the Lathe.
3. To set the machine type to **the C Axis Slant Bed Lathe** select the plus in front of **Properties** to expand the Machine Group Properties.

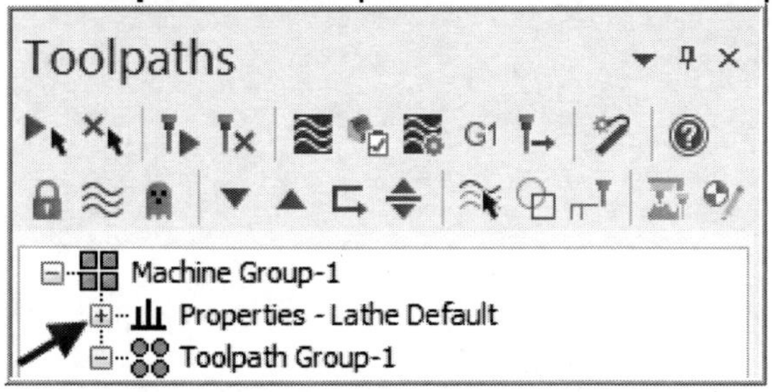

4. Click on **Files** as shown below:

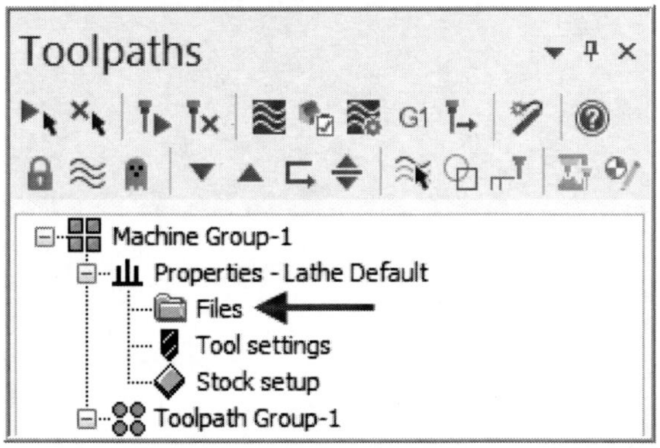

5. Click on the **Replace** icon as shown below:

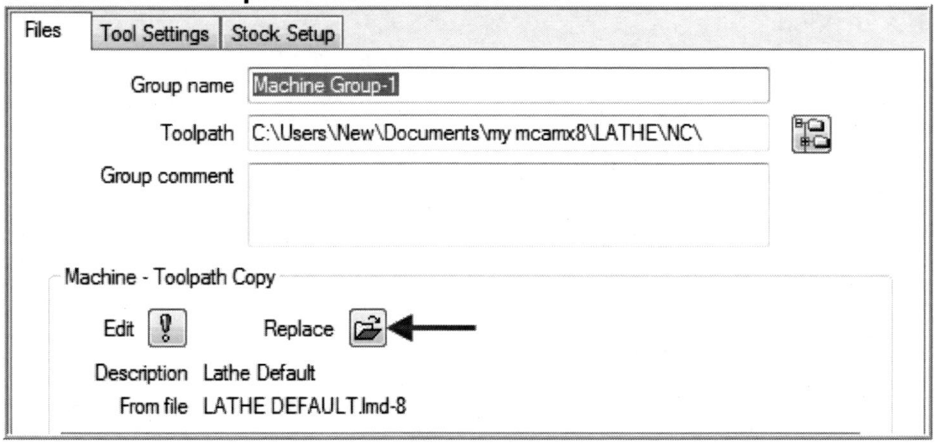

6. Select **Lathe C-AXIS SLANT BED** from the list of files as shown below

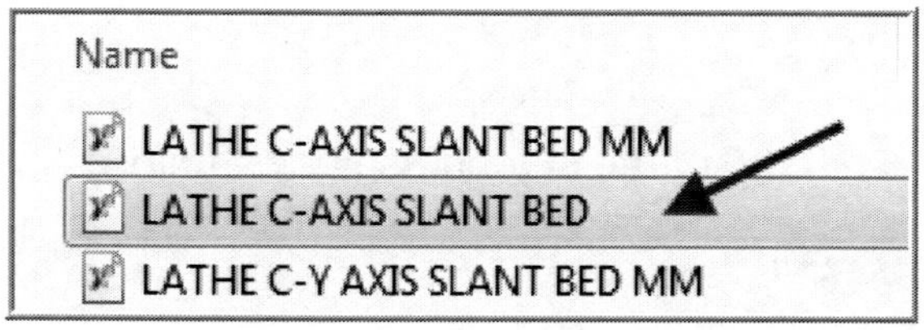

7. Click on the OK icon in the Replace Group Machine window (if it appears).

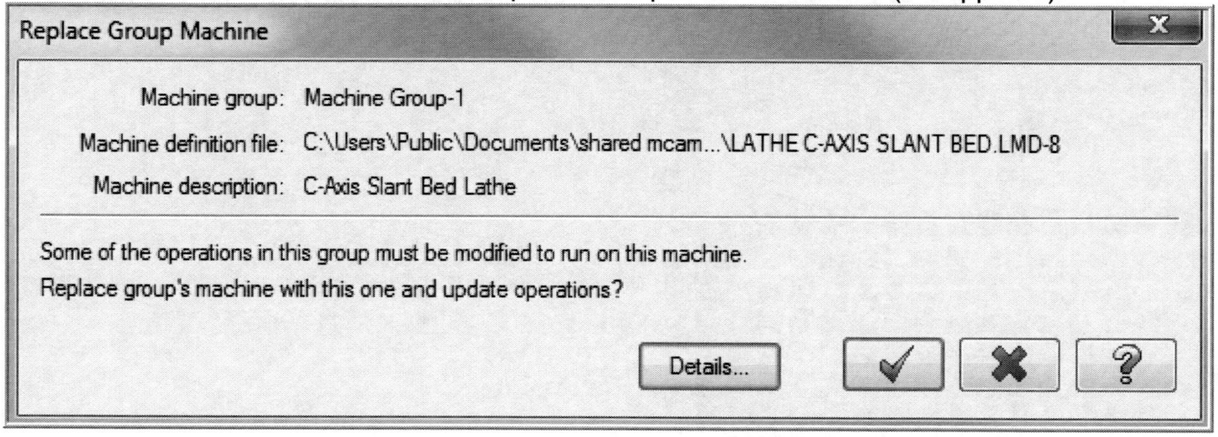

8. Click on the OK icon once again at the Machine group Properties page to exit.
9. Select the Regenerate all dirty operations button to remove the red X from the operations.

➲ **Set the Construction Plane to Lathe diameter +D +Z (WCS)**

10. Click on **Planes** on the **Status bar** at the bottom of the screen.
11. Click on **Lathe diameter>+D +Z (WCS)** as shown below:

TASK 3:
CREATE THE POINTS

1. Click on **Wireframe Color** on the Status bar at the bottom of the screen as shown below:

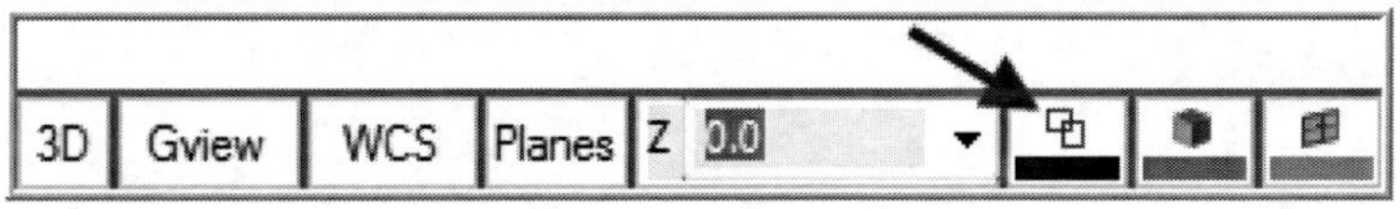

2. Click on color **11 (Cyan)** as shown below: Note: this will change the color of the points that you will be creating.

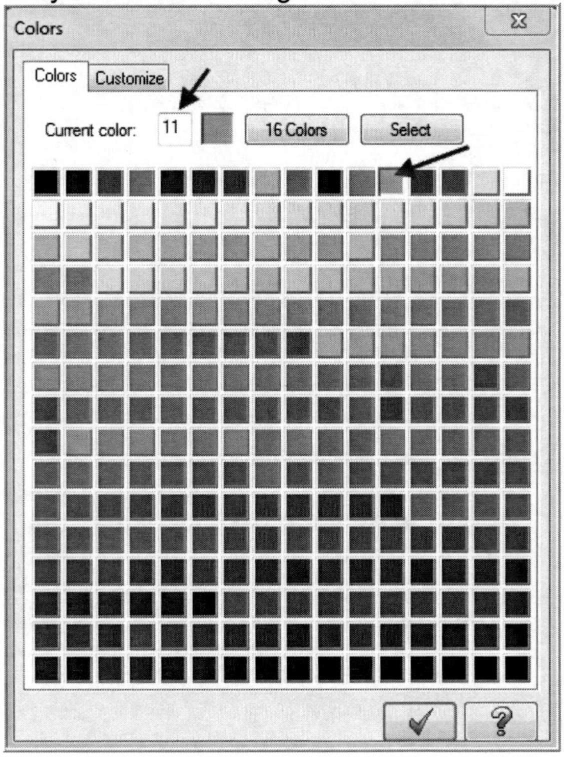

3. Click on **OK.**
4. Select **Alt-T** on the keyboard to hide the display of toolpaths.
5. Click on **CREATE>Point> Position…**

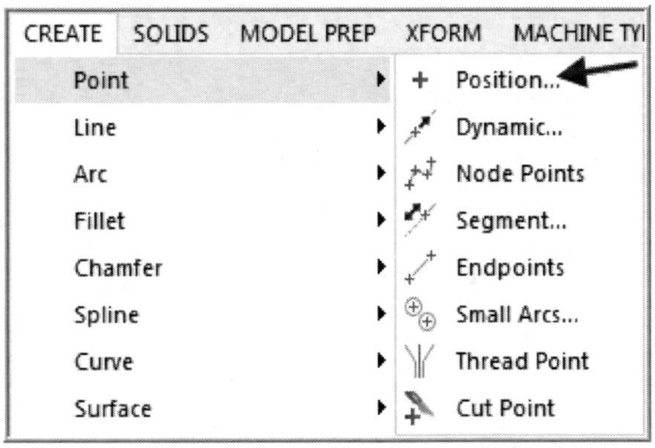

6. You are prompted to **Sketch a Point**. Click in the **D** entry point window as shown below and type **1.0** and hit the **Enter key**. Type in **-0.25** for the **Z value** and hit the **Enter Key**. Note the value of Y is set to Zero, this does not need to be input.

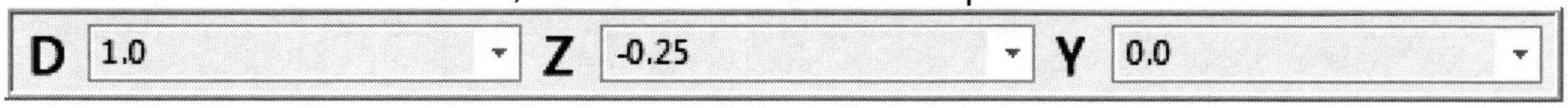

7. Click on **OK**.
8. A point will be displayed on the geometry like the diagram shown below:

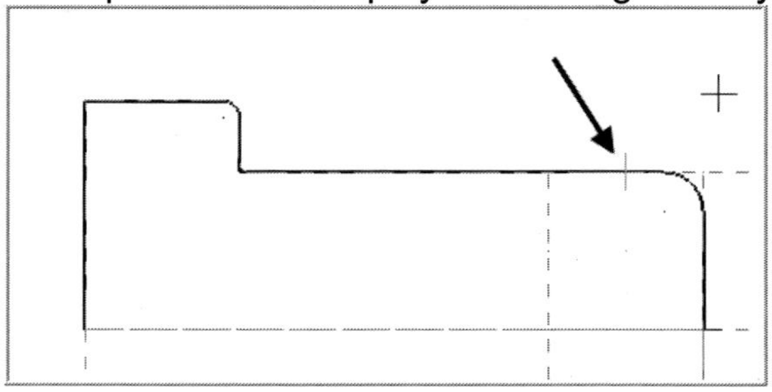

9. Select the **Isometric View** by clicking on the **Isometric Icon**  .
10. Select the screen fit icon .
11. Your screen should look like the diagram shown below:
12. Click on **XFORM>Rotate…**

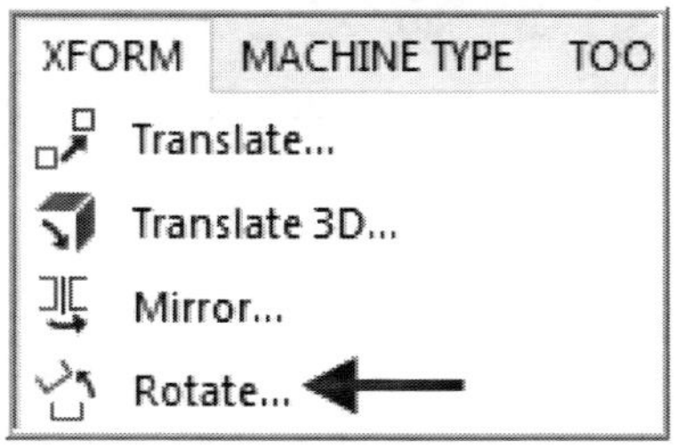

13. You are prompted to **Rotate: select entities to rotate.** Click on **Only** as shown below:

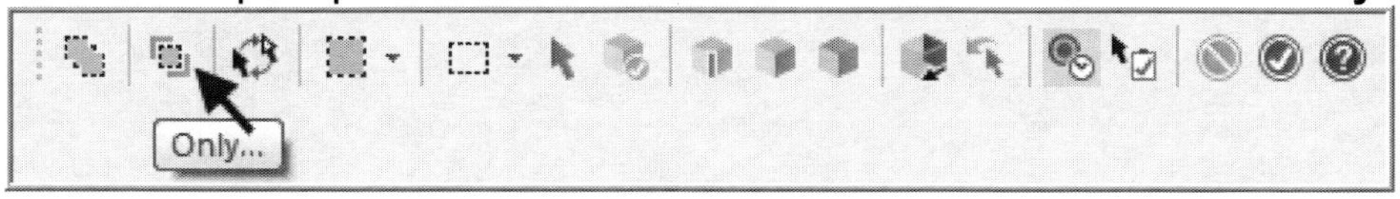

14. Activate checkmark for **Entities**. Click on **Points** and **OK** as shown below: **Note**: this will ensure only the point is selected and not the line attached to the point.

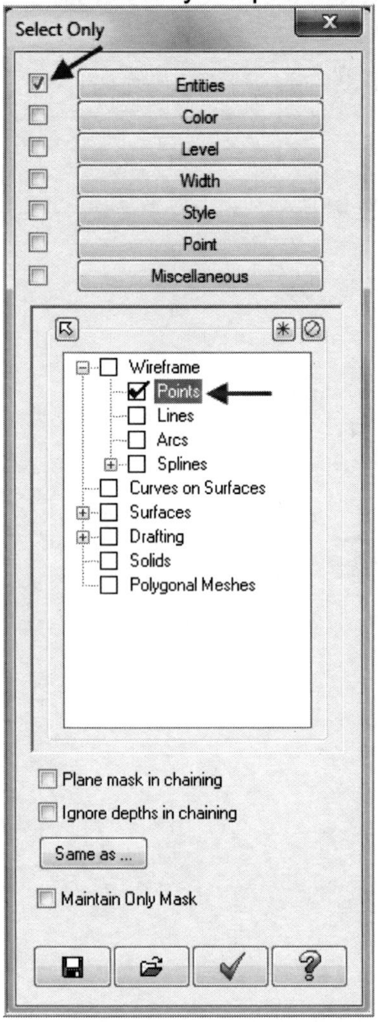

Select Only dialog box
Use this dialog box to set selection masks, which restrict entity selection to defined sets of criteria.

Set the criteria and choose the OK button. This closes the dialog box and lets you manually select any entities in the graphics window that meet the criteria.

This masking method, prohibits you from selecting entities that do not match your criteria.

Entities button
Restricts the entities that you can select based on the type of entity.
When you click the Entities checkbox or button, the corresponding entity selections display in the Criteria List area.

Choosing an entity type in the Criteria List area will disable selection of any other type of entity.

For example, choosing Wireframe enables you to select points, lines, arcs, and splines but disables the selection of surfaces, solids, and other entity non-wireframe types.

15. Select the **Point** as shown below:

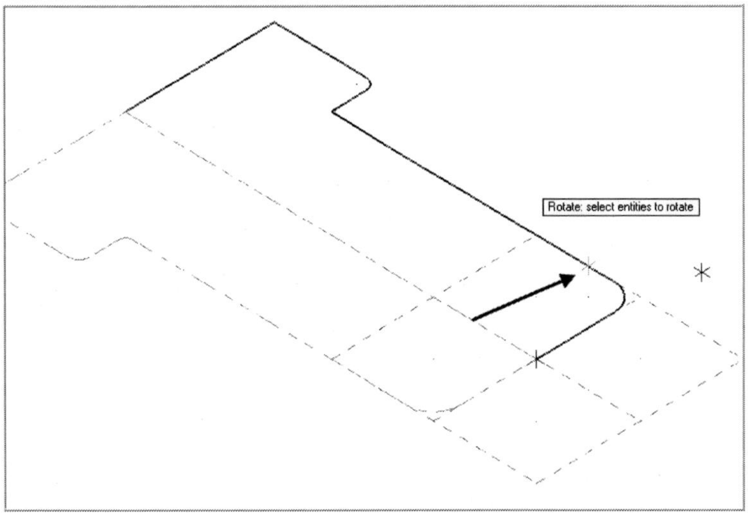

16. Click on **End Selection**.

17. The **Rotate** dialogue window appears. Make the changes as shown in the diagram below:

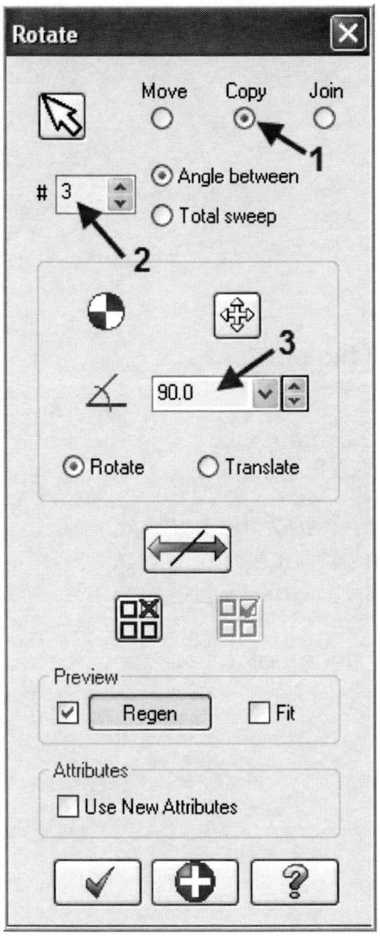

#1 Copy
Copies the points rather than moves them.

 # (2)
The number of points to add, in this case we will be adding 3 more points.

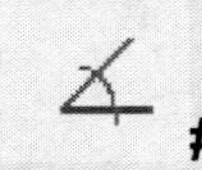
#(3)
How many degrees each point is rotated from the other point.
Since a circle is 360 degrees and we are putting 4 points equally spaced around the diameter of the part, then each point will be 90 degrees.
(360 / 4 = 90)

18. Select the **screen fit** icon .
19. Notice the points are in the **wrong position** as shown in **Diagram 1** below. They should be in the position as shown in **Diagram 2** below.

Diagram 1 – Incorrect Point Position

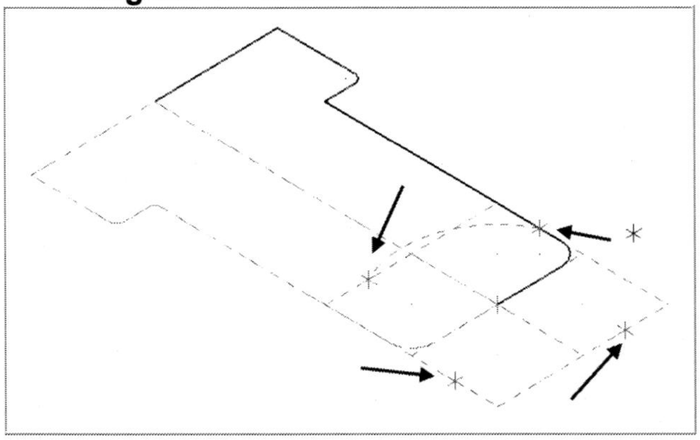

Diagram 2 – Correct Point Position

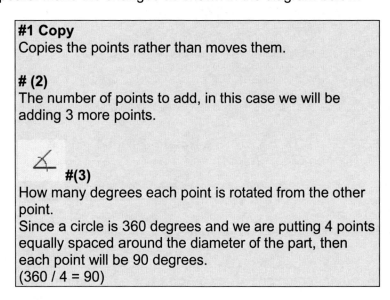

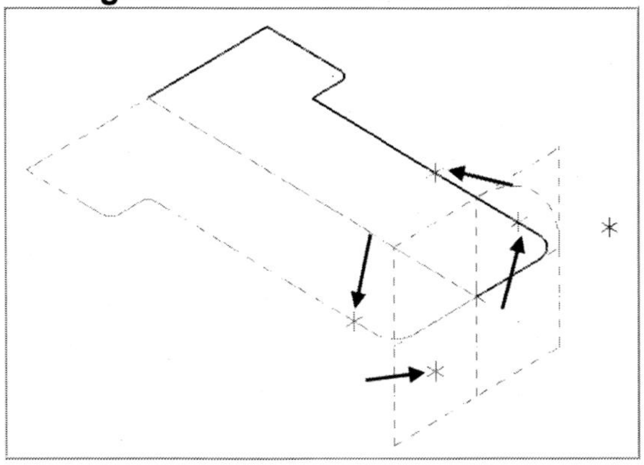

20. To put the points in the correct position click on the **Right (WCS)** icon as shown below:

Changing the **Construction Plane** from **Top** to **Right** will ensure the points are created around the diameter of the workpiece. Notice how the points change to the proper position.

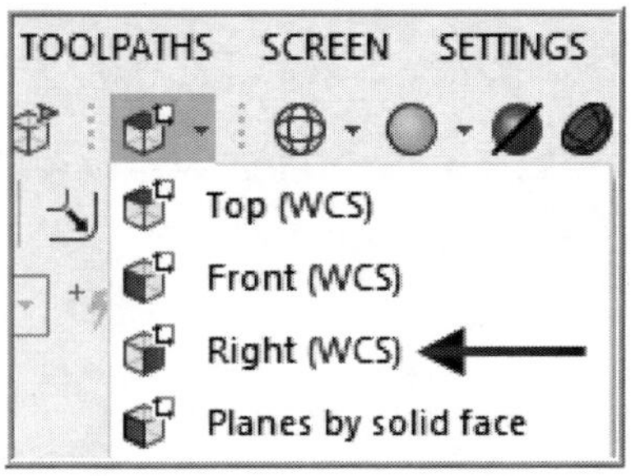

21. Click on **OK**  in the **Rotate** dialogue window.
22. Click on **Clear Colors**.
23. Change the view to Right. . Notice the location of the points.
24. Change the view to **Isometric** .
25. Change the view to **Dynamic Rotation** 
26. When prompted to **Pick a point to begin dynamics** select the **origin** of the part.
27. After picking the origin move the mouse around to view the geometry at a different angle. Notice the location of the points now in the correct position. When finished with Dynamic Rotation **Click a mouse button when done**.
28. Change the graphics view to a Top View by using the toolbar at the top of the screen.

29. Select the **screen fit** icon .

TASK 4:
SAVE THE UPDATED MASTERCAM FILE

1. Select the **save** icon from the toolbar 

.

Toolpath Creation

TASK 5:
DRILL THE POINTS USING C-AXIS DRILL

1. Select the **Isometric View** by clicking on the **Isometric Icon** .
2. Select the screen fit icon .
3. Select **Alt-T** on the keyboard to display toolpaths.
4. In the Toolpaths Manager move the red **Insert arrow** before the Cutoff operation as shown below. Use the Arrow icons shown below right to position the Insert arrow up or down.

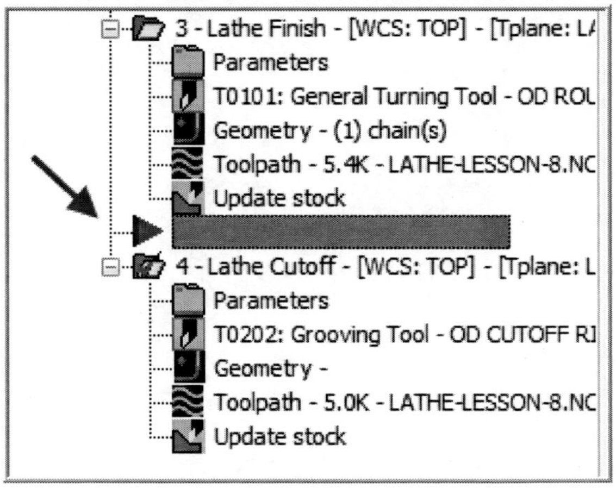

The insert arrow controls where new operations will be inserted.

Its default position is at the bottom of the list of operations

5. Click on **TOOLPATHS>C-axis>C-axis Drill…**

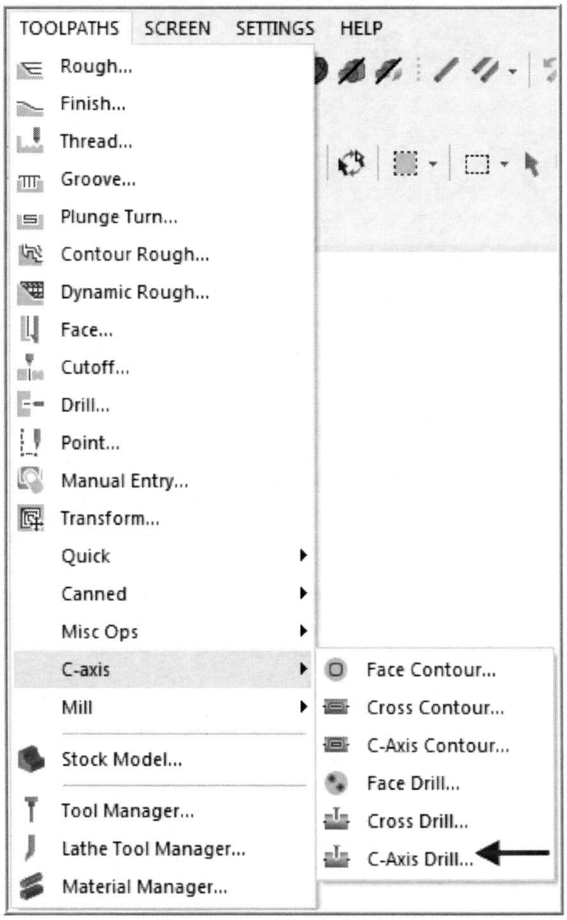

6. You are prompted to **Select Points**. Make sure the Select Drill point position in graphics screen button is selected as shown below:

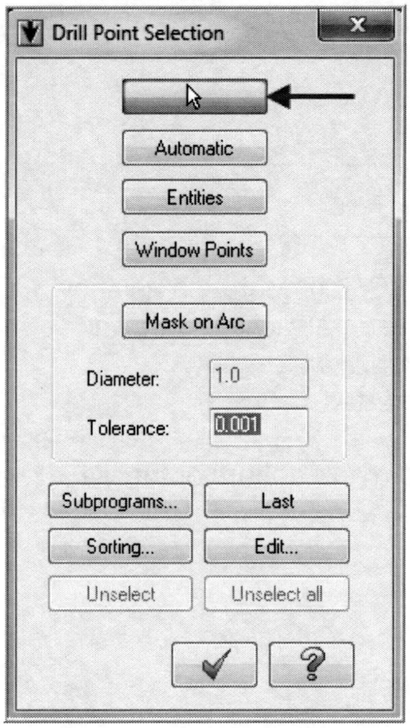

7. Click on the **4 points** in order as shown below:

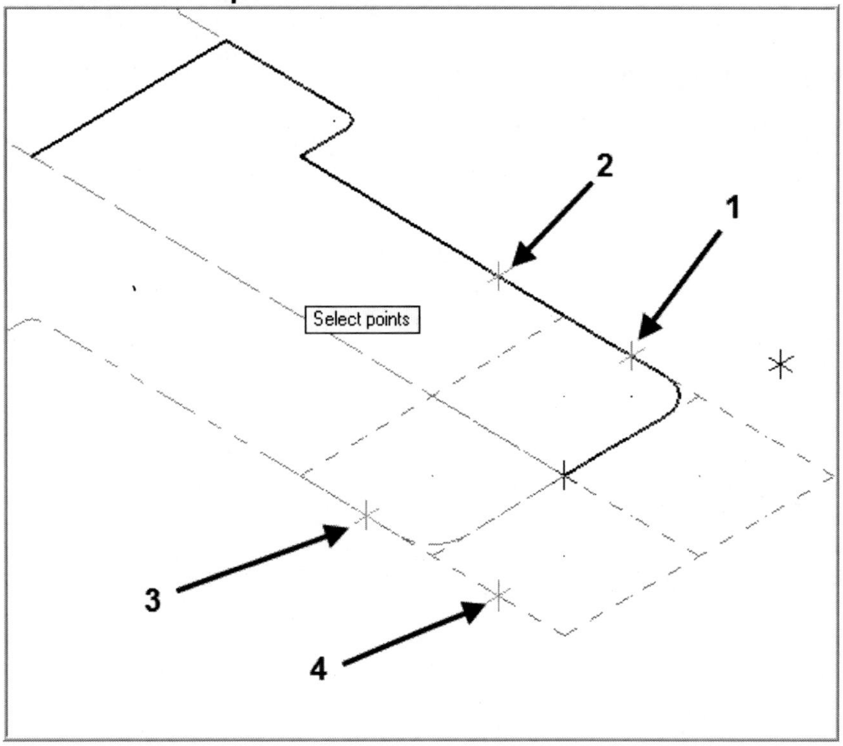

8. Click **OK** .

9. Select the **Tool** menu and then click on **Select library tool…** as shown below:

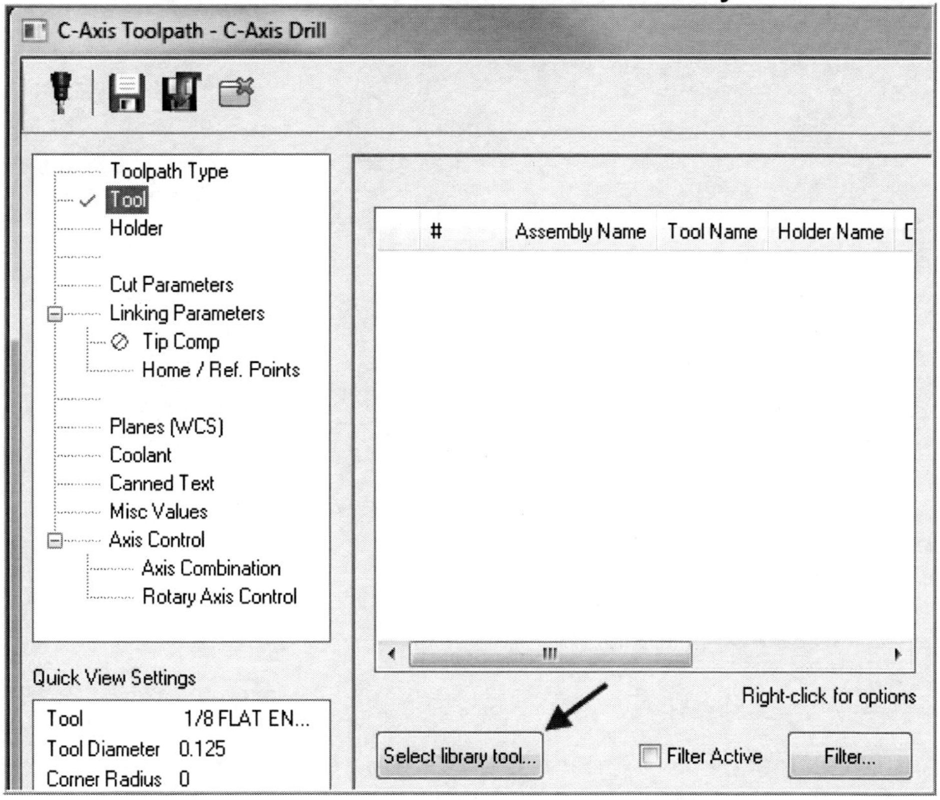

10. Scroll down the Tool Selection window and select the **1/8 Flat End Mill** as shown below:

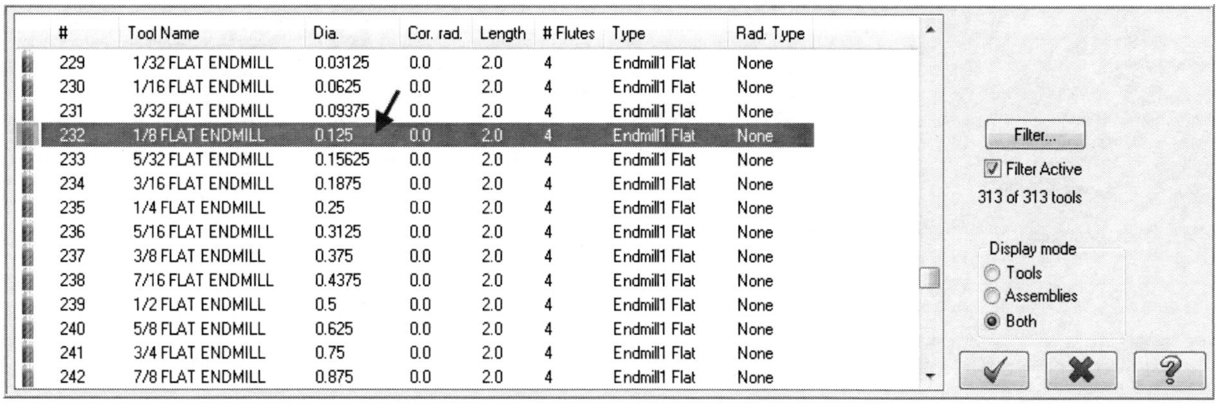

11. Click on **OK** .

12. Make the changes as shown below:

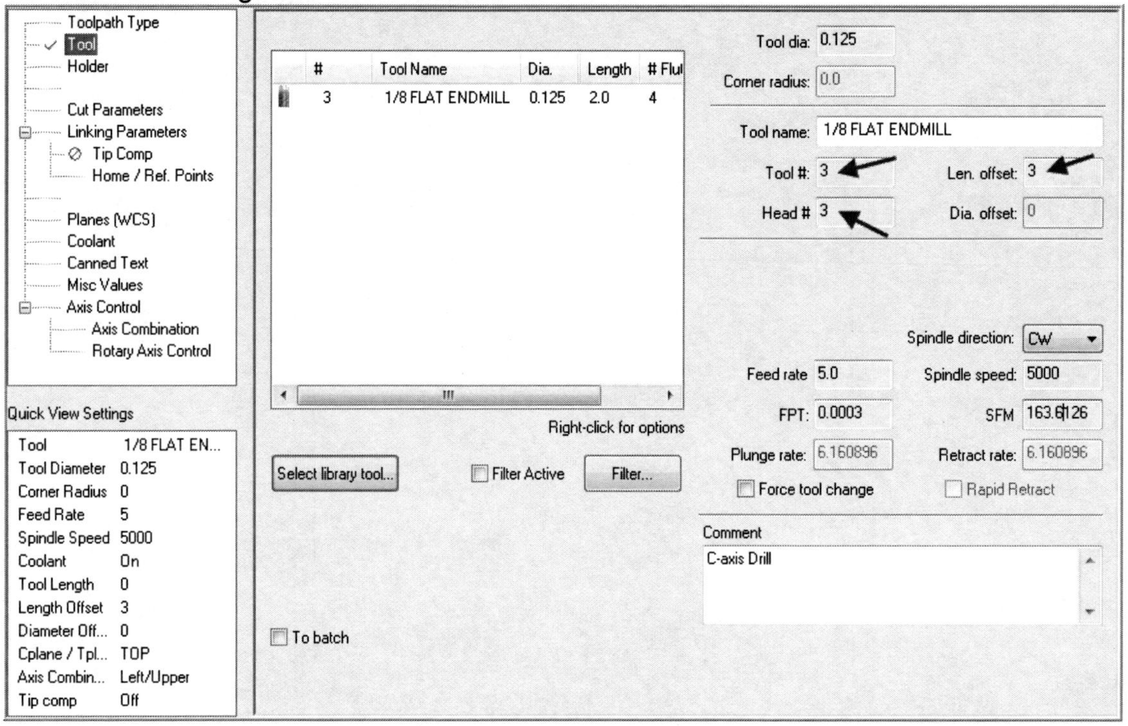

13. Expand the **Axis Control** menu and select **Rotary Axis Control.** Change the **Rotary Diameter** to **1.0** in the **Rotary Axis dialogue screen** as shown below: **Note:** this is the diameter of the part that the holes will be drilled into.

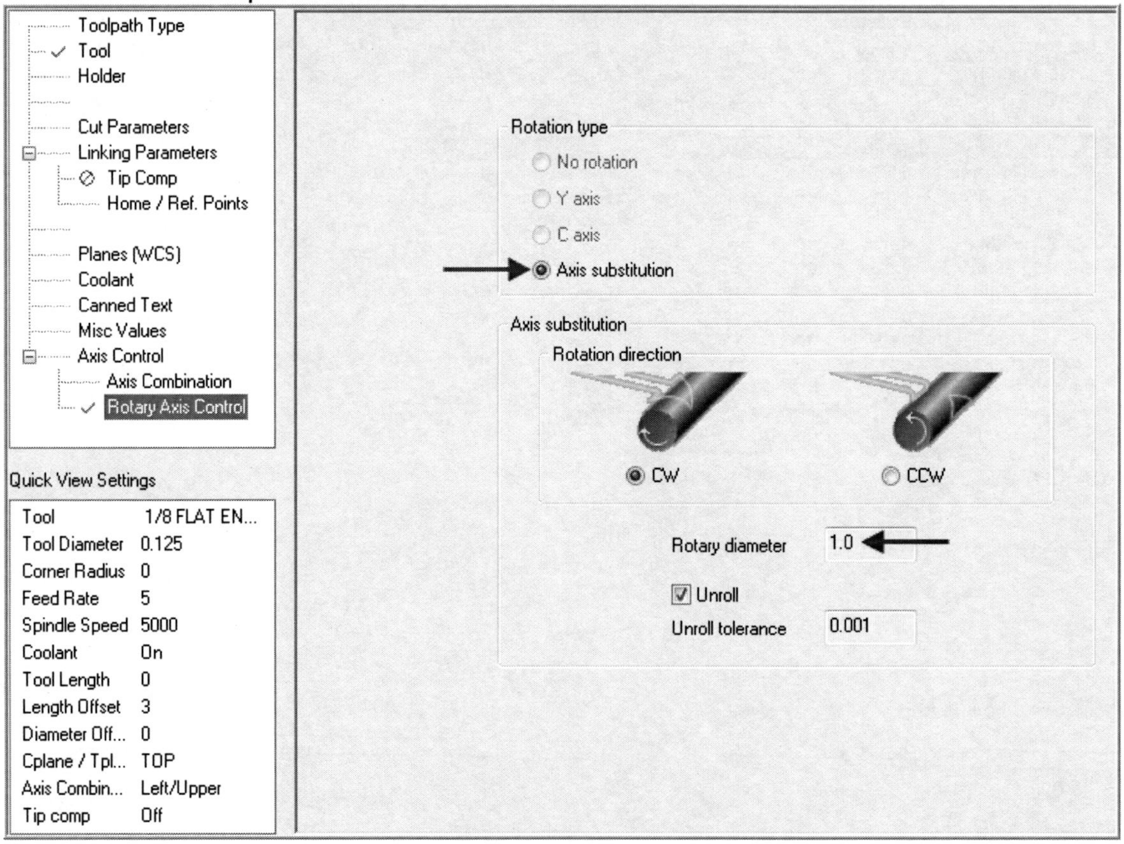

Rotary Axis Control (Lathe) page
Use this dialog box to configure rotary axis motion for Lathe applications.

For **axis substitution**, you need to tell Mastercam more information about how to wrap the geometry.

Select the direction of rotation and the diameter of the cylinder around which to wrap the geometry. Being able to specify these parameters in this dialog box means you do not have to have the cylinder created as geometry in your part file.

Note: Before you can create rotary axis motion, you need to configure the rotary axis components in your machine definition. You will only be able to select rotary axis options which are supported by your machine definition.

Unroll
Unrolls geometry wrapped on a cylinder so it lies flat on a plane. Cutter compensation and retract moves are then calculated relative to the flat geometry. When the toolpath posts, the geometry wraps back onto the cylinder using the Axis substitution and Rotary Diameter parameters. Only available for contour and drill toolpaths.

14. Click on the **Linking Parameters** menu and change the **Depth to -0.125** as shown below:

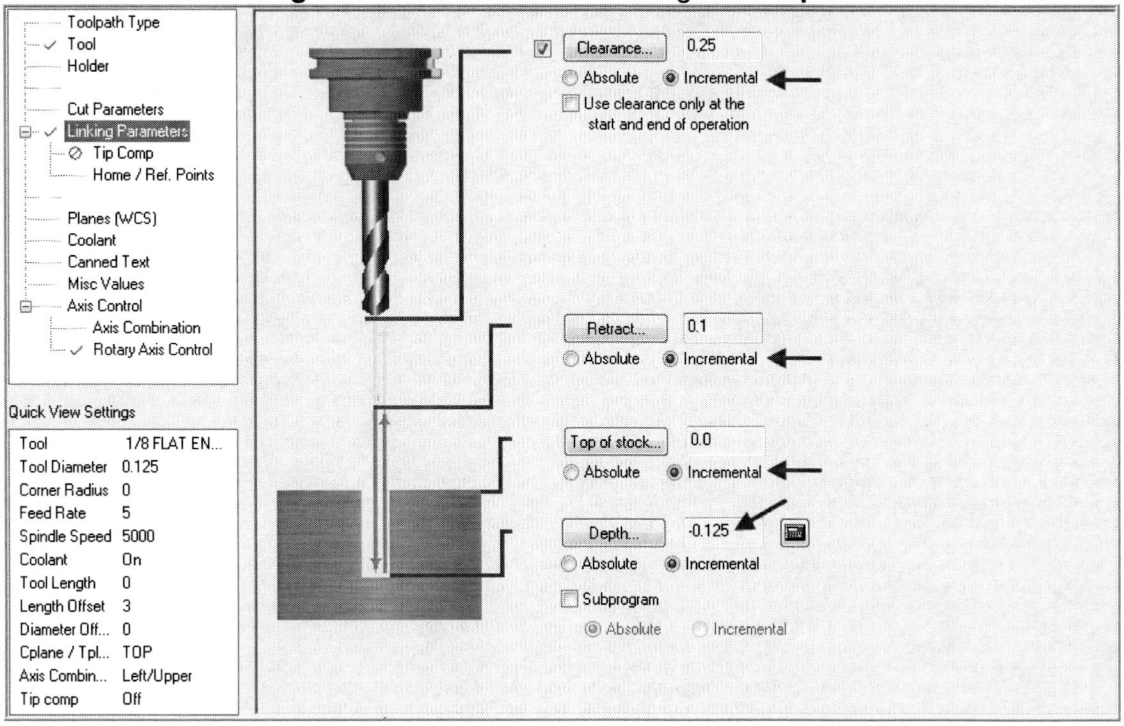

15. Click **OK** .

16. In the Toolpaths Manager move the red **Insert arrow** after the Cutoff operation. Use the red Arrow icons to position the Insert arrow up or down
17. Select the screen fit icon .
18. The view around the part should look like the diagram shown below:

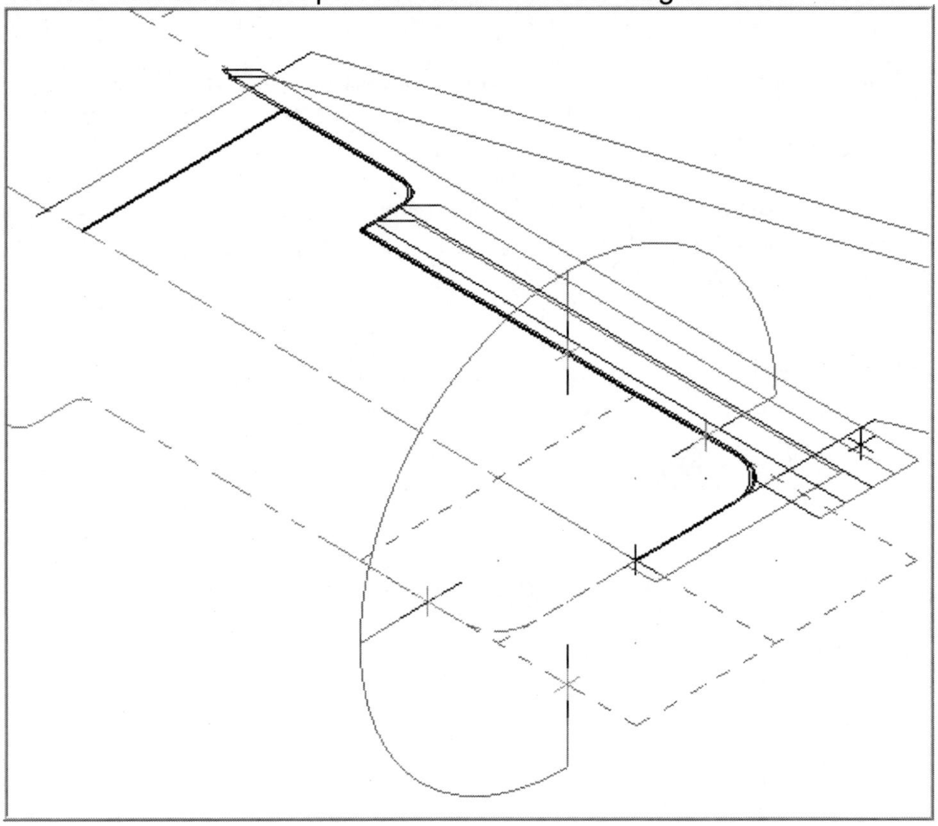

TASK 6:
BACKPLOT THE TOOLPATH

- In this task you will use Mastercam's Backplot function to view the path the tools take to cut this part.
- Backplot will enable us to review the cutting motions and identify any problem areas when cutting the part.

1. To pick all the operations to Backplot pick the **Select All** icon .
2. The next step is to select the **Backplot selected operations** icon shown below:

3. **Maximize** the Backplot/Verify window if required.
4. Select the **Home** Tab if required.
5. Activate the options shown below in the **Visibility** section of the Home tab.

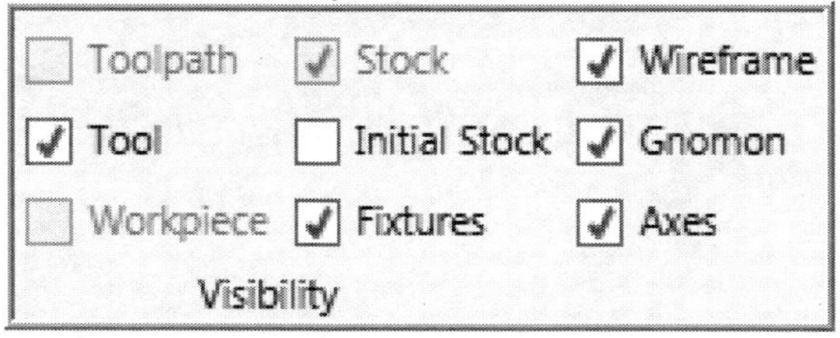

6. At the top of the screen select the **View** tab, the **Isometric** icon and then select **Fit**.
7. Click on the **Backplot** tab at the top left of the screen

8. Activate the **Both** option in the Toolpath section of the Backplot tab.

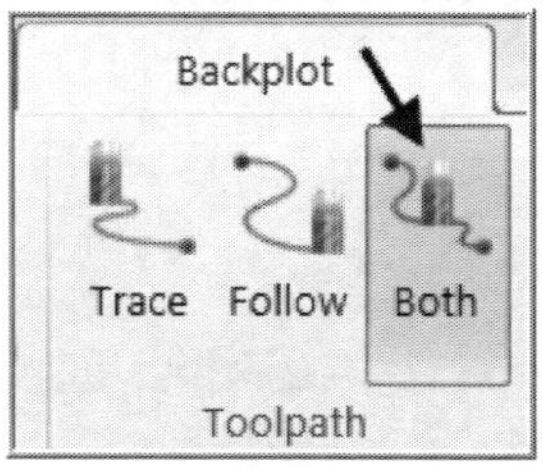

9. In the lower right corner of the screen now set the run Speed to slow by moving the slider bar pointer over to the left as shown below.

10. Now select the **Play Simulation** button to review the toolpaths.

11. After reviewing the Backplot of the toolpaths select the **Close** button 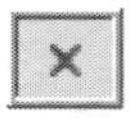 to exit Backplot.

TASK 7:
VERIFY THE TOOLPATH

➲ Mastercam's Verify utility allows you to use solid models to simulate the machining of a part. The model created by the verification represents the surface finish, and shows collisions, if any exist.

1. In the **Toolpaths Manager** pick all the operations to verify by picking the **Select All** icon .

2. Select the **Verify selected operations** icon shown below:

3. **Maximize** the Backplot/Verify window if required.
4. Now select the Home Tab if required.
5. Activate the options shown below in the **Visibility** section of the Home tab. Initial Stock not activated.

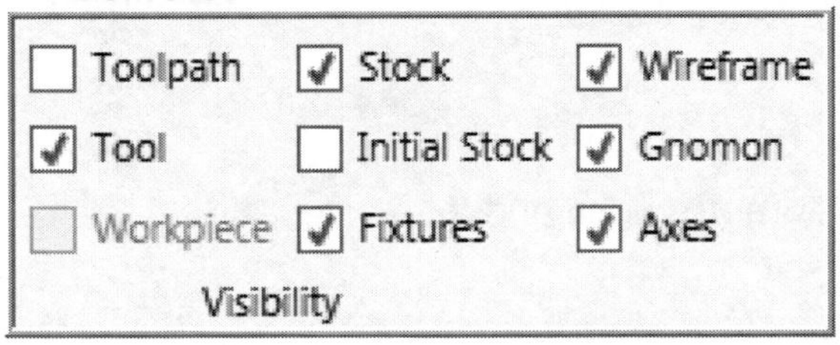

6. Activate the **Color Loop** to change the color of the tools for the verified part.
7. At the top of the screen select the **View** tab, the **Isometric** icon and then select **Fit**.
8. In the lower right corner of the screen now set the run **Speed** to slow by moving the slider bar pointer over to the left.
9. Now select the **Play Simulation** button to review the toolpaths.

10. Select the **Close** button  in the top right hand corner to exit Verify.

TASK 8:
SAVE THE UPDATED MASTERCAM FILE

1. Select the **save** icon from the toolbar .

TASK 9:
POST AND CREATE THE CNC CODE FILE

1. Before you post the code enlarge the **Toolpaths Manager** window to the right as shown below. Click on the **right hand pane** and **slide to the right**.

➲ At present the **Program** number is set to 1 and the toolpath data file is set to **Lathe-Lesson-1.NC** because we initially made a duplicate of Lathe-lesson-1. You will now change the 1 to 8 for both of these as this is Lesson 8.

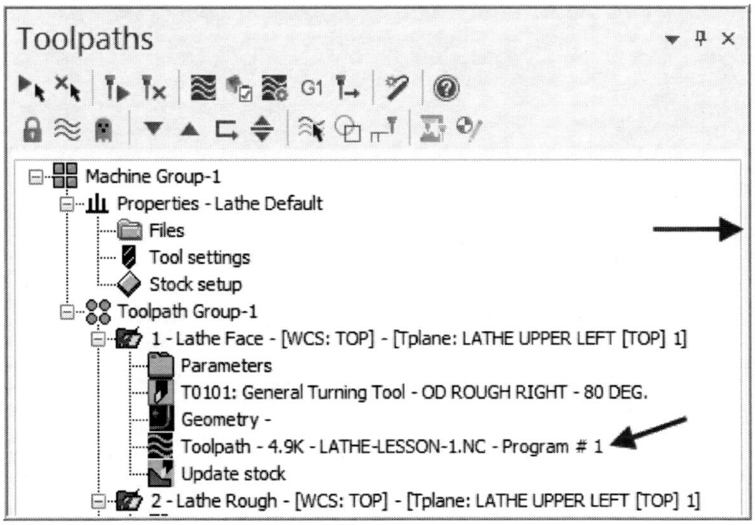

2. Right mouse click over the first operation folder. Select **Edit selected operations** and then pick **Change Program #.**

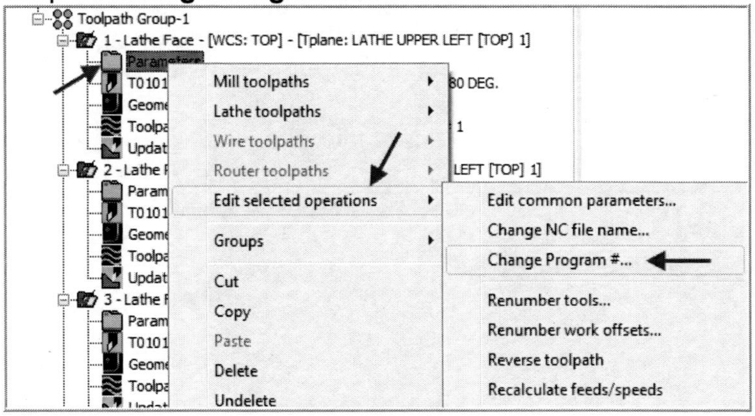

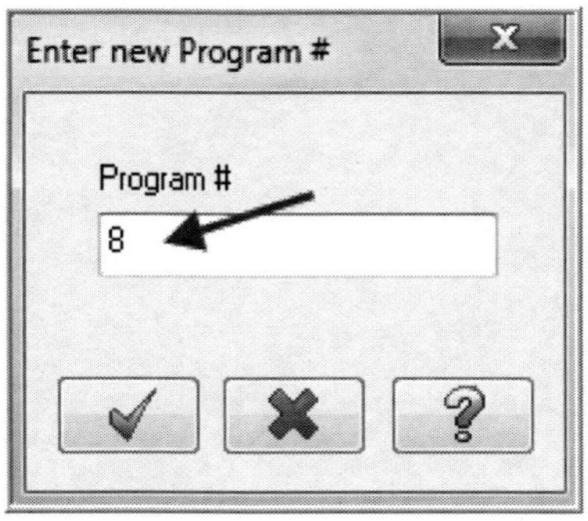

3. Enter **8** for the new Program number as shown above.

4. Right mouse click over the first operation folder. Select **Edit selected operations** and then pick **Change NC file name.**

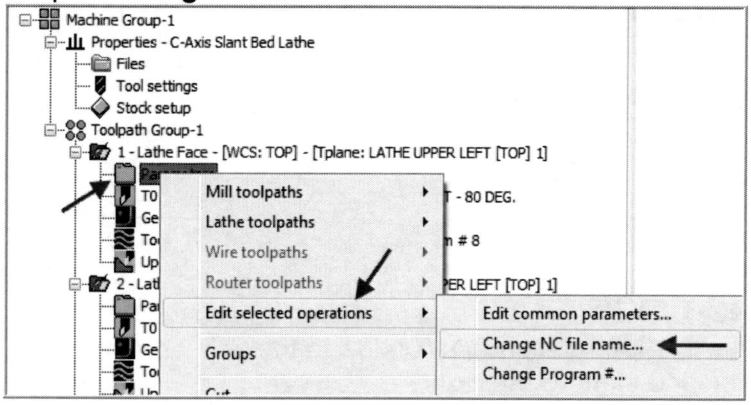

5. Enter **LATHE-LESSON-8** for the new NC name as shown below.

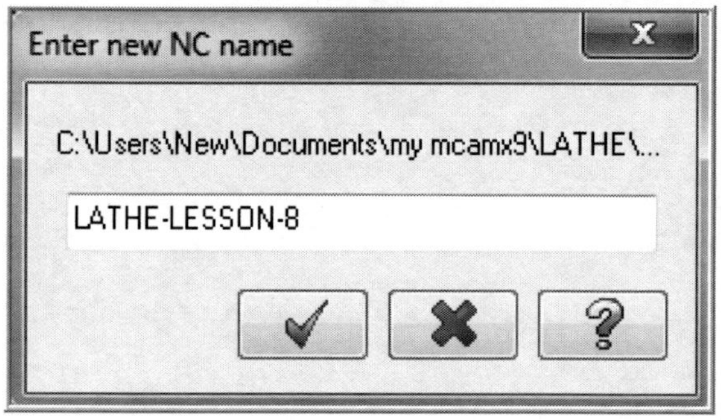

6. Ensure all the operations are selected by picking the **Select All** icon  from the **Toolpaths Manager.**
7. Select the **Post selected operations** button from the **Toolpaths Manager.**
8. In the Post processing window, make the necessary changes as shown below:

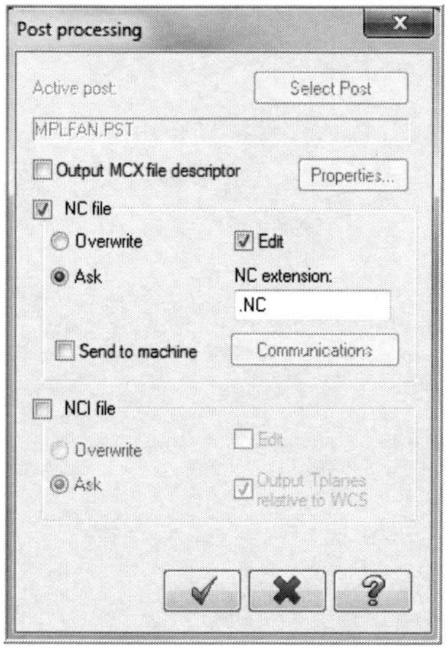

About Post Processing

NC file: Select this option to save the NC file. The file name and extension are stored in the machine group properties for the selected operation. If you are posting operations from different machine groups or Mastercam files, or batch processing, Mastercam will create several files according to the settings for each machine group.

Edit: When checked, automatically launches the default text editor with the file displayed so that you can review or modify it.

9. Select the **OK** button  to continue.

10. Enter the same name as your Mastercam part file name in the **NC File name** field **LATHE-LESSON-8.**
11. Select the **Save** button.
12. The CNC code file opens up in the default editor.

LATHE-LESSON-8.NC ×

```
(MATERIAL - ALUMINUM INCH - 6061)
G20
(TOOL - 1 OFFSET - 1)
(OD ROUGH RIGHT - 80 DEG.  INSERT - CNMG-432)
G0 T0101
G97 S449 M03
G0 G54 X1.7 Z0.
G50 S3600
G96 S200
G99 G1 X-.0625 F.01
G0 Z.1
X1.2784
Z.2
G1 Z.1
Z-1.495
X1.2975
G3 X1.47 Z-1.5813 R.0862
```

13. Scroll down the CNC code until you locate the commands to rotate the chuck (C-Axis) when drilling the four holes.

```
(TOOL - 3 OFFSET - 0)
( 1/8 FLAT ENDMILL)
(C-AXIS DRILL)
G0 T0300
M23
G0 G55 X1.5 Z-.25
C0.
G97 S2500 M51
G81 X.75 R1.2 F5.
C90.
C180.
C270.
G80
G28 U0. W0. H0. M55
T0300
M01
```

14. Select the × in the top right corner to exit the CNC editor.

➲ This completes LATHE-LESSON-8.

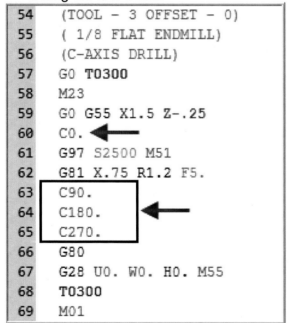

LATHE-LESSON-8 EXERCISE

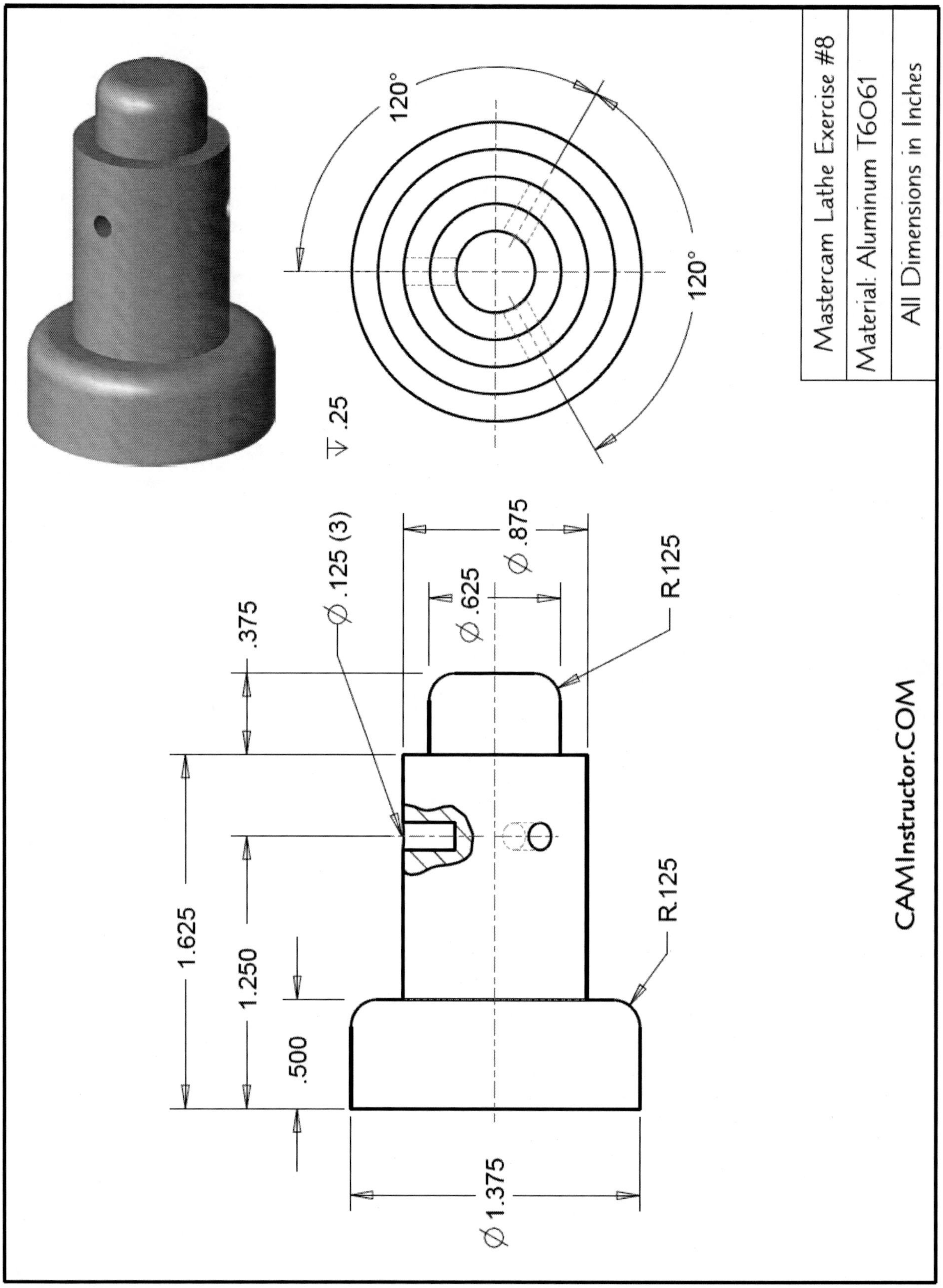

Mastercam® X9

TRAINING GUIDE

LATHE-LESSON-9

C-AXIS CROSS CONTOUR

camInstructor

Objectives

You will create the geometry for Lathe-Lesson-9, and then generate a toolpath to machine the part on a CNC lathe. This lesson covers the following topics:

➲ **Create a 2-dimensional drawing by:**
Creating lines.
Creating fillets.
Creating lines rotated about the diameter.

➲ **Establish Stock and Chuck settings:**
Stock size.
Chuck Configuration.
Material for the part.
Feed calculation.

➲ **Generate a C-Axis lathe toolpath consisting of:**
Lathe Face.
Lathe Rough.
Lathe Finish.
Lathe Drill.
Lathe Bore.
C-Axis Cross Contour.
Lathe Cutoff.
Modify geometry and update toolpath operations

➲ **Inspect the toolpath using Mastercam's Verify and Backplot by:**
Launching the Verify function to machine the part on the screen.
Using Backplot to identify the correctness of the toolpaths.
Generating the NC- code.

LATHE-LESSON-9 DRAWING

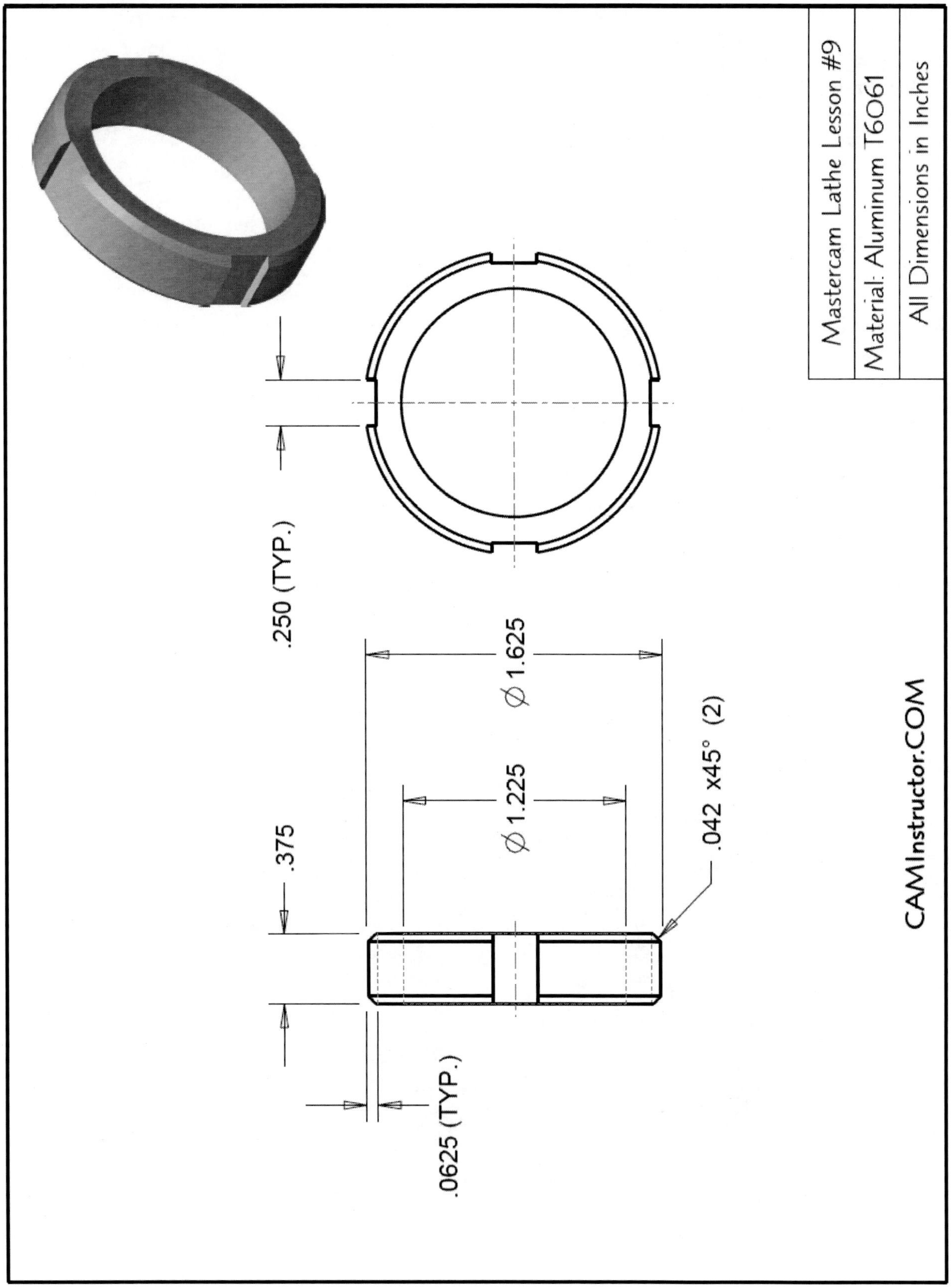

TOOL LIST

Eight tools will be used to create this part.

- **Tool #1 Face and Rough**
  Holder: Outside Diameter Rough Right Hand - DCGNR-164D.
  Insert: 80 Degree Diamond Insert – CNMG-432

- **Tool #2 Finish the outside diameter**
  Holder: Outside Diameter Finish Right Hand - MVJNR-164D.
  Insert: 35 Degree Diamond Insert – VNMG-431

- **Tool #3 Center drill**
  Centre Drill – body diameter 0.250"

- **Tool #4 0.375 diameter drill**
  Drill 0.375" diameter

- **Tool #5 0.500 diameter drill**
  Drill 0.5" diameter

- **Tool #6 Boring Tool**
  Holder: Boring Bar – minimum diameter 0.375".
  Insert: 75 Degree Diamond Insert

- **Tool #7 ¼" Flat End Mill**
  End Mill 0.25" diameter

- **Tool #8 Cutoff tool**
  Holder: Outside Diameter Groove Right Hand - Narrow.
  Insert: 0.125" Wide - GC-4125

LATHE - LESSON - 9 - THE PROCESS

Geometry Creation

TASK 1: Setting the Environment
TASK 2: Setting the Construction Planes
TASK 3: Create the Geometry
TASK 4 Create the Chamfers
TASK 5: Save the Drawing

Toolpath Creation

TASK 6: Define the Stock and Chuck Parameters
TASK 7: Face the Front of the Part
TASK 8: Rough the Outside Diameters
TASK 9: Finish the Outside Diameters
TASK 10: Center Drill the hole
TASK 11: Pre drill the 1.125" hole 0.375" diameter
TASK 12: Pre drill the 1.125" hole 0.500" diameter
TASK 13: Rough the bore
TASK 14: Finish the bore
TASK 15: Machine the first slot using C-axis Cross Contour
TASK 16: Machine the remaining three Slots using Transform Toolpath
TASK 17: Cut off the Part
TASK 18: Modify 1.625" diameter and regenerate operations
TASK 19: Backplot the Toolpath
TASK 20: Verify the Toolpath
TASK 21: Save the Updated Mastercam File
TASK 22: Post and Create the CNC Code File

Geometry Creation

TASK 1:
SETTING THE ENVIRONMENT

➲ Before starting the geometry creation you should set up the grid and toolbars as outlined in the **Setting the Environment** section at the beginning of this text:

1. Set up the Grid. This will help identify the location of the origin.
2. Load the Workspace – **SETTINGS>Load Workspace>Lathe** to machine a part on the Lathe.
3. Set the machine type to the **C Axis Slant Bed** Lathe.
4. Click on **Machine Type>Lathe>C-AXIS SLANT BED.LMD** as shown below. If the machine type is not displayed, follow the step 5-8.

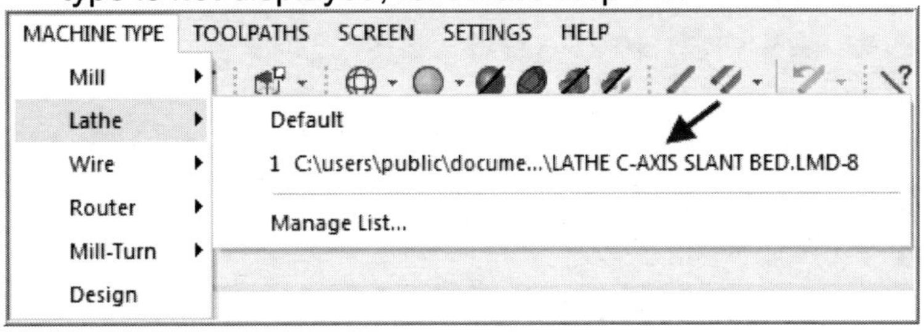

5. Click on Machine **Type>Lathe>Manage list** as shown below.

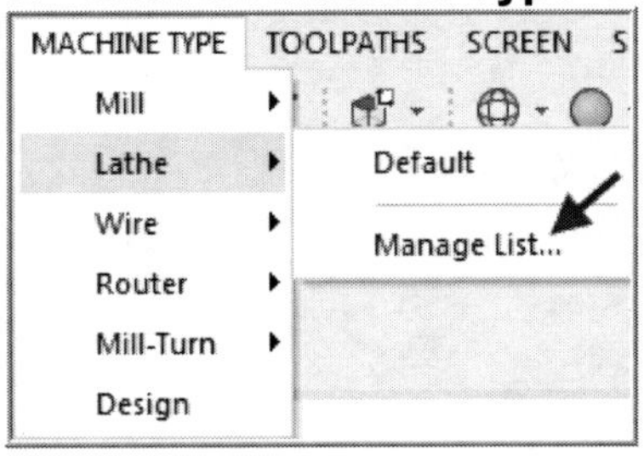

6. The **Machine Definition Menu Management** window appears. Select **LATHE C-AXIS SLANT BED.LMD** from the list and click on **Add** button  as shown below:

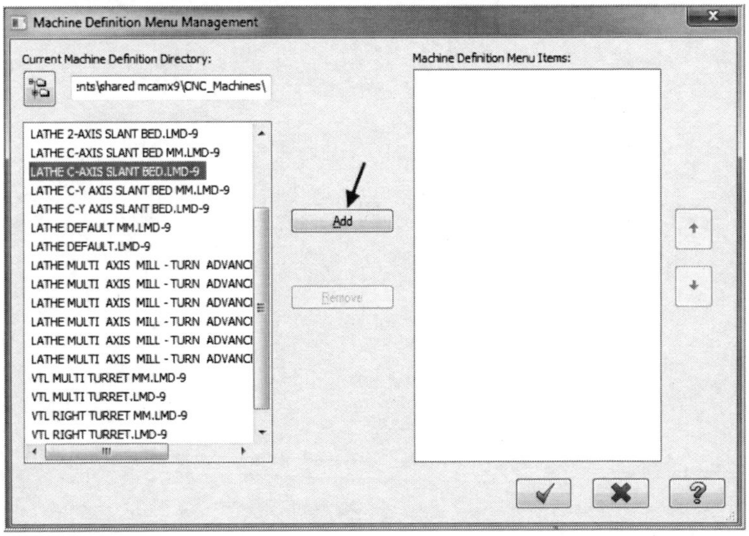

7. Click on the OK icon .
8. Click on **Machine Type>Lathe>C-AXIS SLANT BED.LMD**

TASK 2:
SETTING THE CONSTRUCTION PLANES:

➲ **Set the Construction Plane to Lathe diameter +D +Z (WCS)**

1. Click on **Planes** on the **Status bar** at the bottom of the screen.
2. Click on **Lathe diameter>+D +Z (WCS)** as shown below:

TASK 3:
CREATE THE GEOMETRY – THE RIGHT HAND FACE IS AT Z0

➲ This task explains how to create the geometry of this part. In this lathe part you only need to create **half of the geometry**, the geometry above the center line.
➲ Lines 1, 2 and 3 will be created using the Create Rectangle command.
➲ Lines 4 and 5 will be created using the Xform Offset command.
➲ The Chamfers will be created last.

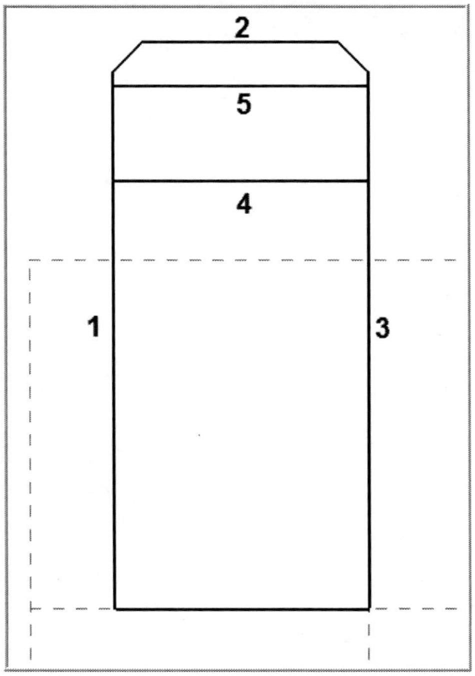

➲ Create Lines 1, 2 and 3

1. Select from the pull down menu **Create>Rectangular Shapes…**

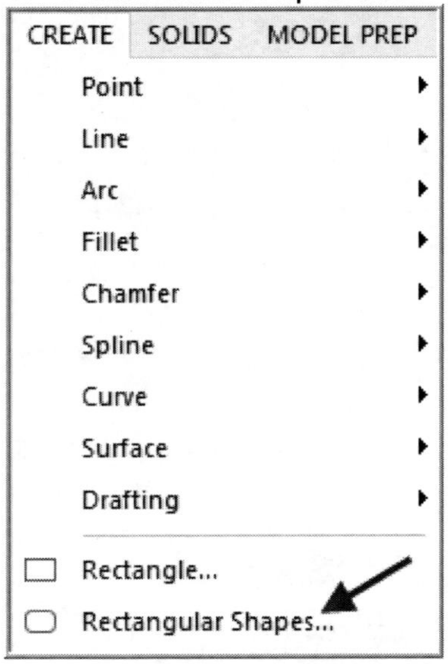

2. The **Rectangular Shapes Options** window appears. You are prompted t**o "Select position of base point".** Move the cursor over the **center of the grid** and as you get close to the origin a visual cue appears.  This is the cue that will allow you to snap to the origin. With this visual cue highlighted pick the origin as shown below:

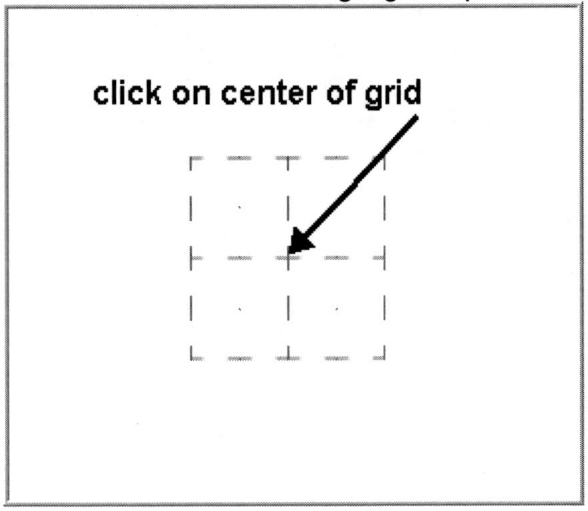

3. Fill in the **Rectangular Shapes Options** window as shown below:

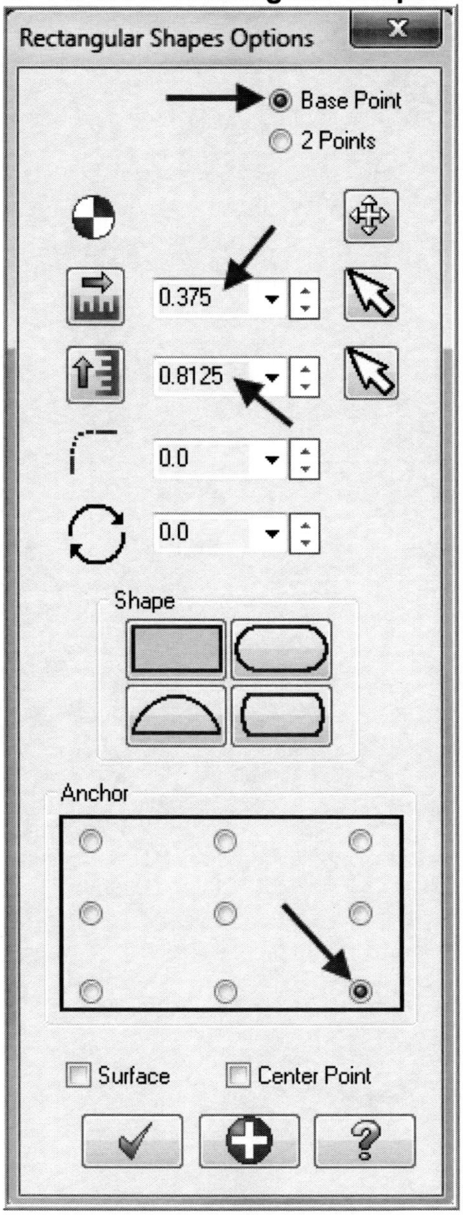

4. Click on **OK**.

5. Select the screen fit icon .
6. Select **Un-Zoom Previous / .5** 

.
7. A **rectangle** should be visible as shown below:

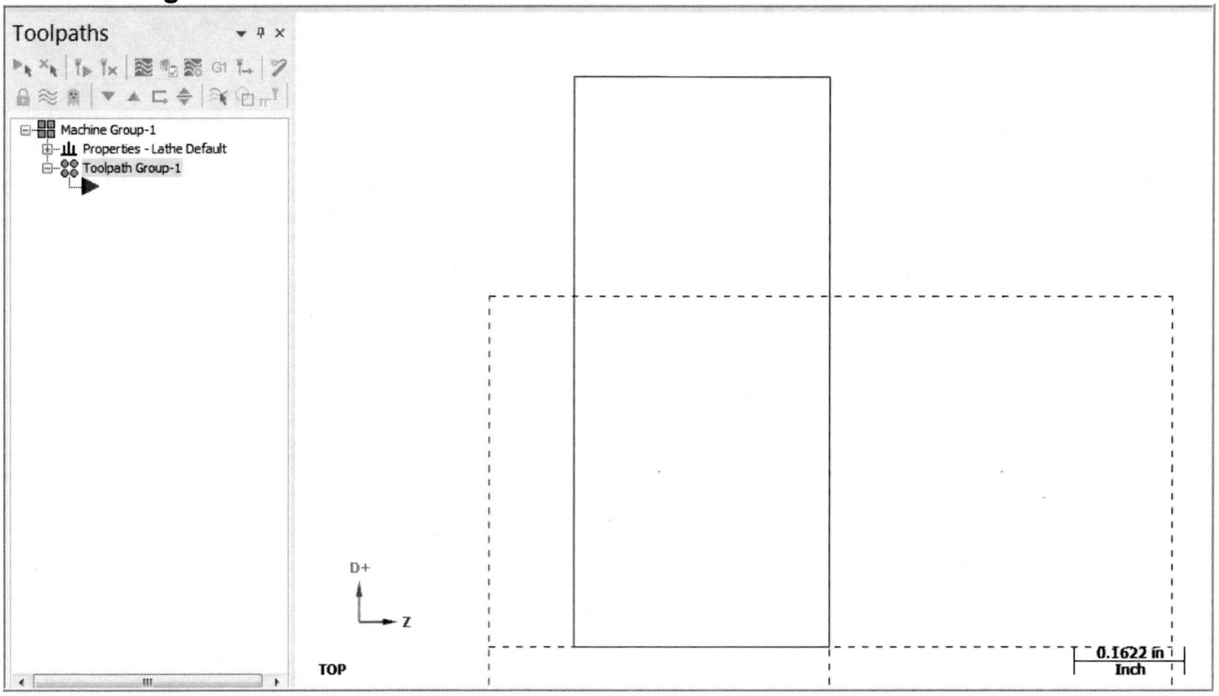

NOTE: If you make a mistake creating lines, click on the **Accept** icon and click on the **Undo** icon . Then redo the Line.

➲ **Create Lines 4 and 5 using the Xform Offset command.**

8. Select **XFORM>Offset…**

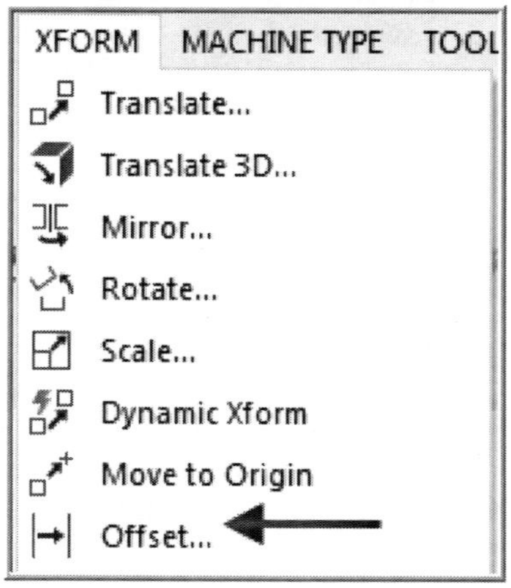

9. The Offset parameters window appears and you are next prompted to **"Select the line, arc, spline or curve offset".** Make the necessary changes in the **Offset parameters** window as shown below:

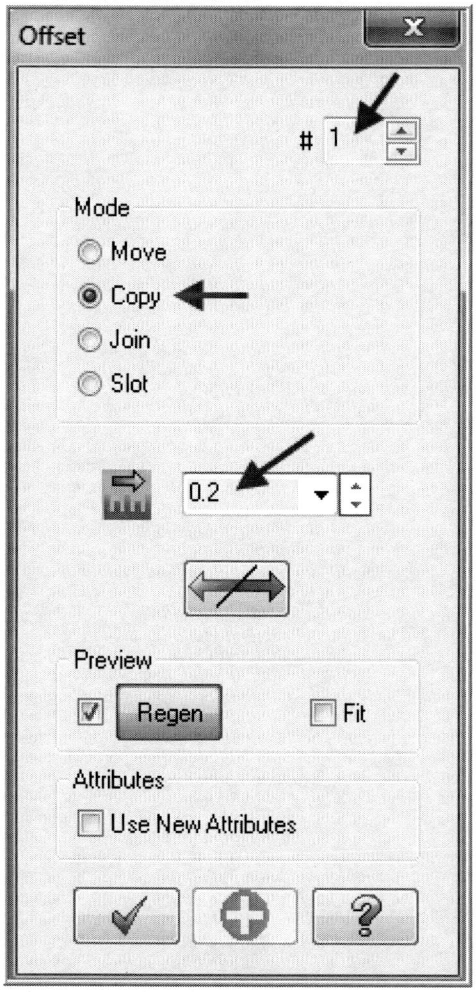

10. Click on **line 2** and move the cursor **below line 2** and click the **left mouse button** as shown below left:

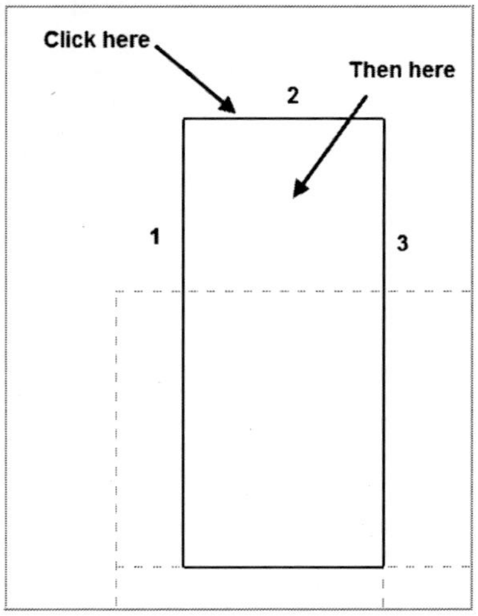

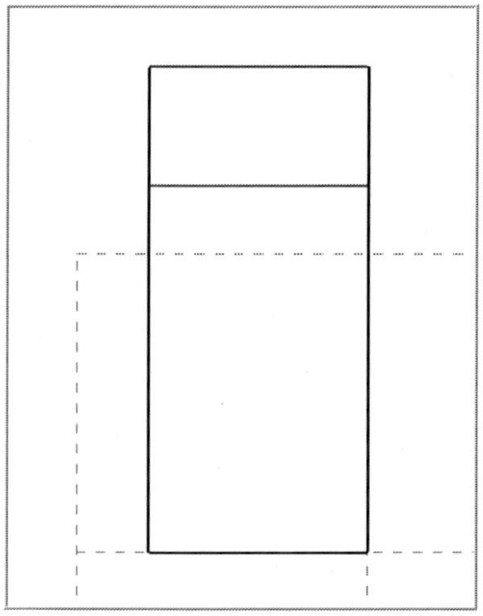

11. A new line should be created just **below line 2** as shown above right:

12. Click on **Apply** .

13. Make the necessary changes in the **Offset parameters** window as shown below:

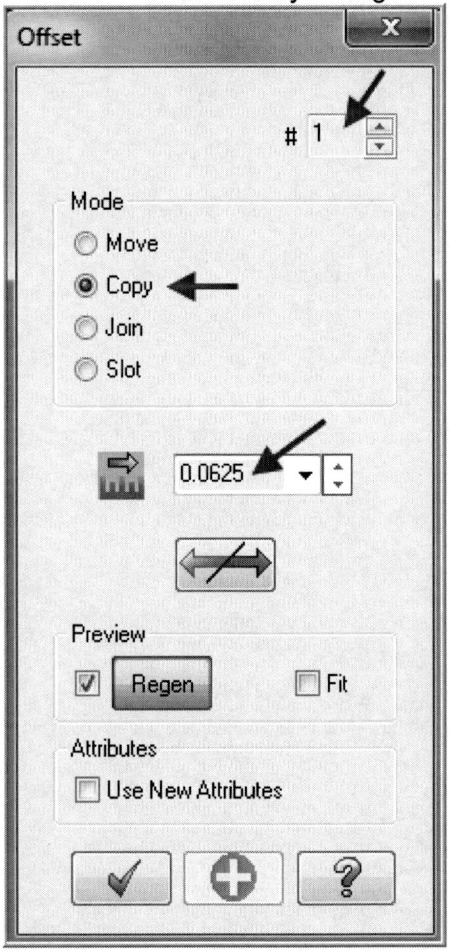

14. Click on **line 2** and move the cursor **below line 2** and click the **left mouse button** as shown below left:

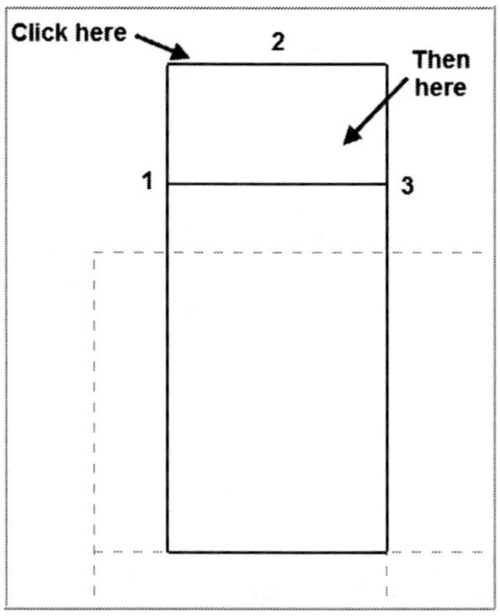

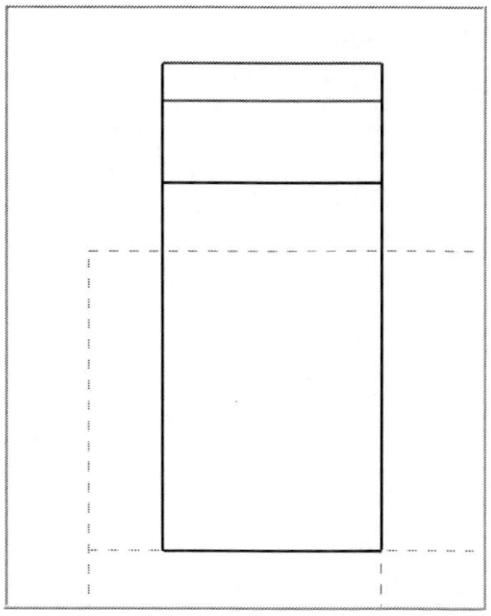

15. A new line should be created just below **line 2** as shown above right:

16. Click on **OK** .

17. Click on **Clear Colors** at the top of the screen .

TASK 4:
CREATE THE CHAMFERS

➲ **Create the .042 chamfer**

1. Select **Create>Chamfer>Entities …**

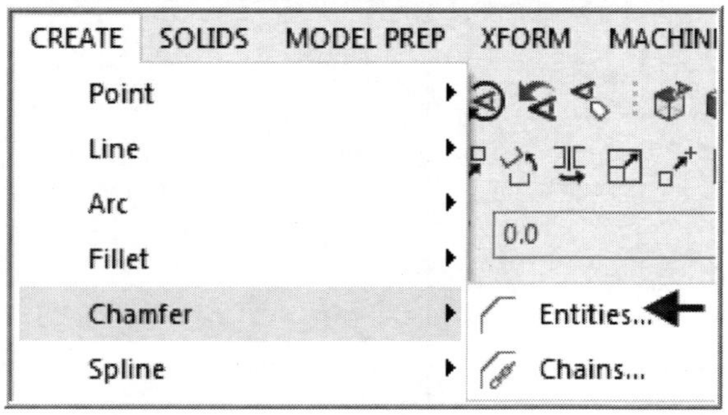

2. The **Chamfer Entities** ribbon bar appears and you are prompted to **"Select line or arc".**

3. Open up the **Style** drop down menu and select **Distance/Angle** as shown below:

4. Click in the space for **length**, and input **.042** and then hit the **tab key**.

5. Click in the space for **angle**, and input **45.0** and then hit the **enter key**.

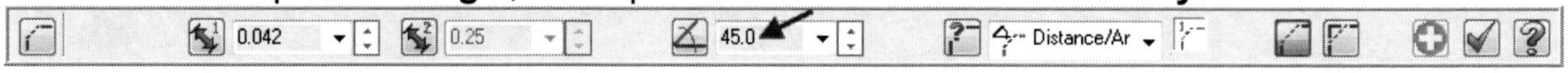

6. Ensure the **Trim** option for chamfer is activated and the icon is depressed as shown below:

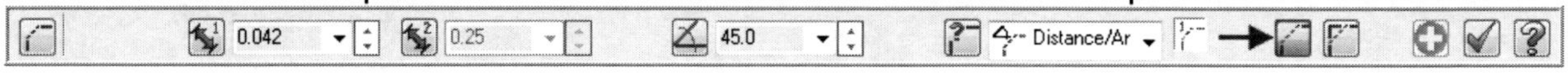

7. Click on **line 1** and then click on **line 2** as shown below:

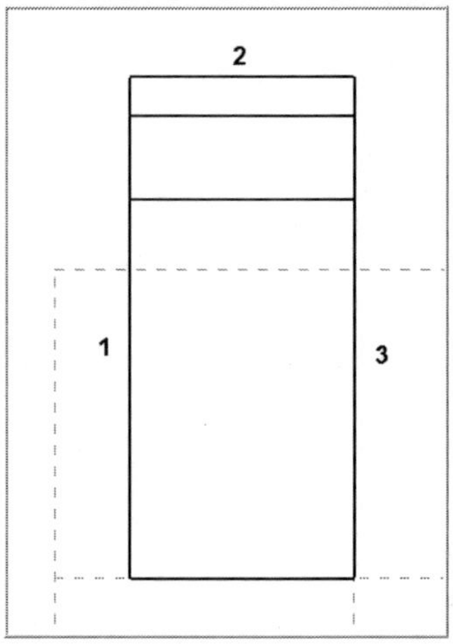

8. Click on the **Apply**  icon.
9. Click on **line 2** and then click on **line 3** as shown above.
10. Click on **OK** .

11. The completed chamfers are shown below:

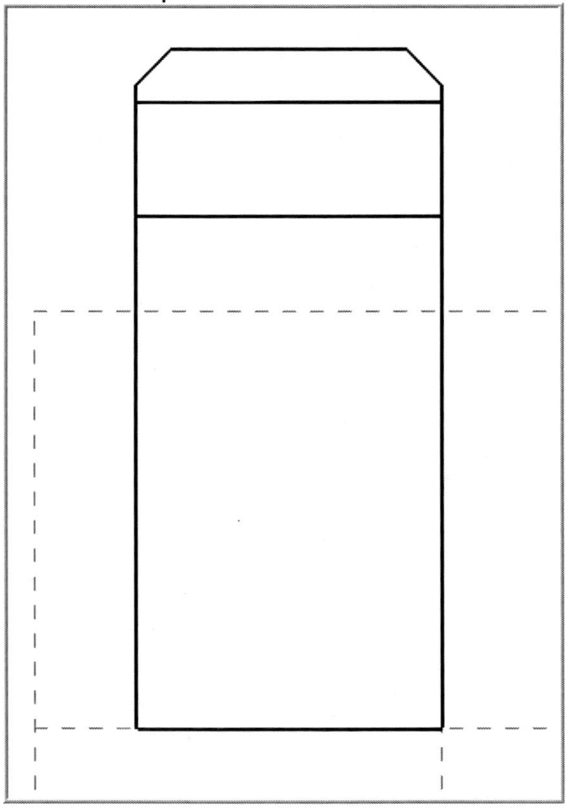

TASK 5:
SAVE THE DRAWING

1. Select **File.**
2. Select **Save As…**
3. In the "File name" box, type **Lathe-Lesson-9**.
4. Save to an appropriate location.
5. Select the Save button to save the file and complete this function.

Toolpath Creation

TASK 6:
DEFINING THE STOCK AND CHUCK PARAMETERS

1. Select the **Top View** .
2. Select the **screen fit** icon .
3. Select the **Un-Zoom Previous / .5** icon as shown below:

4. Select the plus in front of **Properties** to expand the **Machine Group Properties**.

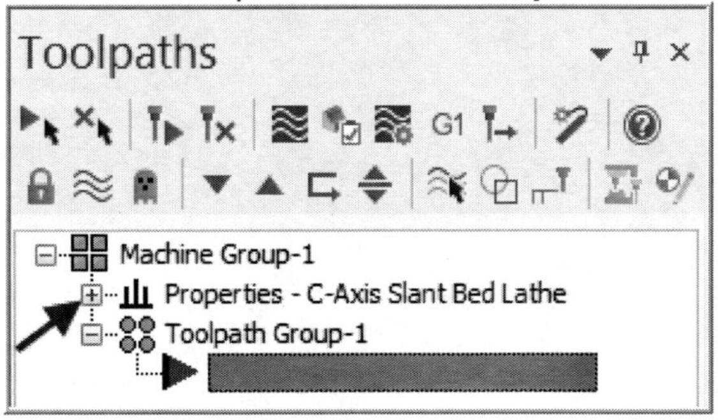

5. Select **Stock setup** in the Toolpaths Manager window.

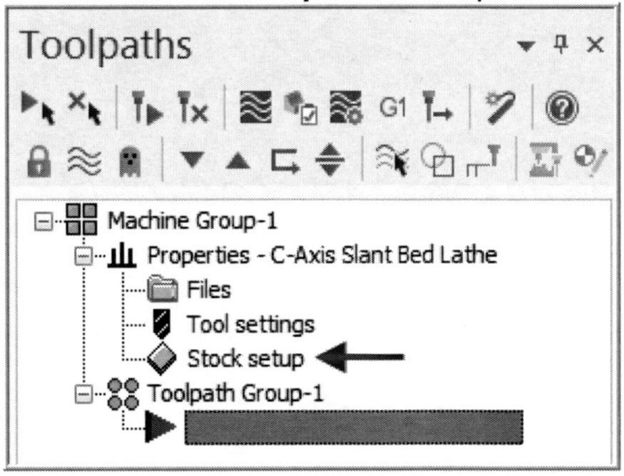

6. Select the **Stock Properties** button in the Stock Setup page as shown in the screenshot below:

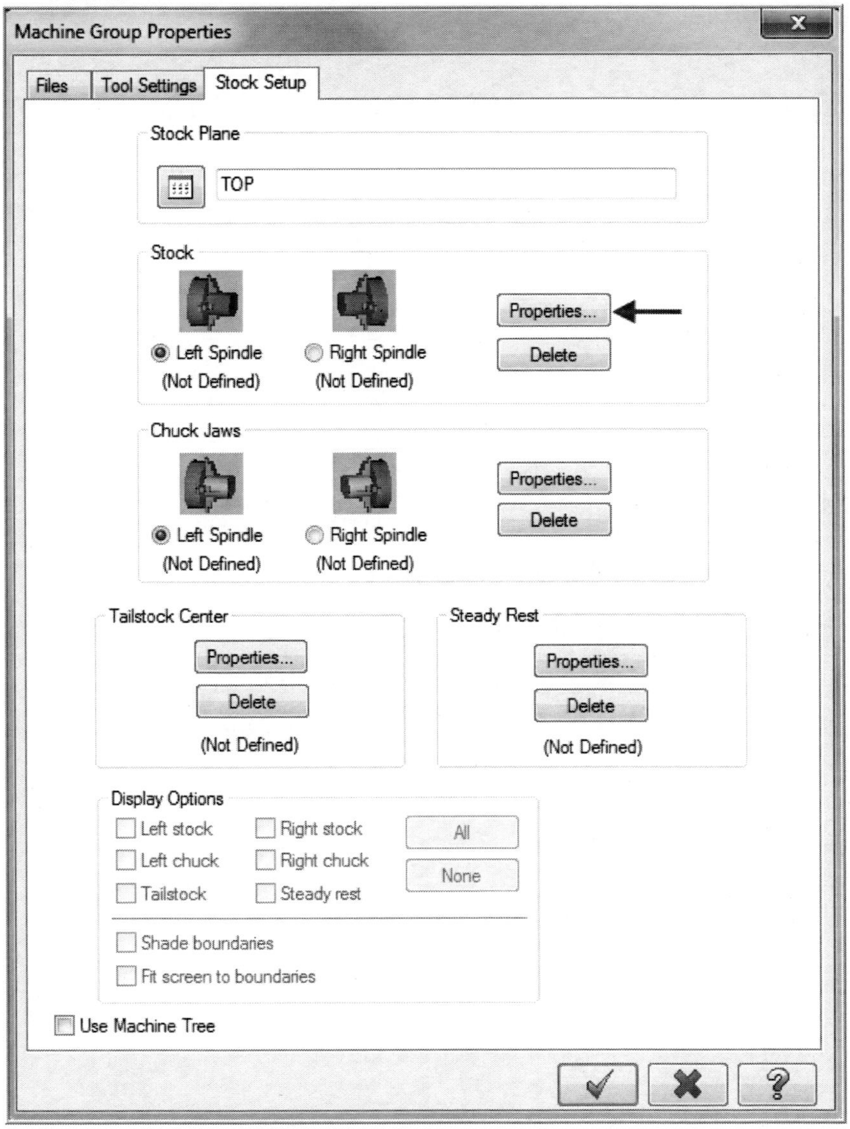

7. In the **Machine Component Manager-Stock** window click on the Geometry button and select Cylinder as shown below:

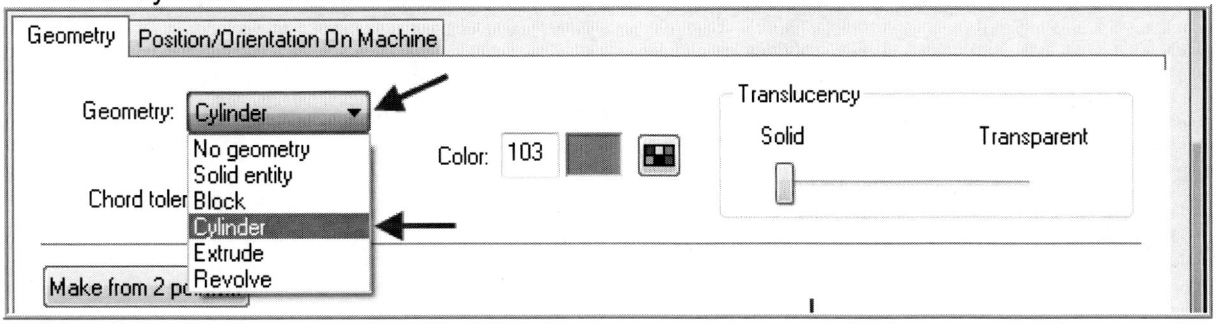

8. In the **Stock** setup set the values as shown below. **Axis is set to -Z**.

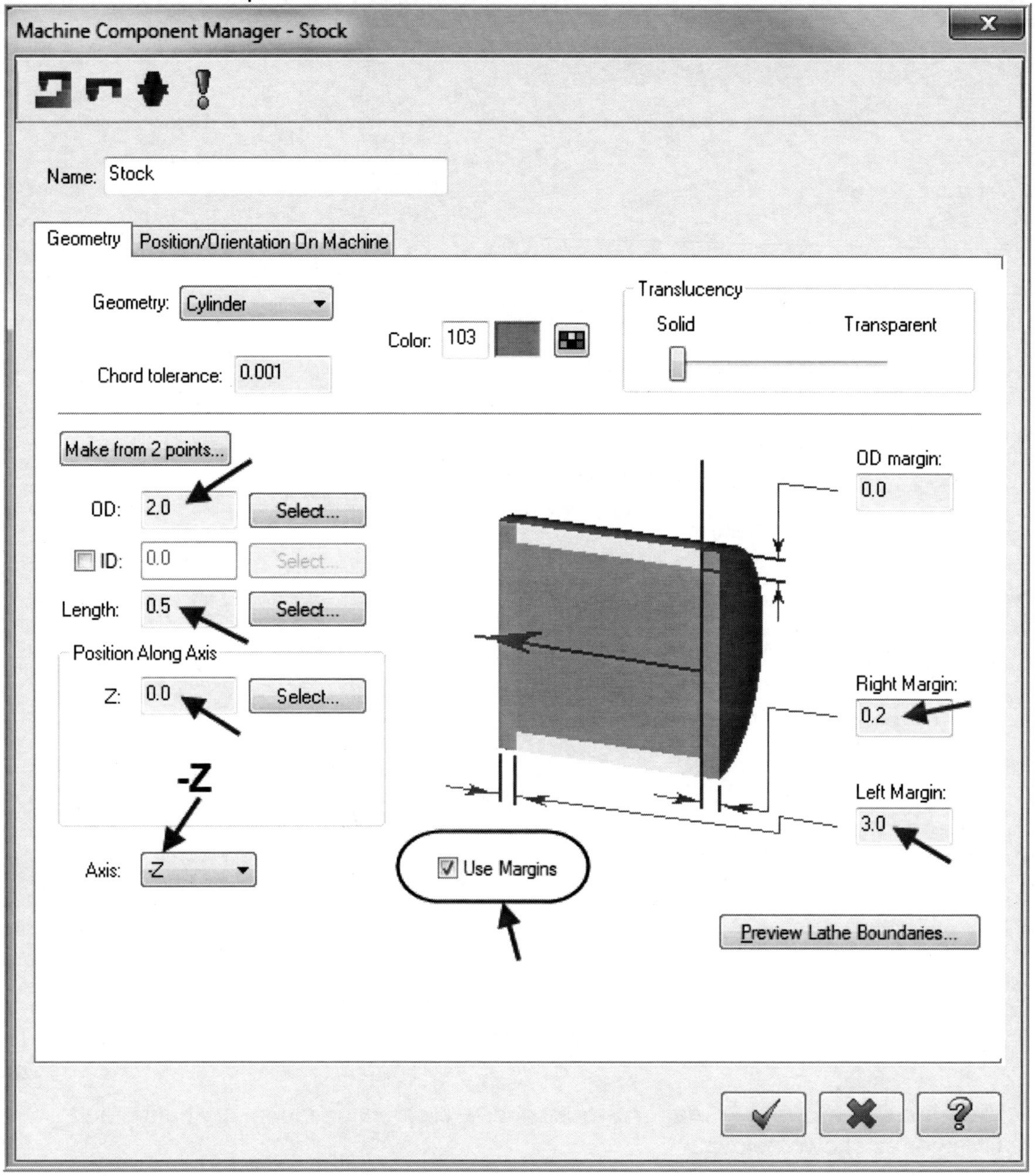

9. Click on the **OK** icon  to complete this feature.
10. Select the **Chuck Properties** button in the Stock Setup page as shown in the screenshot below:

11. In the **Chuck Jaws** setup set the values as shown below:

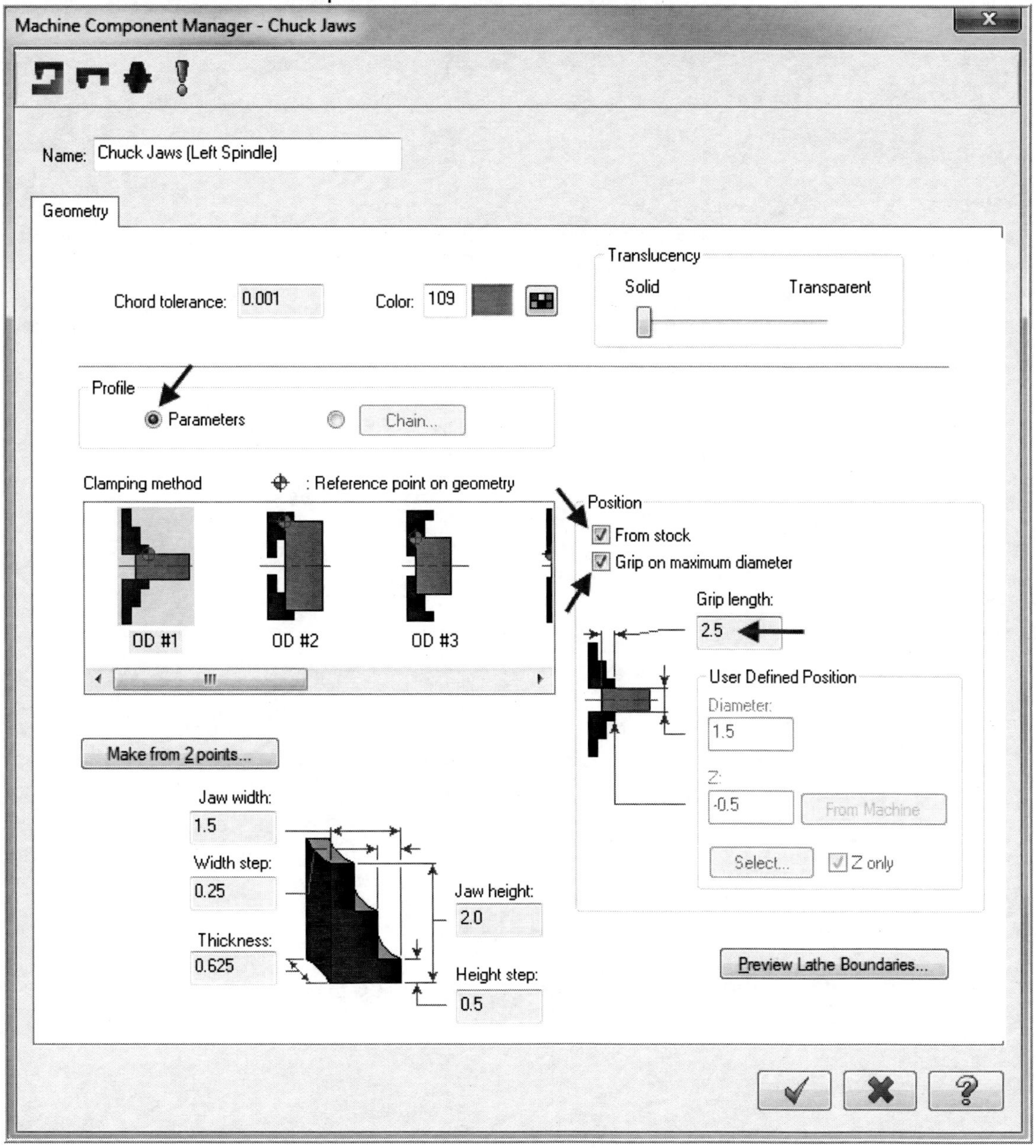

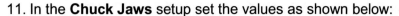

12. Click on the **OK** icon  to complete this feature.

13. Click on the **Tool Settings** page and make changes as shown below and then click on the **Select** button:

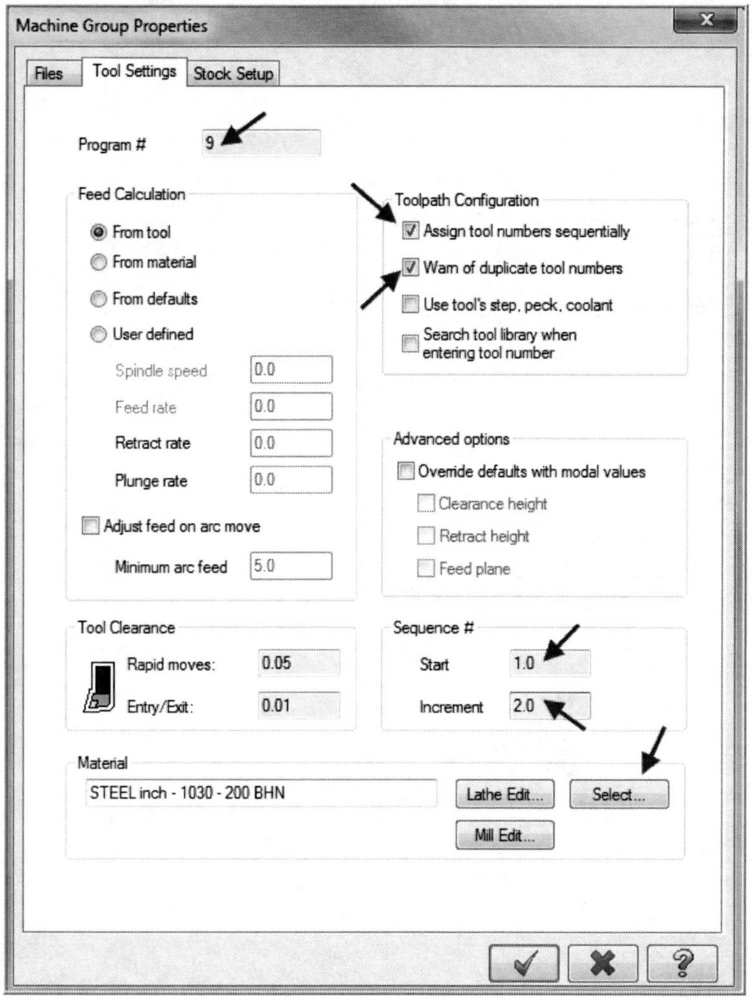

14. Select **Lathe – library** from the drop down **Material List** dialog box as shown below:

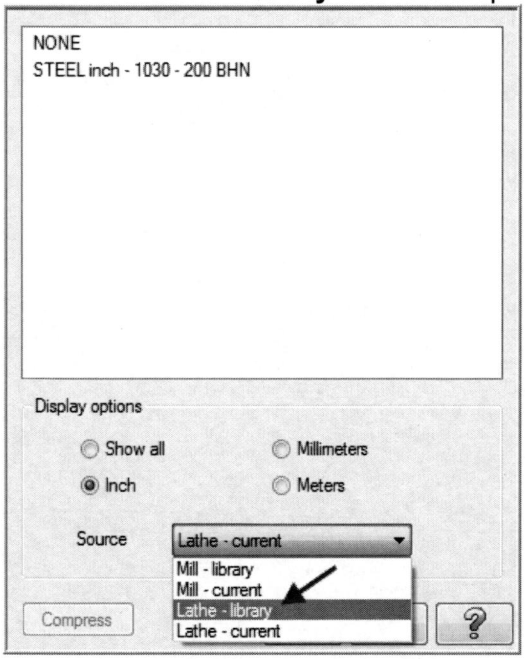

15. Select ALUMINUM inch - 6061 from the Default Materials list.

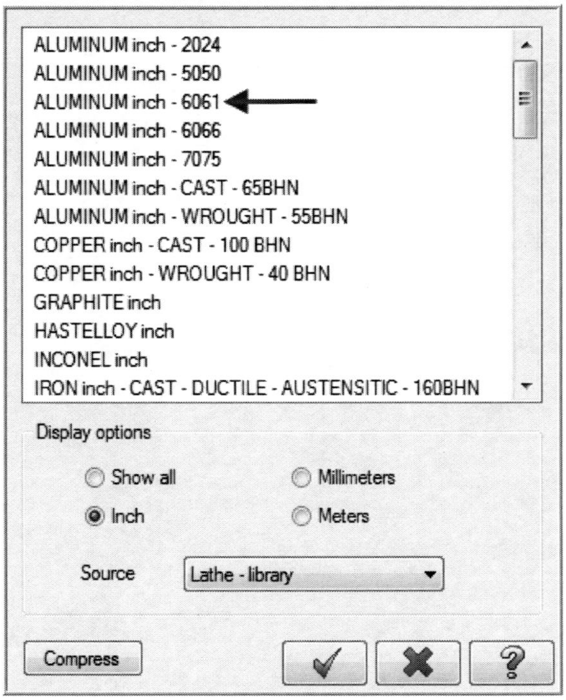

16. Select the **OK** button .

17. Select the **OK** button  again to complete this Stock Setup function.

18. Zoom out by clicking on the **Un-Zoom Previous / .5** icon

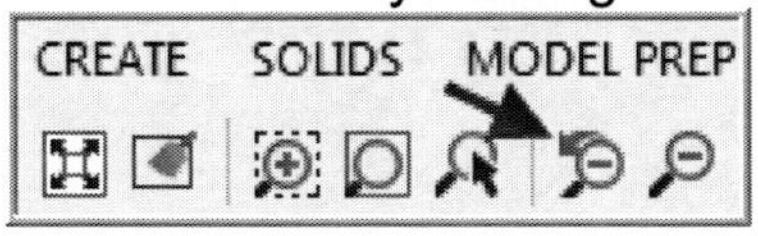

Notice: the stock setup outline as indicated by broken lines as shown below: (Note, you may have to click the **unzoom** button a number of times to see the entire image.)

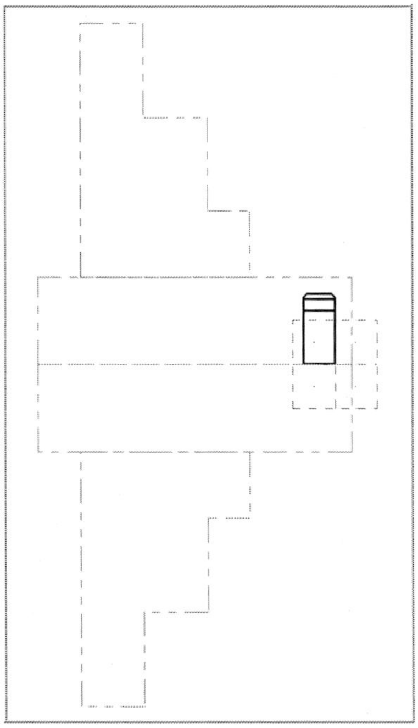

TASK 7:
FACE THE FRONT OF THE PART:

➲ In this task you will use a facing tool to face the front of the part in one cut.

1. Select the **Fit** icon. 
2. Click on the **Un-Zoom .8** icon as shown below:

3. From the menu bar select **TOOLPATHS>Face…**

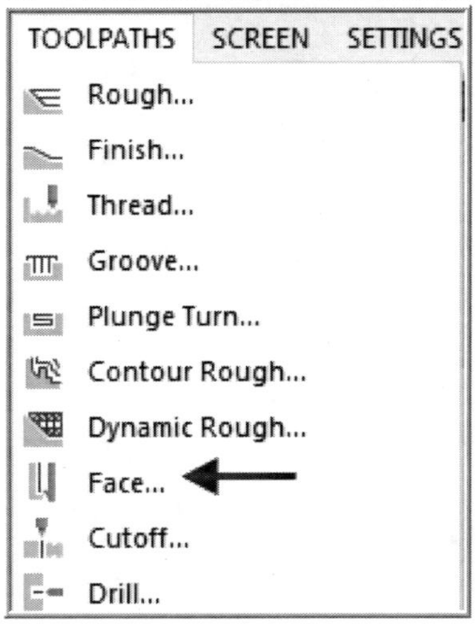

4. When prompted to **"Enter new NC name"** select the OK button  to accept LATHE-LESSON-9 as shown below:

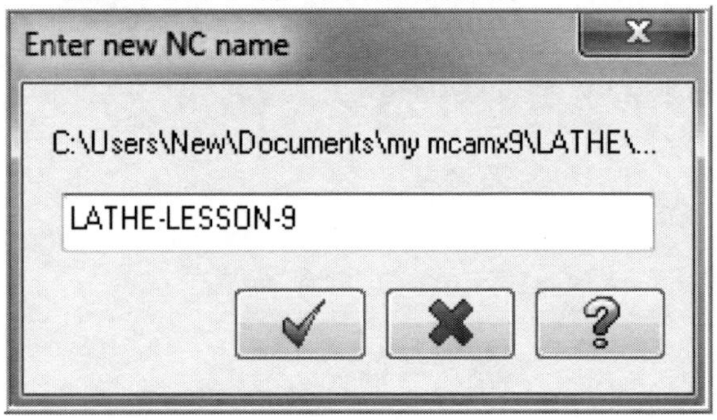

➲ After selecting the OK button you are confronted with **Toolpath parameters** page. The first task here will be to select **Tool #1 an OD Rough- Right – 80 deg.**

5. Click on **Tool #1 OD ROUGH RIGHT** and make changes in the **Toolpath parameters** page as shown below:

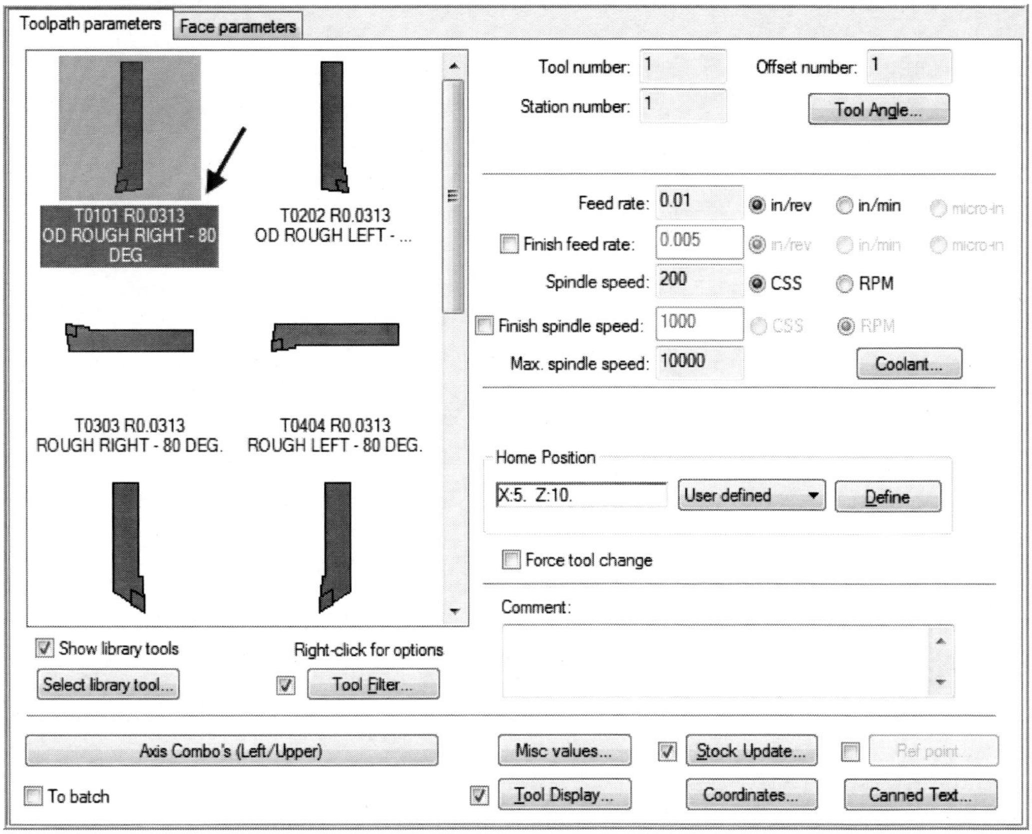

6. Select the **Face parameters** page and make changes as shown below:

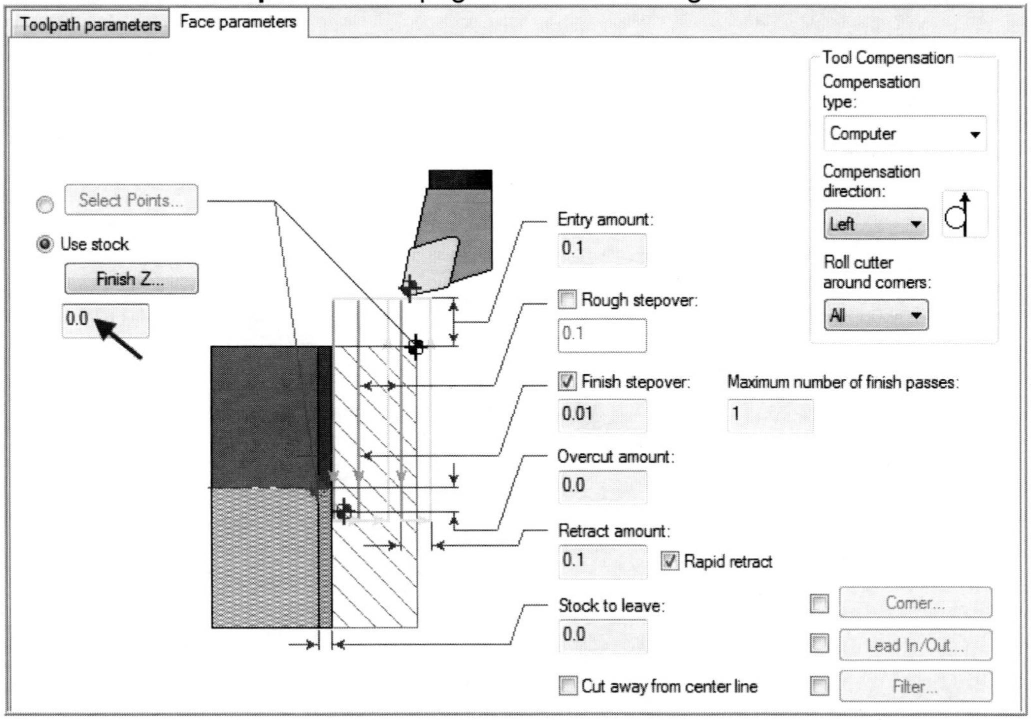

7. Select the OK button  to complete this **Lathe Face** operation.

TASK 8:
ROUGH THE OUTSIDE DIAMETERS

➲ In this task you will use the same tool as used for the previous facing operation **Tool #1 an OD Rough- Right – 80 deg.**

1. From the menu bar select **TOOLPATHS>Rough…**

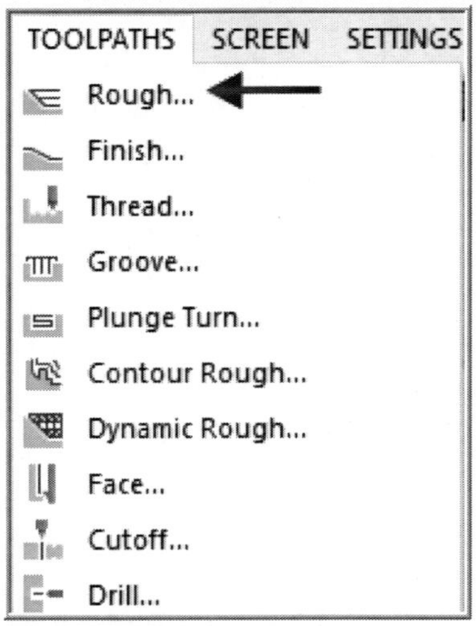

2. In the **Chaining** window Chaining mode is set to **Partial** by default.

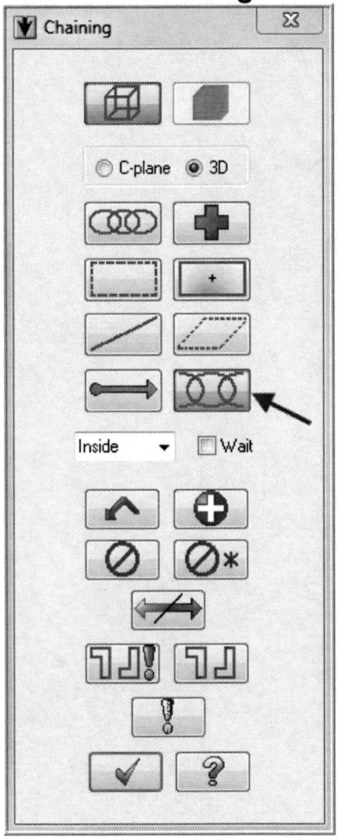

3. **Zoom** the part so it looks similar to the diagram below: **Note:** You can Zoom by using one of the following methods:

    a. By clicking on the **Zoom Window** icon 
    b. By **Scrolling the wheel** on your mouse (if your mouse has a wheel)
    c. Using the **Page Up** key on your keyboard. (The **Page Down** key unzooms the part).

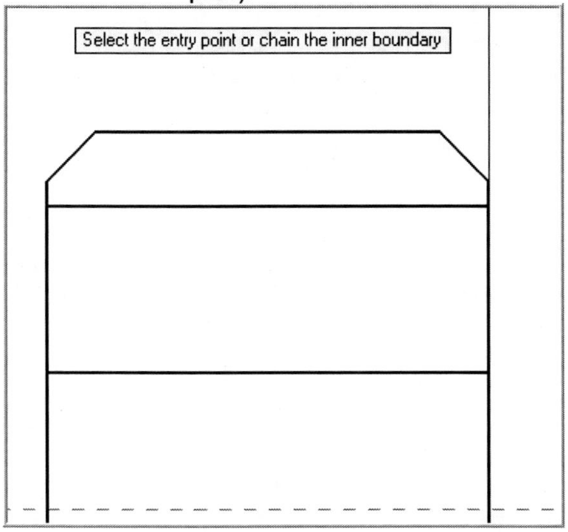

4. Select **Line 1** as the start of the **Partial chain**.

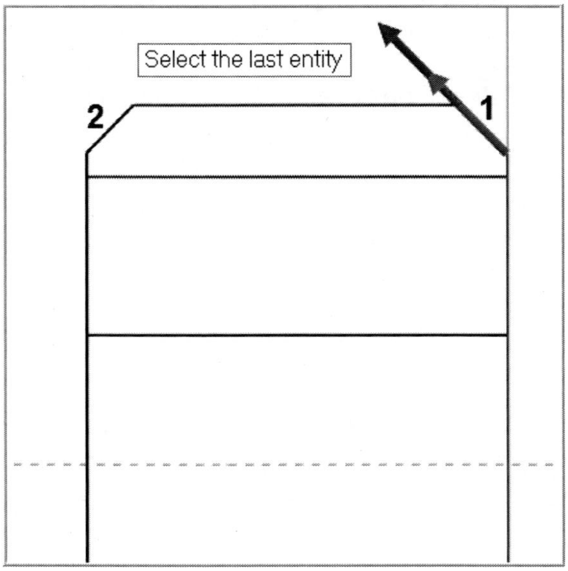

5. After you have selected the line **ensure** that the arrows are pointing up as shown above on **line 1**. If it is not, select the **reverse button** in the **Chaining dialog box**:

6. Then select **Line 2** as the end entity in this chain as shown above.

7. Select the **OK** button  to exit the Chaining dialog window.

8. In the **Toolpath parameters** page select the same tool used to face the part **Tool #1 OD ROUGH RIGHT** and make sure the settings are the same as shown below:

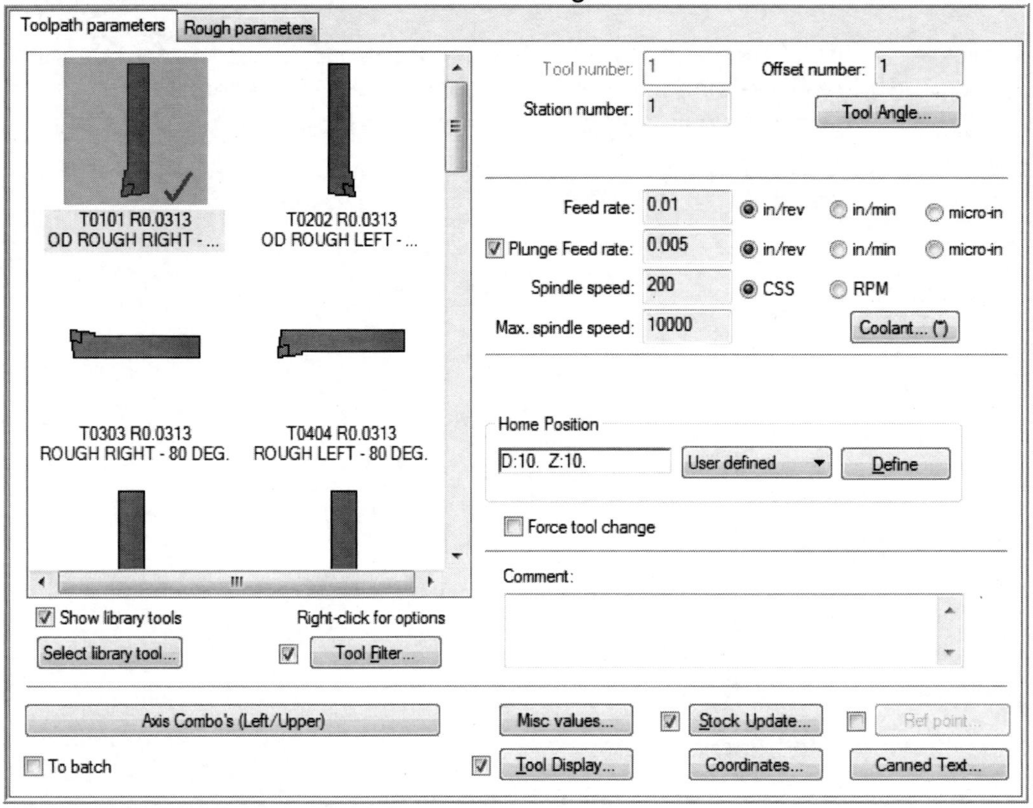

9. Select the **Rough parameters** page and make sure the settings are the same as shown below:

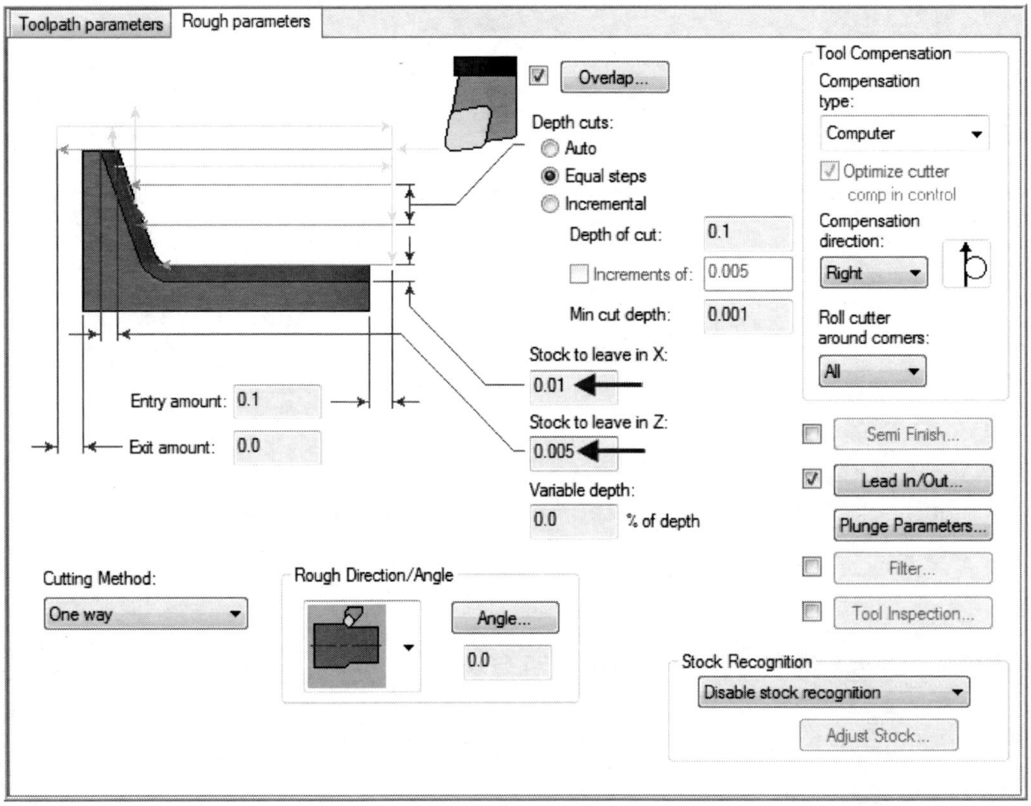

10. Select the **Lead In/Out** button select the **Lead out** page and extend the contour by **.2** as shown below

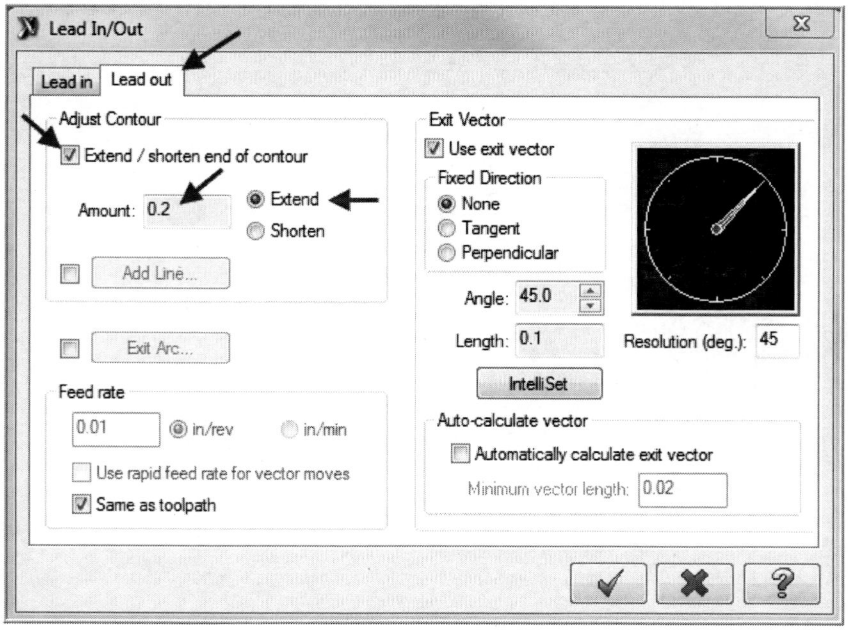

11. Select the **OK** button  to exit this function.
12. Select the **OK** button  to exit Rough Parameters.

TASK 9:
FINISH THE OUTSIDE DIAMETER

➲ In this task you will finish the outside diameters in one cut using **Tool #2 an OD Finish-Right – 35 deg.**

1. From the menu bar select **TOOLPATHS>Finish...**

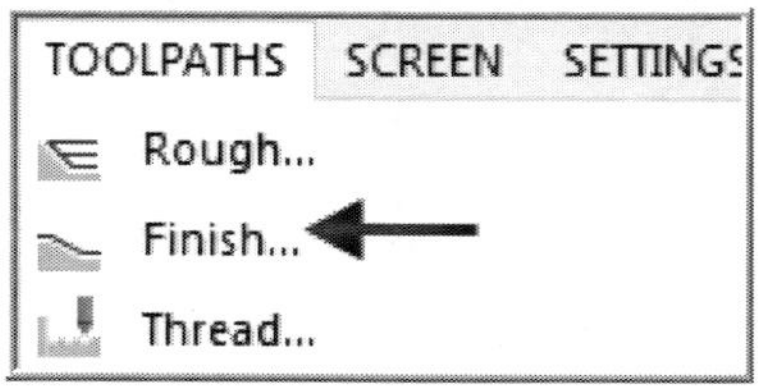

2. Select **Last** in the **Chaining dialog box**.

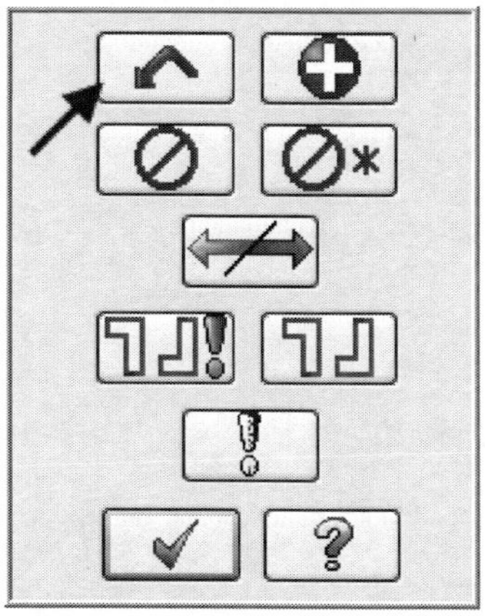

3. Select the **OK** button  to complete the selection.

4. Select **R0.0156 OD Finish Right 35 DEG** tool from the tool list and make changes as shown below:

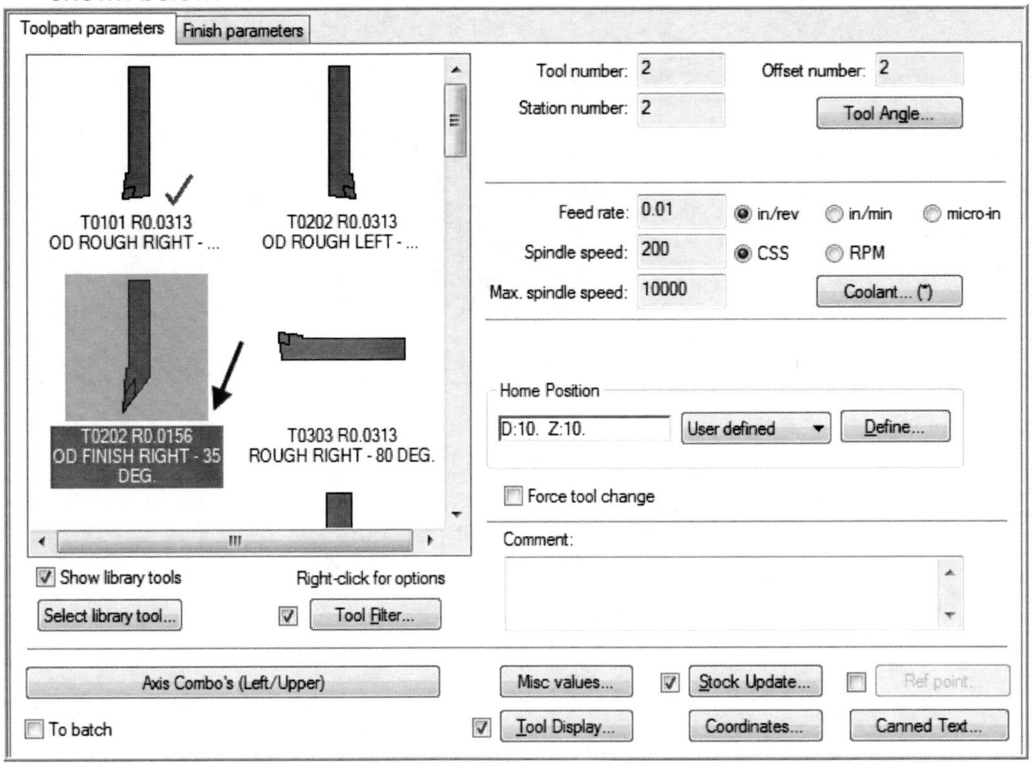

5. Select the **Finish parameters** page and make changes as shown below:

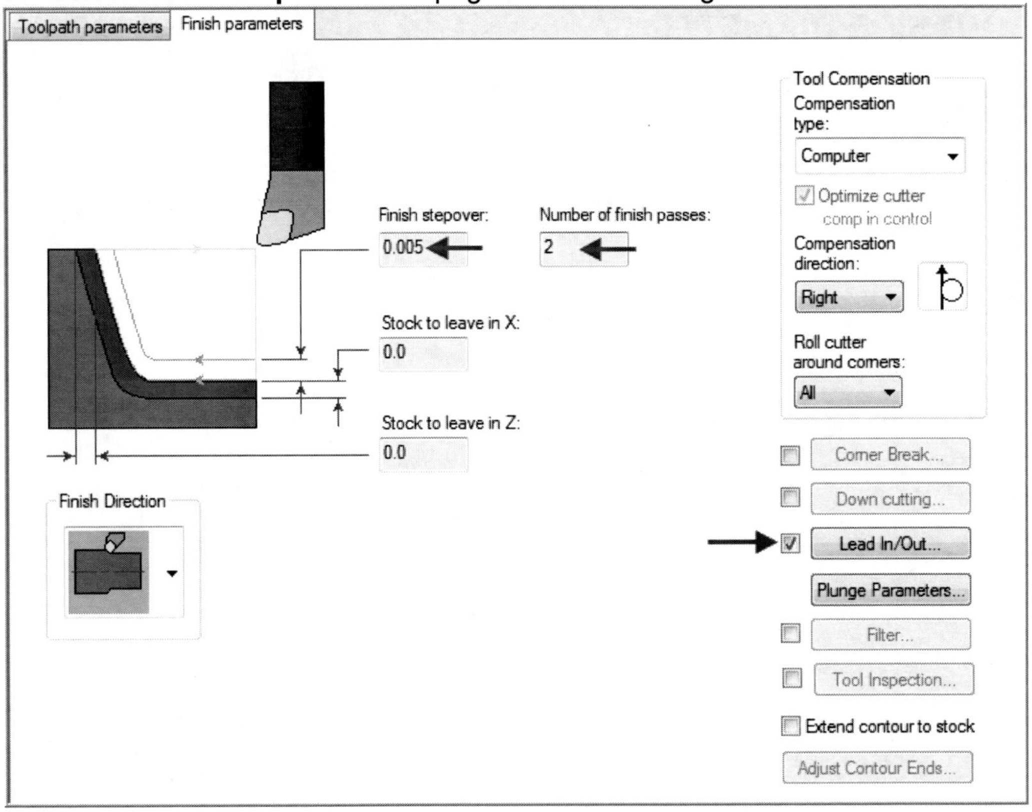

6. Select the **Lead In/Out** button select the **Lead out** page and extend the contour by .01 as shown below:

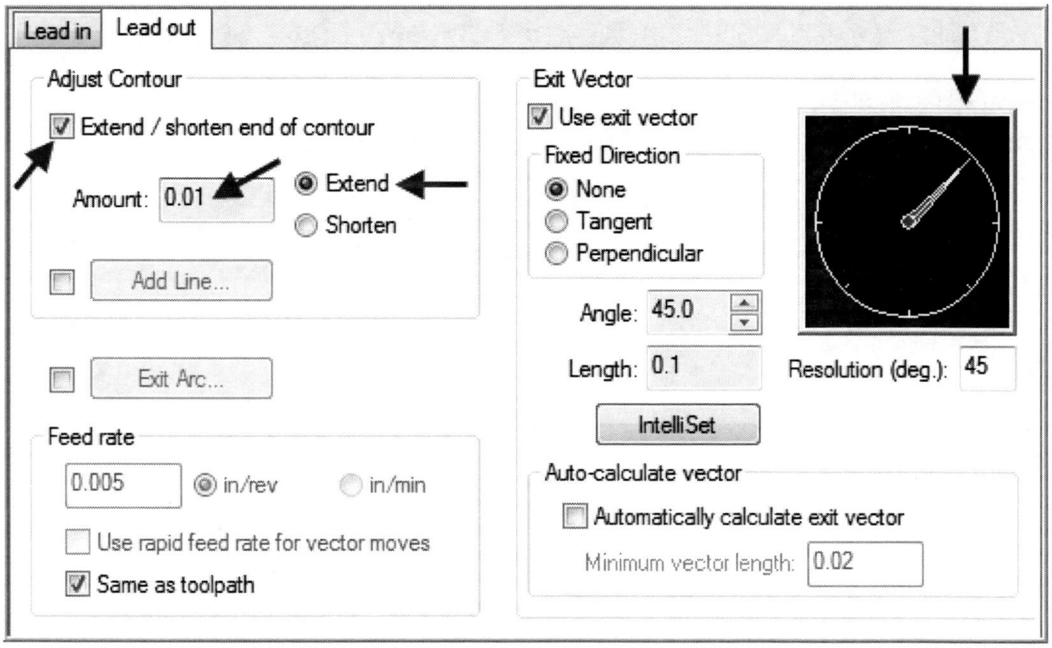

7. Select the **OK** button ✓ to exit this function.
8. Select the **Plunge Parameters…** button [Plunge Parameters...] and select the **Plunge Cutting** option shown below:

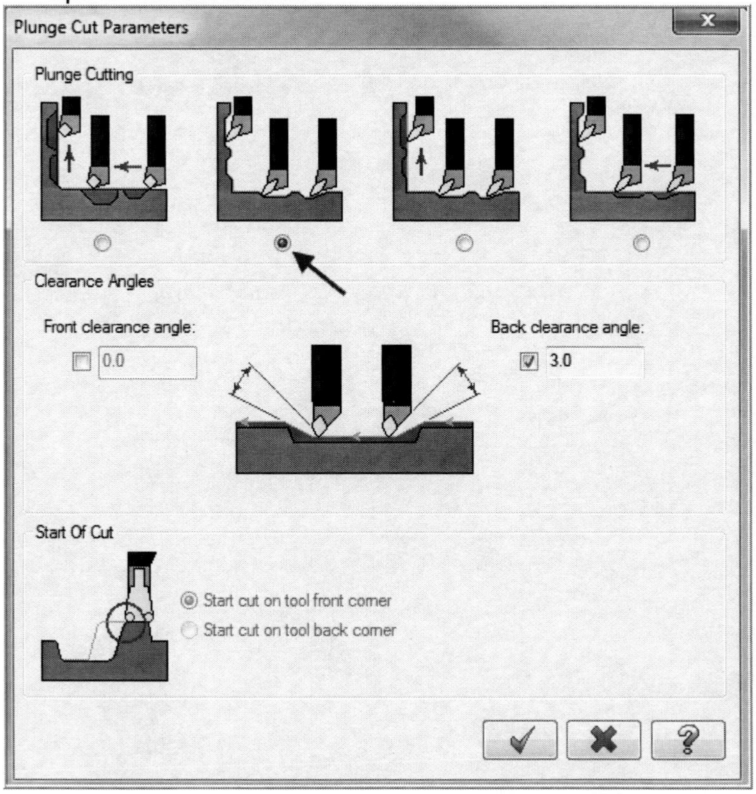

9. Select the **OK** button ✓ to exit this function.
10. Select the **OK** button ✓ to exit **Finish parameters**.

TASK 10:
CENTER DRILL HOLE

➲ In this task you will center drill **.125"** depth using **Tool #3 Centre Drill - .25 diameter.**

1. From the menu bar select **TOOLPATHS>Drill…**

2. Select the **Centre Drill .25 diameter** tool from the tool list and make changes as shown below:

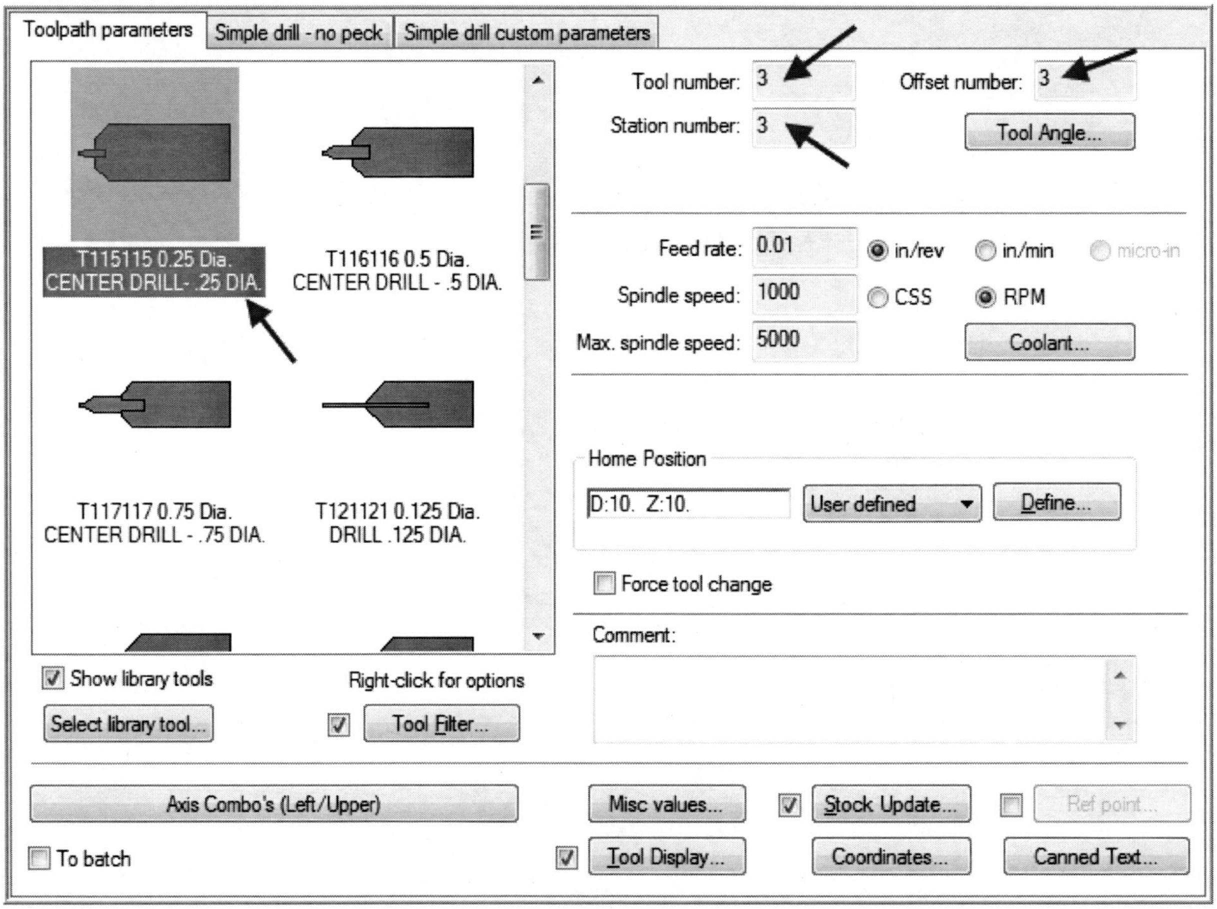

3. Select the **Simple drill – no peck** page and make changes as shown below:

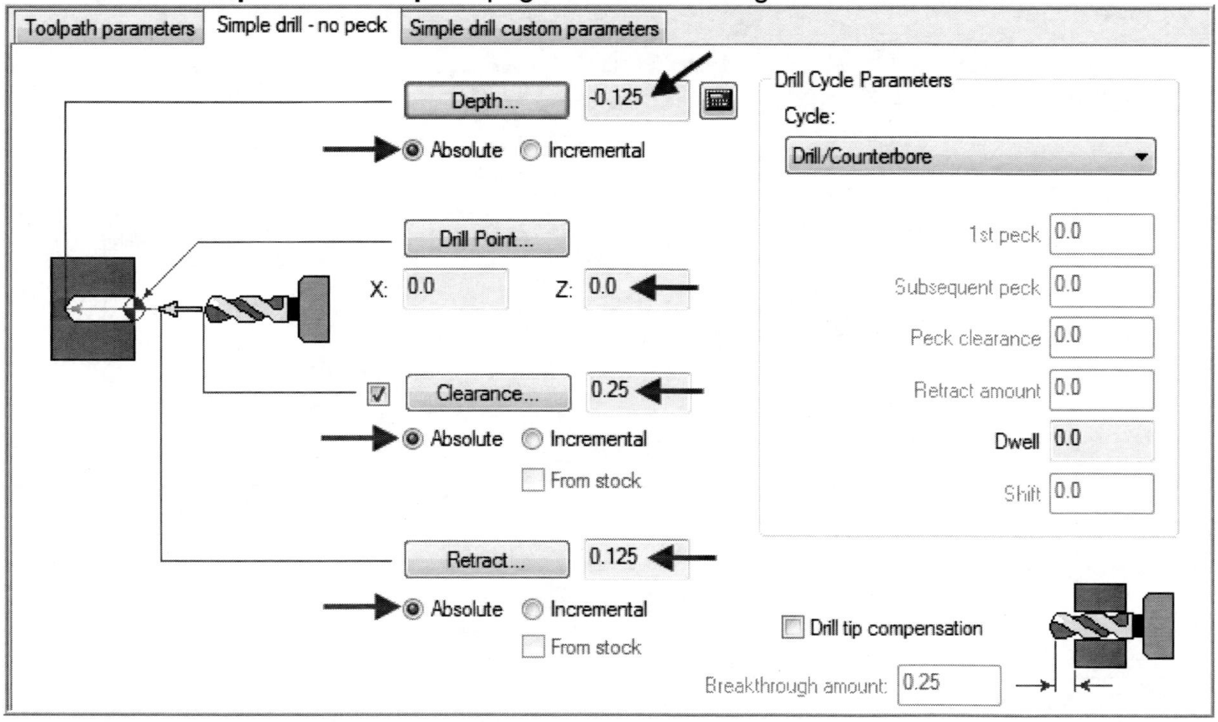

4. Select the **OK** button ✓ to exit **Simple drill – no peck**.

TASK 11:
PRE DRILL THE 1.125" HOLE 0.375 DIAMETER

➲ In this task you will pre drill the 1.125" hole through the part using **Tool #4 Drill - .375 diameter.**

1. From the menu bar select **TOOLPATHS>Drill...**

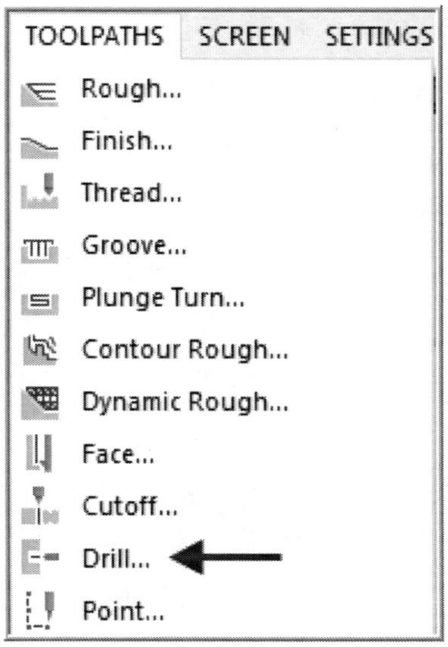

2. Scroll down and select the **Drill - .375 diameter** tool from the tool list and make changes as shown below:

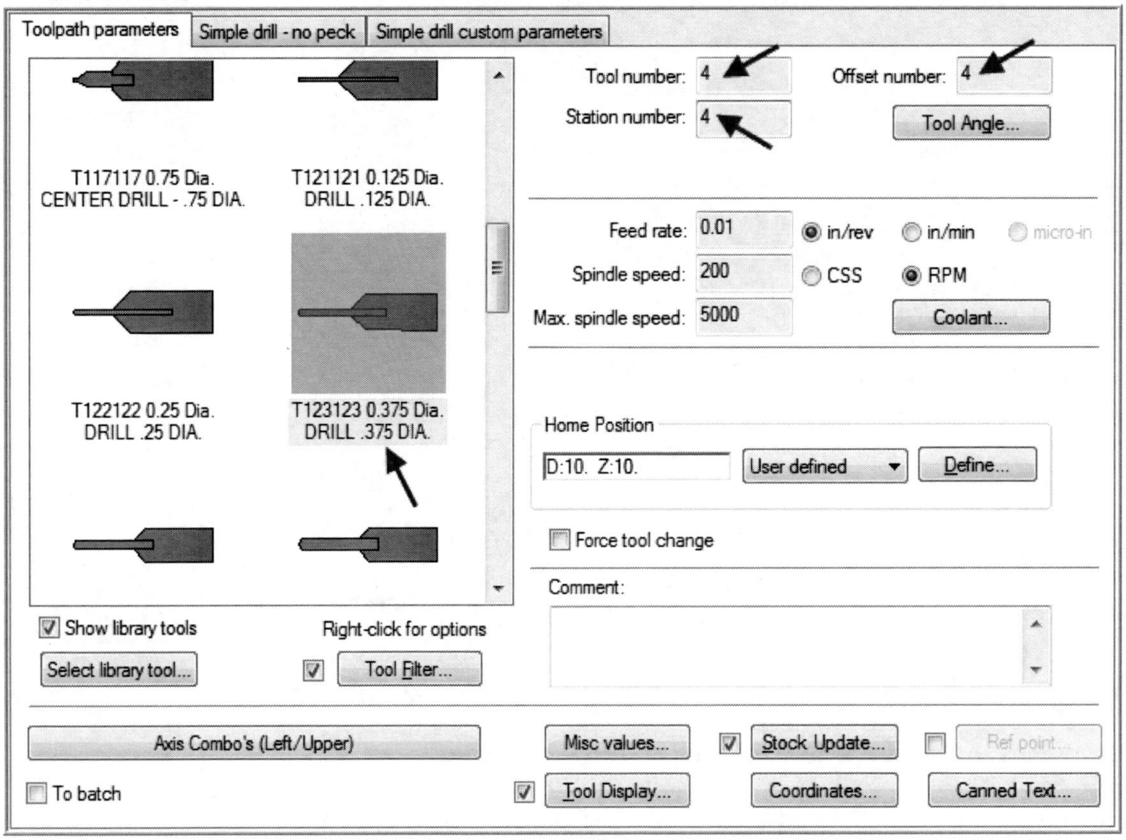

3. Select the **Simple drill – no peck** page and make changes as shown below. This hole will be **peck drilled through the part**. Make changes as shown below:

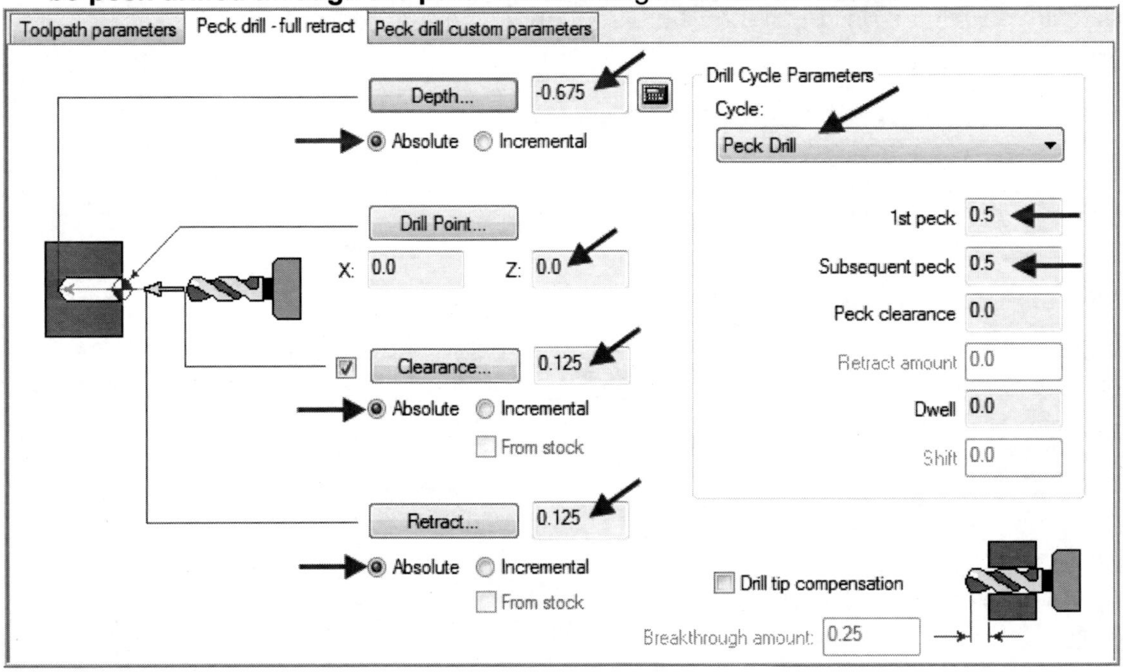

4. Select the **OK** button ✓ to exit **Peck drill – full retract**.

TASK 12:
PRE DRILL THE 1.125" HOLE 0.5 DIAMETER

➲ In this task you will peck drill through the part with a 0.5 diameter drill prior to boring.
➲ You will copy the previous peck drill operation and then modify into this peck drilling operation.

1. On the left of the screen in the Toolpaths Manager the 0.375 drill peck drilling operation is the **fifth** operation. To copy this operation hold down the **Right mouse button** over the folder for this operation. Keep holding the right mouse button down and drag below the red arrow and release.
2. Select **Copy after** from this menu.

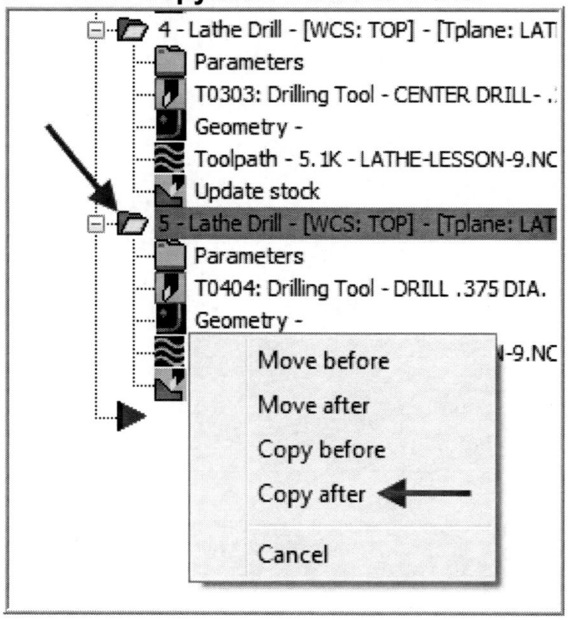

3. Move the Insert arrow 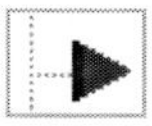 to the bottom of the list of operations by clicking the  icon on the Toolpaths Manager toolbar.
4. In the Toolpaths Manager click on the folder Parameters for the **sixth** operation as shown below:

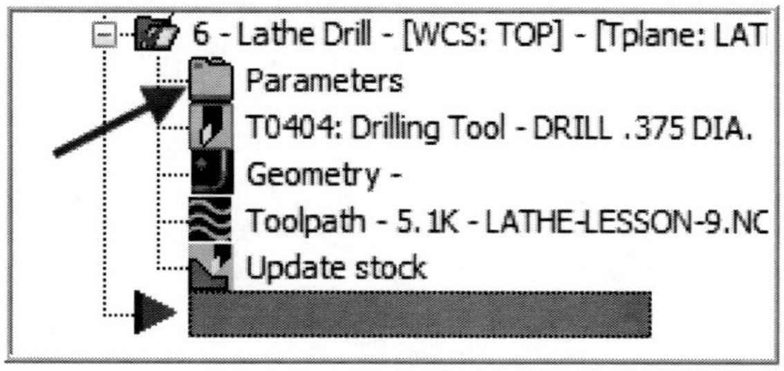

5. Select the **Toolpath parameters** page.
6. Scroll down and select the **.50 diameter drill** as shown below:
7. Make changes to the **Toolpath parameters** page as shown below.

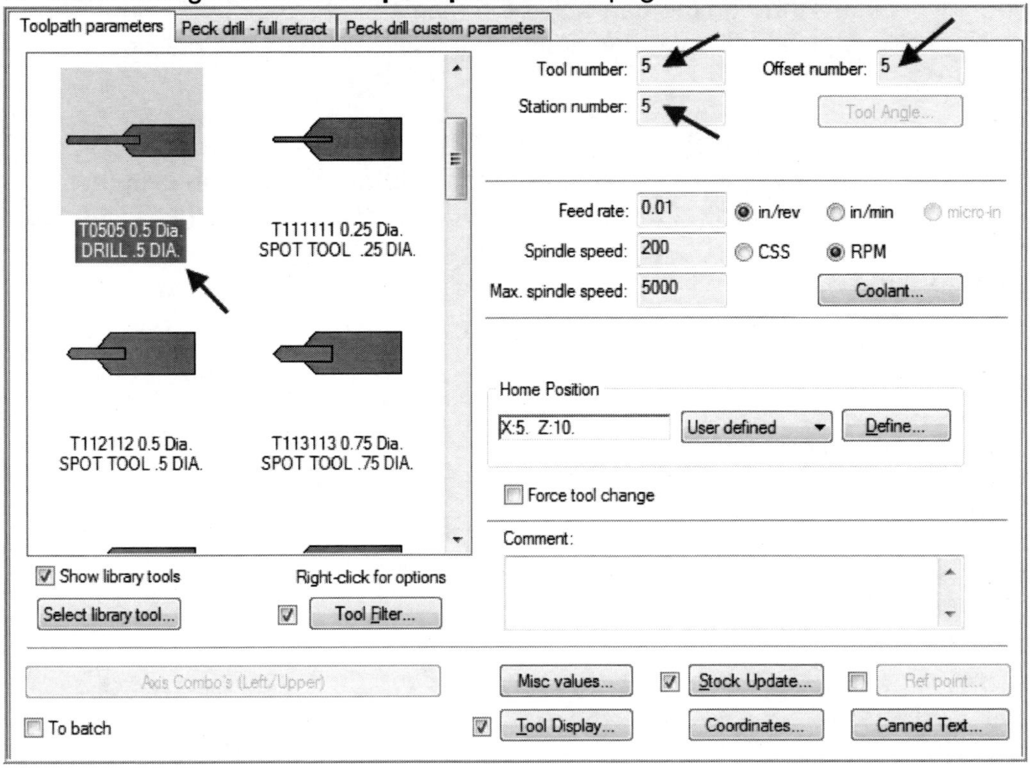

8. Select the **Peck drill – full retract** page and make changes as shown below.

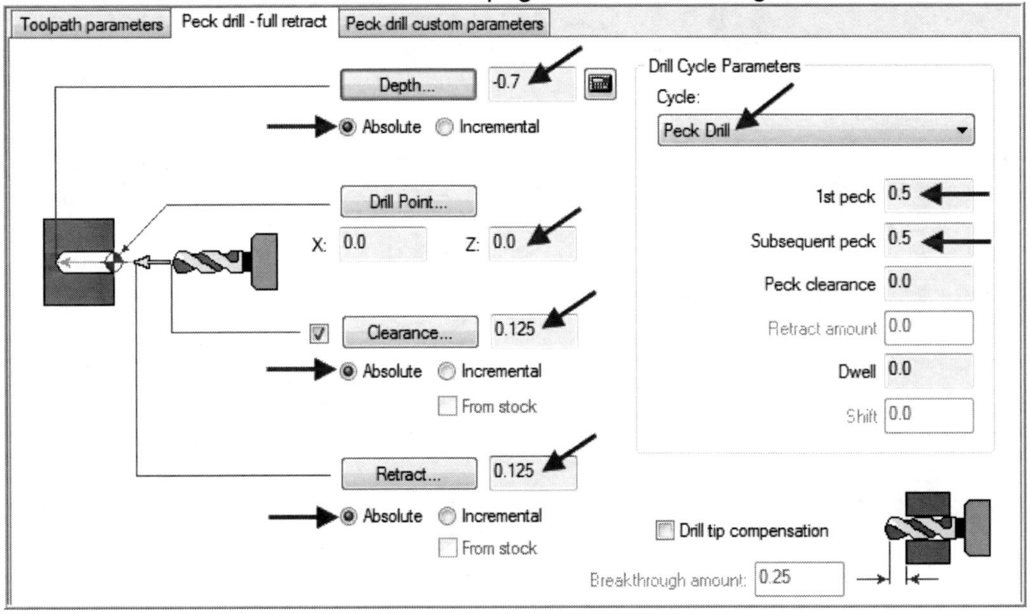

9. Select the **OK** button  to exit **Peck drill – full retract**.

10. Select the **Regenerate all dirty operations button**  to remove the red X from the drilling operation you have just edited. You need to update the toolpath with the new parameters you have just input.

TASK 13:
ROUGH THE BORE

➲ In this task you will use a boring tool to rough out the 1.225" diameter bore.

1. From the menu bar select **TOOLPATHS>Rough...**

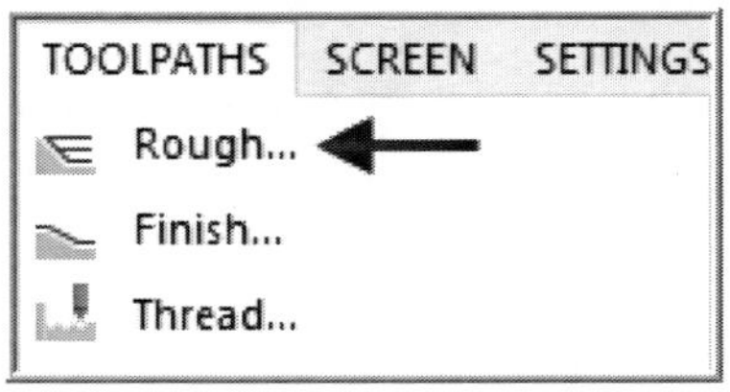

2. In the **Chaining** window Chaining mode is set to **Partial** by default.
3. Select **Line 1** as the start of the **Partial chain**.

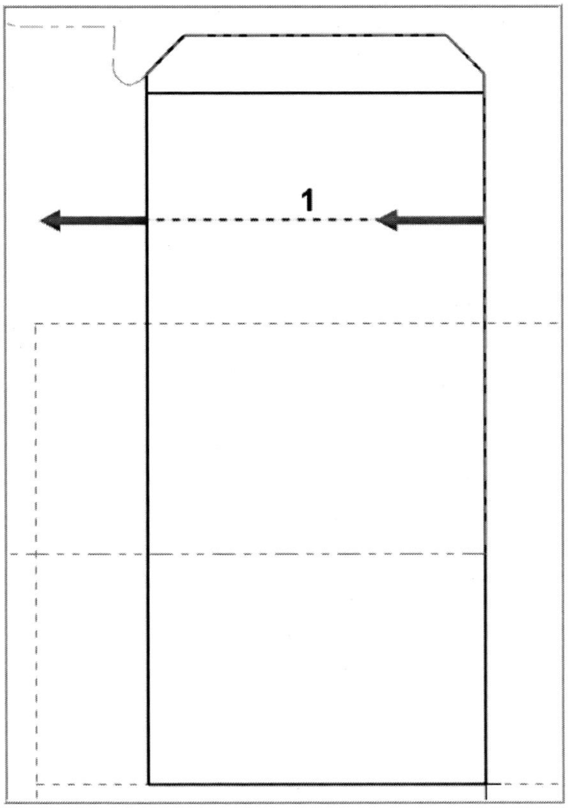

After you have selected the line ensure that the arrows are pointing towards the part as shown above. If it is not select the reverse button in the Chaining dialog box

4. Select the **OK** button  to exit the **Chaining dialog window**.

5. In the **Toolpath parameters** page scroll down and select a boring tool **ID ROUGH MIN .375 DIA – 75 deg**.

6. Double click on the picture  for this boring tool in the tool list window.
7. On the **Inserts** page change the thickness of this insert to 1/32 as shown below:

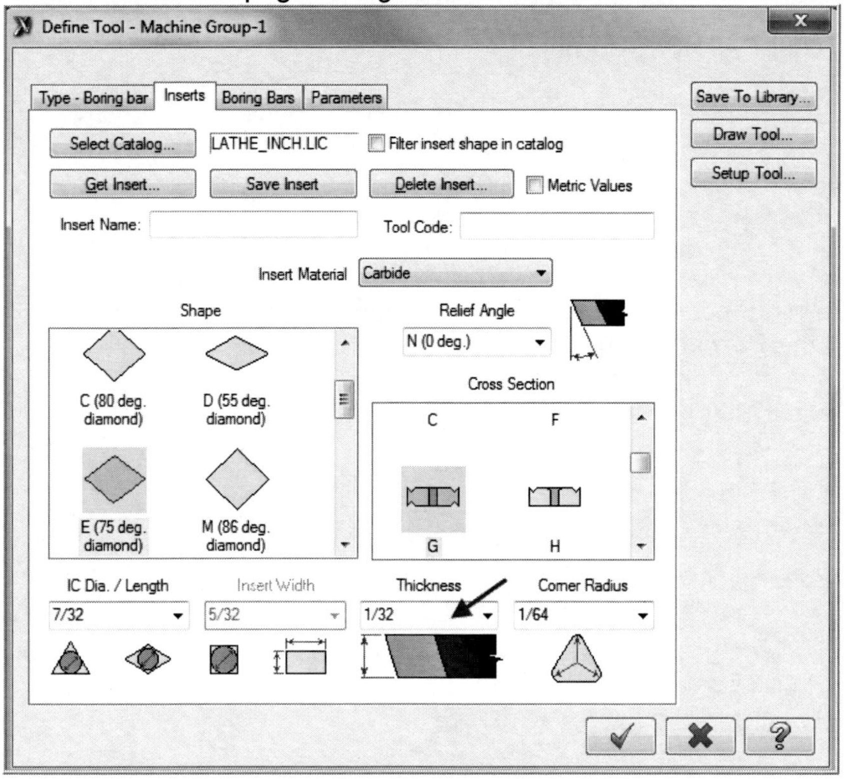

8. Select the **OK** button  to exit the **Inserts** page.
9. In the **Toolpath parameters** page make any necessary changes as shown below:

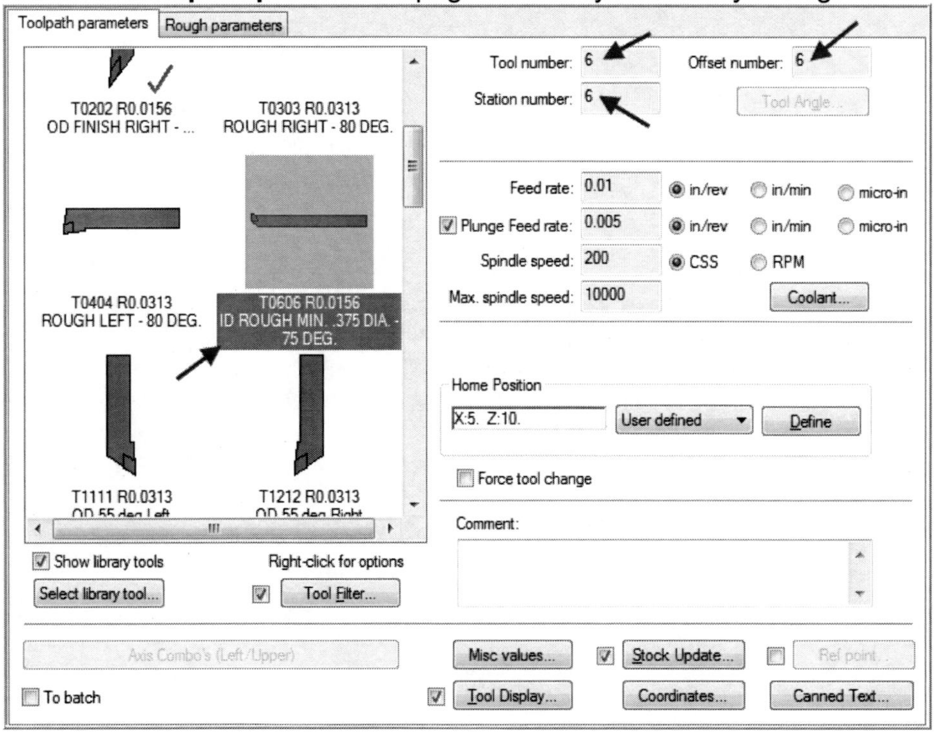

10. Select the **Rough parameters** page and make any necessary changes as shown below:

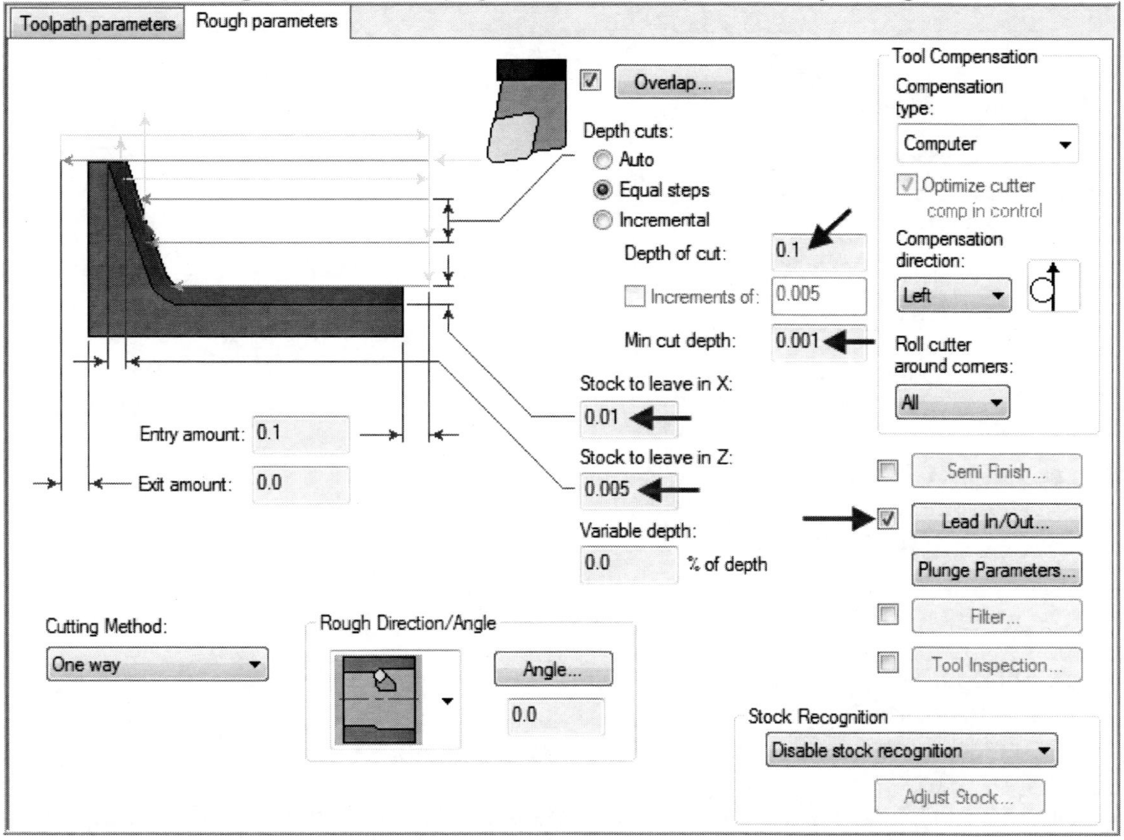

11. Select the **Lead In/Out** button select the **Lead out** page and extend the contour by **0.05** as shown below:

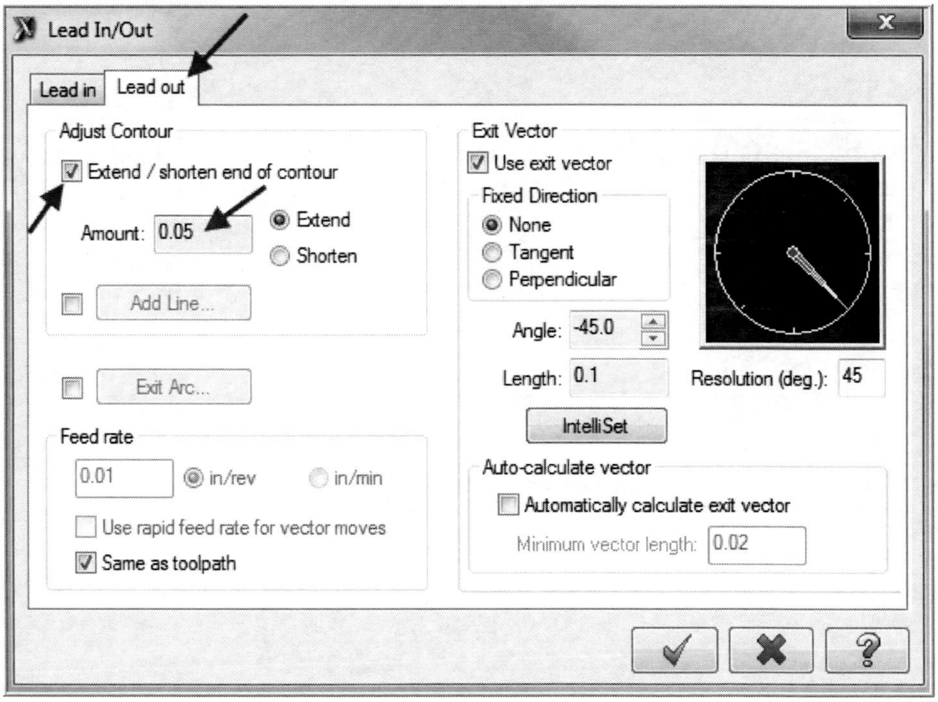

12. Select the **OK** button ✔ to exit this function.

13. Open up the **Stock Recognition** drop down menu and select **Use stock for outer boundary**.

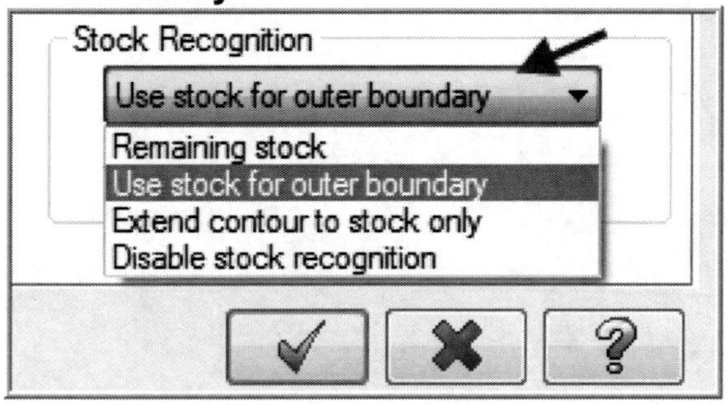

14. Now Click on the **Adjust Stock....** button.

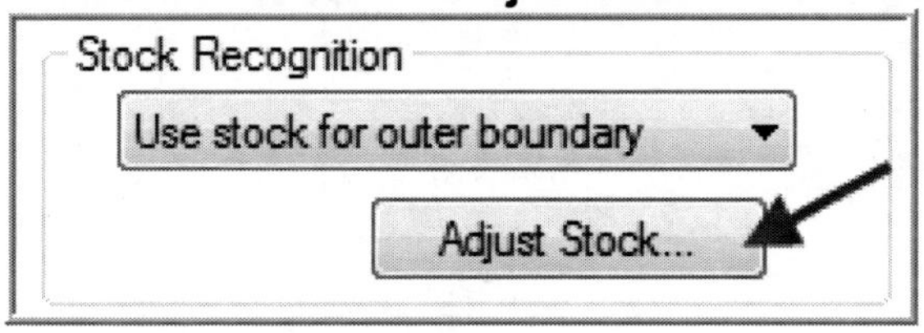

Adjust Stock dialog box
Use these options to tell Mastercam how to integrate the contour that you've chained for the toolpath with the stock boundary, so that the tool will approach and come off the part the way you intend to.
First, select an End to Adjust. The first radio button lets you adjust the start of the toolpath, the second lets you adjust the end. You can adjust the stock individually for each.
Then, for each end of the toolpath, select a stock adjustment method. Each option results in an imaginary line from the selected end of the toolpath to the stock boundary, in either of the following orientations:
- tangent to the toolpath
- perpendicular to the Z axis
- to the Z axis
The area of remaining stock between the stock boundary and chained contour is highlighted in orange. A yellow point indicates the start of the chained contour, while a red point indicates the end of the chained contour.
As you select different options, you will see them previewed on the screen. If the dialog box is in the way, choose Auto hide and it will hide when you move the cursor over the graphics window.

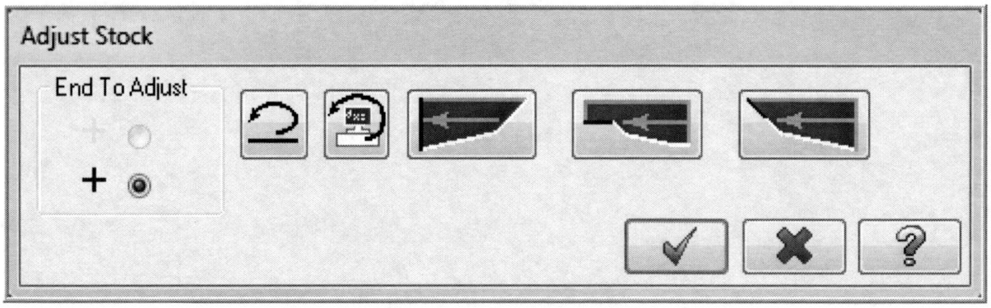

15. Select the **OK** button to exit Adjust Stock.
16. Select the **OK** button to exit Rough Parameters.

TASK 14:
FINISH THE BORE

➲ In this task you will use the same boring tool as used for the previous rouging operation.

1. From the menu bar select **TOOLPATHS>Quick>Finish …**

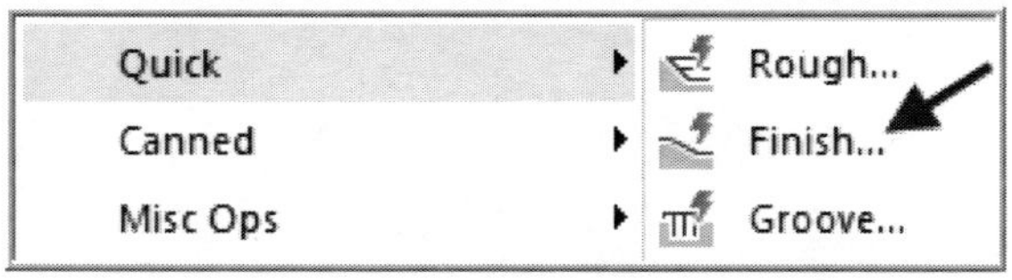

2. In the **Quick Toolpath parameters** page select **Tool #6 a boring tool ID ROUGH MIN .375 DIA – 75 deg** and make any necessary changes as shown below:

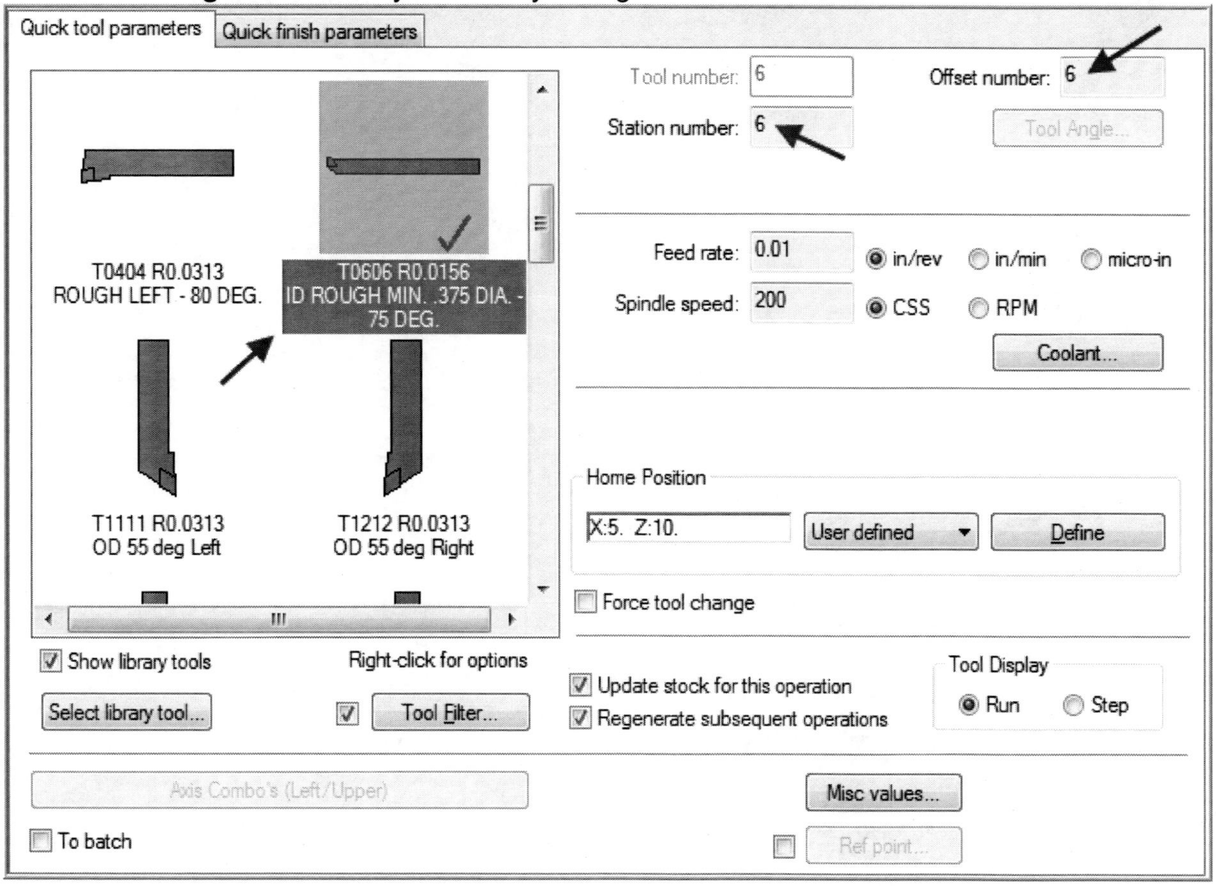

3. Select the **Quick finish parameters** page and make any necessary changes as shown below. Open up the drop down menu for operation and select the operation at the **bottom of the list**, this is the previous rough boring operation.

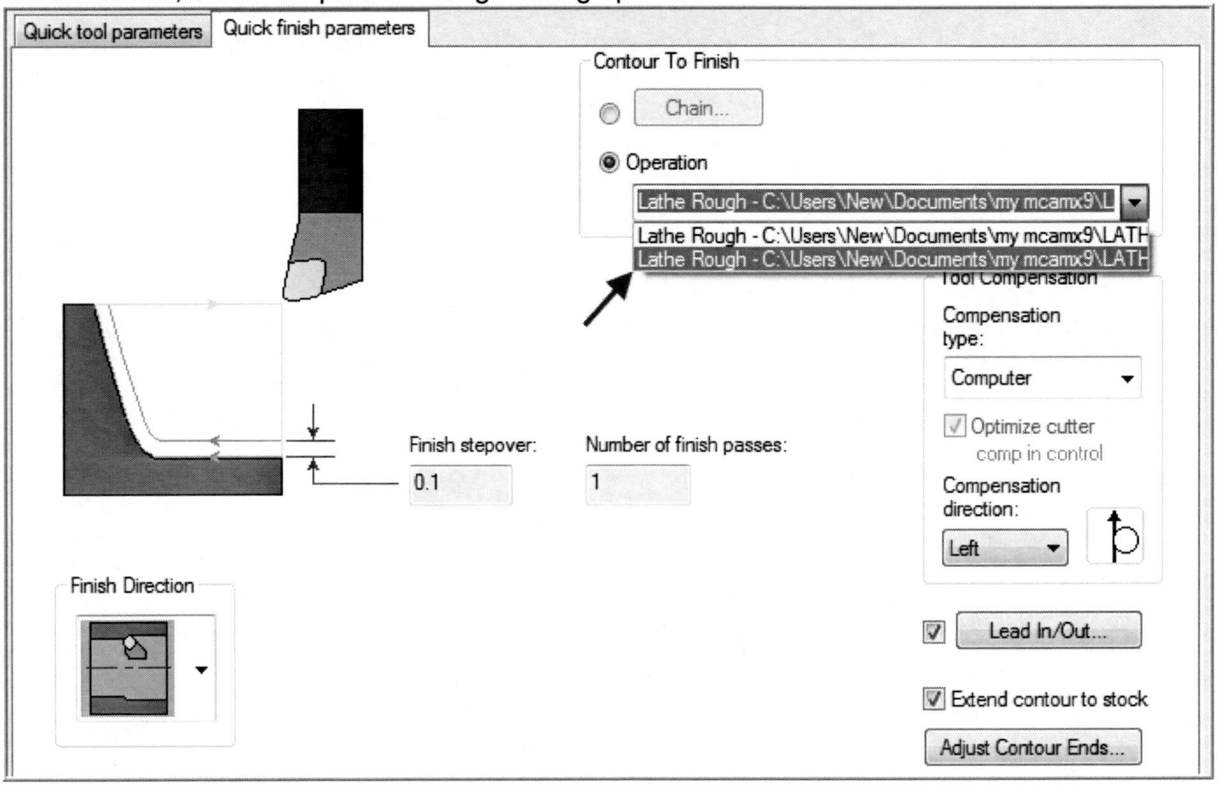

4. Select the **Lead In/Out button** select the Lead out page and extend the contour by .05 as shown below:

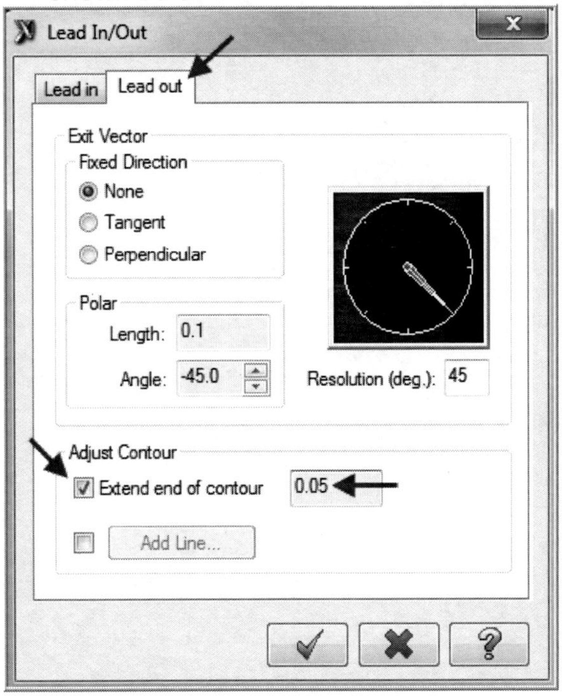

5. Select the **OK** button to exit this function.
6. Select the **OK** button to exit **Quick finish** parameters.

TASK 15:
MACHINE THE FIRST SLOT USING C-AXIS CROSS CONTOUR

1. Change the view to **Isometric** .
2. Click on the **Fit** Icon. 
3. Click on **TOOLPATHS>C-axis>Cross Contour…**

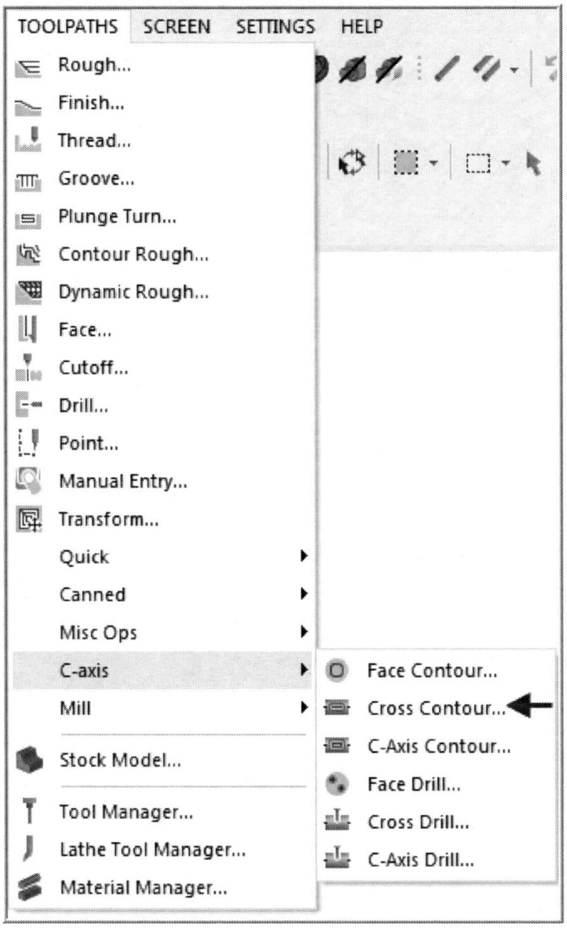

Cross contour toolpaths
Use Mastercam Lathe cross contour toolpaths to cut parallel to the axis of rotation.

These toolpaths are most often used to cut slots. Mastercam sets the tool plane (Tplane) and construction plane (Cplane) so that the tool is placed perpendicular to the axis of rotation (typically the part spindle).

Choosing this toolpath also sets the default cutter **compensation** to **Off** so that the center of the tool follows the chained geometry.

4. You are prompted to **Select Contour chain 1** and the Chaining parameter window appears. Select the **Single** button as shown below left:

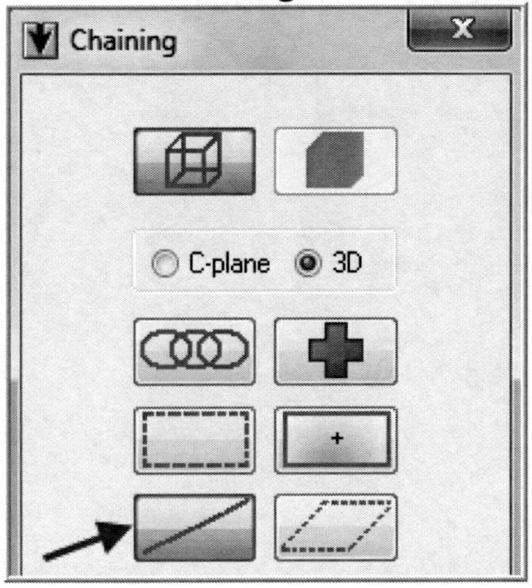

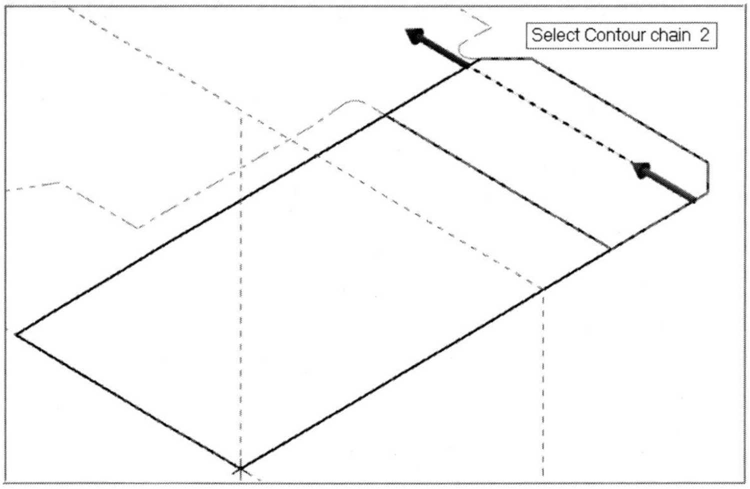

5. To satisfy the prompt click on the right end of the line as shown above right. Arrows are pointing towards the part.
6. Click **OK** in the Chaining dialog box.
7. Select the **Tool** menu and then click on **Select library tool...** as shown below:

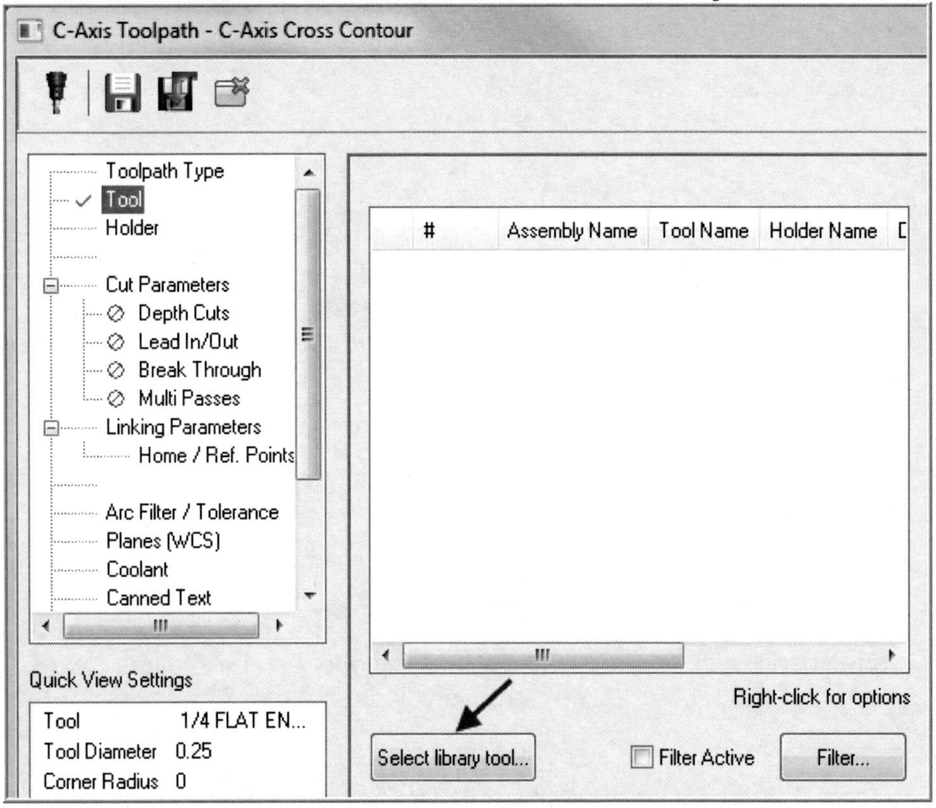

8. Select the **1/4 FLAT END MILL** as shown below:

#	Tool Name	Dia.	Cor. rad.	Length	# Flutes	Type	Rad. Type
233	5/32 FLAT ENDMILL	0.15625	0.0	2.0	4	Endmill1 Flat	None
234	3/16 FLAT ENDMILL	0.1875	0.0	2.0	4	Endmill1 Flat	None
235	1/4 FLAT ENDMILL	0.25	0.0	2.0	4	Endmill1 Flat	None
236	5/16 FLAT ENDMILL	0.3125	0.0	2.0	4	Endmill1 Flat	None

9. Click on **OK** for the selection of the 0.25" Flat End Mill.
10. Make the changes in the **Toolpath parameters** screen as shown below:

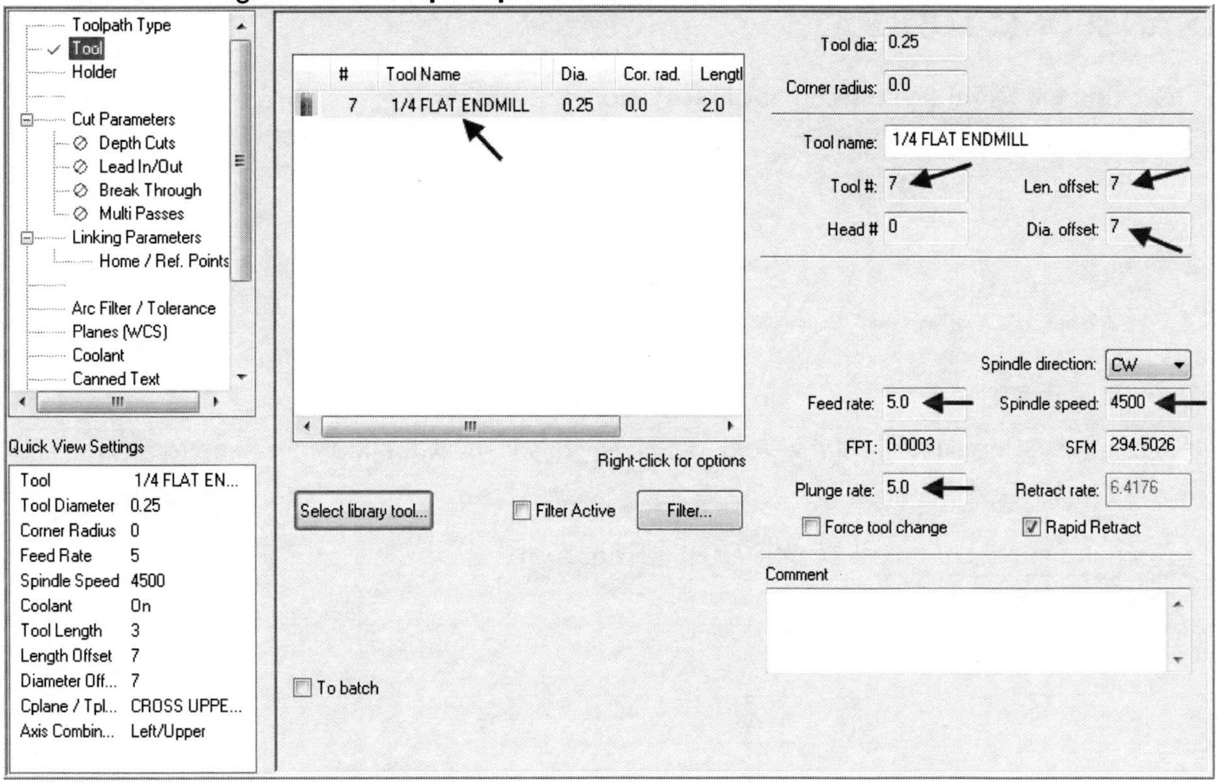

11. Click **OK** .
12. The screen should look like the image shown below:

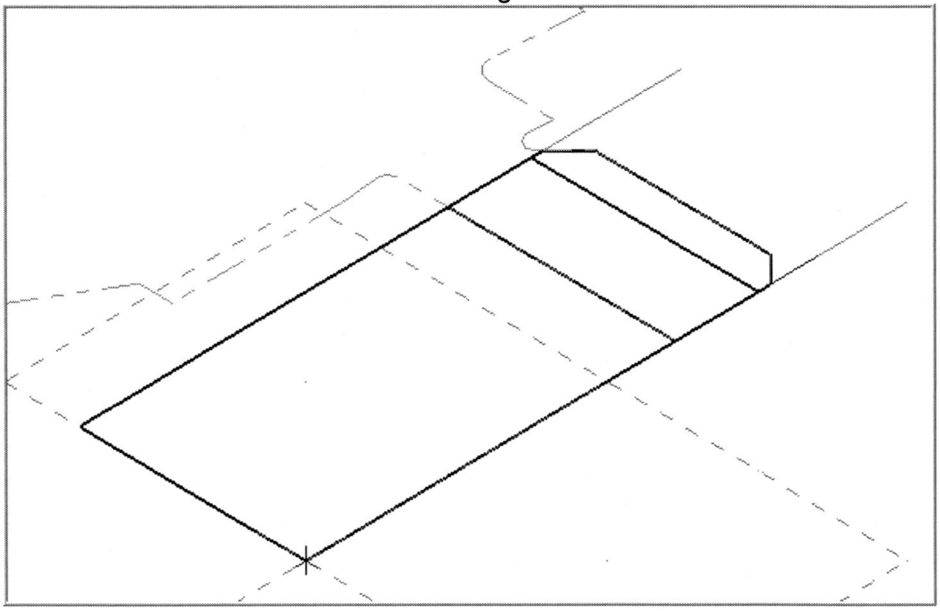

TASK 16:
MACHINE THE REMAINING THREE SLOTS USING TRANSFORM TOOLPATH

1. Click on the **Right (WCS)** icon as shown below:

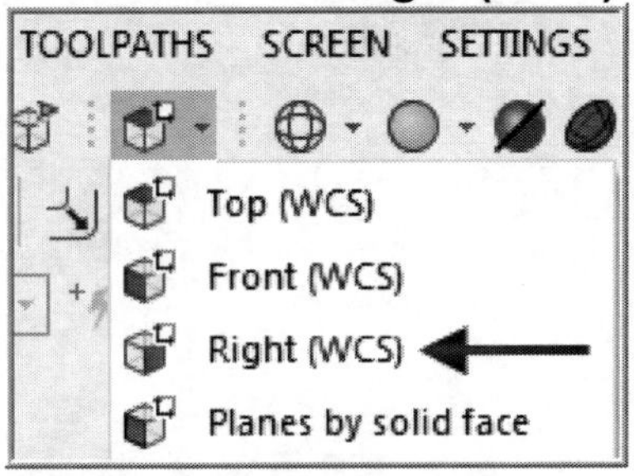

Changing the **Construction Plane** from **Top** to **Right** will allow the toolpath to be rotated correctly.

2. From the menu bar select **TOOLPATHS>Transform ...**

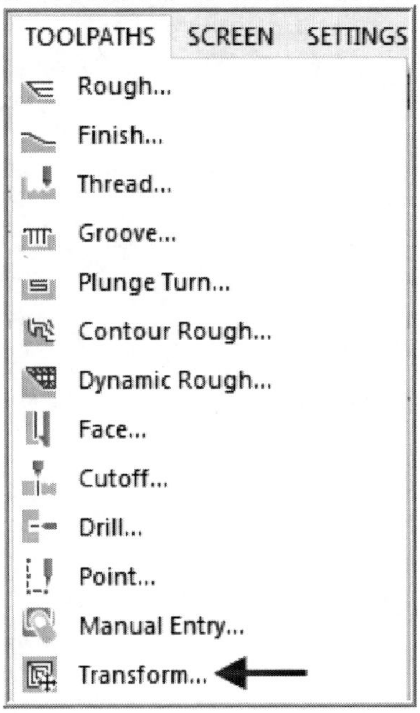

3. The **Transform Operation Parameters** dialog box appears. In the **Source operations** list ensure you have a check mark on only the **C-Axis** operation. Activate the radio button for **Method** to **Tool Plane**. Activate the radio button for **Type** to **Rotate**.

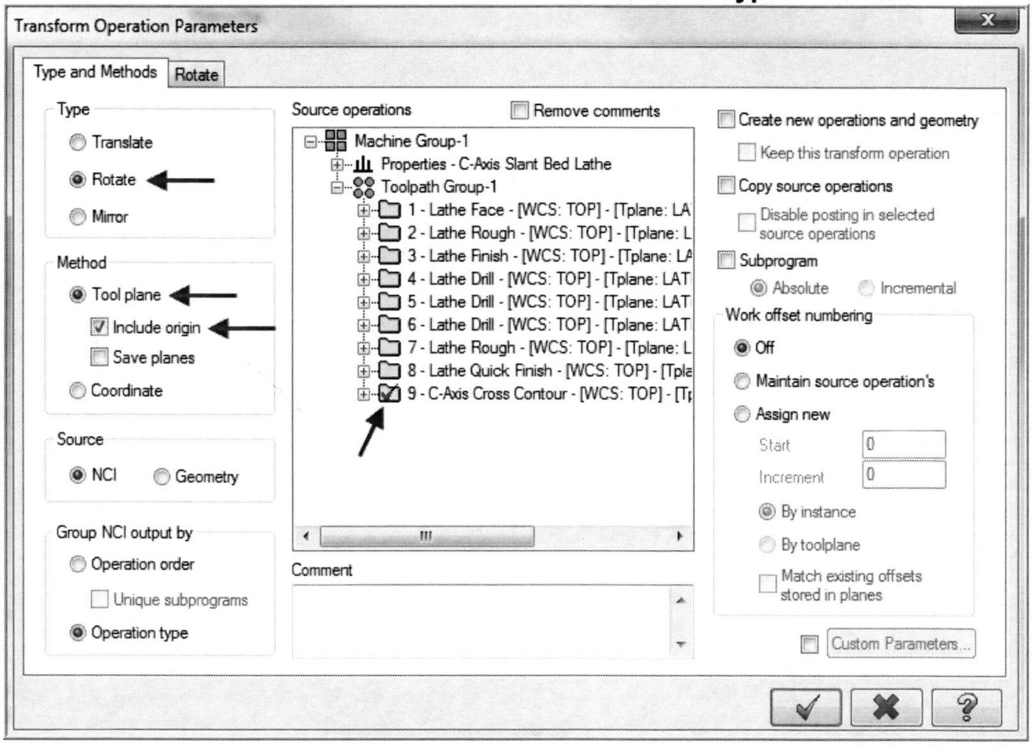

Transform Operation Parameters dialog box
Use this dialog box to begin creating a transform operation.

Here you can select the source operations, the type of transform, and how you want to organize the toolpaths which result.

After you select the type of transformation, choose only one of the remaining dialog box tabs to complete the operation. For example, if you choose a Rotate transformation, the Translate and Mirror tabs will be unavailable.

4. Click on the **Rotate** tab at the top of the dialog box and set the following as shown below:

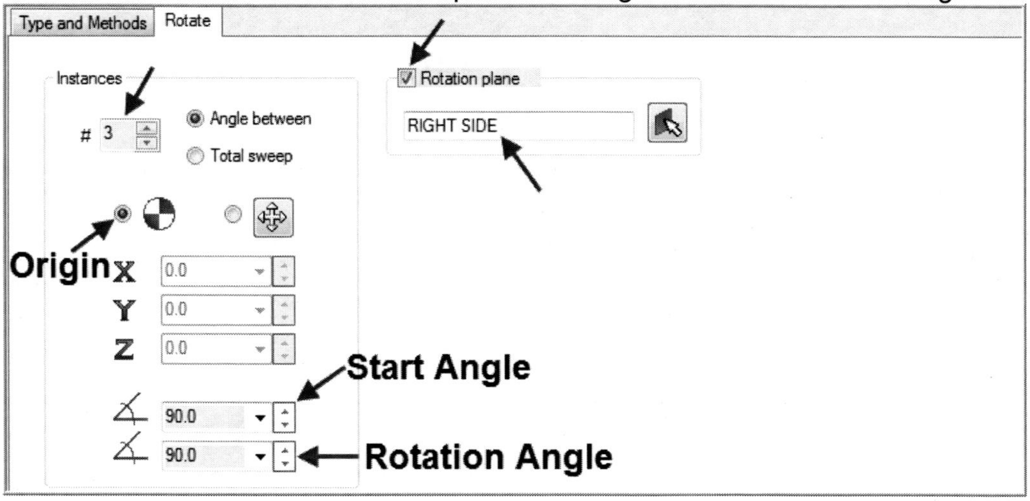

5. Select the OK button  to complete this function.
6. To review the completed transformed toolpaths **Zoom** out by clicking on the **Un-Zoom Previous / .5** icon 

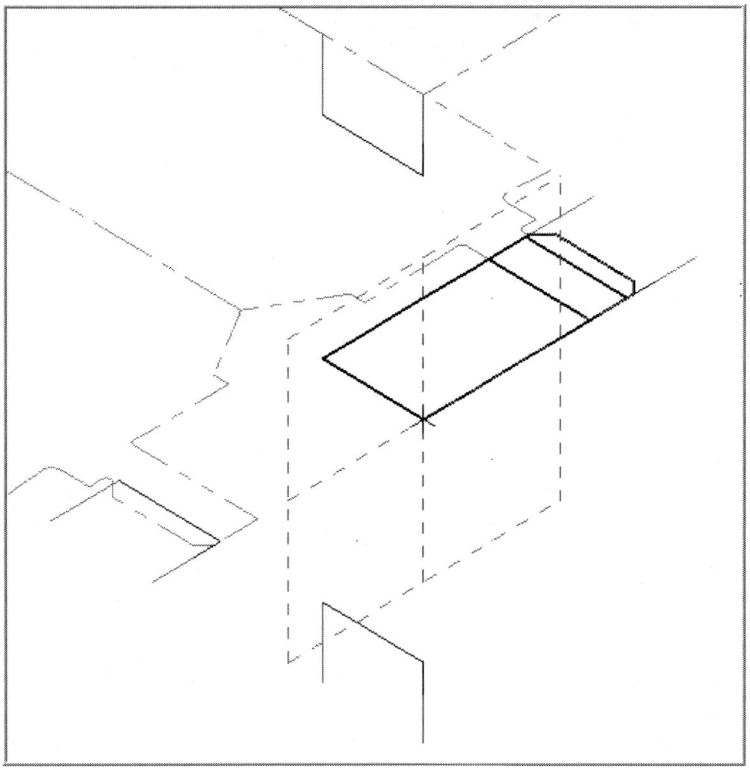

TASK 17:
CUTOFF THE PART

➲ In this task you will cutoff the part using a **0.125" wide cutoff tool**.

1. Change the view to **Top** .
2. Click on the **Top (WCS)** icon as shown below:

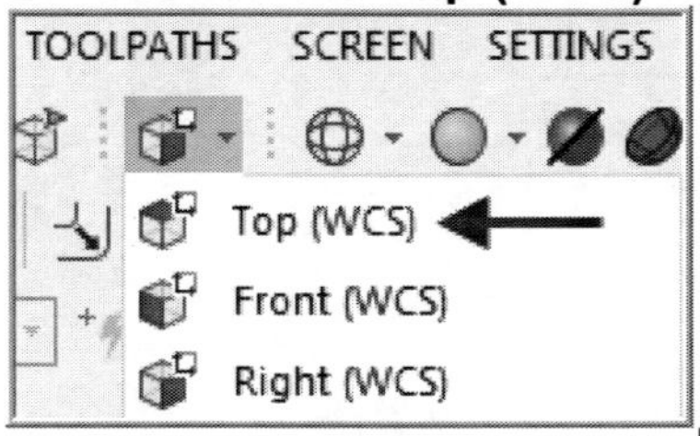

3. Select the **screen fit** icon .
4. From the menu bar select **TOOLPATHS>Cutoff…**

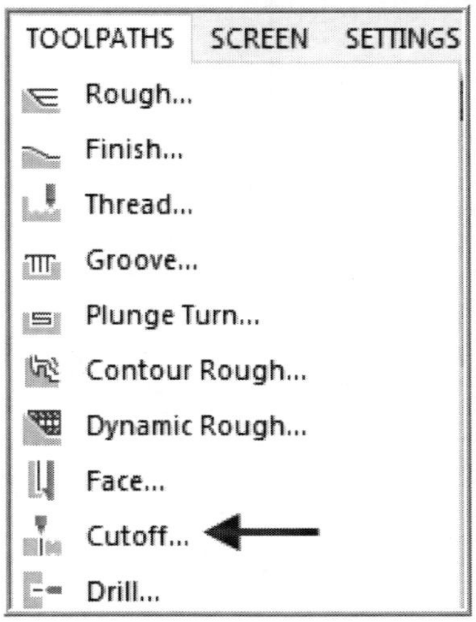

5. Hold down the **Alt key** and hit the **T key** on the keyboard to hide the toolpath lines.

Toolpath Lines visible:

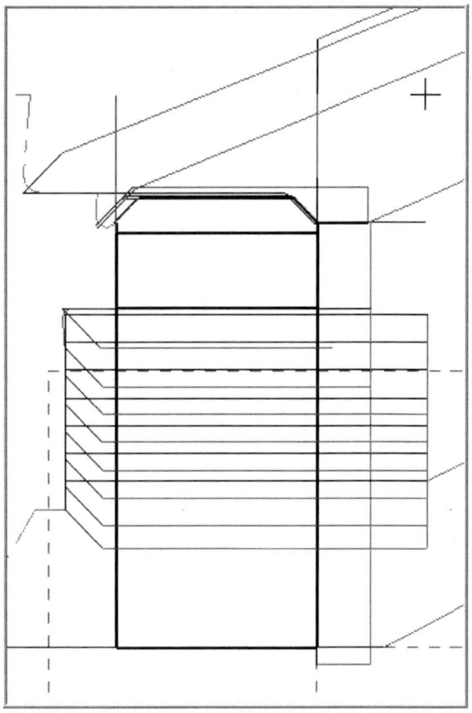

Press Alt T to hide toolpath Lines:

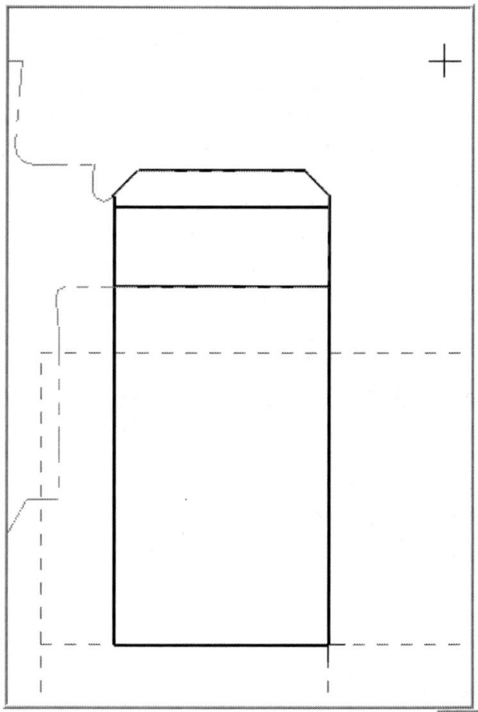

6. Move the cursor over the corner (where **Line 1** and **Line 2** meet) until the visual cue  for **End point** displays and then click on this point as shown below:

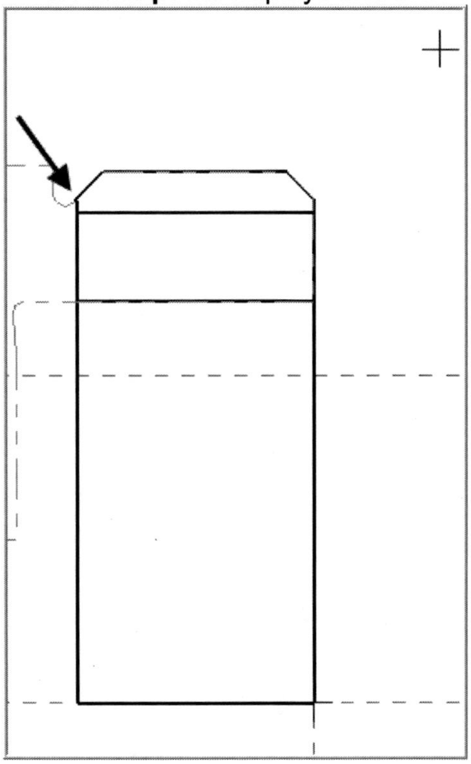

7. Scroll down the tool window and select the **OD Groove Right Width .125** tool and make changes as shown below in the **Toolpath parameters** page:

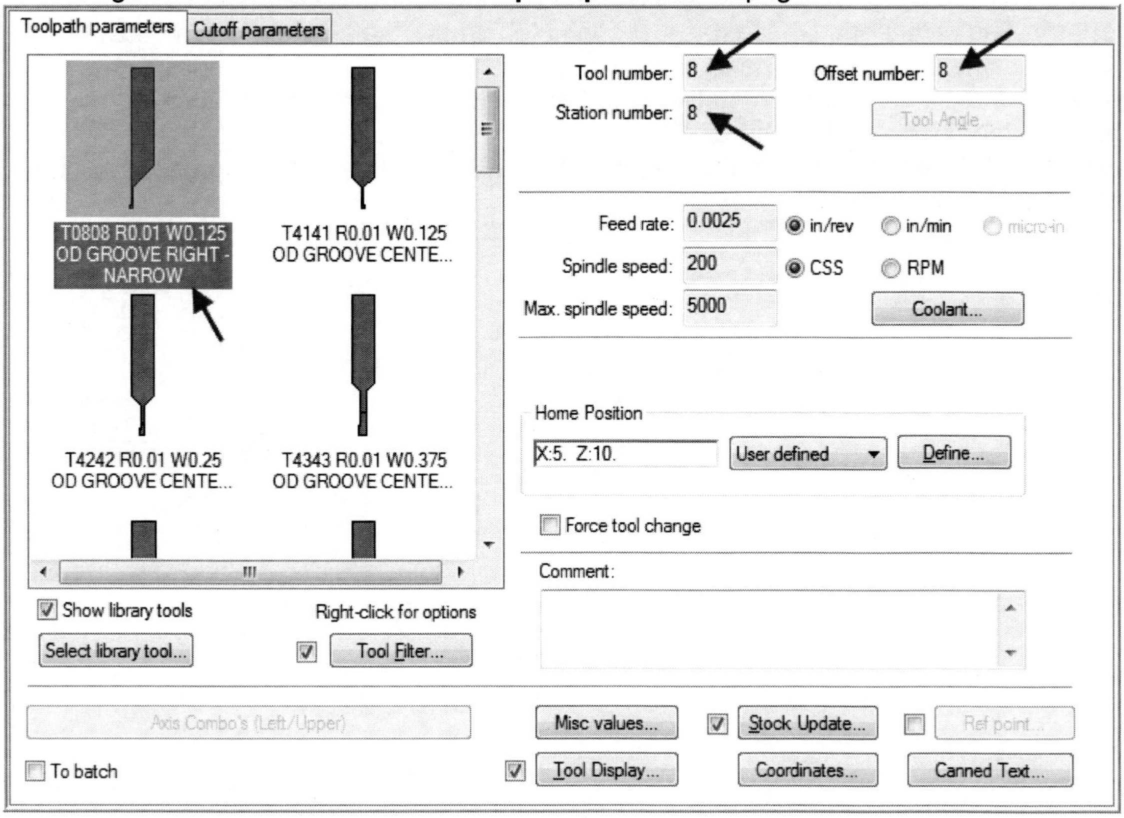

8. Select the **Cutoff parameters** page and make changes as shown below:

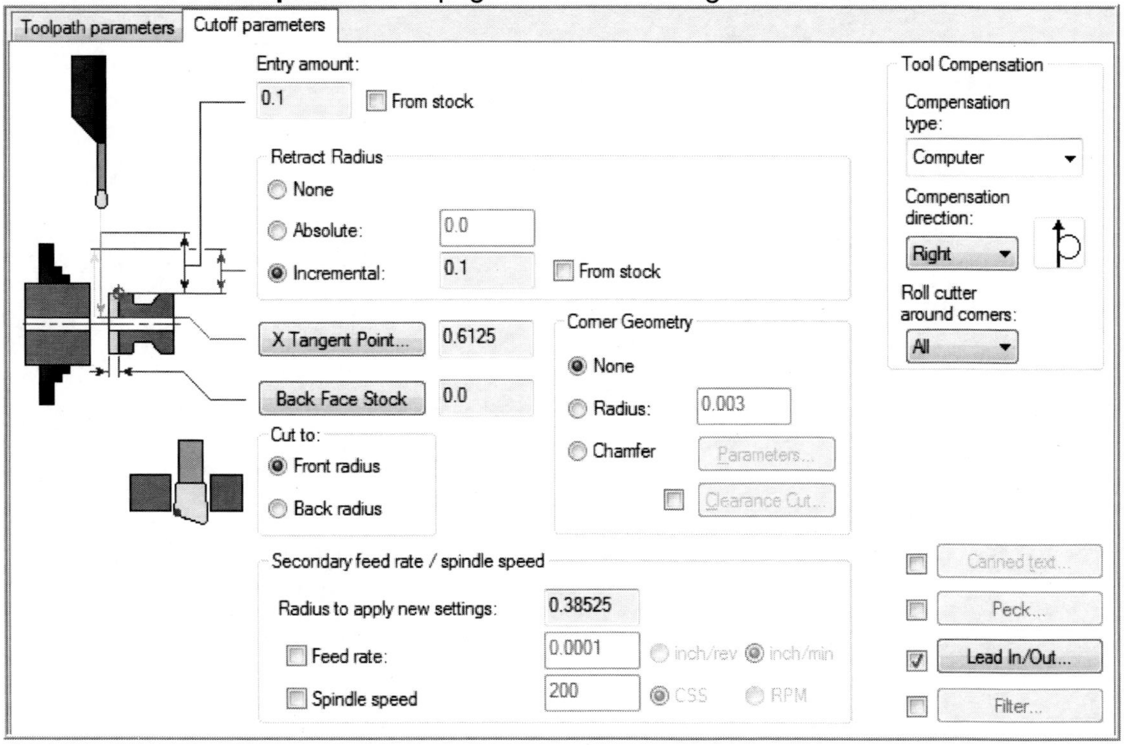

9. Select the **OK** button  to exit **Cutoff parameters.**

TASK 18:
MODIFY 1.625" DIAMETER AND REGENERATE OPERATIONS

- **Newsflash**: The engineering office has just contacted you with a change to this part.
- The 1.625" diameter has been changed from 1.625" to 1.425".
- In this task you will modify the geometry using **Xform Stretch** and then update the machining operations to reflect this change.
- Mastercam is fully associative, so after regenerating all the toolpaths the operations will now reflect this geometry modification.

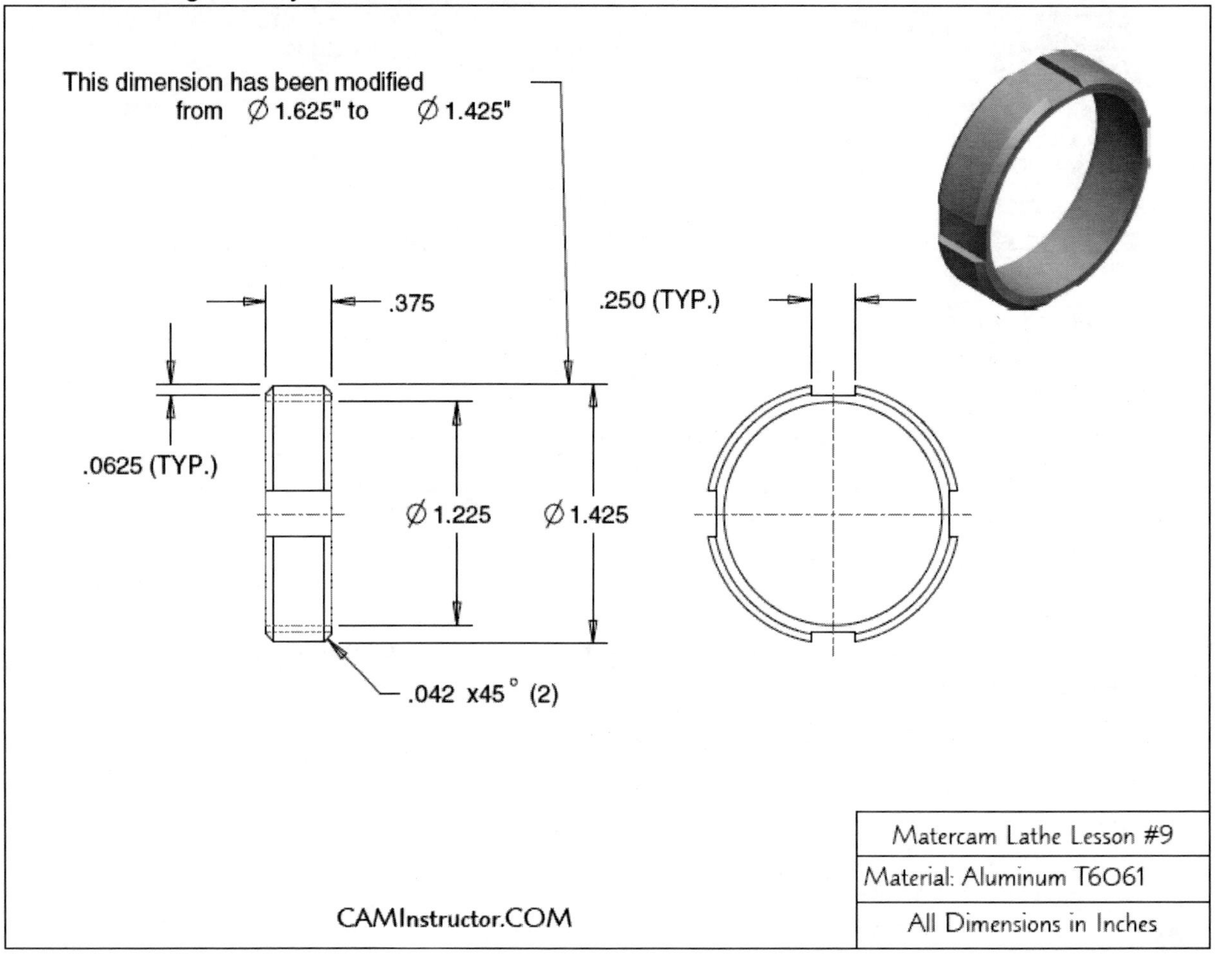

1. Click on **Xform>Stretch...**

2. You are prompted to **Stretch: Window intersect entities to stretch.** Now draw a window around the entities by first picking a point at **position 1** and then dragging the window to **position 2** and then pick this point.

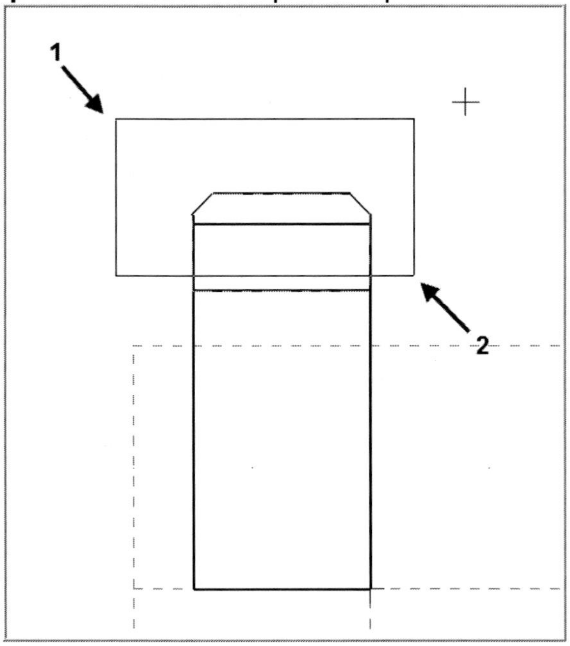

3. Click on **End Selection** 

.

4. The **Stretch dialogue** window appears. Make the changes as shown in the diagram below:

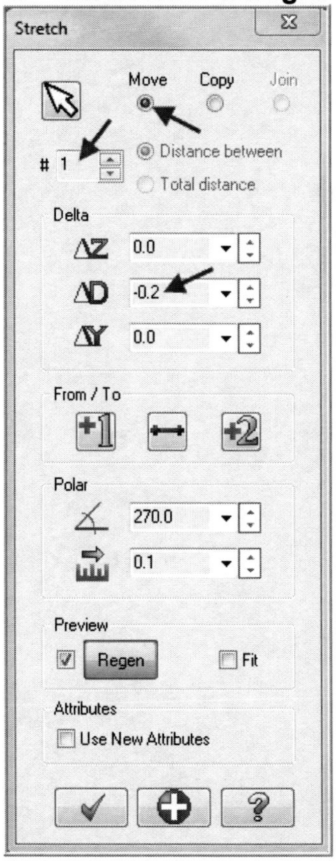

5. Click on **OK**  in the **Stretch** dialogue window.
6. Click on **Clear Colors** .
7. Now pick all the operations by selecting the **Select All** icon  as shown below:

8. Select the **Regenerate all dirty operations button**  to remove the red X from the machining operations that have been modified by this geometry change.

TASK 19:
BACKPLOT THE TOOLPATH

- In this task you will use Mastercam's Backplot function to view the path the tools take to cut this part.
- Backplot will enable us to review the cutting motions and identify any problem areas when cutting the part.

1. Change the view to **Isometric** .
2. To pick all the operations to backplot pick the **Select All** icon .
3. The next step is to select the **Backplot selected operations** icon shown below:

4. **Maximize** the Backplot/Verify window if required.
5. Select the **Home** Tab if required.
6. Activate the options shown below in the **Visibility** section of the Home tab.

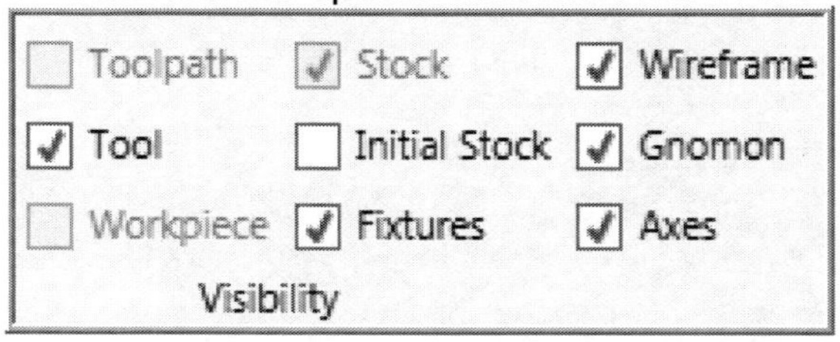

7. At the top of the screen select the **View** tab, the **Isometric** icon and then select **Fit**.
8. Click on the **Backplot** tab at the top left of the screen

9. Activate the **Both** option in the Toolpath section of the Backplot tab.

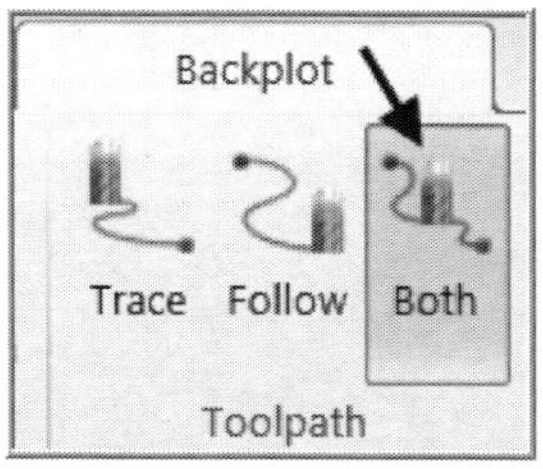

10. In the lower right corner of the screen now set the run Speed to slow by moving the slider bar pointer over to the left.
11. Now select the **Play Simulation** button to review the toolpaths.
12. After reviewing the Backplot of the toolpaths select the **Close** button 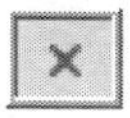 to exit Backplot.

TASK 20:
VERIFY THE TOOLPATH

➲ Mastercam's Verify utility allows you to use solid models to simulate the machining of a part. The model created by the verification represents the surface finish, and shows collisions, if any exist.

1. In the Toolpaths Manager pick all the operations to backplot by picking the **Select All** icon .
2. Select the **Verify selected operations** icon:
3. **Maximize** the Backplot/Verify window if required.
4. Activate the options shown below in the **Visibility** section of the **Home** tab. Initial Stock not activated.

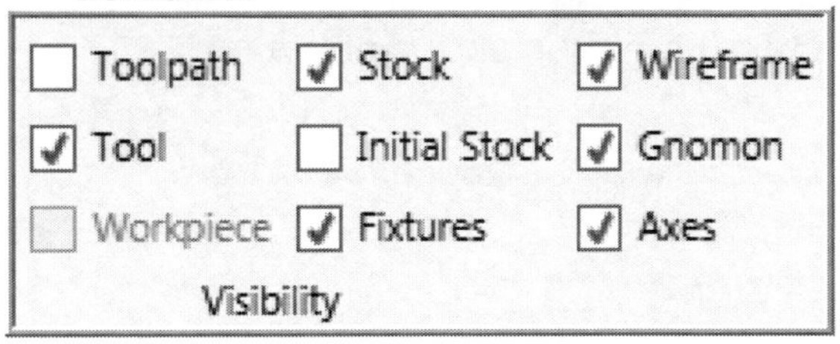

5. Activate the **Color Loop** to change the color of the tools for the verified part.
6. At the top of the screen select the **View** tab, the **Isometric** icon and then select **Fit**.
7. In the lower right corner of the screen now set the run **Speed** to slow by moving the slider bar pointer over to the left.
8. Now select the **Play Simulation** button to review the toolpaths.

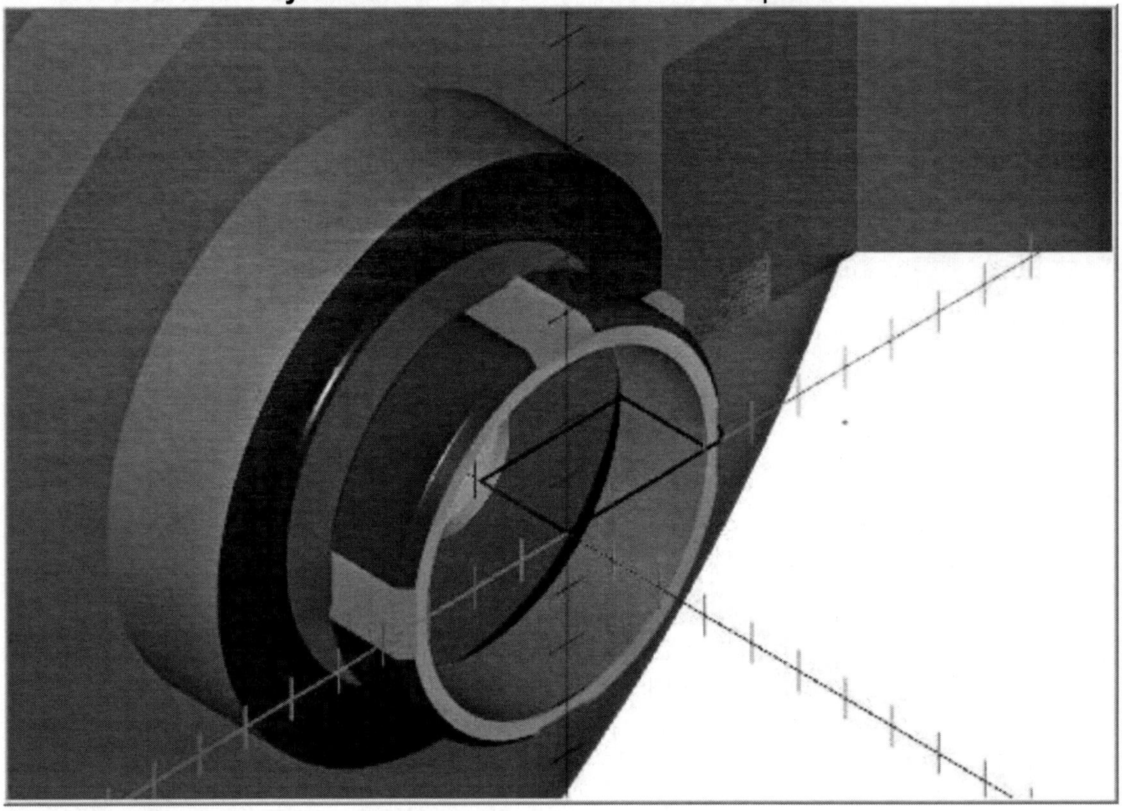

9. Select the **Close** button 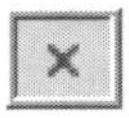 in the top right hand corner to exit Verify.

TASK 21:
SAVE THE UPDATED MASTERCAM FILE

1. Select the **save** icon from the toolbar .

TASK 22:
POST AND CREATE THE CNC CODE FILE

1. Ensure all the operations are selected by picking the **Select All** icon  from the **Toolpaths Manager.**
2. Select the Post selected operations button from the **Toolpaths Manager.**
3. In the Post processing window, make the necessary changes as shown below:

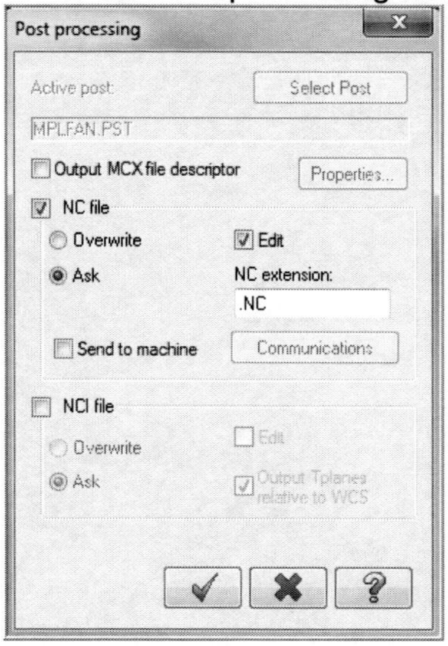

4. Select the **OK** button  to continue.
5. Enter the same name as your Mastercam part file name in the **NC File name** field **LATHE-LESSON-9.**
6. Select the **Save** button.
7. The CNC code file opens up in the default editor.

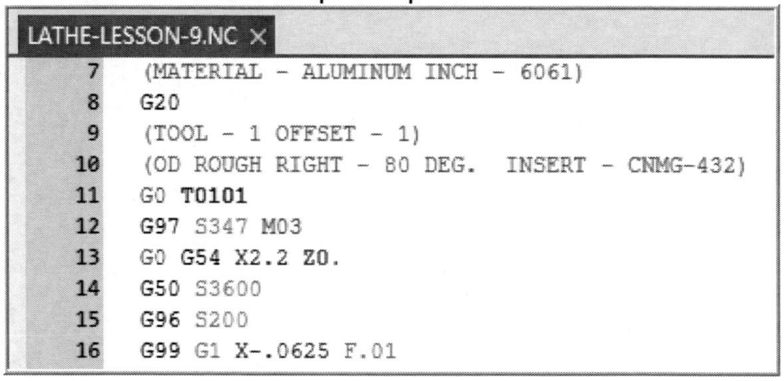

LATHE-LESSON-9.NC

```
7   (MATERIAL - ALUMINUM INCH - 6061)
8   G20
9   (TOOL - 1 OFFSET - 1)
10  (OD ROUGH RIGHT - 80 DEG.  INSERT - CNMG-432)
11  G0 T0101
12  G97 S347 M03
13  G0 G54 X2.2 Z0.
14  G50 S3600
15  G96 S200
16  G99 G1 X-.0625 F.01
```

8. Scroll down the CNC code until you locate the commands to rotate the chuck (C-Axis) when machining the slots.

```
M01
(TOOL - 7 OFFSET - 7)
( 1/4 FLAT ENDMILL)
G0 T0707
M23
G0 G55 X1.8 Z0.
C0.
G97 S2500 M51
X1.5
G98 G1 X1.3 F5.
Z-.375
G0 X1.8
G56 X1.8 Z0. C90.
X1.5
G1 X1.3
Z-.375
G0 X1.8
G57 X1.8 Z0. C180.
X1.5
G1 X1.3
Z-.375
G0 X1.8
G58 X1.8 Z0. C270.
```

9. Select the × in the top right corner to exit the CNC editor.

➲ This completes **LATHE-LESSON-9**.

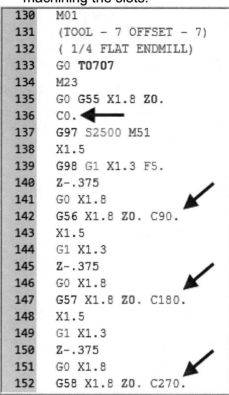

LATHE-LESSON-9 EXERCISE

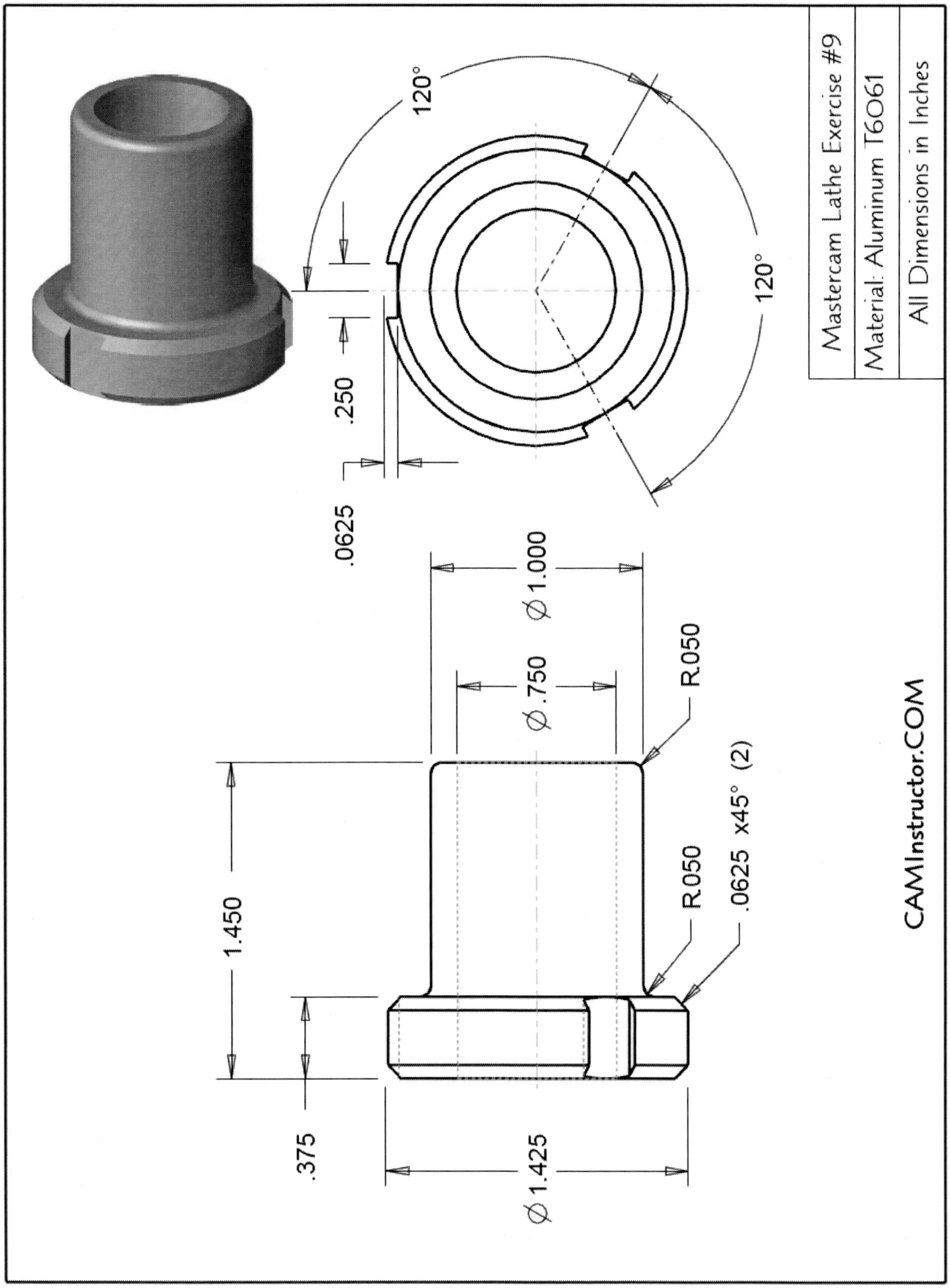

Mastercam® X9

TRAINING GUIDE

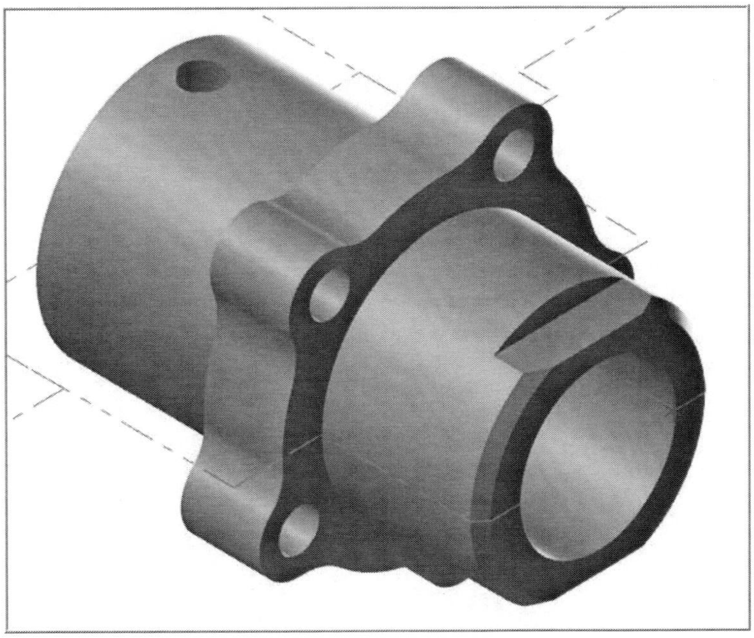

LATHE-LESSON-10

NOTE:
This Lesson is located on the **CamInstructor** Course site.

1. Just go to **www.caminstructor.com** and click on **Login** at the top of the home page.
2. For the email use: **mill3dstudent@caminstructor.com**
3. For the password use: **x8mill3dstudent**
4. Click on **Continue/ View** beside **Mastercam X8 Mill 3D Training Guide Supplement.**
5. After reading the course intro click on **Lathe Lesson 10.**
6. The Lesson can be printed or you can follow the instructions on the computer screen.

camInstructor